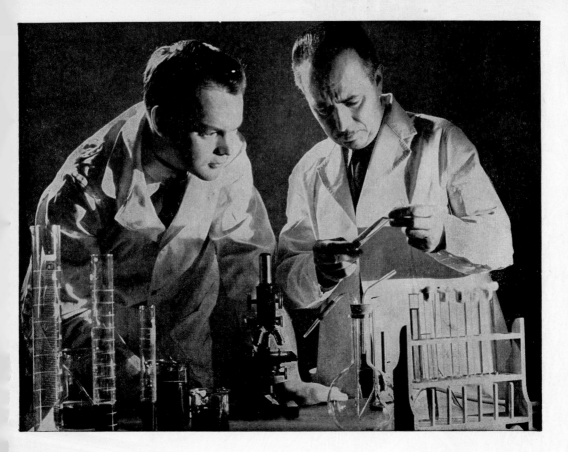

MODERN BIOLOGY

Truman J. Moon

Paul B. Mann

James H. Otto

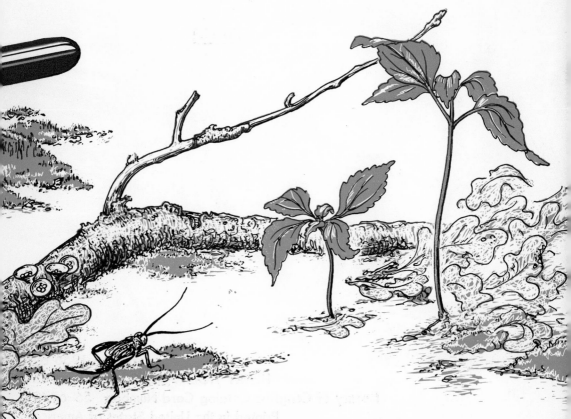

HENRY HOLT AND COMPANY · New York

JAMES H. OTTO is head of the Science Department in George Washington High School, Indianapolis, Indiana. . . . Mr. Moon was head of the Science Department in the Middletown (N.Y.) High School. . . . Mr. Mann was head of the Department of Biology in Evander Childs High School, New York City, and deputy chairman of the city's Science Council.

59 BK 10

Preface

This complete revision of MODERN BIOLOGY is designed as a basic textbook for the standard course in high school biology. The utmost care has been given to all the factors that support teaching and aid in learning biology as a challenging and richly rewarding experience in science. In view of the wide variations in emphasis and in student abilities, MODERN BIOLOGY combines breadth with balance and unitary completeness with the simplest essentials for beginners. This general plan of presentation and the sequence within units provide maximum adjustability that is easily administered to meet varying needs.

MODERN BIOLOGY combines the best features of the type, systematic, and principles course. In the study of type organisms, the beginner has an opportunity to study a complete plant or animal and the interrelation of all its organs and life activities. Such an approach emphasizes the unity of life. On the other hand, the systematic study of plant and animal groups shows the relationship of all living things, the development of life through various stages of complexity, and the wide variety of organisms which compose our living world. Finally, the study of principles is accomplished largely by the inductive approach. The parts relating to the structure, function, behavior, and adaptations of living things lead the student through generalization to an understanding of principles. Beginning with the natural interest in particular living things, MODERN BIOLOGY applies the scientific method in expanding knowledge and developing understanding.

The organization follows a logical and sequential pattern. Unit 1 introduces biology as a science and explains and illustrates the research and technical methods as well as essential scientific attitudes. Other chapters of the first unit lead into the basic properties of living things, problems in maintaining life, the cell as the structural unit of life, functions of the cell, and the basic chemical relations of plants and animals. Unit 2 relates the organism to its physical and biological environment, and illustrates the basis of scientific classification and the structural relationships of various plants and animals.

With this broad background of living things in general, the student is prepared to consider specific groups of organisms. Unit 3 presents the seed plants, thus starting the study of plant life with familiar examples. The less familiar flowerless plants follow the seed plants in Unit 4. The student has only a short step from the simplest plants to the simplest forms of animal life as he begins Unit 5. In the chapters of this unit and Unit 6 he surveys the animal kingdom from the less to the more complex and finishes the vertebrates before studying the human body.

Unit 8 includes a practical study of human biology. Therefore, with this knowledge of plants, animals, and man, the student is prepared for the more advanced units dealing with disease and heredity. Although conservation problems are continually discussed in appropriate places throughout the study of plants and animals, the total conservation problem is treated fully in Unit 10 as a climax to the study of biology.

The authors recognize the reading problems that exist for many high school students. Hence they have kept the sentences and paragraphs short. Words having important scientific meaning are printed in **boldface type** and are pronounced phonetically, with the accented syllables in *italics*. Each of these is defined where it first appears in the text, and again in the *Glossary* at the back of the book.

Illustrations have been carefully chosen for learning value to supplement reading comprehension. These include both line drawings and photographs. Color has been used as an aid to learning by emphasizing detail in the line drawings. The quality and abundance of line drawings, charts, and tables of comparison cannot be overemphasized for their usefulness to high school students.

Each chapter opens with a short introduction which directs the thinking of the student to the chapter content. A brief summary at the close of each chapter reviews the principles presented and leads into the next chapter or unit. Teaching and learning aids at the end of each chapter have been carefully differentiated to meet individual or group differences. They are arranged into two categories: *Questions for Review* are factual and recall questions which every student should be able to answer; the second group of questions, *Applying Facts and Principles*, consists of items which require some inductive thinking. *Biologically Speaking* is vocabulary drill to help students know the meaning and pronunciation of all essential terms. *Research on Your Own,* at the close of each unit, contains a list of suggested outside activities for individual and group projects. This is followed by *More About Biology,* a list of carefully selected books for supplementary reading in the topical area of the unit.

Grateful acknowledgment and deep appreciation is made to all who have assisted in the preparation of this revision. Special thanks are due to Mr. Thomas F. Morrison, of Milton Academy, Milton, Massachusetts, and Mr. William Hubbard of Boys' High School, Anderson, South Carolina, who have read the entire manuscript critically and given many valuable suggestions. Dr. Herbert Taylor, Department of Botany, Columbia University has read the proofs for Units 1, 2, 3, 4, 9, and 10, while Dr. Edward Hodson, Department of Zoology, Columbia University, has read those for Units 5, 6, 7, and 8. Thanks are due to each of them. Mr. Paul Klinge of Thomas Carr Howe High School, Indianapolis, Indiana, has been of great assistance in revising the units dealing with flowerless plants, simpler forms of animal life, and human biology. Miss Mildred F. Campbell, of Shortridge High School, Indianapolis, Indiana, helpfully provided the author with data concerning nearly extinct birds and bird migration. Information relative to the preparation and production of vaccines was obtained through the kindness of Dr. J. O. Macfarlane of the Eli Lilly Company, Indianapolis, Indiana. Users of MODERN BIOLOGY across the nation have been most kind in giving comments and suggestions. The following biology teachers have been especially helpful: Mr. Philip T. Piaget, Clifton High School, Clifton, New Jersey; Mr. Rex Conyers, University City High School, University City, Missouri; Miss Georgia Arnold and Mr. Virgil Kirkpatrick, Bakersfield High School, Bakersfield, California; Mr. Thomas H. Wilson, Evanston Township High School, Evanston, Illinois; and Mr. Robert Ehn, Wauwatosa High School, Wauwatosa, Wisconsin. The book lists in *More About Biology* were prepared by Mrs. Mildred I. Ross, Science Librarian, George Washington High School, Indianapolis. Finally, deep appreciation is extended to my wife, Eloise B. Otto for her help in typing manuscript and in reading proof. **J. H. O.**

Contents

Practical Pointers

Here are some suggestions which will enable you to get the most from your biology course.

1. Keep your eyes and your mind open. In biology, as in all the sciences, we base conclusions *only on facts*. You will want to apply the scientific methods and attitudes which you will learn in Chapter 1 throughout your course. These methods and attitudes will become habits of straight thinking for intelligent living.

2. The more you learn about living things, the more interested you will probably become. Let your natural curiosity and special interests go beyond this book. Observe living things every time you meet them. Read some of the books that especially appeal to you from the list entitled *More About Biology* at the end of each unit.

3. After you have finished reading your assignment, check your understanding of it by glancing over the **boldface paragraph headings.** If you cannot make accurate statements from what you have just read, go back and reread those paragraphs until you can. When you get to the end of the chapter, read the short summary called *In Conclusion* and then answer the questions which follow under *Questions for Review*. You may want to try your skill at somewhat more difficult questions which require a little thought, and if so you can do those called *Applying Facts and Principles*.

4. Biology is a laboratory science. You can observe many of the facts and important discoveries by actual experiments. If you are so fortunate as to have valuable laboratory equipment available, use it most carefully. Participate in making your classroom a laboratory experience by bringing in specimens for observation. Do as many of the special projects, listed at the end of each unit as *Research on Your Own,* as appeal to you.

5. The drawings and photographs as well as the tables of comparisons are important features of this book. Train yourself to remember and to interpret accurately by seeing as well as by reading.

6. Familiarize yourself with the *language of biology* in your day-to-day study of the text. You will understand and remember biological words best by associating them with their use in your discussions. Each special biological word or term of real importance is printed in **boldface type** the first time it appears in the text. Pay particular attention to the meaning given and to the subject with which the word deals. These important words are also listed for you at the end of each chapter for a quick check-up review under the heading, *Biologically Speaking*.

7. Later in the text when you meet one of the biological words whose meaning you may have forgotten, stop and look it up in the *Glossary* at the end of the book. Then go back to your reading. You are not very apt to forget it again; if you use the *Glossary* correctly, you will find that you are developing a working knowledge of the language of biology.

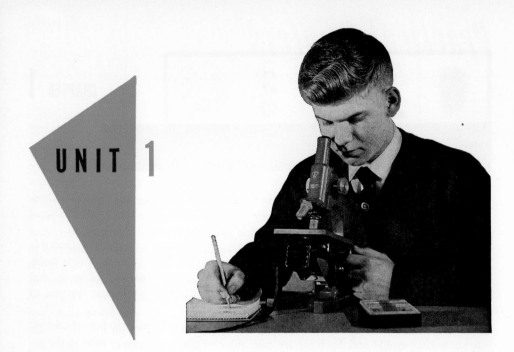

UNIT 1

Biology: The Scientific Study of Living Things

Biology is the study of life — plant life, animal life, and the life of human beings. The substance of life, called protoplasm, is the most remarkable of all substances. It carries on amazing chemical activities, responds to conditions around it, and even produces more of itself. It forms all living things.

Your study of biology will lead you into complex societies, where plants and animals live in vital relationship with each other. You will study the life of the forest and field and the ocean depths. You will explore miniature worlds where animals no larger than a pinhead feed on still smaller forms of life. Within a school year, you will explore the findings of biologists over a period of nearly two centuries.

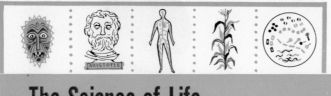

CHAPTER 1

The Science of Life

It was quite an event when biologists discovered that the big, green tomato "hornworm" could fly 35 miles an hour as an adult sphinx moth. They were thrilled, too, when they found that the golden plover, a relative of our killdeer, flew 8,000 miles twice a year, and that it traveled south over one route and returned to the north by another. Stop a moment and think where the food which will reach your dinner table in the weeks to come is being produced. It is being formed in the tiny chemical factories of the leaves of green vegetables and fruits. Have you followed the dramatic conquest of polio in recent years? Do you know that crop rotation increases yield and that contour plowing prevents gullies on hillsides? Do you know that molds and bacteria are our allies in the war against infectious microbes?

These are only a few of the fascinating discoveries of biologists during the past years. New discoveries are being made every day. You will review many of these discoveries in your course in biology. And you will do it in the way in which scientists make their discoveries. When you have finished your course, you will have a better understanding of the principles which govern your life.

Superstition versus science. Have you ever heard that hoop snakes take their tails in their mouths and roll down hills? What about milk snakes milking cows? Do toads cause warts? Will a gold wedding ring make a wart disappear? If you plant a seed upside down, will the roots grow upward while the stem pushes into the ground?

These are some of the ideas and superstitions which have come down to us from early times. Before scientists knew how to prove or disprove ideas and to provide reasonable explanations for the events around them, peoples' lives were full of superstitions.

Primitive man lived in constant fear of his environment. He could neither explain a windstorm in terms of a passing weather front, nor lightning in terms of electricity in the atmosphere. He did not know that blood surged through his arteries or that thought originated in his brain. Most of all, he could not understand infectious disease because he had no idea that germs lurked on his hands, in his food, and in the air around him.

It is not hard to see then why he turned to magic and superstition in an effort to account for the many strange happenings in the living world. Is it any wonder that disease-ridden victims would appeal to a witch doctor to drive out the demons which possessed them?

Biology is the science of life. The Greeks had a word for it. In fact, they had two words for it. One word was "bios," which means *life*. The other was "logos," meaning *science* or *study*.

Fig. 1-1. These common superstitions have no scientific basis. A true scientist does not accept any ideas until he has proved or disproved them.

Together, they form the word *biology* which means the **science of life.**

The Greeks gave us more than the name biology. Medicine, one of the many fields of biology, has its roots in ancient Greece. Hippocrates (hih-*pah*-kra-teez), who lived from 460–370 B.C., cast aside the superstition and witchcraft associated with disease during his time and began hunting causes for sickness in his patients. He studied symptoms, tried various cures, and kept records of the success or failure of his treatments. He was scientific in that he avoided making the same mistake twice. We honor his great wisdom when we speak of him today as the *father of medicine.*

A short time later, another famous Greek, Aristotle (*ar*-iss-tah-tal), who lived from 384–322 B.C., turned his attention to the study of plants and animals. He watched the development of a chick in an egg. He studied the stomach of cud-chewing animals, like the cow. His dissections included over 50 different kinds of animals. Probably his greatest contribution was the grouping and classifying of over 500 different kinds of plants and animals on the basis of their body structure. We still admire Aristotle and honor him as the *father of biology.*

Biology has progressed rapidly in the past fifty years. Had biology progressed steadily from the time of Aristotle, there probably would have been no great plague and smallpox epidemics during the Middle Ages. We might have had penicillin a hundred years or more ago. By now, we might even have a cure for advanced cancer and heart disease. However, people were hostile to new ideas. Scientists were even cast into dungeons for trying to find out more about the unknown.

Fig. 1-2. Hippocrates, the father of medicine, is responsible for the Hippocratic oath which is part of the code of medical ethics. Today all prospective doctors take this oath before entering the medical profession.

Knowledge of biology was advanced very little during the Middle Ages. Not until the 17th century could William Harvey, an English doctor, convince the king, and later his fellow doctors, that blood circulated in the body. Only a little more than 150 years ago, Edward Jenner discovered vaccination against smallpox. However, he was ridiculed and condemned for trying to save lives by using it. Even the doctors of France laughed at Pasteur when, less than a hundred years ago, he tried to convince them that disease could be caused by invisible forms of life which could float through the air. And only about 75 years ago did Sir Joseph Lister show doctors how to scrub their hands and sterilize their instruments before performing hospital surgery. These are milestones in medicine and biology.

Walk through a modern hospital, visit a biological research laboratory, tour a conservation project, or study a modern farm and you will see how far biology has come in the past 50 years. Then, consider sulfa drugs and antibiotics, X-ray and radium treatment for cancer, hybrid corn and 300-egg hens, blood banks, and the Rh factor. These are discoveries and achievements of recent years. They are some of the reasons you now have the greatest opportunity in the history of the world for a long life and for health and happiness.

Science consists of attitudes and methods. In part, **science** is a vast accumulation of knowledge or facts, added to by each generation and passed on to the next. But science is more than knowledge. It consists of *attitudes* and *methods.* An **attitude** is a pattern of thought, or a way of regarding things. In scientific thinking, reason replaces superstition. A mere idea is never accepted until it has become a proved fact.

In the past, scientific attitudes and methods were, for the most part, limited to scientists themselves. Today, through education, radio, television, newspapers, and other channels of information, most of our population live close to the science laboratories and research centers. Attitudes and methods of science are now part of the thinking of millions of people. This is the scientific age.

A scientist must have certain attitudes. As you review the following five scientific attitudes, think of a doctor, a chemist, a horticulturist, a laboratory technician, or an engineer. See if they do not reveal these qualities. How many do you have? Whether you enter the ranks of a professional, or **producer scientist,** or live in close contact with scientific achievements as an interested layman, or **consumer scientist,** your life

Fig. 1-3. A modern farm with its clean and well-equipped building shows the progress biology has made in the last 50 years. The higher the standards of cleanliness, the greater the insurance against disease.

will have much more meaning if you adopt these scientific attitudes.

1. *Open-mindedness.* The scientist must free his mind of prejudice. The scientist never rejects knowledge because it happens not to agree with an idea of his own.

2. *Careful judgment.* The scientist must not jump to conclusions. He must base his decisions on reliable information and proved facts. Snap judgment could cost a life or bring disaster in some other way.

3. *Desire to learn.* Every scientist has a healthy curiosity. He wants to know the *why* of things. Every discovery opens new fields for study. The scientist never stops learning.

4. *Belief in cause and effect.* The scientist believes that, as far as the physical world is concerned, things happen for a reason. Nature is orderly, and events are controlled by natural laws. Therefore, there must be a cause for each occurrence. If this were not true, and if the scientist did not attempt to look for these causes as explanations of the events, we would have made little progress thus far. We would still be living in the age when superstition ruled our method of thinking.

5. *Active concern for human welfare.* This attitude is a tremendous force behind medical science and many other fields of biology. Much of our scientific effort is directed toward saving lives, lengthening lives, and producing better things for better living.

There are several scientific methods. We often speak of the scientific method as though there were one universal method used by all scientists in investigating a problem. Actually, there are many. The method used depends on the type of investigation. An atomic scientist depends on *mathematical calculations* to predict the outcome of an experiment. Often trial and error ex-

Fig. 1-4. A laboratory technician here is sterilizing blood by means of a special ultra-violet radiation tube. How does this illustrate the technical method? The special goggles protect the operator's eyes from damage.

perimentation would be fatal. The *technical method* is widely used in testing. Much of our new knowledge of science results from use of the *research method*.

The technical method is probably the most widely used in science today. Here the scientist is not working hard toward a new discovery. Nor is he trying a new procedure. Instead, he is making an extremely accurate check.

For example, no operation can be performed until a medical technician has determined the kind of blood a patient has, the clotting time, the corpuscle count, and other important facts. The surgeon follows a carefully outlined procedure, tested over and over and described by leading surgeons. Before the operation has been completed, it may be necessary to send part of the removed organ to the laboratory for microscopic study.

Similarly, technicians follow outlined procedures in checking the bacteria content of milk and water, the strength of drugs, or the various parts for the presence of disease. Here are three steps in applying this important method.

1. *Follow an outlined procedure carefully.* The technician must not vary the procedure in any way.

2. *Make accurate observations.* A slip in observation might make the whole test valueless.

3. *Record and report all findings.* Again, the technician must use great care in recording all results of a procedure.

Much of the laboratory phase of your biology course, whether demonstration, group, or individual study, will involve the technical method. If you observe a demonstration, study the procedure carefully, observe the progress of the demonstration, and make an accurate report of the results.

The research method is used to prove or disprove an idea. The research method differs from the technical method in that there is no definite outlined procedure. You will have opportunities to use this method in your biology course. It may be an experiment performed by the class, or a project you have planned. Let's look at the steps of the research method as the scientist follows them.

1. *Recognizing and defining a problem.* The more you study biology, the more questions you will want answered. Such questions present a problem to the scientist. He wants to find the answer to it. Why does a plant bend toward the light? How do roots take in water? What causes a heart to beat?

2. *Collecting information related to the problem.* When a research problem

leads into the unknown, the scientist uses known facts to take him to the fringe of knowledge. He gathers all available information relating to his problem. For this reason, a scientific library is as important as a laboratory. Your textbook and supplementary readings (found in the lists at the end of each unit in this book) will aid you in solving biological problems included in your course.

3. *Forming an idea or hypothesis.* You might call this a scientific " hunch." The scientist usually has an idea of what an experiment might prove. However, he must not make up his mind in advance. He must prove or disprove his idea.

4. *Experimenting to prove or disprove the hypothesis.* The scientist thinks up an experiment to prove or disprove the hypothesis. This part of this procedure requires imagination, careful planning, and skill. Frequently, several experiments may be required.

5. *Observing the experiment.* What does the experiment prove? Perhaps something quite unexpected appears in the experiment. The scientist is, of course, a keen observer, and so will notice this. Many of our most important scientific discoveries were not expected until an experiment revealed them.

6. *Organizing and recording data from an experiment.* Every part of the experiment — the way it was set up, what happened during its progress, and the results — must be recorded accurately. These records may be in the form of notes, drawings, tables, or graphs.

7. *Drawing conclusions.* Scientific data are of value only when they are put to use. Drawing a conclusion leads to the discovery of a principle which can be applied to other situations. For example, Dr. Alexander Fleming found in experiments that a mold called *Penicillium* killed certain kinds of bacteria. His conclusion from this observation led to his discovery of the wonder drug, penicillin.

How do you set up a scientific experiment? We will now plan a simple experiment, using two sets of plants, and see how it should be set up. Then we shall see how the same experiment could be made quite worthless with a few slight oversights. The experiment will show the influence of light on the growth of bean seedlings. Our hypothesis is that light is necessary for normal growth and activity of a green plant.

Plant a bean in each of six three-inch pots filled with garden loam. All six pots should be watered regularly and equally. Set three pots on a window shelf in a warm room. The other three should be placed in a dark place at the same temperature as the room. In selecting these locations, be careful to find places where the temperature is the same. The seedlings should be left for four weeks.

Notes must be made of all results during the experiment. At the end of four weeks, the length of all stems can be found by counting the leaves and measuring the distance between them. The color of all plants should also be noted. Data from the three plants in the light, as well as those in the dark, can then be averaged.

The experiment should show that the plants in the light were green, had sturdy stems, and large, healthy leaves. The plants in the dark had longer, spindly stems and small, yellow leaves. We can conclude that light is somehow necessary for growth of a young bean plant. Both sets of plants were grown under the same conditions except for light. Light was the *variable factor;* all other factors were ruled out.

Fig. 1-5. This biologist is sectioning plants that have been treated with radioactive materials. As a result of a study of these parts, the movement of substances through the plant's body can be determined. Explain how this shows the research method.

What if the plants in the dark were growing in clay or sand, while those in the light were in loam? Or what if we had watered one set more often than the others? Suppose one set had been in a warmer place than the other? The difference in the seedlings could have been due to any one of these variable factors. The experiment would have proved nothing. Similarly, if we had used only one plant in the light and one in the dark, the difference in the rate of growth might have been due to a weak plant. This was the reason for using several plants.

When you plan an experiment, be sure to control conditions so as to test *only one variable factor*. When you are dealing with several factors, plan an experiment to test each factor separately.

What does biology include? Although biology is a single science based on the study of all living things, it includes many special branches. The bacteriologist, after gaining a knowledge of biology in general, usually specializes in one or more of these branches.

We usually separate biological science into these broad areas:

1. *General biology* includes the study of living things in general, the principles governing life, and the relationship of

living things to their surroundings and to each other.

2. *Botany,* the specialized study of plant life and the relationship of plants to other living things.

3. *Zoology,* the specialized study of animal life and the relationship of animals to other living things.

4. *Human biology* deals with man as a living organism and his relationships with other living things.

These general areas are, in turn, separated into further fields of specialized study.

What can biology do for you? Some of you will choose a branch of biology as a career. For those who do, your biol-

ogy course is an introduction to a life-work. For those of you who do not take up biology as a career, your knowledge of living things will be useful in daily life. You will look at a piece of woodland, a field, a bog, or a river with much greater interest when you understand the plants and animals which live there, and the principles which govern their lives.

We can summarize goals and objectives of a biology course as follows.

1. *To answer questions about life and living things.* Can identical twins be of different sexes? Can a child inherit an acquired skill from its parents? How does your body produce immunity

Fig. 1-6. One variable factor, light, was used in an experiment with these two plants. Note the tall, spindly stems of the plant on the left grown in the dark. The plant on the right, however, grown in light, has sturdy stems and large leaves.

to a disease? How is energy stored in food? Is the mother or father responsible for the sex of a child? The answers to these and countless other questions about life are part of the knowledge of biology.

2. *To acquire scientific attitudes and methods.* Biology will help you solve problems. It will increase your powers of observation. It will help you evaluate your observations and draw correct conclusions from what you see.

3. *To understand the basic principles of life.* As you study biology, you will see that all living things fit into an orderly pattern. Basic principles and natural laws govern all of the events in the world of life.

4. *To aid the conservation program.* No organism has been more destructive to living things than man himself. He has slaughtered wildlife, destroyed their homes, poisoned their streams with refuse, leveled forests, and has even destroyed the soil itself. Civilization need not be responsible for such destruction!

5. *To improve our general health standards.* Probably the greatest advances in biology have been in control of disease and improvement of health. At least half of the deaths from diseases caused by germs could have been avoided. Health education can reduce the number of deaths from heart disease and cancer enormously.

6. *To increase outdoor recreation.*

Fig. 1-7. Water polluted by factory wastes can be a serious health menace. Conservation of natural resources should be a goal of everyone.

Fig. 1-8. Bird hikes give you the chance to get together in groups and be out-of-doors as well. Learning about birds is an interesting and worthwhile hobby.

There is no better place to relax and forget the cares and worries of modern complex living than in the out-of-doors. Miles of paved highways lead to forests, lakes, state and national parks, and other places where man can be alone with nature. Biological knowledge will add to the enjoyment of every hike and trip you make.

7. *To acquaint you with some of the outstanding biologists.* Biology is a record of human achievements. Every phase of modern living has been improved in some way by the contributions of great biologists. We, who enjoy these benefits, should know more about the men and women who gave them to us.

8. *To introduce worthwhile hobbies.* Biology is full of fascinating hobbies. Have you ever watched angelfish glide gracefully through columns of water plants in a tropical aquarium? Many species of tropical fish thrive in the tanks of thousands of amateur aquarists.

Others prefer fancy goldfish or the many small fish of our native waters. Bird hikes, nature photography, flower and vegetable growing, insect collecting — biology is full of interesting hobbies.

9. *To improve daily life.* Seeding and fertilizing a lawn, spraying insect pests, protecting food from spoilage, and a great many other contacts you will have with the living world might be classed as biological necessities. Biology will help you perform these tasks more skillfully.

10. *To introduce biological occupations.* Every high school pupil is giving thought to career opportunities for a lifework. The food industries are always eager to have people who are trained in biology. Nurses, doctors, dentists, and optometrists require courses in biology. And if you plan to go into the fields of agriculture, bacteriology, or forestry you must have a knowledge of biology.

Fig. 1-9. In fighting garden insects, dusters and sprayers are important weapons. However, especially early in the season, it pays to pick off by hand the first arrivals of the larger bugs, such as squash bugs and tomato worms.

In Conclusion

You are now ready to explore the living world. We will use various scientific methods and procedures in our exploration. A page in your text may represent many years of research and study conducted by a biologist of past years. An experiment you conduct in the laboratory might have been an outstanding discovery a few years ago. At times, your study of biology will bring you to the fringe of knowledge — a problem which may be under investigation in a research laboratory at this very moment.

What is life? What does it mean to be alive? Let's begin the study of living things with these basic questions. We will not find an answer, but we will show you many fascinating things that biologists have discovered about life.

Questions for Review

1. Some primitive people have resorted to magic and superstition. Give as many reasons as you can to account for this.

2. Explain why superstition has been a foe of science through the ages.

3. Discuss the contribution of the early Greeks to medicine and biology.

4. List five attitudes associated with modern science.

5. List seven steps of the research method.

6. Explain what is meant by the variable factor in an experiment.

7. What was the single variable factor tested in the experiment with bean seedlings? How were the other factors ruled out of the experiment?

8. List some of the specialized fields in the biological sciences.

9. List ten goals and objectives of a high school course in biology.

10. What are some effective ways to fight garden insects?

Biologically Speaking

attitude	human biology	superstition
biology	hypothesis	technical method
botany	producer scientist	variable factor
consumer scientist	research method	zoology

Applying Facts and Principles

1. Compare the technical and research methods in terms of purpose and procedure.

2. Why is scientific curiosity an important quality of a research scientist?

3. A person cannot believe the principle of cause and effect and still believe in superstition. Why is this true?

4. In recent tests of the polio vaccine, children of the same age group were given one of two kinds of injections. One group received the Salk vaccine. The other group was given a useless solution made to look exactly like the vaccine in regard to color and consistency. Even the doctors who gave the injections had no idea which substance they were injecting. The vaccine and useless solution were identified by code numbers so that only those who were conducting the experiment knew which children received each of the substances. Why were some of the children given a useless substance, looking exactly like the vaccine? Why was it necessary to use children of about the same age in the experiment?

CHAPTER 2

What It Means To Be Alive

Let's take a trip to a quiet pool in a woods. Several rocks are lying in the shallow water. A frog is sitting on one of the rocks, ready to leap to the safety of the pool if danger comes. Nearby, a bird is perched on a dead branch. A rabbit is partly hidden in the grasses and ferns which surround the pool. These grasses and ferns are growing in rich woodland soil.

If you were asked to separate all the things just mentioned into two groups, what would be your basis for dividing them? Undoubtedly, you would put the water, soil, and rocks into one group and the frog, the bird, the rabbit, and the grasses and ferns into another. The basis for this grouping is life. Some of the things are *living* and some are *nonliving*. You would need a third group, *having lived*, to include the dead tree.

Living and nonliving things. The pool we described is shown in Fig. 2-1. Each of the plants and animals you see is an **organism,** or a complete, entire living thing. Each possesses a condition we call *life*. This life came from another organism of the same kind and will be passed on to a similar offspring. You might compare this transfer of life to the lighting of new fires from one which has been burning. When a fire goes out, it cannot be relighted. But if new supplies of fuel are lighted from older fires, the fire can be preserved endlessly. Thus, life is preserved, age after age, in organisms. Water, rocks, and all other nonliving substances never possessed life.

Would it surprise you to find out that all plants and animals are alive because of the same substance? We call this basic substance of life **protoplasm** (*proh*-toh-plazm). It is the only living substance. The water and rocks in Fig. 2-1 do not have protoplasm as part of their make-up. The frog, bird, rabbit, and grasses and ferns do have it. You have and all other people have it.

Living things are fundamentally alike. They must be alike if they are made of the same basic substance and share the condition we speak of as life. Look at the picture in Fig. 2-2. They are so different in appearance that no one could mistake the plant for the animal. You can name many ways in which they seem to be different.

Let's consider some of the characteristics of all living things which make them similar and which distinguish them from nonliving things.

Living things have a certain form and size. You can describe a pine tree, a Persian cat, a geranium plant, and a cottontail rabbit with reasonable accuracy. You also can predict the approximate size each will become when it is mature. This is because all living things have a certain form and size.

While two plants and animals of the

Fig. 2-1. Examine the drawing carefully and name the living things that are shown in it; likewise, name the nonliving things. Tell why you have classified them as living or nonliving.

same kind are never identical in appearance, they are of the same general form as all others of their kind. A tiny rainbow trout will grow to be like all other rainbow trout. It will develop a certain form and color and will reach a certain size. It does not resemble a bass, a perch, or a catfish. Its life and substance came from its parents, two other rainbow trouts. While it may vary slightly, it will preserve the basic qualities of its kind.

Living things have a definite life span. The *life span* of a plant or animal is its period of existence — the time between its beginning and its death. No form of life can exist indefinitely. There are four stages in the life of every individual organism: (1) beginning or origin; (2) growth; (3) maturity; and (4) death. Even though living things repair and maintain themselves for long periods of time, the substance composing them finally breaks down. Then they lose their life activity and die.

The life span of any particular plant or animal, barring disease or accidental death, is about the same as that of all others of its kind. The petunia, marigold, and zinnia plants of your flower garden last only a season. The oak tree may thrive 500 years. A Big Tree of California would still be young at this age. These remarkable trees live several thousand years.

Many members of the insect world have a life span of only a few weeks. Five years is old for some fish. Horses may reach an age of 30 or more. Man's life span averages between 66 and 68 years. Some people live to be much older, while some die younger.

Regardless of what the life span may be, however, eventual death of a living organism is inevitable. This isn't true of nonliving things. The substance composing nonliving things isn't active in the sense that protoplasm is. A rock you pick up may be millions of years old.

Radium and other radioactive substances do have a definite period of existence. It may be a few seconds or millions of years. The matter compos-

Fig. 2-2. One geranium of this species is like all other plants of the same species. The same is true of all cats. This similarity is characteristic of all living things of the same kind.

ing these substances changes slowly to energy in the form of radiation. And with this release of energy other substances are formed. Scientists speak of the life of radioactive materials in terms of the time it takes the matter composing them to change to energy. But this "life" is quite different from the plant or animal which produced by another of its kind, grows, matures, and dies.

Living things maintain constant activity. They cannot just exist. When activity ceases, life also ceases.

Life activity does not refer just to visible signs of life, such as moving around. A tree may look lifeless, but its living

Fig. 2-3. You can identify this fish as a rainbow trout because fundamentally it is like all other rainbow trouts. Both the parent and offspring are basically alike.

parts are in a constant state of activity.

Protoplasm can remain active and alive only as long as energy is released in it. In other words, energy is the force which gives life to living substance. This power must be present throughout life. You use this energy in your living substance when you read this page, when you think, when you move around. You use it just to stay alive.

The activities of plants and animals are called their **life functions,** or life processes. Like the substance which carries them on, life functions are universal. They are performed by every living thing. This explains why the grasshopper is no more alive than the grass it eats. Life functions make all organisms fundamentally alike and different from nonliving things.

We will discuss these functions, the substance which performs them, and the energy which makes them possible in Chapter 4.

Living things have a critical relationship with everything around them — their environment. The *environment* includes all of their surroundings. Factors such as temperature, rainfall, humidity, or water vapor in the air, winds and air currents, soil conditions, and variations in the surface of the earth, have a direct influence on life. Environmental conditions differ in various localities. As these conditions vary, plant and animal life in the region varies. Desert plants and animals cannot survive in moist woods. Nor can prairie life survive in swamps. From the arctic wastelands to the tropics and from mountain to valley, you find certain kinds of plants and animals which find each environment ideal.

The environment must supply plant life with materials with which to pro-

Fig. 2-4. Some of the California redwoods have lived over 2,000 years; some are 4,000 years old. The lumber from one of these is enough to build 20 five-room houses.

Fig. 2-5. The robin and the tree are carrying on many life functions which are alike. Name some of these.

duce a food supply. Animals, in turn, eat the plants as food. Thus, plants become part of the necessary environment of animal life. Water is essential to all living things. Some plants and animals require a water environment and thrive in oceans, lakes, or streams. Others require the less abundant water of a bog or a marsh. Still others thrive in the dry surroundings of the desert.

Light is another critical factor of the environment. The dark floor of a forest is an ideal place for young sugar maples and beech trees. The American elm grows better in bright sunshine.

With the exception of certain kinds of bacteria, plants and animals require air (oxygen) for life. The earthworm finds sufficient air in the soil. The fish depends on oxygen which is dissolved in water. The atmosphere supplies the host of plants and animals that live on the surface of the earth.

The food supply, water, light, and air are **requirements** for life. The environment must supply them, along with other necessary conditions.

Living things have a survival problem. Plants and animals face a constant struggle for life. Much of this struggle centers around requirements for life. A severe drought, extreme heat or cold, storms, fires, and other catastrophes take a heavy toll of plant and animal life. Famine is a constant threat to animal life. Plants often sprout in unsuitable places where seeds happen to fall. They struggle for a time, then die because the soil is not of the right type, or because there is too much or too little water or light.

Even if the environment is proper, a plant or animal must compete with other living things. Sometimes the struggle is competition for the needs of life. Other times it is a struggle against enemies. A small tree growing from the forest tree floor must compete with many other trees for a place to grow. The robin is a constant threat to the worm and caterpillar. But hawks, crows, bluejays, cats are a constant threat to robins. The **struggle for existence** is a problem to all living things.

Extinct organisms. Many plants and animals which thrived on the earth are now gone forever. We classify them as **extinct organisms.** Once the earth supported a large population of dinosaurs. No one knows exactly why these great reptiles disappeared so completely. They had dominated the earth in many regions for millions of years. The saber-toothed tiger, wooly rhinoceros, giant sloth, Irish elk, mastodon, and mammoth are extinct animals which flourished more recently than the dinosaurs.

Once the forests of North America were made up of giant ferns and plants called club mosses rather than the trees we have today. As the environment changed, they perished. Today, tree ferns are found only in scattered areas where the climate is warm, as in Jamaica and Hawaii.

The curious dodo, shown in Fig. 2-10, was a relative of the pigeon, with a body about the size of a turkey. Sailors found this bird on the island of Mauritius in the Indian Ocean. The name, dodo, means "simpleton" in Portuguese. It was well-named, for it had no fear and could be killed with a club. Sailors were responsible for the extermination of the dodo many years ago because it was a good source of food.

The heath hen, passenger pigeon, and great auk are also numbered among extinct birds. Unless we continue to guard them closely, the whistling swan, ivory-billed woodpecker, whooping crane, California condor, and several other species may be added to the list of extinct birds.

Variations cause changes in living things. How do plants and animals change and become better suited to an environment? The answer lies in **varia-**

Fig. 2-6. A marsh is one kind of environment. Here all living things must adapt themselves to this environment in order to survive.

Fig. 2-7. For dry land plants which require little water, a desert environment is ideal.

Fig. 2-8. Besides the right environment to survive, animals like this frog have a constant struggle against predatory animals.

Fig. 2-9. Tree ferns are not a common sight today. At one time, they made up large forests and grew 30 to 40 feet high. However, as environmental conditions changed, they were unable to compete with more adaptable varieties.

ern forest. Wolves and other flesh-eating animals would have exterminated it years ago. But neither could the larger, northern whitetail deer find shelter in the marshes of Florida.

In referring to adaptation, we often speak of an organism as modifying to fit its environment. This does not happen. No bird can voluntarily change its color to blend with its surroundings. The ptarmigan (*tar*-mi-gan) of the north does not willingly grow white plumage to blend with the snow in winter. Plants and animals do not change *in order to* survive. They survive *because of* change. For every change which improves the chances of survival, there have been countless variations which were of no benefit or even caused destruction. By taking advantage of variations in organisms in plant and animal

tions. This means that no two offspring are exactly alike, nor are they exactly like their parents. Sometimes a slight change is a benefit to an organism. It has a better chance to survive. Often, the change isn't an improvement and may hasten its death. By these chance variations which improve the possibility of survival, plants and animals become better suited to their surroundings. This is called **adaptation.**

Nature is full of examples of adaptation. We will consider one in the deer family. The whitetail deer ranges over most of North America, Mexico, and Central America. In the north, it is a slender, long-legged animal. It can run at top speed through a dense forest and hurdle logs five feet or more off the ground. In Florida, a tiny deer known as the Key deer lives in the marshes. This " toy " variety of the whitetail deer weighs 50 pounds or less. It can easily hide in a clump of marsh grass. The Key deer could not survive in the north-

Fig. 2-10. The Dodo, a relative of the pigeons, was about the size of a turkey. Its heavy body and weak wings prevented it from escaping its human enemies.

Fig. 2-11. The whistling swan is rapidly decreasing in numbers. It may be added to the rising number of extinct forms unless definite steps are taken to protect its breeding grounds and favorite haunts.

able for growth, and the high death rate of seedlings. Insects, fish, frogs, and many other animals produce large numbers of young, many of which are destroyed. In cases where fewer young are produced, as in the case of bears, squirrels, deer, and other higher animals, the chances of young surviving are greatly increased by parental care.

Man is the supreme form of life. As living organisms, human beings face the same problems of life which confront plants and animals. But one superiority of the human race has placed man far above other living things in the ability to meet these problems. Man is the most intelligent organism. What he lacks in instinct and physical ability, he more than makes up for in intelligence.

breeding we have produced high-yielding crop plants and fruit trees, race horses, saddle horses, and draft horses, beef cattle, and dairy cattle.

Living things must reproduce. Since the life span of any plant or animal is limited, reproduction is essential if a race of plants or animals is to survive. Reproduction is the ability to produce new living things that are similar to the parents.

Methods of reproduction are strange and interesting. Fruits may have edible pulp to attract an animal as a means of carrying seeds to a new location. Others are equipped with parachutes and ride the air currents. Animals frequently travel long distances to find conditions suitable for the production and rearing of young. The plant or animal must be able to produce at a rate at least equal to the death rate of its kind. Plants usually produce large quantities of seed. The number must be large enough to allow for destruction of seed, failure to lodge in a place suit-

Fig. 2-12. The whitetail deer is a good example of how an animal has adapted itself to its surroundings. The long, slender legs enable it to run swiftly through thick forests.

Fig. 2-13. Since bears do not produce large numbers of young, the bear's mother instinct to protect her young cubs is a big factor in their survival.

He learned long ago that food could be grown in cultivation. This solves the greatest problem facing all other living things. True, people still face famine at certain times and in certain places of the earth, but even this problem can be solved in time.

Man has spread his civilization from the tropics to the frigid realms. This does not necessarily indicate great adaptability of man to various environmental problems. If it were not for man's intelligence, human life would probably exist only in the tropics. But he modifies his environment to suit his needs. Clothing, shelter, and heating devices allow people to live in the coldest of climates. Shelter and cooling devices protect them from the summer heat.

He controls his natural enemies and, in many cases, puts them to work for him. Even disease microbes, man's greatest enemies in the living world, are coming under his control.

Man's brain has enabled him to become the most successful form of life.

In Conclusion

To be alive is to be different from all nonliving things, and to be alive is to be like all other living things. Plants and animals are composed of the same life substance and they carry on the same life functions.

Being alive is a problem. You cannot just exist. Your body substance responds to conditions around it. The environment must supply the organic needs of life, as well as a suitable place in which to live.

As we continue the study of life and the similarities of living things, we turn to the physical make-up of plants, animals, and people. For this study, we need a microscope, for the individual units of life called cells are too small to be seen without magnification. The microscope is as necessary to the biologist as the telescope is to the astronomer. We will study this instrument and find out what it reveals about life.

Questions for Review

1. What does a biologist mean when he refers to an organism?
2. How is protoplasm different from any other substance?
3. Explain how living things may be distinguished from nonliving things on the basis of definite form.
4. Discuss the term *life span* and indicate the approximate life span of several common plants and animals.
5. In what respect are life functions universal?

6. Describe some of the important varying factors which make up the environment of a plant or animal.
7. What do we mean by the term *organic needs?* List the basic organic needs of life.
8. By using a plant or animal as an example, illustrate adaptation.
9. Explain the relationship between parental care and number of offspring.
10. Account for the fact that man is superior to all other living things.

Biologically Speaking

adaptation
environment
extinct organism
life function

life span
protoplasm
reproduction
struggle for existence

Applying Facts and Principles

1. Discuss variation in organic needs and variation in environmental conditions as they relate to the distribution of living things.
2. Discuss the relationship between variations in organisms, the struggle for existence, and improvement of plants and animals.
3. The crow, robin, and certain other birds have increased in numbers with civilization. Many other kinds have decreased. Account for this in terms of adaptation.
4. Why do nonliving things lack the possibility of natural improvement?
5. In your opinion, what is the greatest threat to human existence on the earth today?

CHAPTER **3**

The Physical Basis of Life

If you look at a newspaper picture through a strong magnifying glass, you see nothing but a mass of tiny black dots. All these dots combine to form an object you can recognize. Each dot is a unit of the picture. Each is a small part of a greater whole.

When you magnify a plant or animal, you see another kind of unit. We call these units of living things *cells.* Each is a microscopic mass of living substance. Each carries on life functions. In one sense, each cell is a tiny plant or animal; in fact, some plants and animals actually consist of only one cell. Other plants and animals are composed of millions of cells, all working together in close relationship with each other.

The microscope will take you into a world in miniature. This amazing instrument will show you the cells of your blood which carry oxygen to other cells and the wandering corpuscles which wage a constant war against invading microbes. Through the lenses of your microscope you will see the food factories in leaves and the storage deposits in a root cell. You will see nerve cells, muscle cells, bone cells, and many others — all fundamentally alike, yet each a specialist in a certain kind of life activity.

A Dutchman, a hobby, and a great contribution to biology. Nearly 300 years ago, in the city of Delft, Holland, Anton Van Leeuwenhoek (*lay*-ven-hook), 1632–1723, made a hobby of grinding lenses. He used small pieces of glass and ground them into magnifying lenses with which he could enlarge objects 40 to 270 times. By mounting his lenses in holding devices, Van Leeuwenhoek made many microscopes. It is said that he made 247 different ones. Each different type of material to be studied required a special microscope. Today his microscopes seem crude.

One of Van Leeuwenhoek's early microscopes was built in order to examine a small fish. It consisted of a tube in which the fish was put. The frame around the tube held a small magnifying lens. By putting his eye close to the lens, Van Leeuwenhoek enlarged the tail of the fish enough to see blood vessels and circulating blood. With other microscopes he saw the fibers in muscles and other minute structures in various plants and animals. To his amazement, he found stagnant water teeming with microscopic animal life, which he described as " cavorting beasties."

While Van Leeuwenhoek did not make the first microscope, his were far more perfect than any of the earlier and even cruder instruments. For this reason, and the fact that he was the first to view plants and animals with a magnifying lens, we usually credit him with the invention of the microscope.

Light for viewing an object strikes the *mirror*. The mirror directs the rays through the opening in the *stage,* through the objective, *tube,* and eyepiece to the eye. This explains why objects to be viewed with this type of microscope must be sufficiently small and thin to allow light to pass through.

The electron microscope. Until recent years, the amount of magnification possible with a microscope was limited by the ability of the human eye to see greatly enlarged images. Light has been another problem in high magnification. Both of these limitations are overcome in the electron microscope. In this instrument, a beam of electrons in a vacuum chamber replaces ordinary

Fig. 3-1. The photograph above shows one of the early microscopes. Science owes much to the contributions of Leeuwenhoek and Hooke in perfecting the microscope.

The modern compound microscope. A compound microscope of the type widely used in high school biology laboratories today is shown in Fig. 3-3. Lenses are contained in the *eyepiece* and in the *objectives.* That is why it is called a **compound microscope.** Most high school microscopes are equipped with 10-power eyepieces. This means that the eyepiece lenses alone magnify 10 times. The objectives contain a series of lenses cemented together. The shorter, or *low power,* objective magnifies 10 times. The usual *high power* objective magnification is 43 or 44 times.

Fig. 3-2. The modern research microscope has enabled scientists to conquer many of the mysteries of life.

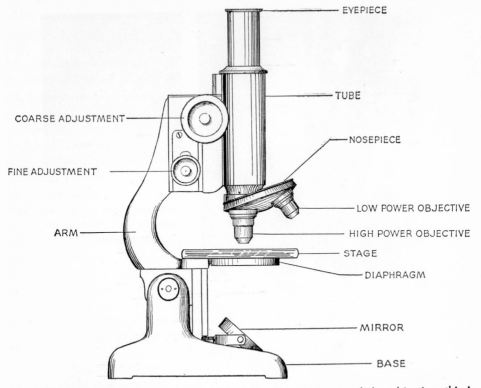

EYEPIECE

TUBE

COARSE ADJUSTMENT

NOSEPIECE

FINE ADJUSTMENT

LOW POWER OBJECTIVE

ARM

HIGH POWER OBJECTIVE

STAGE

DIAPHRAGM

MIRROR

BASE

Fig. 3-3. Because lenses are contained both in the eyepiece and the objective, this is termed a compound microscope.

light. The image is received on a photographic plate which is far more sensitive than a human eye. In some cases, the enlarged image is received on a fluorescent screen.

The electron microscope has been of great value in the study of viruses which cause smallpox, influenza, and other diseases. These extremely small organisms, less than one-millionth of an inch in size, are not visible under the highest power of an optical microscope. Yet, they have been photographed and studied with the electron microscope.

The microscopic structure of living things. Two important discoveries with the microscope revealed the plan of structure of all living things. One of these was the *cell,* the smallest unit of plants and animals. The other was *pro-*

toplasm, the living content of cells and the physical substance of life. The discovery of cells, nearly 300 years ago, was an important milestone in biological science.

The discovery of cells and protoplasm. One day in 1665, the English scientist, Robert Hooke, 1635–1703, was examining various objects with a crude microscope. Among his materials was a piece of cork, sliced thin enough to let light pass through it. To his surprise, he found that the cork was a mass of tiny cavities. Each cavity was enclosed by walls, reminding him of cells in a monastery or a honey comb. **Cell** was a logical name for these tiny cavities.

Hooke did not realize, however, that the most important part of these cells

Fig. 3-4. This bacteria specimen, seen in the electron microscope on the left, was enlarged to 40,000 diameters.

was lacking. He saw only the empty shells or walls of cells which had once contained active, living protoplasm.

In the early 19th century, several scientists conducted investigations of plant and animal cells. In 1835, a French biologist named Dujardin discovered protoplasm. Three years later, in 1838, two German biologists, Matthias Schleiden (*shly*-den) and Theodor Schwann, found protoplasm in plant and animal cells quite independently. The work of these men and other biologists gave us the basis for the cell theory which states that:

1. All living things are composed of cells.

2. All cells come from previously existing cells.

3. The cell is the unit of structure of all living things.

Protoplasm is the most wonderful of all substances. Can you imagine a chemical mixture being alive? Of the millions of different mixtures, only one, protoplasm, has this marvelous quality. What sort of substance is protoplasm? It is usually grayish, but it may appear bluish or even brownish. It is neither entirely liquid nor solid, but rather jelly-like in texture. We often compare it to the white of an egg. Sometimes protoplasm is almost clear; sometimes it contains tiny bubbles or grains.

It appears to be impossible to make an accurate chemical analysis of protoplasm. Since it is alive and active, its composition is constantly changing. Furthermore, biologists and chemists have never succeeded in keeping it alive during the analysis because the chemicals used in the analysis destroy the property of " life." However, nonliving protoplasm contains the substances listed in the next paragraph.

Water forms the liquid portion of protoplasm and makes up on the average about 70 per cent of its composition. Other substances are associated with the water. About half of these are *protein* (*pro*-tee-in). *Sugars, starches, fats,* and *salts* also are present. Certain of these solid substances, including protein, are associated with water in a solution of the type we call a **colloid** (*kol*-oid). Other solid substances, including salts, mingle with water in a true solution. This gives the colloid a semi-

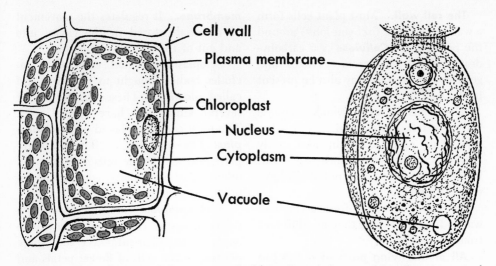

Cell wall

Plasma membrane

Chloroplast

Nucleus

Cytoplasm

Vacuole

Fig. 3-5. The cell on the left is a typical plant cell and that on the right is a typical animal cell. How do they differ and how are they alike?

solid texture. Egg white, face creams, hand lotions, and gelatin desserts are other colloids.

The water present in protoplasm is not alive. Nor is the protein or any other of the solid substances. Yet, when living protoplasm builds more of its own substance, life is passed into it. What gives it life and how does this happen? Biologists haven't yet found the answer, and probably never will. This is one of the marvels of life.

The cell, a unit of protoplasmic structure. The protoplasm composing a plant, an animal, or man is contained in its cells. Thus, each cell is a unit mass of protoplasm. It is the individual part of which the whole plant, animal, or man is composed. In a many-celled organism the size of the individual depends, not on the *size* of its cells, but on the *number* of cells present.

The protoplasm within a single cell is specialized. That is, there are distinct and different parts of the cell all made up of protoplasm. When you see various types of cells under a microscope, you will probably be amazed that a

structure so small can be that complex.

In addition to living protoplasm, cells contain nonliving substances. These nonliving parts are really essential for the cell to carry on its functions.

In the study of cells, you will find also that plant cells differ in several ways from animal cells. However, the protoplasm in all cells is fundamentally the same. Fig. 3-5 shows a typical plant cell and a typical animal cell. Notice the ways in which they are alike and those in which they are different.

In classifying the parts of a cell, we can group the living and nonliving structures as follows.

1. The *cell wall*. This nonliving structure, formed by living protoplasm, especially in plant cells, forms a case which surrounds and encloses the cell structures inside.

2. The *protoplast*. This includes all the protoplasm or living content of the cell.

3. The *inclusions*. These are nonliving substances in the protoplasm.

Now we will discuss each of these three groups in detail.

The cell wall. Most plant cells form a wall of cellulose (*sel*-you-lohs) around the protoplast. **Cellulose** is a carbohydrate related to starch. Waxes and gelatinous materials may also be present in the wall.

The walls of cells which compose leaves, petals, pulpy fruits, and other soft plant parts are thin and easily crushed. Cells which make up wood, various plant fibers, and nut shells have very thick walls.

Animal cells seldom form a cellulose wall. In this respect, they are different from plant cells.

All of the living parts of a cell are included in the protoplast. The principal divisions of a cell protoplast are (1) *cytoplasm* (*sy*-toh-plazm); and (2) the *nucleus* (*new*-klee-us).

We include in the **cytoplasm,** or cell substance, all the protoplasm lying outside the nucleus. Various parts of the cytoplasm are specialized and form distinct cell structures. We will refer to the bulk of the cytoplasm as **general cytoplasm.**

Where cytoplasm lies against the cell wall, it becomes clear and almost colorless and hardens slightly, forming a thin membrane. This is the **plasma membrane.** Pressure inside the cell presses the plasma membrane firmly against the wall in a plant cell, much as air presses the inner tube against the casing in a tire. This makes the membrane hard to see. In many animal cells, the plasma membrane forms the outer surface of the cell. This membrane is extremely important to the life of the cell since it controls the movement of materials into and out of the general cytoplasm.

Another membrane forms where cytoplasm borders on a central cavity within the cell. We refer to this type of membrane as a **vacuolar** (*vack*-you-oh-lar) **membrane.** It regulates the movement of materials stored in the cavity into and out of the general cytoplasm.

Cytoplasm of plant cells often includes bodies thought to be living and called **plastids.** These plastids are of several kinds and have special uses. The most common plastid is the **chloroplast** (*klo*-roh-plast). These chloroplasts, present in the cells of leaves and other green plant parts, contain the familiar green pigment, **chlorophyll.**

A **chromoplast** (*kro*-moh-plast) is a colored plastid containing yellow, orange, or red pigment. We find these plastids in the cells of flower petals and the skins of fruits, such as the tomato, the cherry, or the pepper. A **leucoplast** (*lew*-koh-plast) is a colorless body and serves as a place in which a plant cell stores food.

The **nucleus** appears as a dense, spherical, or ball-shaped mass of protoplasm, often near the center of the cell. It lies in the mass of general cytoplasm. When you examine a cell under the microscope, the nucleus usually looks slightly darker than the general cytoplasm. This is because its substance is thicker, or more dense. You can use special stains, such as iodine or methylene (*meth*-ee-leen) blue, to color the nucleus much darker than the cytoplasm and thus make it quite distinct.

The nucleus is the center of most of the activity of a cell. In addition to controlling cell activities, it is the center of cell reproduction.

Structure of the nucleus. The outer edge of the nucleus is a thin membrane, the **nuclear membrane,** as shown in Fig. 3-6. Inside the membrane lies the nuclear sap, or **nucleoplasm** (*new*-klee-oh-plazm), a dense, gelatinous form of protoplasm. The nucleoplasm contains a small, round body, the **nucleolus** (*new*-klee-oh-lus), which appears as a tiny nucleus within the nucleus. Often, several nucleoli are present. The function of the nucleolus is not known. It may be a reservoir of the materials produced in the nucleus. An interesting fact is that the nucleolus or nucleoli usually disappear during cell division.

When a nucleus is stained with special dyes, a network of granular substance appears. This is **chromatin** (*kroh*-ma-tin). Chromatin is of extreme importance since it carries the hereditary characteristics of the plant or animal. Your hair color, eye color, facial features — all of the characteristics you inherited — are determined by the chromatin in your cells.

The inclusions in cells. These are nonliving materials or parts found in the cytoplasm or nucleus of cells. Cavities in the cytoplasm are called **vacuoles** (*vack*-you-oles). They contain a nonliving, watery fluid called **cell sap.** Do not confuse cell sap with cytoplasm. Cytoplasm is a form of living protoplasm. Cell sap is nonliving. Various

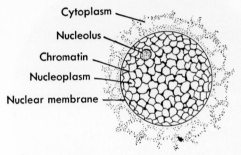

Cytoplasm
Nucleolus
Chromatin
Nucleoplasm
Nuclear membrane

Fig. 3-6. Most of the activities of a cell are controlled by the nucleus.

food substances, especially sugar and mineral salts, are dissolved in water in the cell sap. These nonliving materials are essential to normal activity of the cell. Vacuoles of plant cells are often large, especially in older cells. Starch grains, oil droplets, crystals of various mineral compounds, and other solid materials may also be present in cells as inclusions. The table on this page summarizes the principal parts of a cell.

A glance at several kinds of cells. You could use any part of a plant or ani-

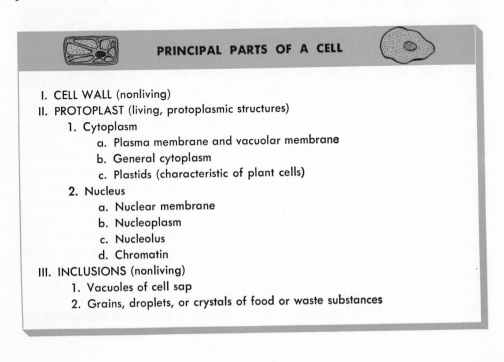

PRINCIPAL PARTS OF A CELL

I. CELL WALL (nonliving)
II. PROTOPLAST (living, protoplasmic structures)
    1. Cytoplasm
        a. Plasma membrane and vacuolar membrane
        b. General cytoplasm
        c. Plastids (characteristic of plant cells)
    2. Nucleus
        a. Nuclear membrane
        b. Nucleoplasm
        c. Nucleolus
        d. Chromatin
III. INCLUSIONS (nonliving)
    1. Vacuoles of cell sap
    2. Grains, droplets, or crystals of food or waste substances

Fig. 3-7. The above shows the cells of an onion skin as viewed under a microscope. They have been stained with iodine to show the nuclei.

mal to examine cells with a microscope. However, certain plant and animal subjects are widely used in high school biology laboratories because they are easy to get and they show cell structures clearly.

The onion skin has always been a favorite subject. If you slice an onion lengthwise and pry the thick scale leaves apart, you can peel a thin, transparent skin from the inner surface of each scale leaf. This skin is only one cell thick. Iodine solution is a good stain for onion cells.

Fig. 3-7 shows onion cells as they appear under the microscope. The cell walls, cytoplasm, vacuoles, and nucleus show very clearly. The outer edge of the cytoplasm is the plasma membrane. Iodine stains the nucleus darker than the cytoplasm. You can see the nucleus and one or more nucleoli. The odor and flavor of onion is onion oil. You can see this as droplets, a form of cell inclusion, in the cytoplasm.

The leaf of *Elodea,* the common little waterweed of ponds and streams, is an ideal subject to show living cells and chloroplasts. In making a slide of an *Elodea* leaf, press the leaf against your hand to warm it a few minutes. Then put it on a glass slide, add a drop of water, and put a thin cover-glass on top of it. You will find many rounded or egg-shaped chloroplasts. Some may be moving. You might think the chloroplasts are swimming in the general cytoplasm. But if you look more closely, you can see that all of the chloroplasts in a cell are moving in the same direction and at the same rate. The cytoplasm is moving around and around the cell with chloroplasts floating in it.

The potato is an excellent subject to show starch grains. You must slice the potato thin enough so that light can pass through it. A drop of iodine colors the cells yellowish and the starch grains dark blue.

The skin of a tomato shows cells with chromoplasts, while the pulp is made of a different kind of cell, filled with fluid and stored food. Sources of plant materials are almost unlimited. Directions for preparing slides of plant cells are given in *Research on Your Own* at the end of this unit.

Animal cells are more difficult to prepare for microscopic study than plant cells. They do not have cell walls to make them stand out so clearly. Beef or heart muscles will show the long, narrow cells forming muscle fibers. A drop of methylene blue, a widely used stain, will make the cells stand out more clearly. You can see some of your own cells easily if you scrape the inside of your cheek with a toothpick and mount the slimy material you gather on a slide. Either iodine or methylene blue can be used as a stain. You will find these and other animal and human cells in Fig. 3-8.

The cell is the unit of structure of living things. We defined a cell as a unit

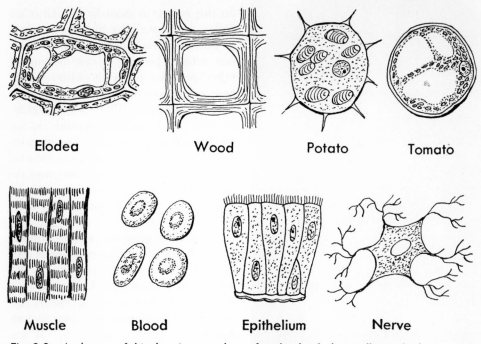

Elodea   Wood   Potato   Tomato

Muscle   Blood   Epithelium   Nerve

Fig. 3-8. At the top of this drawing are shown four kinds of plant cells; at the bottom are four kinds of animal cells.

mass of protoplasm. And we stated that plants and animals are composed of cells — a single cell, or many of them. Regardless of what part of a plant or animal you examine, you will find cells. All the living cells will contain protoplasm. All the nonliving cells contained protoplasm at some stage of their life, but this living material has either been replaced by nonliving substances or disappeared. In other words, *the cell is the unit of structure of all living things.*

Is your body then a mere mass of millions of cells, all alike and living together in a tremendous colony? Of course it isn't! If it were, you wouldn't be the marvelous organism you are. Your ability would be limited to the activity of a single kind of cell.

Your body and those of complex plants and animals are the result of cell specialization. This means that there

are many different kinds of cells. Each kind is highly developed for a particular kind of life activity. This leads us to the subject of tissues.

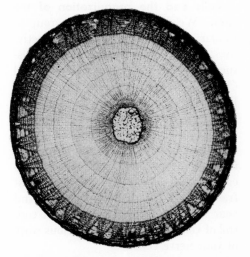

Fig. 3-9. This cross section of a woody stem shows how various tissues are grouped together to form an organ such as a stem.

Fig. 3-10. Just as your heart is an organ, so is the trunk of a tree also an organ. Life activity depends on all the cells, tissues, and organs working together.

Cells and the organization of tissues. We define a tissue as a group of similar cells performing a similar activity. In your body you have muscle tissue, nerve tissue, bone tissue, liquid (blood) tissue, and many others. Plants and animals also have tissues. When you name a tissue of the human body, you think immediately of a certain kind of activity. Your movement is the best movement your muscle cells can provide. Your skeleton is the best framework a bone cell can offer. And your hearing, seeing, tasting, and control of your body are the marvelous work of your nerve cells.

A cell in a tissue is a specialist. The cell must perform all of the life activities required to maintain its protoplasm.

In this respect it must be like all other cells. Here, we have division of labor. A nerve cell can become a specialist in one activity because it can depend on other specialists for needs of life. Other cells prepare food for it, supply it with oxygen, and carry off its waste materials. It's like the doctor who depends on the grocer, the carpenter, and the machinist. These specialists, in turn, depend on the doctor. If each one was required to do everything for himself, he could never have become a specialist. So it is with cells.

Tissues are grouped to form organs. In plants and animals, even a highly specialized tissue cannot perform a life activity to perfection. This requires a group of tissues, working closely together. We call such a complex part an *organ*. A hand is an organ. It has skin, muscle, bone, tendons, ligaments, blood, and other parts made of different specialized tissues. Your heart, stomach, liver, brain, and kidneys are other organs. The stem or trunk of a tree is an organ. It has bark, wood, pith, and other tissues, all working together. This organ supports the leaves, flowers, and fruit and moves materials up and down between the roots and leaves.

Organs may be grouped into systems. In the higher forms of life, especially among animals, several organs often perform related functions. Such a group of organs working together is called a *system*. For example, the digestive system performs functions related to the preparation of food for the body. It is composed of many organs, including the stomach, liver, and intestines. The circulatory system includes such organs as the heart, arteries, and veins. These organs, and the tissues which compose them, are all united in the work of circulation.

Complex organisms. The complex plant or animal and man himself are organized in the following way:

1. Protoplasm is contained in all the living cells.

2. Cells are unit masses of protoplasm which make up the organism.

3. Tissues are groups of similar specialized cells.

4. Organs are formed by several tissues, grouped together.

5. Systems are groups of organs performing related functions.

6. The organism is the plant, animal, or man as a whole. It may be complex enough to have systems or so simple that it consists of only a single cell.

In Conclusion

We have discussed the physical basis of life, starting with protoplasm and the organization of protoplasm in a cell. Each cell is a unit of life and, in a sense, a tiny living organism. As living things become more complex, cells become specialists. Tissues, organs, and systems allow specialization of protoplasm to the utmost. They make possible the wonderful activities of our own bodies. Still, the most marvelous activity of the human body is an activity of a cell, or a group of them.

Just as the cell is the unit of structure of all plants and animals, so it is the unit of their life activities or functions. In the next chapter, we will examine cells again. This time, we will approach the cell not from the viewpoint of how it is made, but of what it can do.

Questions for Review

1. What two parts of a modern compound microscope contain lenses which are used in series with each other?

2. Robert Hooke discovered only part of a cell. Explain.

3. Name three ideas in the cell theory.

4. Describe the physical appearance of protoplasm.

5. Protoplasm is a colloid. Distinguish between a colloid and a true solution. What are some other examples of colloids you can name?

6. List the various substances associated with water in the formation of protoplasm.

7. What carbohydrate substances, formed by plant cells, are contained in cell walls?

8. (a) List the various parts of the cytoplasm. (b) List also the parts of the nucleus of a cell.

9. Name several cell inclusions.

10. Doctors speak of blood as a tissue. What do they mean when they use the word tissue?

11. Give an example of a plant and an animal organ.

12. Discuss how your body is organized from protoplasm on up to systems.

Biologically Speaking

cell	compound microscope	organ
cell sap	cytoplasm	organism
cell theory	electron microscope	plasma membrane
cell wall	general cytoplasm	plastids
cellulose	inclusion	protoplasm
chlorophyll	leucoplast	protoplast
chloroplast	nuclear membrane	system
chromatin	nucleolus	tissue
chromoplast	nucleoplasm	vacuolar membrane
colloid	nucleus	vacuoles

Applying Facts and Principles

1. Biology as we know it today could not have developed before the invention and perfection of the microscope. Why is this true?

2. Why is it almost impossible to make an accurate chemical analysis of protoplasm?

3. Explain how the various parts of a cell protoplast illustrate specialization of protoplasm.

4. Discuss the importance and significance of highly specialized cells in the make-up of your body.

5. The more specialized a cell becomes, the more it must depend on other cells. Explain.

CHAPTER 4

The Functional Basis of Life

Have you ever wondered why you fill your lungs with air every few seconds, why you must eat regularly, and why your blood must surge constantly to all parts of your body? To live, of course, is the simple explanation. But have you thought in terms of millions of masses of protoplasm depending on your next breath, your next meal, and your next heartbeat? Have you thought of your lungs, your digestive organs, and your heart as specialists in serving cells?

In this chapter, we will explore the wonders of a living cell. Scientists cannot explain what life is, but they can define it in terms of a group of processes. Our example can be any plant or animal. All we need is active protoplasm, the functional basis of life. Life cannot function without protoplasm.

The cell carries on life activities. There are various ways of separating the life activities of a cell into different processes. The ten *life functions* common to protoplasm and carried on by every living cell are as follows:

(1) Food-getting or food production; (2) digestion; (3) absorption; (4) respiration; (5) assimilation and growth; (6) excretion; (7) secretion; (8) motion; (9) sensitivity; and (10) reproduction.

While we will discuss each of these life functions separately, remember that they are interrelated. Each can be performed only as long as the others are being carried on.

A cell is like a tiny power plant. Its product is life activity. Its fuel is food. Thus the food you eat today will supply the force behind your thoughts, your movements; in fact, your very life today and tomorrow.

But *energy* for life is only one requirement supplied by food. Protoplasm constantly makes more of its own substance. From what? Food must supply this need, too. Thus, every living cell transforms food substance into the living substance, protoplasm.

Can you think of a food that does not come, directly or indirectly, from a green plant? The green plant holds the key to the living world because it is the food producer. The earth yields *water* to the green plant. The air supplies *carbon dioxide,* the same gas you exhale from your lungs. These, however, are not foods and protoplasm cannot use them. But inside certain plant cells are chloroplasts. These chloroplasts contain the green-colored substance, chlorophyll. These cells are the food factories of the green plant. Inside and around these green chloroplasts and with the aid of certain special chemicals called *enzymes* (*en*-zymes), the substances which make up water and carbon dioxide are rearranged to form sugar. During this process, the chloroplasts absorb energy from the sun and store it in the sugar. This cell activity,

Fig. 4-1. The green plant is the food-producer for the living world.   Here wheat is being harvested to make flour.

the food-making of green plants, is known as **photosynthesis** (foh-toh-*sin*-the-sis).   Photosynthesis makes life possible.   Protoplasm " runs " on sunshine, with sugar as a fuel.   Sugar and starch are often changed to fats and oils in cells.

While sugar, starch, fats, and oils

Fig. 4-2. The mold on this bread is a fungus, a plant dependent on a nonliving substance for its food supply.

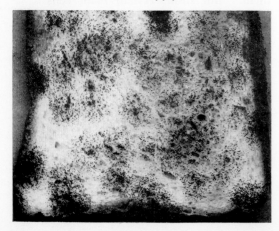

supply the energy requirements, they are not the only substances needed for the formation of protoplasm.   Remember that protein makes up nearly half of the solid ingredients of protoplasm.   Where does protein come from?   We look to the plant for this, too.   In producing protein, the plant adds substances taken from soil minerals to the materials present in sugar.

You can see then why the world is dependent on the green plant for its existence.   A great many nongreen plants are in the same predicament in which animals find themselves.   If they do not have chlorophyll, they cannot make their own food.   Most of these dependent plants belong to the group known as **fungi** (*fun*-jye).   (See Fig. 4-2.)   Among them are bacteria, yeasts, molds, mildews, and mushrooms.

Fungus plants would starve in an environment of soil minerals, water, and air alone.   They must have a food supply.   Some fungi live on dead or nonliving materials, such as decaying wood and other vegetable matter, paper, or food materials like bread, fruits, meat, and cheese. These fungus plants which get their food from nonliving materials are **saprophytes** (*sap*-roh-fites). **Parasites,** on the other hand, attack a living plant or animal or even man himself. The living material is known as the **host.** Included here are such destructive organisms as mildews, rusts, smuts, and disease-causing bacteria.

Not all parasites are destructive to their hosts. In some cases, they are actually beneficial. A certain kind of parasitic bacteria live in tiny swellings, or nodules, on the roots of clover and other plants of the legume family. The root cells of the clover provide moisture and other requirements for the bacteria. The bacteria in turn produce chemical substances called **nitrates** (*ny*-traytes) which are essential to green plants in the production of proteins. This peculiar relationship of living together to the benefit of both is called **symbiosis** (*sim*-bee-oh-sis). We will discuss symbiosis more fully and give other examples in Chapter 19.

Digestion is the preparation of food for cell use. Living protoplasm can make use of only a few simple food substances. Carbohydrate foods, which include sugars and starches, enter a cell in the form of **glucose** (*glu*-kose). Cells use protein foods in the form of **amino** (*ah*-mee-noh) **acids.** Fats are used in the form of **fatty acids** and **glycerin.** These basic foods which enter the cell are quite different from the steak, potatoes, gravy, string beans, and ice cream you eat at the dinner table. Thus, we must make a distinction between the foods *consumed by an organism* and the foods *used by its cells.* We call the change of food into a proper form for cell use **digestion.**

Fig. 4-3. These nodules, containing nitrogen-fixing bacteria, are beneficial to the clover. How does this illustrate symbiosis?

In a plant, digestion may be the simple process of changing starch to sugar. Food is first formed in a plant cell as sugar. Often, the sugar is changed to starch for storage in some other part of the plant. When food is required by the cells, it is a simple matter to change the starch back again into sugar. This same sort of process takes place in the case of both proteins and of fats.

What is absorption? We may define **absorption** as the movement of foods and other substances into cells and internal fluids. In Chapter 3, you learned that the protoplast is enclosed in the plasma membrane. If it is a plant cell, there is usually a cell wall outside this. If the protoplast is enclosed by the plasma membrane, why is it not cut off from food, water, minerals,

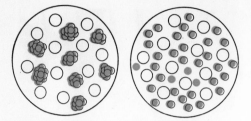

Fig. 4-4. The particles of the insoluble material are shown in color. Notice how in the left-hand diagram they have clung together and have not diffused through the solvent like they have in the right-hand diagram.

oxygen, and other requirements for life?

A cell wall is porous and offers no problem in moving materials into and out of the protoplast. However, to pass through the plasma membrane, foods and minerals must be dissolved in water. That is, their individual particles, which we call **molecules** (*mol*-lih-kyools), must be spread completely through the molecules of water. A plasma membrane will allow particles of these small sizes to pass through it.

Several forces control cell absorption. Water enters the cell by a process known as **osmosis** (oz-*moh*-sis). Since absorption of water by the cells of a root is one of the clearest examples of osmosis, we shall reserve this discussion for Chapter 12. Digested food materials and dissolved minerals pass through the membrane with water. Oxygen, carbon dioxide, and other gases pass freely through the plasma membrane.

Digested foods leave the digestive organs and enter the blood by absorption. Later, the cells absorb these materials from the blood and the blood absorbs waste materials. Part of digestion, then, is making food substances soluble in water so that cells can absorb them.

Respiration is the breath of life to a cell. When a plant cell makes food, it

absorbs energy and stores it in the food. This is the energy which maintains life in protoplasm. The energy is set free when the food substance is broken down inside the cell protoplast. To do this, the cell must have oxygen. When oxygen combines with sugar, two more simple substances, carbon dioxide and water, are formed. This frees the stored energy. Some of it is used to maintain the life processes. Some is released as heat. We call this chemical change **oxidation** (ox-ih-*day*-shun).

Maybe you have noticed that products of oxidation of sugar in a cell are the same as the plant used as raw materials in making the sugar. You see oxidation and the release of stored energy when you burn a piece of paper, a piece of wood, or a lump of coal.

The life process **respiration** is the taking in of oxygen and the release of carbon dioxide by a cell. (See Fig. 4-5.) This life process is closely associated with the chemical process oxidation.

You can see why respiration is essential to life. Cutting off the oxygen supply to a cell is like closing the air intake on an automobile carburetor or smothering a fire by cutting off the draft.

Assimilation is the organization of protoplasm. Part of the food absorbed by a cell, especially protein, serves as building materials for the growth and repair of protoplasm. During compli-

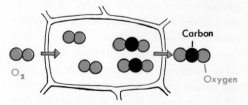

Fig. 4-5. Oxygen, represented in color, is taken in by the cells, while carbon dioxide, represented by black, is given off. This life process is called respiration.

cated and little understood chemical processes, protoplasm forms more protoplasm. This is the life process, **assimilation** (as-sim-ih-*la*-shun).

Excretion is the removal of cell waste materials. The chemical processes carried on in a cell leave various substances which the cell cannot use. The cell discharges these waste materials during **excretion** (ex-*kree*-shun). The accumulation of waste materials in protoplasm may stop its activity and cause death. So it is important that wastes be excreted as they are formed.

One-celled organisms and simple animals, like the sponge, discharge their wastes directly into the water in which they live. However, when billions of cells form a single organism, like your body, the removal of waste becomes a complicated process. Each cell discharges waste into a fluid which washes the cell. This fluid enters the blood stream. The blood, in turn, delivers the wastes to the kidneys, the lungs, and the skin for elimination from the body.

Secretion is the pouring out of essential chemical substances. Every cell is in a sense a tiny chemical factory. It forms chemical substances essential to other life processes. We call the substance by the term **secretion.**

Among the secretions of cells are digestive fluids. The cells of simple organisms secrete all their own digestive fluids and other necessary chemical substances. In animals having organs devoted to the digestion of food, certain tissues are highly specialized in performing this process. The cells forming the lining of the food tube secrete **mucus,** a lubricating substance. Cells of the stomach, liver, pancreas, and intestine secrete digestive fluids.

Highly specialized cells forming glands in higher animals secrete powerful chemical substances known as **hor-**

Fig. 4-6. The growth of these stalagmites results from the addition of lime from dripping water. In living things, growth results on the inside of cells as a result of new protoplasm being formed from food.

mones (*hor*-mones). These secretions influence the activity of cells in the body.

Motion is a basic property of protoplasm. The streaming of cytoplasm inside a cell is primitive cell motion. This motion results from energy released from food during oxidation.

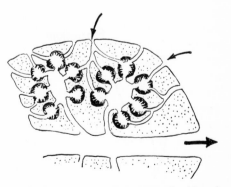

Fig. 4-7. Some simple animals, like the sponge shown here, discharge, or excrete, waste products directly into the water.

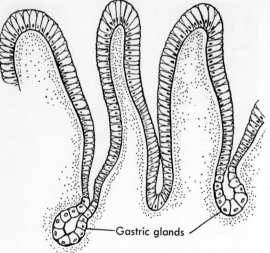

Gastric glands

Fig. 4-8. Gastric glands, located in the stomach wall, secrete a digestive fluid that acts on certain foods. Thus, these foods are made soluble and can be absorbed.

When you study one-celled plants and animals, you will find a slightly more advanced form of motion. Some cells move because the cytoplasm pushes against a flexible plasma membrane. This causes bulges in the membrane in the direction in which the cell is moving. As cytoplasm streams in the bulges, the cell moves along. Many one-celled organisms have threadlike projections of cytoplasm called **cilia** (*sil*-ee-uh), which lash back and forth in the water like tiny oars. Still others have long whiplike strands of cytoplasm, called **flagella** (fla-*jell*-uh), which propel them through the water. (See Fig. 4-9.) We speak of movement of an organism from place to place as **locomotion**.

Cell specialists in motion form muscles. Muscles accomplish such complicated movements as walking, running, swimming, or flying. Muscle cells have the power of shortening, or *contracting*. A single cell contracts only a very slight amount. But when many thousands of cells contract in a single muscle, an arm may bend or a leg may move.

Contraction of heart muscle cells pumps a flow of blood through the vessels. This accomplishes circulation, a result of motion. Muscle layers in the walls of digestive organs cause a churning or squeezing action which moves food along. Muscle cells change the diameter of artery walls and raise or lower the blood pressure.

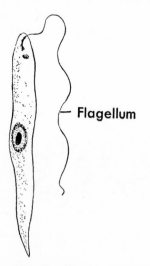

— Flagellum

Fig. 4-9. The flagellum, which enables some one-celled organisms to move through the water, is a long strand of cytoplasm.

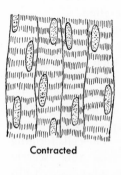

Contracted

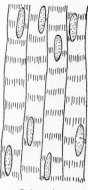

Relaxed

Fig. 4-10. When muscle cells contract, movement results. This shortening of the cells is the result of chemical reactions occurring in the cytoplasm of the cells.

Sensitivity is the response of protoplasm to its surroundings. The high development of this life process has placed man far above all other forms of life. In fact, emotions, thought, memory, and judgment are so marvelous we hardly think of them as cell activities. And they are so complicated, we have no idea how they are accomplished.

To understand sensitivity, or the reaction of protoplasm to conditions around it, we need to study it at a level far below that of a brain cell. Let's consider the plant and its leaves which bend toward the light and its roots which grow toward water. A response of this type is called a **tropism** (*troh*-pizm).

Fig. 4-11. All protoplasm has irritability, or the ability to respond to different stimuli. Hydrotropism is the response to water. What do we call the response which causes this geranium plant to bend toward the light coming through the window?

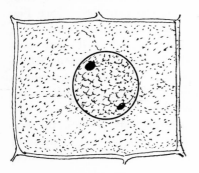

Young cell

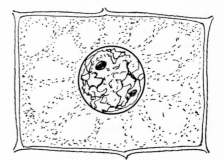

Mature cell

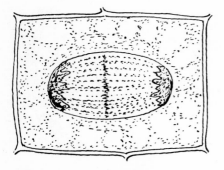

Dividing cell

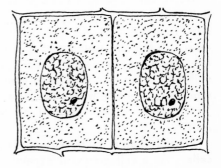

Two daughter cells

Fig. 4-12. During reproduction, the nucleus divides and each cell forms two new cells.

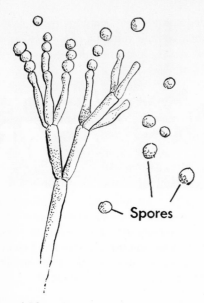

Spores

Fig. 4-13. Some organisms, especially plants, reproduce by means of spores. These spores leave the parent plant and travel to new locations. What is this type of reproduction called?

We name the various tropisms according to the condition or **stimulus** which causes the reaction or **response**. **Phototropism** (foh-toh-*troh*-pizm) is the response of protoplasm to light. **Hydrotropism** (hydroh-*troh*-pizm) is the response to water. There are also responses to the earth, or gravity, pressure, chemicals, heat, and other stimuli.

Nerve cells are specialists in sensitivity. They carry an impulse, or message, from one part of the body to another. If you cut your finger, you irritate a nerve in your skin. You feel it and think about it in your brain, and do something about it with your muscles. Nerve impulses accomplished all this activity.

Reproduction is the formation of new cells. As a cell grows, it expands its wall and increases the size of the protoplast. But the volume of protoplasm increases more in proportion than the sur-

face. This creates a serious problem. The protoplast receives oxygen and nourishment and discharges its waste through the outer membrane. Thus the volume-surface relationship of a cell is critical.

Is the cell forced to stop growing when the protoplast becomes as large as its surface can supply? Certainly not. The solution to the problem is logical. You will probably conclude that the cell must be halved; that two protoplasts half as large are formed, and that a new surface is added between them. This is just what happens.

Cell division starts with splitting of the nucleus. During a complex process, called **mitosis** (my-*toh*-sis), the chromatin of the nucleus divides. (See Fig. 4-12.) Since chromatin carries the hereditary traits of a cell, both new nuclei will be like the nucleus which formed them. We will discuss mitosis more fully in Chapter 48 in the discussion of heredity.

After the nucleus divides, the cell forms a membrane near its center and one large old cell becomes two new small cells.

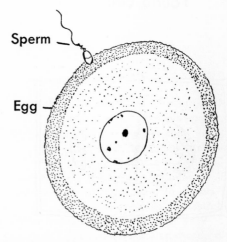

Sperm

Egg

Fig. 4-14. The union of an egg (female gamete) and a sperm (male gamete) is called fertilization.

In the case of one-celled plants and animals, division of a cell results in the formation of two complete organisms and is frequently called **fission** (*fish-zun*). Therefore, it is a method of reproduction. In many-celled organisms, cell division results in growth of the various tissues.

Many organisms, especially plants, produce special reproductive cells which leave the parent organism and travel through the air or in the water to a new location. Here, if conditions are favorable for growth, they establish a new organism by the process of cell division. We term these reproductive cells **spores.** Since spores are neither male nor female, and do not combine with other spores, we call the type of reproduction they accomplish **asexual.**

Plants and animals form another type of reproductive cell known as a **gamete** (*gam*-eet). These cells are either male or female. **Sperm** is a familiar name for a male gamete, and **egg** for a female gamete. (See Fig. 4-14.) Neither a sperm nor an egg is capable of growing into a new organism until the two have combined. The union of the two is termed **fertilization,** and the fertilized egg, or egg and sperm after union, is the **zygote** (*zy*-goat). The zygote grows into the new organism by cell division.

In Conclusion

Life is a group of processes carried on by a living substance, protoplasm. These processes are the functional basis of life in every cell, plant or animal, simple or highly specialized. The processes of the most complex animal are really no different from those of the lowest forms of life. They are merely more highly developed.

Protoplasm is the product of a chemical environment. Its substance comes from food, and foods come from soil minerals, water, and air. This brings us to the chemical basis of life, the subject of the next chapter.

Questions for Review

1. Explain the two basic uses of food by all living cells.

2. In what respect are fungi similar to animals in their food relations?

3. Give an example of symbiosis.

4. In what form are each of the following classes of foods used by cells: carbohydrates, fats, proteins?

5. Why must all the substances which cells absorb be soluble in water?

6. Explain the relation between the life process, respiration, and the chemical process, oxidation.

7. In what way is a cell a chemical factory in performing the process of secretion?

8. Discuss tropisms as examples of cell sensitivity.

9. Describe the various stages in reproduction of a cell.

10. Spores and gametes are special reproductive cells. In what respect are they different?

Biologically Speaking

absorption	glucose	phototropism
amino acid	glycerin	reproduction
assimilation	host	respiration
cilia	hydrotropism	response
digestion	ingestion	saprophyte
enzyme	locomotion	secretion
excretion	mitosis	sensitivity
fatty acid	mucus	spore
flagellum	osmosis	stimulus
food-getting	oxidation	symbiosis
fungi	parasite	tropism
gamete	photosynthesis	zygote

Applying Facts and Principles

1. How do the life processes illustrate the basic similarity of all living things?

2. Explain why the green plant holds the key to the living world.

3. How is the growth of a cell different from the growth of an icicle, a crystal, or other nonliving things which increase in size?

4. Discuss the relation of cell volume and surface to cell division.

5. Why is it important that division of the nucleus occur before the cell divides?

CHAPTER 5

The Chemical Basis of Life

The chemistry of life is a story of elements, the building blocks of matter. Just as bricks can form a walk, a wall, or a house, so do the various chemical elements compose all matter of the earth and atmosphere.

In this chapter, you will study the elements most closely associated with living things. We shall trace them from the atmosphere and the soil to the living cell. We shall follow energy changes from sunlight to the stored energy in food and then to life activity in protoplasm. These are the marvelous changes in matter and energy which transform nonliving materials into plants and animals and give them life. This is the chemical basis of life.

We define matter as anything which occupies space and has weight. We ordinarily think of *solids* and *liquids* as matter because we can see them and weigh them. But *gases,* such as oxygen and nitrogen, which are present in great quantities in the atmosphere, occupy space and have weight just as solids and liquids do.

Matter may be changed from one form to another. This may be a **physical** change, in which it changes form but not chemical make-up. For example, ice melts and forms water. Water, in turn may change to vapor, or gaseous water. Or if heat is applied, it can change to steam. Ice, water, vapor, and steam are, of course, the same substance in different physical forms. Similarly, iron is a solid under ordinary conditions, but the high temperature in a blast furnace can change it to a liquid, or molten iron.

The other kind of change is a **chemical** change. A change of this type takes place when wood burns and forms water vapor, carbon dioxide, and ashes. The heat and light given off during the change are energy which was stored in the wood before burning.

What is the Law of Conservation of Matter? If you burn a log in your fireplace, only ashes are left. These ashes are only a small part of the matter composing the log. What happened to the rest of it? It would seem that the burning destroyed it. But you did not see the carbon dioxide and water which went up the chimney. This was part of the matter which made up the wood. If you could catch these products and add them to the ash, you would have all of the substances present in the wood. This example illustrates the **Law of Conservation of Matter.** This states that matter is neither created nor destroyed during *ordinary* chemical changes.

Elements are the alphabet of matter. All the words in our language are formed from 26 letters in various combinations. When you look through a large dictionary, you realize what an enormous number of combinations may be formed from so few letters. In somewhat the same way, all matter in the world is composed of 92 basic, natural

47

THE MORE COMMON ELEMENTS

NAME OF ELEMENT	SYMBOL	PROPERTIES
Oxygen	O	Colorless, odorless, tasteless gas. Heavier than air; will not burn, but causes things to burn
Nitrogen	N	Colorless, odorless, tasteless gas; lighter than air
Hydrogen	H	Colorless, odorless, tasteless gas; lightest element; burns in oxygen and explodes when mixed and ignited
Carbon	C	Usually a black solid; usually inactive but burns in oxygen to form carbon dioxide or carbon monoxide
Sulfur	S	Yellow solid; burns in air and forms sulfur dioxide
Phosphorus	P	Yellow waxy or red solid; yellow (white) phosphorus glows in dark; **very active and dangerous; highly poisonous**
Iron	Fe	Heavy, gray metal; often magnetic; forms iron oxide (rust)
Calcium	Ca	Gray, brittle metal; reacts with water; never found in pure form in nature
Sodium	Na	Soft, gray metal; very active and dangerous; bursts into yellow flame in water; never found in pure form in nature
Potassium	K	Soft, gray metal; very active and dangerous; bursts into violet flame in water
Iodine	I	Crystalline solid

ESSENTIAL TO ALL LIVING THINGS

WHERE FOUND IN NATURE	SOURCE TO LIVING THINGS	USE BY LIVING THINGS
About one-fifth of atmosphere; one-half of solid material of the earth; water	Atmosphere; water	Respiration; part of all foods; element in protoplasm
About four-fifths of atmosphere; soil minerals (nitrates)	Soil minerals (nitrates)	Found in all protein; element in protoplasm
Water, all acids, wood, coal, gas	Water	Part of all foods; element in protoplasm
Carbon dioxide in atmosphere; soil minerals; fuels	Carbon dioxide	Part of all foods; element in protoplasm
Deposits in ground; soil minerals (sulfates); as hydrogen sulfide in springs	Soil minerals (sulfates)	Part of many proteins; element in protoplasm
Soil minerals (phosphates)	Soil minerals (phosphates)	Part of many proteins; element in protoplasm, especially in nerve tissue; phosphates present in bone
Ore deposits and soil minerals	Soil minerals	Essential element in chlorophyll in plants and hemoglobin (red substance) in blood of animals
Soil minerals and rocks, such as limestone and marble	Soil minerals	As a mineral used in forming bone and teeth; essential in blood and other tissues and bone formation
Soil minerals; including table salt	Soil minerals	As a mineral, essential in blood and other tissues and bone formation
Soil minerals	Soil minerals (potash)	Essential for growth
Mineral salts, especially in sea water	Mineral salts	Production of thyroid hormone

Fig. 5-1. Iron is obtained from its ores by means of a chemical change. Here molten iron pours from the mouth of a blast furnace after it has been separated from the other substances with which it was combined in nature.

substances called **elements.** In addition to these natural elements, eight more have been produced as a result of atomic research. You may think of elements as the letters in a chemical alphabet, which spell all substances of the earth and atmosphere.

Elements are composed of tiny units called **atoms.** The largest atoms are less than one fifty-millionth of an inch in diameter. Scientists have estimated that the smallest atoms, those of hydrogen, are less than one 250-millionth of an inch in diameter. When we say that atoms are basic units of matter, we mean that in ordinary chemical reactions, a substance is reduced no further than its individual atoms. Similarly, you can reduce a word to its letters, but you can't split up the letters.

Elements unite to form compounds. When an element exists by itself, it is called a free element. For example, free oxygen and free nitrogen, along with traces of five other gaseous elements, form the atmosphere. In addition, carbon dioxide is present in varying amounts. This gas contains two elements, *carbon* and *oxygen*. They are combined chemically to form a **compound.** (See Fig. 5-7.)

Compounds are composed of tiny units called **molecules** (*mol*-lih-kyools). The chemist refers to a molecule of carbon dioxide as CO_2. This is a chemical **formula.** It shows that a single molecule of carbon dioxide is composed of the atomic particles provided by a carbon atom and two oxygen atoms.

You can produce carbon dioxide by burning pure carbon in the air. The chemist would show the chemical change which takes place in the following equation:

$$C + O_2 \longrightarrow CO_2$$

Fig. 5-2. Matter is neither created nor destroyed during burning. How does this photograph illustrate the Law of Conservation of Matter?

In a chemical equation, the substances on the left of the arrow change form and become the products on the right. No substance is gained during the change. Nor is any lost. This is according to the Law of Conservation of Matter.

You have probably seen solid carbon dioxide as dry ice. As a gas, it is colorless, odorless, tasteless, and much heavier than air. It has none of the properties of the carbon which entered into its formation. Aside from being a gas, it has no resemblance to oxygen. Oxygen causes substances to burn, while carbon dioxide smothers a fire.

Furthermore, a molecule of carbon dioxide is formed only from the substance provided by one atom of carbon and two atoms of oxygen. Suppose an atom of carbon combines with only one atom of oxygen. An entirely different compound, carbon monoxide, is produced. This is the deadly gas which

comes from an automobile exhaust pipe, especially when the motor is cold. It has entirely different properties from carbon dioxide.

How could you separate the carbon atom from the oxygen atoms in a molecule of carbon dioxide? This would require a chemical change. We can sum up the properties of a compound as follows:

1. The elements producing the compound are combined chemically.

2. A compound has its own physical and chemical properties.

3. The elements forming a compound combine in definite proportions.

4. A chemical change is necessary to split a molecule of a compound and release the elements combined to form it.

Mixtures are different from compounds. In a *mixture,* the elements or compounds forming it are combined physically, but not chemically. No new substance is produced. The mixture

Fig. 5-3. In atomic research certain radioactive elements are used. These are so dangerous that long-handled tongs must be used to prevent burns from radiations.

has the combined properties of the substances forming it. Furthermore, the substances may be mixed in any proportion. They can be separated from each other by physical means.

Air is a mixture of gases. If air were not a mixture of gases, there would be no life on the earth. We breathe air into our lungs, dissolve part of the oxygen into the blood, and exhale the nitrogen and other gases. Aquatic animals absorb oxygen dissolved in water. They cannot make use of the oxygen combined with hydrogen in forming the water itself.

Iron and sulfur may form either a mixture or a compound. You can mix powdered iron and powdered sulfur in any proportion you wish. Having mixed them you can take a hand lens and see the separate particles of iron and sulfur just as they were before mixing. You can pick out the iron with a magnet or remove the sulfur by means of sub-

Normal hydrogen atom

Heavy hydrogen atom

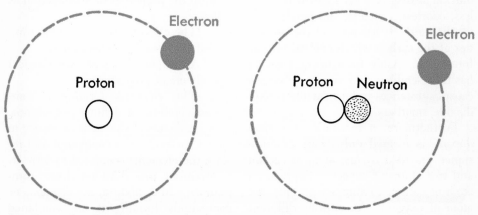

Fig. 5-4. The diagram above shows normal hydrogen and heavy hydrogen atoms. Hydrogen is believed to be the smallest of all atoms.

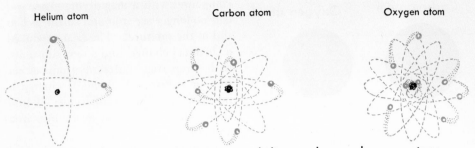

Fig. 5-5. Here are drawings to represent helium, carbon, and oxygen atoms.

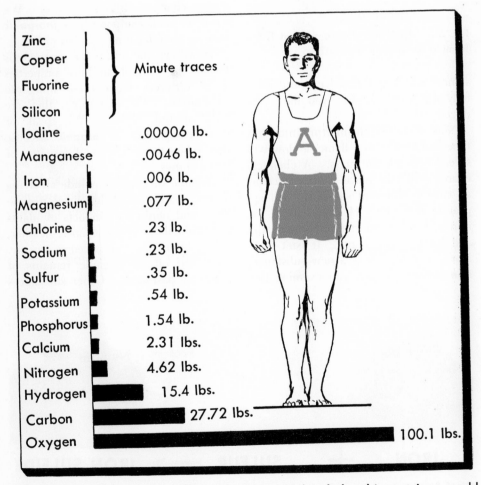

Zinc	
Copper	Minute traces
Fluorine	
Silicon	
Iodine	.00006 lb.
Manganese	.0046 lb.
Iron	.006 lb.
Magnesium	.077 lb.
Chlorine	.23 lb.
Sodium	.23 lb.
Sulfur	.35 lb.
Potassium	.54 lb.
Phosphorus	1.54 lb.
Calcium	2.31 lbs.
Nitrogen	4.62 lbs.
Hydrogen	15.4 lbs.
Carbon	27.72 lbs.
Oxygen	100.1 lbs.

Fig. 5-6. The 18 elements essential to life, if separated and placed in containers, would be represented by the amounts shown on this bar graph.

Carbon atom   Oxygen atom

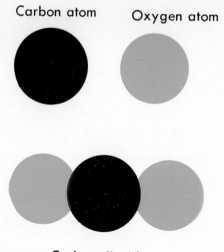

Carbon dioxide

Fig. 5-7. From this diagram, what is the formula for carbon dioxide?

compound with a magnifying glass, you can no longer see iron and sulfur as you did in the mixture. The heat produced a chemical change, and a new substance with properties different from either iron or sulfur. A chemical change is necessary to split the molecules of iron sulfide and form them again into iron and sulfur.

Compounds can be inorganic and organic. Long before life appeared on the earth, chemical changes were taking place. Elements and compounds were reacting with each other in a continuous change in the substances of the earth. These changes still take place. We speak of such compounds as *inorganic* because they have no relation to life.

However, the chemical compounds formed by protoplasm have properties quite different from these inorganic compounds. For one thing, they are built around carbon. We speak of these compounds as *organic* because they relate to the chemical activities of living things.

Organic substances include all living matter, matter which has lived at some time, and nonliving products of plants and animals. Wood, paper, leather, and meat are easily classified as organic. Coal and oil are organic remains of plants of past ages. Other substances

stances which will dissolve it and leave only the iron. So far, you have produced only a mixture.

Now, if you put the mixture into a test tube and heat it in a flame, a glow will spread through the mass. A chemical change will take place. After it cools, an entirely different substance will appear in the tube. Heating caused the iron and sulfur to combine chemically and form a compound. It isn't iron. Nor is it sulfur. It is a new substance, *iron sulfide*. When you examine this

Fig. 5-8. Heating iron and sulfur causes them to combine chemically and form a compound, iron sulfide.

such as sugars, starches, fats, oils, proteins, and vitamins, while never alive, are products of living things and are organic.

We can summarize the complex chemical relation between inorganic compounds, living organisms, and organic compounds in these brief statements:

1. The elements contained in inorganic compounds provide the substance which is used in forming organic compounds.

2. Organic compounds form living matter and nonliving parts of a cell and supply the food and energy necessary to maintain life.

Inorganic compounds which supply the elements necessary for life. Turn back to the table of elements on page 49 and reread the column, *Source to Living Things.* Two inorganic compounds and one group of inorganic compounds supply the elements required by

Fig. 5-10. Oil was formed from plant and animal materials of long ago. These were acted on by bacteria and buried during changes in the earth's crust.

organisms. *Water* supplies both hydrogen and oxygen. Carbon and oxygen come from *carbon dioxide.* The oxygen taken from these two compounds is used in building organic compounds. Do not confuse it with the free oxygen taken from the atmosphere and used in respiration.

All other necessary elements come from **mineral compounds.** They may be soil minerals or minerals dissolved in water, as in the case of sea water.

Organic compounds are products of life. As we mentioned in Chapter 4, plants alone are able to produce organic compounds from inorganic substances. Animals, using these plant products, form many organic substances during chemical changes within their bodies. You will recognize many of these organic compounds as foods. Our chemical supply is a matter of bringing home the groceries, preparing meals, including water with the foods we eat.

The organic compounds both plants and animals use for food are called **organic nutrients.** We group them into

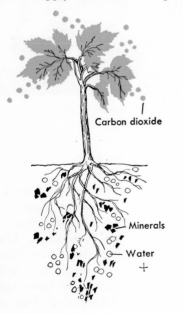

Carbon dioxide

Minerals

Water

Fig. 5-9. This cutaway of a plant shows the intake of water, minerals, and carbon — materials necessary for life.

Fig. 5-11. Carbohydrates, a class of organic nutrients, supply much of the energy that you need to perform your various activities.

three classes: (1) *carbohydrates;* (2) *fats;* and (3) *proteins.* In addition, we require vitamins and enzymes which are complex organic compounds.

What are carbohydrates? A *carbohydrate* is an organic compound containing carbon, hydrogen, and oxygen. The hydrogen and oxygen are present in a ratio of 2:1.

Sugars and starches are examples of carbohydrates. Both are found in the leaves of green plants. The food factories of a green leaf combine the elements in carbon dioxide and water and form sugar. Starch may be formed from the sugar. Sugars may be of various types and may be changed from one form to another by various plants and animals. The more common types include: *sucrose,* or cane sugar, from sugar cane and beet sugar from sugar beets; *lactose,* or milk sugar, from milk; and *glucose,* or grape sugar, from fruits and blood sugar from carbohydrate digestion.

Similarly, starches are of different types. You are familiar with cornstarch, potato starch, tapioca starch,

Fig. 5-12. Which of these foods are rich in fat? Of what elements is fat composed?

and others. Did you know that you have a starch factory in your body? Your liver converts excess glucose to animal starch, or **glycogen** (*gly*-ko-jen). As your blood needs more sugar, the liver changes the glycogen right back to glucose.

A third group of carbohydrates, the **celluloses,** forms the walls of plant cells. We use cellulose in everyday life as paper, wood, cotton, linen, hemp, and other plant fibers. Cellulose is highly important commercially as a source of material for plastics.

Carbohydrate foods are important to all living things as a source of the energy necessary to maintain life. Not only in plants which produce them, but in animals which use them, carbohydrates are vital fuel foods.

What are fats? *Fats,* including oils and waxes, make up a second class of organic compounds. They are composed of carbon, hydrogen, and oxygen, but contain less oxygen than the carbohydrates.

Plant oils are often stored in seeds. Peanut oil, cottonseed oil, corn oil, soy bean oil, castor oil, and linseed oil are important commercially. Animals store food in the form of fat. A diet containing excess sugar and starch results in storage of this excess in fatty deposits. Animal fats, like butter and lard, are important items in our diets. They are highly concentrated energy foods.

What are proteins? Chemically, *proteins* are very complex compounds. They contain carbon, hydrogen, oxygen, nitrogen, and usually sulfur. Some con-

Fig. 5-13. Proteins are tissue-building foods. They help in the growth of new cells and in the repair of worn-out cells.

tain phosphorus and iron as well. Carbon, hydrogen, and oxygen come from air and water and are first organized into a carbohydrate. The addition of nitrogen, sulfur, phosphorus, and iron from soil minerals is a very complex chemical process carried on by plants.

In the discussion of assimilation of protoplasm, we referred to proteins as the building blocks of living matter. No other organic compounds can replace proteins in the growth and repair of protoplasm.

Protein molecules are made up of groups of smaller molecules, called **amino** (ah-*mee*-no) **acids.** Of the more than 30 different forms of amino acids, ten are known to be necessary for growth and repair of protoplasm. Proteins which have all ten of these amino acids are referred to as complete proteins. Among the more common sources of proteins in our diet are: lean meat, milk, eggs, beans, and wheat.

What are vitamins and enzymes? These necessary organic substances are actually not foods. But they are essential for normal activity in both plants and animals.

Foods vary in the kind and amount of vitamins they contain. Therefore, we must have a balanced diet to supply the vitamin needs. Scientists knew little about vitamins until recently. Today we know that there are many different vitamins and that each kind is essential for some phase of body activity. We will discuss them more fully in Chapter 35.

Enzymes (*en*-zymes) are produced in both plants and animals. They're essential in the chemical process of digestion. Like vitamins, they are complex organic substances. You will learn more about them in Chapter 35.

Energy exists in various forms. Energy is often defined as the ability to do work. It has no weight, nor does it oc-

FORMS OF ENERGY

MECHANICAL ENERGY — the energy of motion.

HEAT — the energy given off by heat rays or friction.

SOUND — caused by the vibration of particles of matter by waves of energy.

ELECTRICITY — the flow of electrons.

RADIANT ENERGY — including light, radio waves, heat rays, and cosmic rays.

ATOMIC ENERGY — the force within an atom represented in moving atomic particles.

CHEMICAL ENERGY — energy stored in compounds.

cupy space. It is closely related to matter and produces changes in matter. The different forms are listed in the table above.

We classify energy further as *kinetic* or *potential*. **Kinetic** (kin-*eh*-tick) energy is energy at work. When it is stored, we classify it as **potential** (poh-*ten*-shul).

Electricity in a battery is potential until you hook it up. If it burns a light, or starts a motor, it becomes kinetic energy. Similarly, the chemical energy stored in food you eat is potential. When it is changed to motion of your body and other cell activities, it becomes kinetic. When you set a mouse trap and spring back the jaw, the trap has potential energy (energy of position) until the trap is sprung. When it snaps closed, this energy becomes kinetic.

What is the Law of Conservation of Energy? Suppose we start with a steam boiler and a fuel, such as coal, oil, or gas. We ignite the fuel and start a chemical change, oxidation. Chemical energy which was stored in the fuel changes to heat and light. The heat is transferred to water in the boiler which finally becomes steam under pressure.

Fig. 5-14. Trace the energy changes from the pile of coal to the electric light bulb.

Fig. 5-15. This hydroelectric plant transforms mechanical energy into electrical energy. This in turn may be converted to heat or light energy.

The steam drives a piston and gives off mechanical energy. A flywheel turns and, in turn, drives a generator. This converts mechanical energy into electrical energy. Wires carry the electricity to a light bulb, a toaster, or a motor. The original energy in the fuel has been through many changes. Some escaped during the process, but none was lost. This is according to the **Law of Conser-** **vation of Energy.** Radioactive substances violate this law when matter changes to energy. However, *in ordinary changes,* energy is neither created nor destroyed.

We will deal with energy constantly in the study of biology because it is the force which gives life. And it is expressed through matter in activity of the wonderful substance, protoplasm.

In Conclusion

What does it take to form life substance and to maintain its living condition? It takes about 18 elements, supplied in water, carbon dioxide, and mineral compounds. It takes the marvelous chemical properties of the plant world in the production of carbohydrates, fats, proteins, and other organic compounds. Here are the building materials which produce the organism. And here are the fuel foods which store the energy to give it life and the other substances which regulate its life activities.

The living world is a series of chemical changes. Some balance others in cycles. Plants produce food for animals, and animals return their substances to plants. Cycles like this go on endlessly in the biological world. We will explore some of these cycles in the next unit.

Questions for Review

1. How would you explain to a nonscientist what matter is?

2. In what three forms may matter exist?

3. Give two examples of a physical change and two of a chemical change.

4. (a) List ten essential elements. (b) Indicate whether each is obtained by living things from water, carbon dioxide, or minerals.

5. Explain the relation of elements to compounds.

6. Distinguish a mixture from a compound, using iron and sulfur and iron sulfide as examples.

7. How are organic compounds different in origin from inorganic compounds?

8. What three chemical elements are always present in a carbohydrate and a fat?

9. (a) Why do we call carbohydrates fuel foods? (b) What other class of foods yields body fuel?

10. Name three plant oils and three animal fats.

11. Explain why an organism could not grow on a diet consisting of carbohydrates alone.

12. List the various forms in which energy may exist.

Biologically Speaking

atom	inorganic	molecule
chemical change	kinetic energy	organic
compound	liquid	physical change
element	matter	potential energy
gas	mixture	solid

Applying Facts and Principles

1. Explain why the law of Conservation of Matter does not apply to radioactive substances such as radium.

2. Farmers sometimes find that cattle don't grow and fill out properly in certain fields, even though the grasses and other plants have abundant water and seem to grow normally. Explain how this is possible in terms of what you have learned about organic foods and growth.

3. Study the properties of oxygen and nitrogen in the Table of Elements. Then explain why mountain climbers are often easily exhausted at the higher altitudes.

4. Consider that a log burns to ashes in ten hours. Compare the amount of heat given off in such rapid burning with the amount of heat which would be given off over a period of ten years of gradual decomposition.

Research On Your Own

1. Prepare a report on the life and work of Hippocrates or Aristotle. In discussing the scientific contributions of either man, see if you can discover the attitudes, methods, and achievements which distinguish him as a " father " of medicine or biology.

2. In an encyclopedia or reference book, look up Anton Van Leeuwenhoek. Prepare a report on his life and work with early microscopes.

3. Prepare a similar report including the contributions of Hooke, Schleiden, and Schwann to biology through their work with cells.

4. The response of a root to water is greater than to gravity. Using some bean or corn seeds and boxes of sawdust, plan an experiment to prove or disprove this hypothesis. Be sure to run a control (non-variable factor) in your experiments.

5. Make a chart showing the life processes in one column and explain briefly in another column how a cell performs each of the processes.

6. Prepare a report on the ivory-billed woodpecker, whooping crane, whistling swan, or California condor. Find out its diet, breeding habits, usual number of eggs laid, environment, and any other characteristics which might have a bearing on its future existence. See if you can discover why it is nearing extinction. Make recommendations for preserving it.

7. Select two entirely different environments in your region, such as a deep woods, an open field, a bog, a marsh, a lake, a stream, or a desert, and list various plants and animals which live in them.

8. Collect samples of pond water and look for microscopic plants and animals. Find out, if possible, how the various kinds move.

9. Slice an onion lengthwise and separate the thick scale leaves. Peel the skin from the inner surface of a scale leaf and mount a small piece in a drop of water. Stain it with a drop of iodine. Draw a group of cells under low power, showing their walls and nuclei. Then make a drawing of a single cell under high power, including all the structures you can see.

10. Using an onion cell, show the organization of a complex plant on a chart as follows: start at the bottom of the chart with a drop of protoplasm. Then show a single onion skin cell with its various specialized protoplasmic structures. Next show a group of cells composing a tissue. Above this show a sectioned onion (bulb) as a plant organ. Finally draw an entire onion plant, with its roots, underground stem (the part you sectioned), and the green tubular leaves.

11. Shave some pieces of cork into a drop of water on a microscope slide. Add a cover glass and examine them with the microscope. The following subjects are ideal for showing various cell structures and inclusions:

Anacharis (Elodea) leaf. Mount a whole leaf in water. Set the slide in bright light for a few minutes before examining it. You will find chloroplasts in the cells and may see them moving in the streaming cytoplasm.

Potato cells. Mount a very thin slice of potato in water and stain it with iodine. Many starch grains, stained blue, will be visible in the cells.

Tomato pulp. Smash a small piece of tomato pulp on a slide and add water. The cells are very large and show nuclei and small, elongated chromoplasts.

12. Burn several matches in a bottle. Explain why they turn black. Lift out the matches with tweezers. Add some limewater and shake it. If the limewater turns milky,

carbon dioxide was present. Where did the carbon dioxide come from? Add lime-water to another bottle and blow into it several times. Shake the limewater and check for the presence of carbon dioxide in your breath. Where does this carbon dioxide come from?

13. Add some iron filings to powdered sulfur and mix them. Examine the mixture with a lens. Can you still distinguish the iron and sulfur particles? Pass a magnet through the mixture and separate the iron from the sulfur. Make more of the mixture and heat it over a flame in a test tube. After a glow has appeared, remove the iron sulfide (you may have to break the tube) and examine it. Can you detect the iron and sulfur? Can you separate the iron from the sulfur with a magnet?

14. From a chemistry book, find out what four elements have been produced as a result of atomic research in recent years. You will find them listed as numbers 93, 94, 95, and 96.

 —————————— **More About Biology**

Asimov, Issac. THE CHEMICALS OF LIFE. Abelard-Schuman, Inc., New York. 1954

Berrill, Norman. JOURNEY INTO WON-DERLAND. Dodd, Mead and Co., Inc., New York. 1952

Bischof, George P. ATOMS AT WORK. Harcourt, Brace and Co., Inc., New York. 1951

Brown, Vinson. HOW TO MAKE A HOME NATURE MUSEUM. Little, Brown and Co., Boston. 1954

Coulter, Merle C. THE STORY OF THE PLANT KINGDOM. The University of Chicago Press, Chicago. 1935

Davis, Harry Meyer. ENERGY UNLIM-ITED: THE ELECTRON AND ATOM IN EVERYDAY LIFE. Murray Hill Books, Inc., New York. 1947

Dobell, C. ANTONY VAN LEEUWEN-HOEK AND HIS "LITTLE ANIMALS." Harcourt, Brace and Co. New York. 1932

Fielding, William J. STRANGE SUPERSTI-TIONS AND MAGICAL PRACTICES. The Blakiston Co., Philadelphia. 1945

Freeman, Ira M. ALL ABOUT THE WON-DERS OF CHEMISTRY. Random House, Inc., New York. 1954

Hardin, Garrett. BIOLOGY AND ITS HU-MAN IMPLICATIONS. W. H. Freeman Co., San Francisco. 1952

Hawley, Gessner G. SEEING THE INVIS-IBLE: THE STORY OF THE ELECTRON MICROSCOPE. Alfred A. Knopf, Inc., New York. 1945

Headstrom, Richard. ADVENTURES WITH A MICROSCOPE. J. B. Lippincott Co., Philadelphia. 1941

Hillcourt, William. FIELD BOOK OF NA-TURE ACTIVITIES. G. P. Putnam's Sons, New York. 1950

Jaffe, Bernard. OUTPOSTS OF SCIENCE: A JOURNEY TO THE WORKSHOPS OF OUR LEADING MEN OF RESEARCH. Simon and Schuster, Inc., New York. 1935

Johnson, Gaylord and Bleifeld, Maurice. HUNTING WITH A MICROSCOPE. Sen-tinel Books, New York. 1953

Jordan, Emil Leopold. HAMMOND'S GUIDE TO NATURE HOBBIES. C. S. Hammond and Co., Inc., New York. 1953

Locy, William A. *BIOLOGY AND ITS MAKERS.* Henry Holt and Co., Inc., New York. 1915

Meyer, Jerome S. *PICTURE BOOK OF CHEMISTRY.* Lothrop, Lee, and Shepard Co., Inc., New York. 1950

Meyer, Jerome S. *PICTURE BOOK OF MOLECULES AND ATOMS.* Lothrop, Lee, and Shepard Co., Inc., New York. 1947

Milne, Lorus J. and Milne, Margery. *THE BIOTIC WORLD AND MAN.* Prentice-Hall, Inc., New York. 1952

Moinert, Gairdner. *FOUNDATIONS OF BIOLOGY.* Appleton-Century-Crofts, Inc., New York. 1953

Radford, E. and Radford, M. A. *ENCY-CLOPEDIA OF SUPERSTITIONS.* The Philosophical Library, New York. 1949

Roe, Anne. *THE MAKING OF A SCIEN-TIST.* Dodd, Mead and Co., Inc., New York. 1953

Rothman, S. C. (Editor). *CONSTRUCTIVE USES OF ATOMIC ENERGY.* Harper and Brothers, New York. 1949

Singer, Charles. *A HISTORY OF BIOLOGY.* Rev. Ed. Henry Schuman, Inc., New York. 1950

Snyder, Emily Eveleth. *BIOLOGY IN THE MAKING.* McGraw-Hill Book Co., Inc., New York. 1940

Swartz, Julius. *THROUGH THE MAG-NIFYING GLASS.* Whittlesey House (McGraw-Hill), New York. 1954

Thomas, Henry and Thomas, Dana. *LIV-ING ADVENTURES IN SCIENCE.* Hanover House, Garden City, New York. 1954

Winchester, A. M. *BIOLOGY AND ITS RELATIONS TO MANKIND.* D. Van Nostrand Co., Inc., New York. 1949

Yates, Raymond F. *FUN WITH YOUR MI-CROSCOPE.* Appleton-Century-Crofts, Inc., New York. 1943

UNIT 2

The Relationships of Living Things

In the forests of our central and eastern states lofty oaks and maples tower above a layer of shade-loving shrubs and low-growing plants of the forest floor. Cottonwoods and sycamores thrive on the stream banks and flood plains. Farther west, grasses cover the rolling plains. Evergreen forests cling to the slopes of the Rocky Mountains. And in the far west, dense stands of redwood and Douglas fir send up their magnificent spires 150 feet or more. Pickerel weed and cattails thrive in the bog and water lilies form a marginal zone in lakes. In the desert, the cactus and the yucca survive the scorching sun and parched soil. Each plant society supports its characteristic animal life.

All forms of life are similar in that they are made of protoplasm. All carry on identical processes. All face similar problems of existence. Why, then, do they live in such totally different environments?

You will find the answer in such varying conditions as the composition and texture of the soil, climatic conditions, air movement, light, and other factors. Living things live in a critical relationship with the physical environment. And they live in an equally critical relationship with each other.

CHAPTER 6: Balance in the World of Life
CHAPTER 7: Vital Factors of Environment
CHAPTER 8: Plants and Animals at Home
CHAPTER 9: Classification of Plants and Animals

Balance in the World of Life

When the pioneer first drove his wagon through the eastern hardwood forest, wheels turned over rich, black soil which had grown trees for centuries. Overhead lofty maples, oaks, and ash towered. All about were decaying stumps and fallen trunks of forest giants. As seedlings sprang from the forest floor, they grew in the rich remains of the earlier forest. For some plants, life was just beginning. Nature was engaged in the constructive chemical processes which would yield the forest and support its many animals. For others, life had ended. Nature was reclaiming her chemical stores to build new forests and supply new generations of forest wildlife.

In the destruction of organic substance, nature has recruited other forms of life. Molds, bacteria, and other fungi are indirectly responsible for the forest. Trees cannot grow just from the remains of trees. They require water and carbon dioxide and soil minerals. They need the products of animal decay. Building up and tearing down — food manufacture and food use — growth and decay — this is the balance in the world of life.

Life is a series of processes. The processes of one organism depend on those of another. Plants are benefited by animals. Animals, in turn, are totally dependent on plants.

Life depends on constructive processes. It depends equally on destructive processes. Construction must equal destruction. Food is produced by life and food is broken down by life. Living things store energy and use energy. Oxygen is used up, and oxygen is given off. Throughout life, plants and animals grow through constructive processes, only to be destroyed after death by other living things.

Food is a critical need of all organisms. It supplies the materials for formation of protoplasm as well as the energy for maintaining life. To serve as a food, a substance must possess certain properties which make it usable by living protoplasm. Protoplasm alone can give it these properties. In other words, foods are the result of the constructive processes of life. Nature supplies only those materials which form foods. The foods themselves are products of life.

But the food-producing role of the green plant is only half of the story. Remember that nature operates in cycles. Food production is a constructive process. It must be balanced by equal processes of destruction. Plants must receive a constant supply of the materials which go into the making of foods. Otherwise food-making would in time exhaust those necessary supplies. At this point, all life enters into the food cycle. Not only the green plants, but all animals and dependent plants as well use up food in maintaining the life proc-

Fig. 6-1. Trace the energy in the body of the cat back to its original source.

esses. The waste products excreted following this food use are, in some cases, the very things green plants need to produce more food. Some require further chemical change before the plant can re-use them.

Foods used for growth undergo further processes of construction in the formation of protoplasm. As long as the organism lives, this substance is temporarily "lost" from the cycle. After death, however, bacteria and other fungus plants reduce the complex substances of the plant or animal body to simple compounds. This is **decay.** Products of decay supply substance to the green plant which can be used in forming more food to supply new generations of living things.

What is a food and energy chain? Fig. 6-1 shows a situation which biologists call a **food chain.** It is repeated over and over on a farm. We start the chain with the sun and its never-ending supply of radiant energy. The corn plant absorbs this energy and locks it into molecules of sugar. Air and water

supplied the substance for making the sugar. Soil minerals, taken in by the roots, supply the elements the corn plant uses in making protein.

The ears, with their many kernels, become the storehouse for the extra foods produced by the corn plant during its growing season. Normally, this food would nourish the young corn seedlings which would sprout from the kernels the next season. But the farmer needs this food supply to fatten his cattle and hogs and to feed to his poultry. He picks the ears and stores them in a corn-crib. A mouse raids the crib one night and the corn carbohydrates, fats, and proteins become active mouse tissue. But not for very long. A cat sees the mouse and eats it. Now the cat has the substance which the mouse had. It also has the energy which traveled from sun to corn to mouse. We could carry the chain further if something ate the cat. However, we will assume that the cat dies of old age. Its substance will return to the soil in simple chemical form and enrich it for use by other green plants.

In tracing this food chain, we do not end with the same amount of energy the corn plant absorbed from the sun. The corn plant used some of it in maintaining its own life activities. The mouse used still more. This explains why people in crowded sections of the earth live directly on rice and other plant foods. Feeding corn and other grains to cattle and hogs to produce meat is a luxury. Much of the food substance is used up in growing the animal and maintaining its life activities.

The carbon-hydrogen-oxygen cycle is important in making food. These three elements form the carbon dioxide and water required by a green plant for food production. During the process of making sugar, the plant uses six molecules of carbon dioxide and six molecules of water in forming one molecule of sugar. Eighteen atoms of oxygen are taken in. Only six are needed in a sugar molecule. Therefore, 12 atoms are left over. This extra oxygen passes from the leaf as a by-product of the sugar-making process.

The oxygen released during the sugar-making process is as important to living things as the sugar produced. When this gas is combined with sugar in a living cell, the reaction is reversed and sugar is broken down into carbon dioxide and water. This releases the energy stored in the sugar.

This change is what chemists call **oxidation.** To a biologist, oxidation means the combining of oxygen with sugar resulting in the formation of two other substances, carbon dioxide and wa-ter. Note that in this case oxidation is *exactly the opposite* of the sugar-making process. Thus the carbon-hydrogen-oxygen cycle is a balance between two chemical processes, oxidation and sugar-making. Sugar-making is the constructive process during which food is formed. Oxidation in tissues is the destructive process which reforms the inorganic compounds required for sugar-making.

Fats and proteins are also oxidized with an accompanying release of energy.

The green plant produces much more food than it requires for its own activities. This permits animals and dependent plants to live and to enter into the destructive phase of the carbon-hydrogen-oxygen cycle.

A balanced aquarium consists of plants and animals. Did you ever try to keep fish in an aquarium containing nothing but water? They soon use up the dissolved oxygen and come to the surface to gulp air. Goldfish might live under this condition if you change the water frequently and supply them with prepared food. However, game fish with a greater oxygen need could live in such an aquarium only a short time.

The food and oxygen problem is remedied by adding plants to the aquarium. Fig. 6-2 shows an aquarium containing plants alone. They can survive without any animals. Snails and fish have been added to the aquarium shown in Fig. 6-3. The plants supply oxygen needed by the animals for respiration. The snails feed on slime containing

---

SUGAR–MAKING AND OXIDATION COMPARED

Sugar–making: $6\,CO_2 + 6\,H_2O \rightarrow C_6H_{12}O_6 + 6\,O_2$

Oxidation: $C_6H_{12}O_6 + 6\,O_2 \rightarrow 6\,CO_2 + 6\,H_2O$

microscopic plants and animals. Certain kinds of fish would feed on the plants. Others might eat young snails. However, the fish in an aquarium this small would require artificial feeding. The plants benefit from the animals to some extent. Carbon dioxide, discharged into the water during animal and plant respiration, is used in food manufacture. Organic waste materials from the animals decay in the sand and enrich it for the plants.

A completely balanced aquarium should have more plants and fewer animals. Some of the animals should be plant-feeders. These in turn would be the food supply for flesh-eating animals. Most aquarists overbalance their aquaria with animals. This necessitates feeding the animals and may make an air pump necessary to supply enough oxygen.

The nitrogen cycle is more complicated than the carbon-hydrogen-oxygen cycle. It involves green plants and several kinds of bacteria. It may or may not involve animals. As you read the various steps in the nitrogen cycle, follow them in the diagram shown in Fig. 6-4.

We will start the cycle with the green plant and the formation of protein. Its roots absorb **nitrates,** a group of soil minerals. These compounds contain

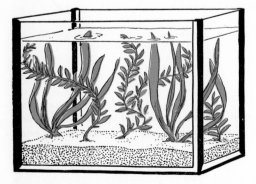

Fig. 6-2. How do plants survive in this aquarium without animals?

Fig. 6-3. In what important ways do the plants supply the animals in the aquarium with necessary materials for their growth and well-being?

nitrogen in chemical combination with oxygen and, usually, sodium or potassium. In building proteins, the plant adds nitrogen to carbon, hydrogen, and oxygen. Sulfur and phosphorus may be added from other soil minerals. During assimilation, protein forms part of protoplasm. This happens many times in a food chain. Protein might travel from plant to rabbit to fox, or from plant to steer, to your table as a steak or a roast.

When protoplasm dies, decay begins. This is a bacterial action. Nitrogen is released from decaying protein in combination with hydrogen as *ammonia*. This is the result of bacterial action. Other soil bacteria act on ammonia, combine the nitrogen with other elements, and form *nitrates*. We refer to these organisms as nitrifying bacteria and call the process **nitrification** (ny-trih-fih-*kay*-shun). Thus we return to the starting point in the nitrogen cycle.

What about the atmosphere? The atmosphere is four-fifths nitrogen. Is this pure nitrogen involved in the nitrogen cycle? It is, in a roundabout way. In the discussion of symbiosis in Chapter 4, we mentioned bacteria which live in nodules on the roots of clover, soy beans, and other legume plants. These

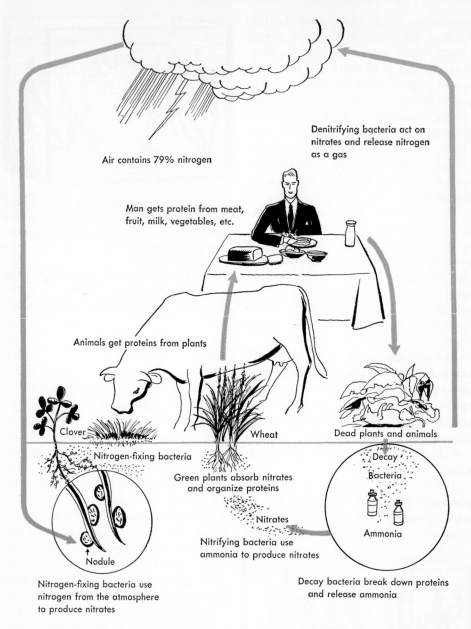

Air contains 79% nitrogen

Denitrifying bacteria act on nitrates and release nitrogen as a gas

Man gets protein from meat, fruit, milk, vegetables, etc.

Animals get proteins from plants

Clover

Nitrogen-fixing bacteria

Wheat

Dead plants and animals

Decay Bacteria

Green plants absorb nitrates and organize proteins

Nitrates

Ammonia

Nitrifying bacteria use ammonia to produce nitrates

Nodule

Nitrogen-fixing bacteria use nitrogen from the atmosphere to produce nitrates

Decay bacteria break down proteins and release ammonia

NITROGEN CYCLE

Fig. 6-4. Follow the steps in the nitrogen cycle from the green plant whose roots absorb the nitrates in the soil to the decay of the plant. Explain what happens during each stage of the cycle.

remarkable organisms receive sugar from the host plant. During their chemical activity, they absorb free nitrogen from the atmosphere and add the other elements necessary to form nitrates. We call the process **nitrogen fixation.**

When a farmer plants clover in a field in a crop rotation schedule, he is building up his soil from unlimited supplies of atmospheric nitrogen. What he is actually doing is raising a crop of nitrogen-fixing bacteria. One phase of the nitrogen cycle is highly destructive to agriculture. This is a path from the soil to the atmosphere. Certain *denitrifying* (dee-*ny*-trih-fy-ing) *bacteria* act on ammonia and other nitrogen compounds and release free nitrogen. This gas leaves the soil and rises to the atmosphere. We refer to the process as **denitrification** (dee-ny-trih-fih-*kay*-shun). It results in loss of valuable soil fertility. Fortunately, denitrification does not take place in well-drained, cultivated soils. Denitrifying bacteria thrive in soils which are water-logged, or packed so tightly that air cannot penetrate readily.

Natural enemies are nature's check on living things. Any living community is a *complex society* or group. It is composed of many kinds of plants and animals living in close association with each other. Some forms of life may be more abundant than others, but no one kind of organism controls the community completely. If you study the day-to-day events in such a living society, you will find out why.

Let's look in on the events in an open-field society. A meadow mouse is running along a pathway through the grasses in search of seeds. In eating seeds, the mouse is reducing the next generation of grasses and other open-field plants. But since plants produce a far greater number of seeds than could possibly grow, the plant population of

Fig. 6-5. Legume crops, like this red clover, are used to help build up the nitrate content of the soil.

the community isn't reduced. Perhaps a barn owl, like the one shown in Fig. 6-6, swoops down and catches the mouse. The barn owl is a natural enemy of mice and other small mammals. We speak of it as a **predator** (*preh*-day-tor) because it preys or feeds on other animals. Suppose there were no owls or other natural enemies of mice. Soon the mice would overrun the field. Their own numbers might bring on starvation. This has happened many times when animals have become too numerous.

The forest, the field, the lowland marsh, and rocky meadows of the mountain top — wherever you find life — there must be a close balance between plant and animal and between prey and predator. Natural enemies are a vital part of the balance of nature.

Civilization has upset the balance of nature. When we clear a forest, plow a field, or landscape a yard, we change

Fig. 6-6. This barn owl is entering her nest with a rat to feed her young. Some animals, like this owl, are a natural enemy of rodents.

a natural, balanced environment. Some plants and animals adjust to the new surroundings. Others cannot make the change.

For example, the crow population is probably larger today than at any time when North America was a wilderness. The crow thrives in an agricultural region. There he will find fields of grain and corn cribs which he can raid. The English sparrow nests under an eave of a house and finds city life more suitable than life in the country with its competition and natural enemies. A lawn is an ideal place for a robin to find a worm. Coyotes have increased in number in the ranch country of the west. Here they add poultry and livestock to their natural diet of smaller mammals.

Whether a plant or animal benefits or suffers from the changes civilization brings depends on its ability to adapt to new conditions. Often the balance of nature is seriously upset and the more adaptable plants and animals become pests.

Destruction of predatory animals can be unwise. As living things ourselves, we face the survival problem common to all life. Because we are intelligent, we understand the problem and have largely solved it. But we have strong feelings about the survival of more helpless animals.

Before we decide whether an animal is destructive and before we destroy any living thing, we should consider three points.

1. Has the predatory animal increased in number to the point that it is destroying far too many other valuable animals? We need a census study to determine this.

2. What is its exact diet? Does it feed more on overpopulated, destructive animals than on those we consider valu-

able? This requires careful study. We must learn the predator's diet and its feeding habits.

3. If the predator is greatly reduced in number, will other forms of life overpopulate the region? In past years, we have introduced birds and animals we thought were ideal for our conditions. We left their natural enemies in the native land. The animals we introduced then became pests and we had to import some of their original natural enemies. This kept the pest under reasonable control.

To sum up, we can say that it takes a trained biologist to decide. He can tell best whether a plant or an animal should be considered destructive.

Fig. 6-8. Minks are very active and bold animals. They kill and eat fish, frogs, and crayfish as well as rats and mice.

Fig. 6-7. Wherever there is life, there is a close balance between prey and predator. This crane is probing in the water for fish on which it feeds.

Man has interfered with the natural cycles. Under natural conditions, all plants and animals depend on each other. Soil destruction and **erosion** (ih-*roh*-zhun), or loss of the soil by wind or water, is a tragedy of civilization. Normally, soil minerals are used by generations of plants and return to the soil with the death of each generation. Each generation adds organic matter. In this way, rich topsoil accumulates slowly through the ages.

Man has unfortunately greatly altered this condition. We cultivate soils to grow crops and then remove the crops from the fields. Much of the phosphorus leaves the farm entirely in the bones of livestock taken to market. Later, crops prove less valuable because of lack of this and other soil minerals. Finally, we begin to pay the price in vitamin and mineral deficiency. We suffer economic loss from poor crops like the one shown in Fig. 6-10. Progressive farmers restore the used minerals in the form of commercial fertilizers, animal manure, and green crops such as clover.

These green crops are plowed back into the soil. Those farmers who do not repay the soil must suffer the consequences.

Stream **pollution** means that water is poisoned and unfit for most living things. It has created a serious problem in our streams and rivers. As game fish die out, the waters are left to such scavenger fish as carp. Many polluted streams no longer support even these species. They become mosquito and bacteria infested, foul-smelling open sewers — a health menace and a discredit to the intelligence of man.

Useless cutting of forests, burning of fields, destruction of fence-row covers, and draining of swamps and marshes have taken a heavy toll of valuable birds and other animals. Many of these are natural enemies of insects. As a result,

insect pests swarm into our gardens and destroy the crops we need for food.

Conservation is our only hope of restoring the balance. Naturally, we cannot restore America to the condition in which our ancestors found it. But we can build cities, grow crops, use lumber, and carry on all of the other activities civilization demands and still not upset the balance of nature.

We can have forests and fertile fields. We can have clear lakes and streams. We can share our natural heritage with abundant wildlife. Biologists can do this and are doing it in a tremendous program of **conservation**, or saving our natural resources.

Biology has shown us the intricate relationships between living things. We can now understand the natural cycles and realize the extent to which we have

Fig. 6-9. Cooper's hawks, though they kill some poultry and wild birds, feed also on field mice, reptiles, and insects.

Fig. 6-10. This worn-out cotton field would have produced a better crop if the soil had been adequately fertilized.

upset them. But the problem is enormous. We must correct the misuse of nature by several previous generations. Conservation will be a constant theme in your biology course. We will deal with the problem in greater detail in Unit 10.

In Conclusion

The living world maintains a natural balance through cycles. Plants and animals carry on constructive processes which use simple inorganic compounds supplied in the soil and atmosphere. Foods are organized and finally plants and animals assimilate their own substance. Equally important are the destructive processes which reduce complex organic matter to simple compounds. In this form, the matter is available to future generations of plants. Thus, cycles continue age after age and living things continue to populate the earth.

Other conditions in nature have a direct and powerful influence on living things. Light, water, and temperature are critical factors in the life of plants. Plants, in turn, control the animal population. In the next chapter, we will consider the factors of environment which make the desert, the forest, and the bog community.

Questions for Review

1. In what way are destructive processes, such as decay, essential to food production by green plants?

2. What important gas is released by a green plant as a by-product of sugar formation?

3. Explain the relation between sugar formation and oxidation as chemical processes.

4. (a) For what requirements do animals depend on plants in a balanced aquarium? (b) How do the plants benefit from the animals?

5. What nitrogen-containing gas is released from decaying protein?

6. What nitrogen-containing minerals are absorbed from the soil by plant roots?

7. Explain why clover is planted to build up soil fertility in a good crop rotation program.

8. (a) Why would an animal be called a predator? (b) Name several predatory animals.

9. Discuss three points to be considered before destroying a predator which someone thinks is a pest.

10. Name several ways in which man has upset the balance of nature.

Biologically Speaking

balance	energy chain	nitrogen cycle
conservation	erosion	nitrogen fixation
constructive process	food chain	oxygen-carbon dioxide cycle
denitrification	natural enemy	pollution
destructive process	nitrification	predator

Applying Facts and Principles

1. People in many parts of the world cannot afford the luxury of raising animals for food. They must eat the plants directly. Explain how food is "lost" in raising domestic animals for food.

2. A farmer has a lowland field which he has fertilized heavily. Crop yield from the field has been good for several seasons. During an unusually rainy spring, the field is flooded for more than a week on several occasions. The corn crop planted later in the season has a low yield. What might have caused this sudden decrease in soil fertility?

3. Give several good arguments for the preservation of predatory animals.

4. As civilization has spread, and more and more natural environments have been destroyed, some native animals have increased while others have decreased. Account for this in terms of adaptability. Give examples of animals which have increased and some which have decreased in your region.

CHAPTER 7

Vital Factors of Environment

Our study of life has shown us that organisms are formed from the chemical substances of the surroundings in which they live. These surroundings must provide, also, conditions suitable for maintaining life and the carrying on of all life activities. Living things are products of a set of complicated conditions in nature which we call *environment.*

Biologists have realized the importance of a knowledge of environment and its relation to the organism. This has led them to study a special branch of biology called *ecology.* Ecology is nature study of a most serious sort. It has led biologists to all parts of the earth in their study of the many kinds of environments in which plants and animals live. Yet any woods or pond or field — even your own backyard — is a part of the great outdoor laboratory of the ecologist.

Environments in nature. When you take hikes, you probably notice the variety of conditions under which plants and animals live. A woods, a field, a deep ravine, or a marsh all provide environments which are totally different from each other. Some of these differences are very obvious; others are not. Still, they all have a direct effect on the organisms which come under their influence.

The ecologist refers to the various conditions or influences present in an environment as *factors.* Each environment is made up of many such factors. Some of these are *physical factors* and include such influences as soil conditions, temperature, light, water, atmospheric conditions, earth changes. Equally important are the biological factors, or the living surroundings of the organism. A plant or animal lives under the constant influence of other living things. The individual organism is a part of a large society of life, closely bound to the nonliving influences of its surroundings.

The earth offers a wide variety of conditions for life. Organisms have spread over its surface until all regions support life in some form. Due to changes in their characteristics, which may occur from time to time, plants and animals have become varied in their requirements. Otherwise, living things would be forced to crowd into small areas of favorable surroundings and much of the earth would be unpopulated.

Soil, a basic factor of environment. To many of us, soil is just dirt which covers the earth. But to the biologist, soil is one of the most important factors of an environment. Careful examination of soil shows that it varies greatly in different localities. The plant and animal life it supports varies accordingly.

Some soils are heavy with clay, while others are loose and sandy. Some we

Fig. 7-1. Virginia pines, growing on these sand dunes, can flourish because of their thin, narrow leaves which reduce water loss.

classify as *loam;* others, as *clay loam* or *sandy loam*. We cannot say that plants prefer any particular type of soil because adaptations have varied their requirements. Sandy soils may support a forest of pine in Michigan, New Jersey, Georgia, or east Texas. Heavy loam supports a beech and maple forest in Ohio and Indiana. Water-logged soils of bogs and swamps provide ideal conditions for larch, white cedar, and cypress forests. The rocky, shallow soils of certain mountain slopes produce luxuriant forests of redwood, yellow pine, and spruce in our western states.

Soils vary also in chemical nature. They may be **acid** (sour) or **alkaline** (sweet). Fertility and richness, which are governed by mineral content and decayed organic matter, likewise alter the conditions of soil.

The character of a soil is always changing. In one place rocks are breaking down and adding to soil. This breaking down is due to the action of weather and of chemical disintegration. In other places, the mineral content of the ground is being weakened because of the quantities of salts removed by plants through their roots. Certain soils may be building up through the decay of successive layers of vegetation, while other soils become exhausted due to heavy crop production and failure to replace the exhausted mineral supplies. Much useful farm land is ruined by bad soil care. As soils change, plants and animals must find other suitable environments.

Temperature, a controlling factor of environment. In temperate regions of the earth, including most of North America, temperature changes range from the narrow fluctuations between day and night to the much more extreme differences of summer and winter temperatures.

All these temperature conditions affect plants and animals. Any organism must be able to withstand the slight variations between day and night. However, seasonal variations between winter and summer present a much greater problem.

Most trees and shrubs in temperate regions flourish through the warm weather of spring, summer, and fall. They enter a dormant or inactive period through the colder months. Leaves may fall and sap may move to parts of the plant which are not injured by freezing. The pine, spruce, and other evergreen trees remain green throughout the winter, even though most activity in the plant has stopped. Plants which are not woody may die to the ground and then reappear in the spring from dormant roots or from seeds.

Animals meet the problems of seasonal temperature changes. Some, like the eastern cottontail rabbit, the whitetail deer, the cardinal, and the bluejay, are permanent residents in their regions. They are active both summer and winter. During extremely cold weather, they find protection in woods and thickets. When the ground is covered with deep snow, securing food often becomes a serious problem.

Many animals **migrate** (*my*-grate) or move to warmer regions when winter comes. We usually associate migration with birds, but some other animals also show the tendency to migrate. These seasonal journeys may cover thousands of miles. Many birds of the far north migrate into the northern regions of the United States during the winter months. Meanwhile, summer residents of these same areas have migrated into the south-

Fig. 7-2. During the cold, winter months, most trees are dormant. Evergreen trees, however, remain green, though most activity stops.

Fig. 7-3. Animals, as well as plants, face the problem of survival during changes in temperature. Elk solve the problem by moving to mountain valleys in the winter.

ern states, or, in some cases, as far south as the tropics of South America.

The bighorn sheep spends its summers in the treeless meadows near the summit of the Rocky Mountains. As winter approaches, it moves down into the protected forests of the mountain slopes. Elk browse in the high altitude forests of these mountains through the summer months. During the winter, the herds move to the more protected mountain valleys and the nearby plains.

The bear, the groundhog (woodchuck), and many other mammals sleep out the cold weather, or **hibernate** (*hy*-ber-nate). During hibernation, the body processes slow down. This reduces the food requirement and allows the animal to maintain itself on food reserves stored in the body.

Intense heat in summer causes survival problems for many animals. The gopher tortoise of the southeastern states finds protection in a burrow deep in the ground. The box turtle digs into the soil or buries itself in a pile of leaves during hot periods. Many animals of

Fig. 7-4. Above you see a woodchuck sitting up beside his hole where he hibernates during the winter. How is he able to maintain life during this period?

Fig. 7-5. Hot summer weather, as well as the cold days of winter, create real problems for many animals. Box turtles, one of which appears in the above photograph, keep cool in summer by digging into the soil or by burying themselves in a pile of dead leaves.

the open field move to the cooler shade of a woods. A frog may bury itself in the mud at the bottom of a pond and *estivate* (*es*-tih-vate), or lie dormant through the hot weather. **Estivation** is a kind of summer hibernation.

Water is essential to life. Probably no environmental factor is more important to living things than the water supply. To meet their critical water needs, plants and animals range from organisms living in a complete water environment to those thriving in sunparched deserts. All living things require water. But the way in which varied plants and animals meet this demand is always interesting to a biologist.

Oceans, lakes, streams, and ponds contain plants and animals which need a constant water environment. Those living in fresh water are called **aquatic.** Those living only in salt water are called **marine.** To the organisms in these environments, water supply is normally no problem. But their body structure

Fig. 7-6. Aquatic plants, like water lilies, must perform all their life functions in a water environment in order to survive.

Fig. 7-7. The cactus plants' adaptation to stand drought have so changed them that many species will die if watered too freely.

must perform all its functions in water. Removed to land, even in the wettest surroundings, they soon die.

Plants and animals of swamps and bogs are modified for life both in the water and on land. Here we find **semi-aquatic** forms, such as cattails, pond lilies, bulrushes, cranberries, frogs, turtles, and muskrats.

Organisms which live on land require less water than marine, aquatic, and semi-aquatic forms, but must still depend on an adequate water supply. Rainfall is a powerful factor in controlling the lives of these land, or **terrestrial** (ter-*res*-tree-al) animals and plants. So with variations in rainfall and atmospheric moisture, terrestrial organisms must find areas of moisture suitable to their individual requirements.

As rainfall decreases and the air becomes drier, plants face a greater problem of water supply. Root areas become larger and leaf areas smaller.

This results in an increased absorbing power and in a reduction of evaporation of water from leaf surfaces into the atmosphere.

Grass-covered plains occur where rainfall is not too high, and hot winds produce periods of drought. The great grasslands of our midwestern states provide ideal conditions for cereal crops, and have become the grain belt of the nation.

The giant cacti inhabit desert regions. They are so modified that they can stand long periods of rainless weather in a hot atmosphere which parches the soil. Many plants in these regions have little or no leaf area and extensive shallow root systems. This adaptation enables them to capture the water during a brief rainy season. Their enlarged stems provide storage room to hold a supply of water lasting many months.

The sparse animal population in a desert has its water problem, too. The kangaroo rat, gopher, rattlesnake, and bull snake are among those animals which live in these areas. They escape the heat of day by burying themselves or seeking shelter under plants. They satisfy their sparse water needs, directly or indirectly, from supplies stored in these plants.

Major climatic zones of North America. Temperature ranges in the various regions of North America divide it into *climatic zones.* We refer to these as (1) *polar climate zone;* (2) *temperate climate zone;* (3) *semi-tropical climate zone;* and (4) *tropical climate zone.* Northern Canada, Alaska, Greenland, and the polar region land masses lie in the **polar zone.** We find similar climatic conditions above timberline on high mountains. Here, we refer to such conditions as being in the **alpine zone.**

Southern Canada and most of the United States lie in the **temperate zone.**

The southern tip of Florida is in the **semi-tropical zone,** as are parts of Mexico and Central America. Gradually those areas became a **tropical zone.**

Within any climatic zone, the plants and animals live in divisions known as **formations.** These divisions are based, usually, on rainfall or soil conditions. A desert and a forest may lie in the same geographic region. The difference in plant and animal life of the two formations is mostly due to water.

Plant formations of the United States. We will take a quick trip across the United States, from the Atlantic coast to the Pacific Ocean, and examine the various plant formations.

If we start our trip in any of the Atlantic coastal states farther south, we will first enter the southeastern evergreen forest. This stand of pine occupies a broad belt from southern New Jersey to northern Florida and continues westward through the Gulf states to Texas. The climate is suitable for broad-leaved trees, but the sandy soil is ideal for pine. Pines have narrow leaves which reduce water loss. Sandy soil holds little water. Plants must conserve water. Thus, an adaptation to sandy soil is the reduction in leaf surface.

Farther inland, the soil becomes richer. Here broad-leaved trees form the eastern hardwood forest. This formation was once the most extensive stand of broad-leaved trees in the world. Rainfall throughout this forest ranges from about 50 inches in the east to 40 inches in the west.

West of this great forest, there was once a tall-grass prairie. Today, it is an area of rich agricultural land in the states of Illinois, Iowa, Missouri, and eastern Oklahoma, Kansas, Nebraska,

Fig. 7-8. Here you see mighty Mt. Rainier ever white with snow, towering above the green alpine meadow below.

Fig. 7-9. Barley, as well as other cereal grains, are grown in the midwestern states where the rainfall and other climatic conditions are adequate to insure good crops.

South Dakota, and North Dakota. Rainfall here varies from about 40 inches in the east to 30 inches in the west. The rainfall is uneven, however. Much of it comes during spring rains, followed by a summer drought.

The plains occupy the land west of the prairie. Plains grasses are short and are adapted to an annual rainfall of about 20 to 30 inches. Parts of Montana, Wyoming, and Colorado lie in the Great Plains. This formation has

Fig. 7-10. Because of the luxuriant growth of grass, this pasture is an important cattle-grazing area.

Fig. 7-11. Unlike many other animals, prairie dogs thrive in exposed places in full sunlight. They live in large colonies.

been developed into one of the principal cattle areas because of the luxuriant growth of grass.

In the Rocky Mountains, forests appear again because of increased rainfall in the higher altitudes. Western pines, firs, and spruces make up much of the beautiful Rocky Mountain forest. They reach up the slopes to timberline, where rocky soil, high winds, and extreme cold prevent trees from growing.

From the Rocky Mountains, and extending westward to the eastern slopes of the coastal ranges, is an area which receives less than ten inches of rain a year. These lands support sagebrush and other semi-desert plants in the north. In the south, they are occupied by true deserts.

Along the coastal ranges of Washing-

Fig. 7-12. Why do the branches of this tree grow in only one direction?

Fig. 7-13. This hillside was once covered with forest growth. Heavy cutting denuded it entirely. In three years, the area has come back by natural seedlings at the time of cutting and from sprouts from the stumps.

ton, Oregon, and California are magnificent stands of pine, spruce, redwood, and other cone-bearing trees of the Pacific coastal forest. Here, forest giants reach a height of 200 feet or more. As you may have guessed, rainfall is heavy here. Winds carrying water from the Pacific Ocean bring a rainfall of 80 inches or more. Fogs frequently blanket much of the area. If it were not for the coastal ranges, the land to the east would not be so dry. The air loses most of its water over the coastal ranges and the winds sweeping over the area to the east have lost their moisture.

Light is a critical factor in the environment of living things. It is essential to all green plants in food making.

We find many plants and animals living in complete absence of light. Blind fish with undeveloped eyes live in underground streams and rivers in the Mammoth Cave of Kentucky. Likewise, deep-sea fish live at depths to which light cannot penetrate. Many bacteria live without light, and are killed by long exposure to direct sunlight. Careful study of these organisms living in darkness shows that they depend indirectly on light for existence. They all require food and its stored energy for their activities. This food can be traced to the green plant and its food-making processes. These processes are dependent on light.

Light conditions vary from place to place just as temperatures do. Deep valleys, the floor of a forest, or the north side of a hill are places where plants and animals which prefer less light can thrive. Here we find snails, toads, and salamanders as well as ferns and mosses. These organisms do well in the shaded, cool environment.

Fig. 7-14. This photograph shows the invasion of a field by trees. The seeds from which they developed were carried by wind from the parent plants in the background.

Open fields, southern slopes, and other exposed places offer ideal situations for plants which need full sunlight. With these plants we find rabbits, groundhogs, coyotes, badgers, prairie dogs, ground squirrels, and many other animals which live in exposed places.

The atmosphere, a factor of environment. Even the air about us has a direct effect on living things. Oxygen composes about 20 per cent of the volume of the air at sea level. With the exception of certain bacteria and a few other organisms, all living things must have oxygen for life. This oxygen may be taken directly from the atmosphere or as a dissolved gas in water.

Deep-sea life has even a greater oxygen problem. Water receives its supply of oxygen from air. Hence, the oxygen content decreases with depth. The ocean is over 35,000 feet deep in the Mindanao Deep off the Philippine Is-

lands. Yet even the deep-sea fish live less than a mile below the surface.

Plants and animals which live in the soil are most abundant near the surface. Partly because of food supply, and certainly because of oxygen supply, life is limited in the depths to which it can penetrate the soil.

Air pressure, also, has a direct influence on living things. Storms may destroy plants and drive animals to shelter. Air currents and winds have a much greater effect on life than most of us realize. Air causes water to evaporate, and winds greatly increase the rate of evaporation. Plants and animals of windy plains, prairies, and mountainous regions must survive the wind. They must also survive the accompanying loss of water by evaporation. On mountains, high winds force trees to grow close to the ground and to form their branches only on the protected side (see Fig. 7-12). The winds also cause

Fig. 7-15. These beech-maple trees are crowding out all other varieties of trees and eventually will take full control of the forest. What is such a forest called?

a reduction in size of leaves and an increase in root systems.

Land formations provide varied surroundings. Changes in the natural or physical features of the earth, or *topography* (toh-*pog*-ruh-fee), usually occur slowly, but have a great effect on living things. Wind and water carry soils from one area to another. Alternate freezing and thawing during the winter months loosen the soil, and produce cracks in the rocks. These slow processes gradually form new soil.

These changes of the earth, though slow, are constant. As the earth changes, plants and animals must migrate to new and more favorable areas. They are then replaced by other organisms more suited to these conditions.

Life in a passing parade. Plants and animals are continually on the move. That is, the plant population of an area changes gradually. As plants change, animals find new homes. We call this passing parade of living things *succession*.

To see how succession takes place, we will start with a section of exposed soil in an open area. It might be a region devastated by fire or an open field. We will locate the area in the broad-leaved forest area of eastern United States, where beech and sugar maple forests once grew over much of the land.

First, grasses and other open field plants you may call weeds sprout and produce a meadow. These plants may control the region for several years. Next, the seeds of elms, cottonwood, and other sun-loving trees and shrubs find their way into the field. This marks the beginning of a forest. The larger plants shade the lower grasses and field plants. Thus environment changes. It may soon become too shady even for the seedlings of these trees and shrubs. The third stage may be seeds of oaks, ashes, and other trees which can stand more shade. These grow among the elms and cottonwoods and gradually assume control. Finally, a dense woods begins to form. The ground becomes moist and fertile and beech and maple seedlings outdistance all other species in the race for a place in the forest. Eventually, they will crowd out most other trees.

We refer to these beech and maple trees as *climax plants* because they assume final control of the region. If the succession had been on a ridge, the climax species might have been oak and hickory. Grasses are climax plants in the Great Plains.

Winds, fires, and other events in nature, as well as man's clearing, may destroy a climax species. Then, if the area is left to nature, succession starts again. Eventually, the climax plants will reclaim the region once more.

In Conclusion

Living things are under the constant influence of the physical factors of the environment. Soil, temperature, water, light, atmospheric conditions, and earth changes determine where a plant may grow. The plants, in turn, provide the environment for animals.

Nearly any set of environmental conditions is ideal for certain plants and animals. Because of this, living things occupy the land, the bodies of water, and the atmosphere from pole to pole and from mountain top to valley.

As environments change, living things change with them. The plant content of an area changes gradually toward the climax plants in a succession.

The influence of environmental factors on life and the relationship of living things to each other make field biology a fascinating study. The next chapter will introduce this phase of your biology course.

Questions for Review

1. Distinguish physical factors of environment from biological factors.

2. Explain how environment controls the distribution of plants and animals.

3. List some of the variable characteristics of soil.

4. (a) Discuss various ways in which organisms meet the problem of seasonal temperature variations. (b) Give an example of each kind of adjustment.

5. Name three geographic regions.

6. What modifications of the roots, stem, and leaves of a cactus adapt it for life in the desert?

7. Deep-sea fish cannot live much more than a mile below the surface of the ocean. What environmental factor limits the depth to which they can go?

8. How does succession apply to plants and animals?

Biologically Speaking

acid soil	dormant	migrate
alkaline soil	ecology	physical factor
alpine	environment	semi-aquatic
aquatic	estivate	succession
arctic region	formation	temperature
biological factor	hibernate	terrestrial
climate	marine	topography

Applying Facts and Principles

1. Animals, like the bear and ground hog, hibernate during the winter season. Why is it important that the animal be inactive during this period?

2. In hilly parts of the eastern deciduous forest, the trees growing on the south side of a slope are usually different species from those growing on the north side of the same hill. Discuss possible variations in the environmental factors of the two areas.

3. Discuss various ways in which plants may change the soils in which they grow.

4. Wooden ships dating back to the Romans and the Vikings have been found in deep lakes and oceans. Had they sunk in shallow water, they would probably have decayed centuries ago. Explain why they were preserved by being in deep water.

5. Explain how plants modify their own environment and establish conditions which are ideal for other plants, thus causing succession.

CHAPTER 8

Plants and Animals at Home

There is a famous pond near Concord, Massachusetts, which attracts visitors from all parts of the country. Walden Pond is an ordinary pond, or small lake, like many others in New England. It is, however, of special interest because of a man who loved it and made it famous in literature. More than a century ago, Henry David Thoreau, 1817–1862, received the inspiration for much of his writing in the quiet woods and along the shore of Walden Pond.

Have you ever read his book, *Walden, or Life in the Woods?* Undoubtedly, those of you who live in cities have felt the urge to get away from the city life and to relax in such a place as Walden. Thoreau felt this way, too, even though he didn't live in a city. The peace and quiet of Walden appealed to him. He built a hut in the birch woods and lived there more than two years. Few events in the pond and in the woods nearby escaped Thoreau's keen eyes. In the beauty and solitude of nature, he found real inspiration for some of the finest writing in American literature.

How good an observer are you? What did you notice on the way to school this morning? Was the sun shining? Did you pass any trees? What kind were they? What kinds of birds did you see? Perhaps you're one of those people who just doesn't notice things. Far too many people live according to a strict routine. They do the same things in the same way every day. Things happen all around them, but they notice very little.

Science teaches you how to observe. Biology should show you things to look for in nature. This is one of the most important reasons for studying biology.

" Eyes that see " in nature. To many people, there is nothing interesting about a woods. They are more interested in following the path leading out than in seeing what is happening there. They may notice a few trees and shrubs and an occasional wild flower. Chances are, they are more on the lookout for poison ivy or a possible snake. They pass through an outdoor laboratory full of the marvels of nature without taking a real look.

The biologist notices the black, soft earth, the ferns and mosses, and fungus plants growing from decaying stumps. He sees the tall, straight trunks of trees whose branches spread through the forest canopy far overhead. He knows what birds to expect and where they build their nests. He watches the chipmunk dart into a hollow log and the squirrel scamper around a tree trunk. To a trained observer, a woods is a fascinating place.

Field biology. Few city high schools are within walking distance of a natural environment, like a woods, a field, a pond, or a stream. But this does not

Fig. 8-1. A trained biologist does not overlook the squirrel scampering in a tree trunk, the various leaf forms, or the different nests the birds build.

mean that you can't do field work if you live in a city. In fact, congested areas offer problems to plants and animals which do not exist in rural sections.

What about your school lawn? Might it be improved? Is the soil fertile, or could it be improved with good lawn fertilizer? What kinds of grasses grow best in the city lawn? What kind should you plant in sunny lawns? What varieties are suitable for shady areas? There might be a major field project just outside your school window.

Some trees grow well along city streets. Others grow poorly or may be objectionable because their roots clog sewers. What kinds of trees are planted along the streets in your neighborhood? Why not take a walk around the block and find out? You can easily take a census. Be sure to make note of the general condition of each one as *good, fair,* or *poor.* You might record the trunk diameter of each tree, measured four and one-half feet from the ground.

Fig. 8-2. The city, too, offers its opportunities for field biology. If you have trees like these in your neighborhood, is their general condition good or could it be improved?

Fig. 8-3. Compare the oak tree (left) with the elm tree (right) as to branching, leaf arrangement, leaf form, and any other " personality " characteristics which distinguish them.

Foresters do this. They take their measurement at this height and refer to it as **d.b.h.** (diameter breast high). If you don't know the names of the trees, bring a leaf from each one and look them up at school in a tree guide.

A bird census is equally interesting. You can learn to identify the birds which live in your community without much difficulty. See how many of each kind you can find on a field trip. This is the method bird students use in determining the annual census of the bird population.

How to bring the field to your classroom. If you can't get into nature, bring nature to your classroom, or your laboratory. You should not try to bring a large number of plants and animals into the school, but many natural habitats can be constructed in aquaria or terraria on the window ledge.

One of these might be a miniature desert. Mix soil and sand and plant it with small cacti. A few rocks will add desert atmosphere. Animal life can be horned toads and other small desert lizards. Water the plants lightly once a week and hide a small container of water behind a rock for the lizards. A culture of small worms (golden grubs are good) should be maintained for food for the lizards.

You can make a bog in an aquarium with a thick layer of peat moss. Leave a small pool of water in one end. Plant pitcher plants, Venus' flytrap, sundew, sphagnum moss, and other bog plants in the peat. This is an ideal environment for small frogs, turtles, salamanders, and other bog animals.

Various vines, such as philadendron and trailing plants like Spanish moss, make an ideal tropical terrarium. Chameleons and tree frogs thrive in this environment. Be sure to cover it with

Fig. 8-4. Here you can see how the vocal sac of a toad expands when it sings. By listening to the different sounds animals make, you can learn to distinguish one from another.

glass to keep the air moist and to prevent chilling at night.

In a woodland terrarium, make a miniature ravine with small, flat rocks and bank it with various mosses. Ferns can be planted in this terrarium, along with other plants of the deep woods. Be sure the plants you get are small and that they won't outgrow the terrarium. Toads live well in the woodland terrarium as long as you keep them supplied with worms.

A pond aquarium is an ideal class project. Because it will probably be overloaded, the aquarium should be equipped with an air pump. The class members can add a great variety of small plants and animals. These might include tadpoles, salamanders (aquatic stages), diving beetles, water boatmen, various insect larvae, bullheads, and plants from nearby ponds and streams.

As a more advanced project, you might try a tropical fish aquarium. For this you will need an air pump, a thermostat, a heater, and tropical water plants. Fresh-water tropical fish in all colors and from many parts of the world are available for a tropical aquarium.

Biological supply companies stock the equipment and the specimens for most of the habitats we have suggested. Many supply detailed instructions for constructing and maintaining these exhibits.

Field identification. At one time, collecting was the major activity in a course in biology. A good botanist could name nearly all of the plants of his region. In his training, he would have collected, pressed, mounted, and classified literally thousands of plants. The zoologist devoted much of his time to the classification of animals. Field identification is still a major part of biology, but our course now includes branches of biology which were unknown a few generations ago.

Fig. 8-5. Studying environmental conditions will help you understand why the trunks of these forest trees grow tall and straight, rather than short and crooked.

Collections are valuable in high school biology courses. Insects, leaves, seeds, and fruits, and flowers (not the entire plant) are popular subjects for collections. In many schools, especially during the spring semester, classes take bird identification hikes and students spend time in individual field work. The name of each bird seen, and the date and place of observation, are recorded on a calendar in the classroom.

Field identification is excellent training in observation. All living things have distinct "personalities." They have characteristics of their kind. Someone familiar with trees can tell an oak tree from an elm at a glance. He uses characteristics of the bark, branching pattern, leaf arrangement, leaf form, flower, fruit, and bud characteristics in distinguishing trees. These are parts of the personality of a tree.

In bird identification, we rely on such characteristics as size, shape, color, habits, sounds, and habitat.

Sounds in nature. Sometime when you are out in the field, stand perfectly still for a few minutes and see how many different sounds you can hear. A naturalist can identify many animals by their sounds alone. Ever hear a frog chorus coming from a marsh on a warm, spring night? The deep bass grunts of a bullfrog blend with the croaking of a leopard frog or the banjo-like twang of a green frog. Tiny tree frogs, cricket frogs, and the common toad add their high-pitched trills and chirps.

All of us recognize the chirping of a cricket and the singing of the katydid and 17-year locust, or cicada. On the other hand, many insects make sounds so high and shrill they cannot be heard by the human ear.

Field study of environment. The biologist is interested not only in the *kinds* of plants and animals he find but also in the type of surrounding environment, in which he find Accurate records should be m

Fig. 8-6. A quail, buried in a thicket, blends in almost perfectly with its environment. What adaptation does this illustrate?

date, place, and environment of each organism identified.

While studying the plants and animals in a forest, notice the environmental conditions. How do light intensity, moisture, soil characteristics, and air currents compare with those of an open field? What causes the trees in a forest to grow tall and straight, while the same trees in an open place probably have short trunks and large, spreading crowns? What kinds of tree seedlings are growing on the forest floor? These young plants will be the forest of the future. What kinds of animals live in the forest? How do they depend on plant life?

As you make trips into other environments, the plant and animal populations will change completely. Keep in mind the effects of light, soil, moisture, and air currents. Notice how they vary from place to place.

Animal camouflage. Did you ever hear a katydid singing on a branch and

trace the sound without being able to find the insect? Probably it was sitting right before you, watching you all the time. But its green wing covers blended so perfectly with the leaves around it that you could hardly see it even when you were looking for it. The blending of an animal with its surroundings is a kind of **camouflage** (*kam*-oo-flaje). Many animals owe their existence to this protection.

Animal camouflage involves several principles. Sometimes the animal is colored and marked like its surroundings. When it is, we refer to the camouflage as **protective coloration**. Nature is full of examples. The orange background and black stripes of the tiger blend almost perfectly with the grasses and shadows of its environment. A covey of quail crouched in a thicket go unnoticed until they become frightened and fly into the air. The common tree frog has irregular markings of brown and ashy gray which blend with the

Fig. 8-7. In the water as well as on land animals show camouflage. It is hard to see the pike in the water, for example, because of countershading.

bark of a tree. The green background and black blotches of the leopard frog and the pickerel frog blend with the grass and water plants of a pond. As you can see, examples of protective coloration are very common in nature and very important to the organisms for survival. Some of the animals blend so perfectly with their surroundings that only the most careful observer is aware of them.

Fish illustrate a slightly different principle, called **countershading.** In this case, darker colors on the upper side fade into light colors on the lower side. The large-mouth black bass is a good example. The upper region of the body is greenish. This blends with colors on the bottom of a lake or stream. It is nearly white on the lower side. This color blends with the reflection of sky in the water, thus protecting the bass from enemies above and below it. The yellow perch has similar countershading. It is greenish on the upper

side and creamy yellow underneath. The dark bars on its sides blend with shadows in the water. The effectiveness of countershading is proved when you realize how hard it is to see a fish in the water.

Protective resemblance is still another principle of animal camouflage. In this case, the animal resembles something other than itself. Certain wormlike insect larvae which feed on leaves look almost like short twigs. When disturbed, they stiffen and hang out from a twig. It is almost impossible to tell which is plant and which is larva. Several kinds of butterflies resemble brown leaves when their wings are folded. The walking stick, a relative of the grasshopper, actually looks like a stick with legs. You have probably seen walking sticks without recognizing them.

Mimicry (*mim*-ih-kree) is one of the strangest of all protective resemblances. However, in this case the animal resem-

Fig. 8-8. Above is a robber fly that closely resembles the bumblebee shown in Fig. 8-9.

Fig. 8-9. Does this bumblebee remind you of the robber fly? This resemblance is called mimicry.

Fig. 8-10. The opossum plays dead when captured, and this fact has given rise to the familiar expression " playing possum."

bles another animal rather than a part of its environment. For some reason, the robber fly resembles a bumblebee. This gives the fly the protection the bee has earned with its stinger. Another common example of mimicry is found in two butterflies, the viceroy and the monarch. The monarch is the common orange and black butterfly you see around milkweed plants. The viceroy looks almost like the monarch, except that it is darker orange and has black bars in its lower wings. It has been said that the monarch has a bitter flavor and, therefore, is avoided by birds. The more tasty viceroy escapes because it looks so much like the monarch which birds do not like. However, scientists have disputed this belief that birds do not eat monarch butterflies. If this is true, the viceroy is not as safe from destruction as we once thought.

In studying animal camouflage, we must keep in mind the principle of cause and effect discussed in Chapter 2. The animal does not blend with its surroundings *in order to live*. Rather, it survives *because* it blends with its surroundings. Today, we see the result of many years of survival of animals best adjusted to their surroundings. Through slight variations in form and color, certain individuals resembled their surroundings more than others. They had a better chance to survive and remained to produce more of their kind. These variations appear slowly. It has taken thousands of years for the animals we have just mentioned to develop. In the process, many millions perished because they were not able to adapt themselves to their environment.

Animal adaptations for protection.
Many animals survive because of vari-

Fig. 8-11. The bobcat, with its sharp claws and ability to run swiftly, has its own method for protecting itself from its enemies.

ous ways they have of protecting themselves in time of danger.

Rapid movement is the best defense of many animals. The deer can run through dense forests and thickets at top speed. If cornered, it uses its sharp hooves and powerful legs for kicking. A squirrel can outrun almost any animal in the treetops. On the ground, it is more defenseless. We are all familiar with the highly effective weapon of the skunk. The slow, awkward opossum cannot outrun an enemy on the ground so it plays dead when captured. You can pick him up by the tail and carry him around and he will remain stiff and motionless. But put him down and step away and in a short time off he scampers to the nearest tree.

The powerful legs and claws of a bear are no match for any animal of the forest. The bobcat, while much smaller, can protect itself well with sharp claws and lightning speed. The fox, wolf, badger, wolverine, mink, and weasel use sharp teeth and powerful jaws in defense as well as in food-getting. Among smaller animals, we find the stinger of the bee and wasp, the pincer jaws of beetles, the poison fangs of spiders, and the claws of crayfish and lobsters efficient weapons of defense.

Field study of plant and animal behavior. Why do living things behave as they do? Is it a natural urge, or instinct? Or is it the capacity to learn, or intelligence? Is it a combination of both?

Animal behavior is one of the most fascinating of all subjects for field study. It takes knowledge of various kinds of behavior and very close observation.

We frequently credit animals with more intelligence than they actually possess. How intelligent is a bird? It can build an intricate nest and migrate long distances without getting lost. Could you build a nest or fly a plane a thousand miles or more over unknown territory without radio or compass? Of course you couldn't. Does this mean that birds have super-intelligence? Let's examine a bird more closely. A robin builds a nest of mud and grass. An oriole makes a deep, hanging bag nest. You can identify a nest as easily as you can the bird which made it, if you know your nests. If all birds of the same kind make the same kind of nest, it must be instinct and not intelligence which directs them. If it were intelligence, the quality of the nest would vary with the intelligence of the bird. They might even improve on the materials used. But if it were intelligence, a bird would have to learn to make a nest. As you know, they do this instinctively. Instinct directs the bird on its migratory flight. It serves as the automatic pilot which guides it through the darkness and over the water to its summer or winter home.

To study instinctive behavior in the insect world, find an anthill. Sit down and study it closely for an hour or more. Watch the endless columns of these tiny creatures moving through a jungle of grass, each performing its task for the colony. If you have never seen the soldiers of two different species of ants lock jaws in deadly combat, you have missed one of the greatest thrills in nature.

Many animals show definite evidence of intelligence and learning in their behavior. A hunter would certainly disagree if you said that all bird behavior is instinctive. Anyone who has hunted will agree that crows seem to know when you're carrying a gun. You can walk fairly close to a crow if you are unarmed. But walk across a field with a gun on your arm and a lookout gives an alarm and all the crows in the vicinity fly away with a noisy protest.

Among mammals, there are many

Fig. 8-12. The different types of nests which birds make are characteristic of the birds themselves. The robin makes clumsy nests, usually in crotches of trees, of mud or clay.

Fig. 8-13. Ants are fascinating animals to study. Here you see the inside of an anthill and the eggs.

signs of intelligent behavior. These are difficult to distinguish from instinct in many cases. Generally speaking, if the animal behaves automatically and like all others of its kind in a similar situation, its actions are controlled by instinct. If an action is the result of learning from a previous experience, a higher form of behavior which may be intelligence has taken over.

In Conclusion

A zoo is a good place to see animals you will probably never see in their native haunts. But a fenced enclosure or a barred cage is no substitute for a natural environment. Similarly, you can learn much about plants and animals in a classroom or a laboratory, but certain phases of biology require study in the field. There are limits to the field work you can do with a group as large as a class. If, during your year of biology, you can make a few trips of your own, the whole class can benefit from your observations and biology will have a new and different meaning for you.

If you enjoy getting out-of-doors, one of the first questions you may ask is, " What kind of bird is that? " or " What kind of a tree, or flower, or insect is it? " All living things have names. All are classified into groups showing likenesses in form. These are topics we will discuss in Chapter 9.

Questions for Review

1. Explain what we mean by the term " eyes that see " in nature.

2. Name some of the characteristics of trees which can be used in identifying them.

3. How does camouflage apply to animals?

4. Describe color blending as a form of camouflage and give several examples of animals which illustrate color blending.

5. Discuss countershading and explain how a fish is marked to blend with its surroundings.

6. Describe several animals which illustrate protective resemblance.

7. Give two examples of animals which mimic other animals.

8. Name five different adaptations for protection and illustrate each with an animal.

9. What distinct advantage does field biology offer that is lacking in laboratory study, especially of animals?

10. Name several ways in which animals show instinctive behavior.

Biologically Speaking

adaptation
behavior
camouflage
countershading

d.b.h.
field biology
instinct
intelligence

mimicry
protective coloration
protective resemblance

Applying Facts and Principles

1. No animal was ever able to change its markings to blend with its surroundings. How, then, do you account for protective coloration, countershading, and protective resemblance?

2. How could you prove that migration and nest building among birds is instinctive behavior rather than behavior based on intelligence?

3. Mammals have become the rulers of the earth because of their capacity for learning. Why do these animals have a great advantage over those which rely entirely on instinct?

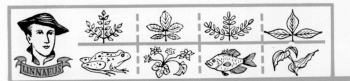

CHAPTER 9

Classification of Plants and Animals

Suppose someone dumped a thousand different postage stamps in a pile and asked you to arrange them in some systematic way. How would you begin? You would probably start by separating them into countries. With this completed, you might have 20 or so smaller piles. Then you would continue sorting the piles for each country. The next division might be into issues, or sets of stamps in use at one time. You might have ten or more issues from a single country. Within each issue, there might be stamps ranging from one to 50 cents. These are denominations. You would arrange them in order. Finally, after sorting through all of the countries, you would be able to find any stamp easily.

Now then, instead of stamps, what if you had a million different living things to group and sort? You would follow the same system — large groups to smaller ones, and these into still smaller ones until you would finally come to a single kind of plant or animal.

Common names of organisms. From the earliest times, plants and animals have been given common names by the people who lived among them. The name often referred to a characteristic, a habit, or a use of an organism. The early pioneers found plants and animals in the North American wilderness which were quite different from those of the old country. They couldn't understand the names the Indians had already given many of them, so they chose names of their own. We still use many of them such as: pine, oak, sunflower, cowslip, bluebell, buffalo grass, bluegrass, cattail, rattlesnake, groundhog, and prairie dog. They have been handed down from generation to generation. As long as a name means a particular plant or animal to you and you stay in the community where it is used, names of this kind are satisfactory. But as you will see, common names of organisms have created many difficult problems.

Common names are confusing. No system was used in choosing common names. In many cases, various regions had their own names for the same plant or animal. Take the "flicker" for example. It is a common woodpecker of eastern United States. Maybe you call it a "yellow hammer." Others know it as the "golden-winged woodpecker" or the "high-hole." It is said that this bird has over 50 different names. If it migrated to Mexico, it would have another set of names in Spanish. In Brazil, there would be still other names in Portuguese.

In some cases, a single name refers to several different plants or animals. What is a "bluebell"? Dozens of plants with blue, bell-shaped flowers are called "bluebells." "Buttercup" is just as confusing. What is a "black-

Fig. 9-1. Both the names groundhog and woodchuck can apply to the animal above.

bird"? It is a crow, a raven, a bronzed grackle, a purple grackle, or a rusty blackbird.

Common names are misleading. Common names have no scientific basis. To a biologist, a fish is a vertebrate animal with a backbone, fins, and gills. Bass, perch, cod, halibut, and salmon are fish. Do you know the "silver fish"? It's an insect. We call clams and oysters "shellfish." And people call other animals in no way resembling the biologist's idea of a fish, "crayfish," "jellyfish," and "starfish."

Scientific classification. By the 18th century, science was becoming international. Common names had long caused hopeless confusion. During this time Carolus Linnaeus (lih-*nee*-us), 1707–1778, a Swedish botanist, devised a system for naming and classifying all the organisms of the earth. His system is used today internationally.

Linnaeus discarded the common names of plants and gave each one a scientific name. He took the scientific name from Latin words. None of the names was taken from his own native Swedish language or from any other modern language.

There are several reasons why Linnaeus chose Latin as the language of scientific classification. It is unchanging. Furthermore, many modern languages contain words taken directly from this ancient language. Latin was understood by scientists of all countries. And its descriptive powers are ideal in identifying the many characteristics of organisms referred to in scientific names.

Linnaeus published his list of plant names in 1753 and his list of animal names in 1758. The scientific name of each plant had at least two parts. Usually, the name referred to some characteristic of the organism or to the person who named it. His system spread rapidly and became so popular that he used it later in naming animals. Many of his names are in use today. You can tell them by the **L.** which appears after the scientific name.

Fig. 9-2. This may be a woodpecker to you, but it may be a "flicker" or a "yellowhammer" to someone else, depending on the locality in which he lives.

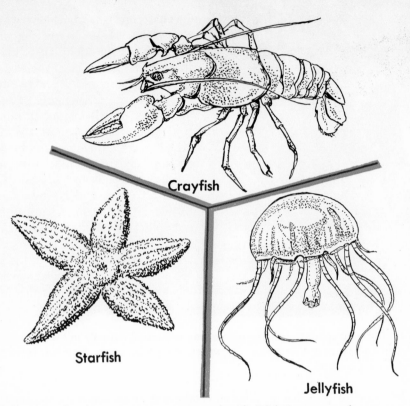

Fig. 9-3. Animals whose common names end with " fish " are not always structurally alike nor are they necessarily related.

How scientific names are written. Linnaeus' system of giving each organism a scientific name of two or more parts is called **binomial nomenclature.** This might be spoken of as two-word naming. The first name refers to the *genus* (*jee*-nus) [pl. genera (*jen*-er-ah)] and always begins with a capital letter. The *species* (*spee*-sheez) name follows and usually, but not always, begins with a small letter. The genus name is usually a noun and the species name is an adjective. The placing of the genus name before the species name is regular Latin order. We use a similar system in official lists of names where John Smith appears as Smith, John.

Now, we can straighten out the confusion about the flicker with its 50 or more common names. Call it what you will, all scientists call it *Colaptes auratus* (koh-*lap*-teez au-*ray*-tus). This is its name the world over and in any language. This name seems strange to you, but it has meaning to a biologist. He knows that any other bird with the genus name, *Colaptes,* is a relative of the flicker. And *auratus* refers to yellow, a noticeable characteristic of the flicker.

Scientific names have more meaning when you see how they are used. For example, *Pinus strobus* is the scientific name of the eastern white pine. It is a species, or kind, of pine. *Pinus resinosa* is the red, or Norway pine; *Pinus rigida* is the pitch pine; *Pinus pungens,* the western yellow pine. You will note

Fig. 9-4. Different species of the sycamore tree are found not only in the United States, but also in Europe and Asia Minor. However, the genus name, *Platanus*, remains the same all over the world.

that each kind of pine has a different species name. The fact that they belong to the same genus indicates close relationship. Pine trees the world over belong to the genus *Pinus*. (See Fig. 9-5.)

Salix nigra is the black willow and *Fraxinus nigra* is the black ash. These names show no close relationship even though the species names are the same. A **genus** is a group of closely related species. A **species**, in turn, is an individual kind of plant or animal like all others of its kind in form and capable of producing more of the species.

In your biology course, you will study many organisms which have no common names. And it is well to know that every kind of living thing has one scientific name known the world over. Man, by the way, is *Homo sapiens*. The species name means *wise*.

The basis of scientific naming and classification. When we say that certain plants and animals are related to each other, how do we know? Why is

WHY WE USE SCIENTIFIC NAMES

1. They are absolutely definite and never duplicated.
2. They are used by people of all countries.
3. They are usually descriptive.
4. They show a systematic relationship to other organisms.

the cow related to the bison more closely than it is to the fox or wolf? The answer lies in the fact that the cow and bison both have hooves while the fox has claws.

All scientific classification is based on similarity in form, or *structural similarity*. This is the only real basis for grouping living things. Biologists have classified all living things into groups, showing structural similarity. They start with very large groups and continue dividing groups into smaller groups until they arrive at a single species of plant or animal. This is the principle we discussed in connection with classifying stamps.

Scientific classification. If you had a specimen of each of the more than one million kinds of plants and animals known to exist and started grouping them, where would you start? The beginning would be rather obvious. Some are plants and some are animals. This division is where the biologist begins his classification. He separates living things into two very large **kingdoms**, plant and animal. Next, he divides each kingdom into smaller groups, known as **phyla** (*fy*-la) [sing. phylum (*fy*-lum)].

Biologists have for many years recognized four plant phyla. Most animals belong to eleven animal phyla.

Phyla are large groups. Some phyla contain thousands of species. We divide each phylum into smaller groups, called **classes**. A class, in turn, is divided into **orders**. A division of an order is a **family**. A family contains related genera, and a **genus** is composed of one or more **species**. In some cases, individuals of a single species vary slightly, but not enough to be considered separate species. We refer to them as **varieties**. This adds a third part to the scientific name in some cases.

Fig. 9-5. Although there are differences in cones and needles, these are all species of pine. Top: *Pinus ponderosa;* middle: *Pinus pungens;* bottom: *Pinus rigida.*

FOUR PHYLA OF THE PLANT KINGDOM

PHYLUM	MEMBERS
Thallophyta (thah-*loff*-ih-tah)	Algae (pond scums and seaweeds), fungi (bacteria, yeasts, molds, mushrooms), lichens
Bryophyta (bry-*off*-ih-tah)	Mosses, liverworts
Pteridophyta (ter-ih-*doff*-ih-tah)	Ferns, club mosses, horsetails
Spermatophyta (sper-mah- *toff*-ih-tah	Seed plants (pines and their relatives and flowering plants)

ELEVEN PHYLA OF THE ANIMAL KINGDOM

Protozoa (pro-toh-*zoh*-ah)	One-celled animals
Porifera (poh-*riff*-fer-ah)	Sponges
Coelenterata (seh-len-ter-*ay*-tah)	Jellyfish, sea anemone, coral
Platyhelminthes (plat-ee-hel-*min*-theze)	Flatworms (tapeworm, fluke)
Nemathelminthes (nem-uh-thel-*min*-theze)	Roundworms (hookworm, trichina, vinegar eel, " horsehair " snake)
Rotifera (roh-*tih*-fer-ah)	Rotifers (wheel animals)
Annelida (an-*neh*-lih-dah)	Segmented worms (earthworm, leech, sandworm)
Arthropoda (ar-*throh*-poh-dah)	Crayfish, lobster, insects, spiders, centipedes, millepedes
Mollusca (mol-*luss*-kah)	Clam, oyster, snail, squid, octopus
Echinodermata (eh-kyne-oh-der-*mah*-tah)	Starfish, sea urchins
Chordata (kor-*day*-tah)	Amphioxus and all the vertebrates
Vertebrata (subphylum) (vert-ah-*bray*-tah)	Lampreys, sharks and rays, fish, amphibians, reptiles, birds, mammals

Fig. 9-6. What similarities of body structure does this bison show that enable biologists to group it with cattle? Notice the hooves.

Plant and animal phyla. We can begin the classification of living things with the great groups, or phyla, which make up each of the two kingdoms. Study the examples of each phylum in the table on page 108 and see if you can find similarity in the plants or animals included in each one. Of course, in a group as large as a phylum, similarities would not necessarily be close.

The classification of an animal. Examine closely the grasshopper shown in Fig. 9-7. It is one of the larger short-horned grasshoppers. Scientists call it *Schistocerca* (skis-toh-*sir*-kah) *americana*. We'll follow it through the various groups from kingdom to species as shown in the table below.

As we follow this grasshopper through its classification, each group we take it

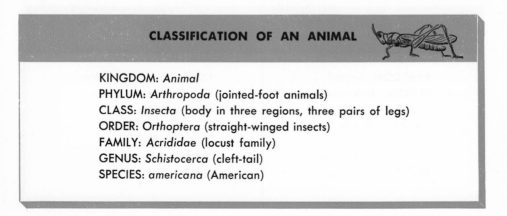

CLASSIFICATION OF AN ANIMAL

KINGDOM: *Animal*
PHYLUM: *Arthropoda* (jointed-foot animals)
CLASS: *Insecta* (body in three regions, three pairs of legs)
ORDER: *Orthoptera* (straight-winged insects)
FAMILY: *Acrididae* (locust family)
GENUS: *Schistocerca* (cleft-tail)
SPECIES: *americana* (American)

Fig. 9-7. Classify this grasshopper from kingdom to species according to the table on this page. Name some other animals that belong to the same phylum.

into becomes smaller. The individuals making up the group become more closely related.

The kingdom includes all animals. The phylum, *Arthropoda* (ar-*throp*-oh-dah), includes only such animals as the insects, spiders, crayfish, centipedes, and millepedes. All have an outer skeleton and jointed appendages such as legs.

The class, *Insecta*, rules out all Arthropods which are not insects. The order, *Orthoptera* (or-*thop*-ter-ah), includes only a certain group of insects with the peculiar *straight wings* found on crickets, roaches, praying mantis, and grasshoppers. The family, *Acrididae* (ak-rid-ih-dee), separates grasshoppers from the other straight-winged insects. The genus, *Schistocerca,* includes a small group of closely related grasshoppers, while the species name, *americana* (amer-ih-*kah*-nah), is given to this one kind of grasshopper. We use only the genus and species names in its scientific name.

We may compare the classification system to the address on a letter, listed in reverse order. Mail clerks read the address in this order when they sort it in various stations.

Classification is a specialized branch of biology. *Taxonomy* (tax-*on*-oh-mee) is the name given to the naming and classifying of plants and animals. All biologists deal with classification in some phases of their work. But many biologists work in this field almost exclusively. We call them **taxonomists.** It may surprise you to learn that new species of plants and animals are discovered each year. The biologist who finds a new species can give it a scientific name. Of course, he must place

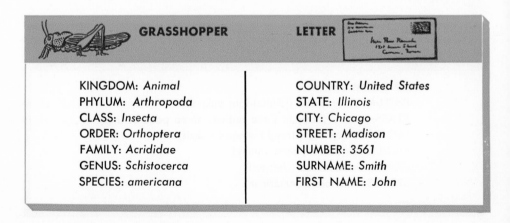

GRASSHOPPER	LETTER
KINGDOM: *Animal*	COUNTRY: *United States*
PHYLUM: *Arthropoda*	STATE: *Illinois*
CLASS: *Insecta*	CITY: *Chicago*
ORDER: *Orthoptera*	STREET: *Madison*
FAMILY: *Acrididae*	NUMBER: *3561*
GENUS: *Schistocerca*	SURNAME: *Smith*
SPECIES: *americana*	FIRST NAME: *John*

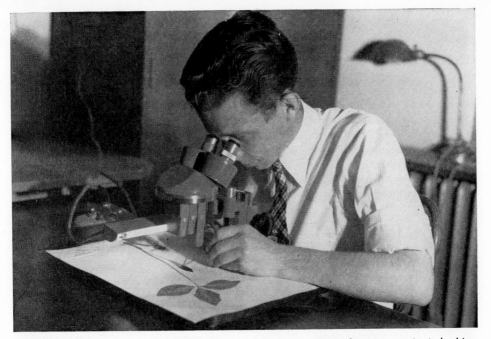

Fig. 9-8. Taxonomy is an important phase of biology. Here this taxonomist is looking through a microscope at a mounted plant in order to find out to what species or genus it belongs.

it in the proper genus. The species name can refer to a characteristic of the organism, or to the person who discovered it.

You will find in the Appendix a partial classification of the plant and animal kingdoms. The four plant phyla and the eleven most important animal phyla are included. In addition, classes and orders of the more familiar organisms are given. Study this classification carefully.

In Conclusion

Scientific classification is one of the best examples of the close cooperation of the scientists of the world. Their nationalities, customs, and native tongues may be different, but in the realm of science, they speak the same language. Through international cooperation, most organisms of the earth have been given places in orderly groups, based on structural characteristics.

We are now ready to start our study of groups of living things. We will begin with seed plants, the most familiar and most advanced members of the plant kingdom.

Questions for Review

1. Discuss several ways in which common names of organisms are confusing.

2. List several reasons why Latin is an ideal language for scientific classification.

3. Explain the binomial system of naming plants and animals.

4. List four advantages of scientific names over common names.

5. On what characteristics of an organism is classification based?

6. Name the classification groups from the largest to the smallest.

7. What do we call the specialized branch of biology which deals with the naming and classification of plants and animals?

Biologically Speaking

binomial nomenclature
class
classification
common name

family
genus
kingdom
order

phylum
scientific name
species
taxonomy

Applying Facts and Principles

1. Give examples to show that such similarities in animals as size, habitat, and diet show no true relationships which could be considered in classification.

2. Make a list of plants and animals of your region which have more than one common name.

3. Scientists do not all agree on the exact meaning of a species. What in your opinion do you think a species should represent?

4. What are some of the ways that scientific classification can be made useful to the nonscientist?

Research On Your Own

1. Set up a balanced aquarium in your classroom or laboratory, including various aquatic plants and animals which live in the ponds and streams of your region. If the aquarium is to be maintained for several weeks or months, it should have about an inch of clean coarse sand on the bottom. Set rooted aquatic plants in the sand. Include several kinds of floating plants. Animals to be included may be several small fish, tadpoles, aquatic salamanders, and aquatic insects. When you add the animals, watch them closely for several days to be sure that the plants supply enough oxygen for them. If you have a balance between the plants and animals, the aquarium should need little attention for several months.

2. Select one bird or other animal of your region which seems to be increasing in number and one which seems to be decreasing. Make a thorough study of both animals, including their habits, diet, natural enemies, adaptability, and reproductive processes. See if you can determine why the animal is increasing or decreasing. Report your findings to the class.

3. Analyze two environments in your region, such as a deep woods, a hillside, an open field, a ravine, or a ridge. Make notes on such factors as soil conditions, air movements, light, moisture, and approximate temperature. List as many of the plants and animals in each region as you can identify. Compare the two environments and present your findings to the class.

4. Prepare one or more habitats, using terraria or aquaria with glass covers. Include plants and animals which belong in the habitats you construct. Your display might include a desert, a woodland, a bog, a tropical habitat, a pond life aquarium, a collection of small native fish, or a tropical fish aquarium. Many biological supply houses can provide the plants and animals, soil, and detailed directions for making the habitats.

5. Make a large wall chart showing the plant and animal kingdoms as trees. Make the phyla branches, with the phylum name on each branch. The branches should come off the trunk in order of complexity of the phyla. You will find them in this order in the Appendix. To make the chart more graphic, you might sketch an animal and a plant representing each phylum at the end of the branch. The illustrations might be taken from magazines, rather than drawn. If your chart is large enough, you may wish to divide some of the phyla into smaller branches representing classes, with an example of each illustrated.

 —————————————— **More About Biology**

Anderson, M. S. *GEOGRAPHY OF LIVING THINGS.* Philosophical Library, New York. 1952

Andrews, Roy Chapman. *NATURE'S WAYS: HOW NATURE TAKES CARE OF ITS OWN.* Crown Publishers, New York. 1951

ANIMAL TRACKS; THE STANDARD GUIDE FOR IDENTIFICATION AND CHARACTERISTICS. Stackpole Co., Harrisburg, Pa. 1954

Buck, Margaret. *IN WOODS AND FIELDS.* Abingdon-Cokesbury Press, Nashville, Tenn. 1950

Carr, William H. *DESERT PARADE.* The Viking Press, New York. 1947

Disney, Walt. *THE LIVING DESERT.* Simon and Schuster, Inc., New York. 1954

DuPuy, Wm. A. *OUR PLANT FRIENDS AND FOES.* John C. Winston Co., Philadelphia. 1948

Earle, Olive L. *PAWS, HOOFS, AND FLIPPERS.* William Morrow and Co., New York. 1954

Garland, Joseph. *ALL CREATURES HERE BELOW.* Houghton Mifflin Co., Boston. 1954

Grange, Wallace. *THOSE OF THE FOREST.* The Flambeau Publishing Co., Babcock, Wisc. 1954

Hylander, C. J. *SEA AND SHORE.* The Macmillan Co., New York. 1949

Jaeger, Edmund C. *OUR DESERT NEIGHBORS.* Stanford University Press, Stanford. 1950

Jacques, H. E. *LIVING THINGS AND HOW TO KNOW THEM.* Wm. C. Brown, Dubuque. 1946

Lorenz, Konrad Z. *KING SOLOMON'S*

RING: NEW LIGHT ON ANIMAL WAYS. The Thomas Y. Crowell Co., New York. 1952

Mason, George F. ANIMAL HOMES. William Morrow and Co., New York. 1947

Mason, George F. ANIMAL SOUNDS. William Morrow and Co., New York. 1948

Mason, George Frederick. ANIMAL TOOLS. William Morrow and Co., New York. 1951

Mason, George F. ANIMAL WEAPONS. William Morrow and Co., Inc., New York. 1949

Parker, Bertha. ADAPTATIONS TO ENVIRONMENT. Row, Peterson and Co., Evanston, Illinois. 1946

Schwarzkopf, Chet. FUR, FIN AND FEATHERS. The Thomas Y. Crowell Co., New York. 1954

Thoreau, Henry David. WALDEN: OR LIFE IN THE WOODS. Dodd, Mead and Co., New York. 1946

The Biology of Plant Life

Which appeared first on the earth — plant or animal life? From our study of the relationship of living things, the answer is obvious — plant life. Animal life exists due to the link between the inorganic world and the living world by means of the green plant.

It is logical to begin our study of a specific kind of organism with the green plant, our chief food producer. We shall find out how it makes food from the carbon dioxide in the air and the water in the soil, and where it stores the excess food.

When you explore the tissues forming the various plant organs and the specialized processes they perform, you will probably agree that a root, a stem, and a leaf are marvelous organs. The story of reproduction from flower to fruit and seed and the dispersal of the seed to a new location is, indeed, a fascinating one.

CHAPTER 10

The Seed Plants

Long years ago, when giant dinosaurs roamed the earth, a new kind of plant was slowly invading the forests of ferns and fernlike plants. The age of the seed plants had dawned. Since that time, more than 200 million years ago, other forms of vegetation have been forced to yield more and more of the land to seed plants, the most advanced of all plants.

Today, seed plants dominate the land masses of the earth. Mosses and ferns, which once grew in great numbers, are now reduced for the most part to scattered clumps and patches. Seed plants form our forests and spread over fields and plains. They have invaded dry lands and deserts. Their frontiers lie in the windswept, treeless plains of the far north and the rocky slopes of high mountains. Beyond here, the mosses hold the shallow, barren ground in their last retreat.

On the land seed plants reign supreme. Their specialized tissues and highly developed organs are the most perfect of the plant kingdom.

Spermatophytes — the seed plants. This fourth phylum of the plant kingdom, the Spermatophytes, includes all plants which produce seeds. A **seed** is a complete young plant surrounded by one or more protective seed coats. Food stored in a seed nourishes the young plant until it is established in its new location. In a sense, a seed is a packaged plant, ready for delivery to new surroundings.

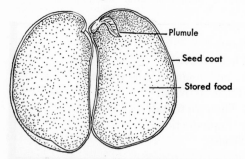

Fig. 10-1. A seed is a young plant containing the seed coat and stored food.

A seed may travel through the air, float in the water, be carried on the fur of an animal, or lie dormant for many months. When conditions are favorable, the seed coats soften and the young plant pushes out its root and its shoot. By means of seeds, plants spread to new locations. This is a highly efficient method of reproduction. It is one of the reasons the seed plants have gained domination of the earth.

Two great classes of seed plants. We divide the phylum, Spermatophyta, into two large classes: (1) the *Gymnosperms* (*jim*-noh-sperms); and (2) the *Angiosperms* (*an*-jih-oh-sperms). The Gymnosperms are the more primitive and older seed plants. Their name means literally *naked seeds*. It refers to the fact that seeds of gymnosperms are not enclosed in a fruit. Gymnosperms flourished in earlier stages of the conquest of the land by seed plants.

Fig. 10-2. The gymnosperms flourished during the Carboniferous and related periods. The great swamps in which they once grew have now become coal beds.

Some of their members lived as far back as the Carboniferous (kar-bon-*if*-er-ous) or coal-forming period. Today, large numbers of gymnosperms are extinct. We know them only in the form of fossils. **Fossils** are the remains of living things of long ago preserved in rocks. However, many gymnosperms, including the pine, spruce, fir, and several other forest trees, are of great value in our modern civilization.

The class, *Angiosperms*, includes all of the flowering plants. The flower produces the fruit which, in turn, encloses the seeds. The everyday plants you know best belong to this class. We might say we live in an age of flowering plants, or angiosperms.

A living fossil. Many years ago, priests of China found a curious tree in the forests of the interior. They planted it in the temple gardens. Later, it was introduced into gardens in Japan. Little did these ancient priests know that they had found and preserved the last species of an order of gymnosperms, the *Ginkgoales* (gink-oh-*ay*-leez). You may know the Ginkgo tree (*Ginkgo biloba*), for it is now cultivated in yards and parks of the United States and other countries.

The leaves of the ginkgo are wedge-shaped and two-lobed, unlike those of any other tree. Most of the leaves grow in clusters at the tips of curious spurs spaced along the branches. Some of the branches lack these spurs. The ginkgo is often called the maidenhair tree because its leaves closely resemble those of the maidenhair fern. Its fruits look like large berries and are extremely foul-smelling.

The ginkgo is a fine tree for planting in the yard. In time it will grow as high as 100 feet with a diameter of nearly four feet. If you do plant a ginkgo in your yard, remember that you have one of the rarest of all living plants — a single species of a single genus — the last survivor of an entire order.

Fig. 10-3. The cycads were widely distributed in early geological eras and many species are now extinct. These tropical and semi-tropical plants usually have unbranched stems which bear a crown of palmlike leaves.

Cone-bearing gymnosperms — the conifers. The word *conifer* refers to the cones which these trees produce. The woody cones bear winged seeds on the upper surface of the scales. Conifers depend on the wind for scattering their seeds.

Conifer leaves are either in the form of needles or flat scales. Most coniferous trees keep their needles all winter. The new ones which are formed in the spring take the place of the old ones which fall to the ground. Exceptions to this are the bald cypress and the larch. These two conifers lose their needles each autumn.

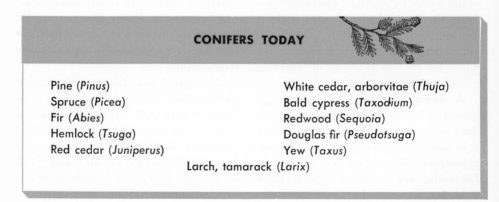

CONIFERS TODAY

Pine (*Pinus*)	White cedar, arborvitae (*Thuja*)
Spruce (*Picea*)	Bald cypress (*Taxodium*)
Fir (*Abies*)	Redwood (*Sequoia*)
Hemlock (*Tsuga*)	Douglas fir (*Pseudotsuga*)
Red cedar (*Juniperus*)	Yew (*Taxus*)

Larch, tamarack (*Larix*)

Of all the kinds of gymnosperms which ever lived, the conifers are best suited to present world environments. Many coniferous species have disappeared, but the conifers remain today in many parts of the world. They still flourish and are dominant in many parts of North America.

The table on page 118 shows you some of the genera of modern North American conifers.

We have included the scientific names of these genera because you will see them if you look at nursery catalogs. Conifers are widely used in yard plantings. Cultivated varieties of the red cedar, white cedar, hemlock, and yew are ideal for planting along the foundations of houses. Larger conifers are widely planted as windbreaks around farm houses and as trees in city yards. Pines, spruces, and hemlocks are ideal for these purposes. The Colorado blue spruce is unsurpassed as a single tree in a yard planting.

Fig. 10-5. The Ginkgo tree, a gymnosperm once found only in China and Japan, is now a familiar sight in the United States where it is grown as a shade tree. In the upper left-hand corner, you can see a close-up of the leaves and fruit.

Fig. 10-4. The Colorado blue spruce, a conifer, has improved the appearance of many a yard. If you were to plant only a single tree, why would this tree be a good one?

As timber trees, conifers are ideal. Many species thrive in the poorer soils, unsuitable for the broad-leaved forest trees. Sand and rocky soils are no barriers to the conifers.

Before leaving the conifers, we might mention that they hold the record for height, trunk diameter, and age among trees. A *Sequoia,* or giant redwood, in the Caleveras Grove of California, towers 300 feet above the ground. This tree is over 30 feet in diameter and is estimated to be 4,000 years old. However, this trunk diameter and age are surpassed by a cypress tree growing about 200 miles south of Mexico City. The Big Tree of Tule, as it is called, is 50 feet in diameter. Biologists estimate that it is over 5,000 years old.

Flowering plants. The angiosperms, or flowering plants, are divided into two large subclasses: (1) the *monocotyle-*

Fig. 10-6. This photograph shows various stages in the development of a plant. The seeds were planted at different times and the cotyledons appear in different stages of development. What are the functions of the cotyledons?

dons (*mon*-oh-kot-ee-*lee*-duns), or *monocots;* and (2) the *dicotyledons* (*dy*-kot-ee-*lee*-duns), or *dicots*. A **cotyledon** is a special kind of leaf which develops in the seed. It absorbs, stores, and digests food and nourishes the young plant after the seed has sprouted and until it is well established. **Monocots** produce a single seed leaf, while **dicots** have two. As we study the various parts of flowering plants, we will point out other differences between monocots and dicots. These will include differences in the arrangement of root and stem tissues, the form of leaf veins, and the number of flower parts.

Flowering plants are represented by over 40 orders, including more than 140 families. Species of flowering plants number approximately 195,000.

You are probably familiar with many of the families of flowering plants listed in the table on page 121.

The plant body of a flowering plant. Each organ of a flowering plant is highly developed for performing certain activities. The root, stem, and leaf are vegetative organs. They perform all of the processes necessary for life *except* the formation of seeds. This does not mean, however, that plants do not multiply directly from their roots, stems, or leaves. If you have sprouted roots on a pussy willow stem in a jar of water, you know you can plant the stem and grow a new plant. Root, stem, and leaf cuttings, as well as budding and grafting, are methods of vegetative reproduction.

SOME FAMILIES OF MONOCOTS

FAMILY	FAMILIAR MEMBERS
Cattail	Common cattail
Grass	Cereal grains, bluegrass, sugar cane, bamboo, timothy
Sedge	Sedges
Arum	Indian turnip (Jack-in-the-pulpit), skunk cabbage, calla lily
Pineapple	Pineapple, Spanish moss
Lily	Lily, onion, tulip, hyacinth
Amaryllis	Amaryllis
Iris	Flag, iris
Orchis	Lady's slipper, orchis, orchid
Palm	Coconut palm, date palm, palmetto

SOME FAMILIES OF DICOTS

Willow	Willow, poplar (cottonwood), aspen
Walnut	Walnut, hickory
Birch	Birch, alder, hazel
Beech	Beech, chestnut, oak
Pink	Pink, carnation, chickweed
Water lily	Water lily, pond lily
Crowfoot	Buttercup, hepatica, columbine, delphinium, larkspur
Poppy	Poppy, bloodroot
Mustard	Mustard, radish, turnip, cress
Rose	Rose, apple, hawthorn, strawberry, pear, peach, plum, cherry
Pulse (legume)	Bean, pea, clover, alfalfa, locust, redbud
Flax	Flax
Maple	Maple
Mallow	Marshmallow, hollyhock, hibiscus
Parsley	Parsley, parsnip, carrot, sweet cicely
Heath	Laurel, rhododendron, azalea, heather, blueberry, cranberry, huckleberry
Mint	Catnip, spearmint, peppermint, nettle, sage
Nightshade	Tomato, potato, tobacco
Figwort	Mullein, snapdragon, digitalis (foxglove)
Composite	Dandelion, daisy, sunflower, zinnia, aster, marigold, thistle, dahlia

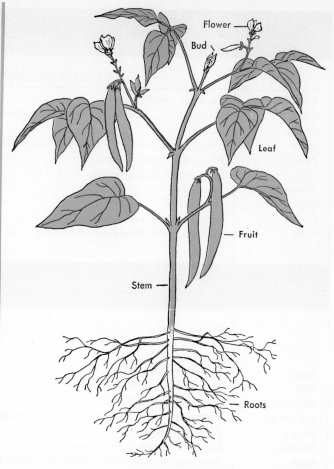

Fig. 10-7. As you look at this drawing of a flowering bean plant, name the activity each organ performs.

The **root** *anchors* the plant in the ground. It spreads through the soil and *absorbs* water and soil minerals. It *conducts* these to the stem for delivery to the leaves. Many roots *store* food reserves and return them to the plant as needed.

The **stem** produces the leaves and *displays* them to the light. It is a busy thoroughfare, for it *conducts* water and minerals upward and carries foods that have been manufactured in the leaves, downward. Like the root, the stem often serves as a place of food *storage*. In many plants, green stems aid the leaves in food manufacture.

The **leaf** is the center of much of the plant's activity. It is the chief center of food *manufacture*. It exchanges gases with the atmosphere during *respiration*. Much of the water absorbed by the root has a one-way trip through the plant. It escapes from the leaf as water vapor during **transpiration** (trans-pih-*ray*-shun).

After a period of growth, a plant usually starts *reproduction*. Flowers are specialized reproductive organs. They are followed by fruits and seeds. As the flower withers, the fruit develops from certain of its parts. Within the fruit are the seeds, each containing an embryo plant, which are ready to be carried to a new environment. There they sprout and establish a new generation of the same kind of plant.

Fig. 10-8. All these are annual plants. In the foreground are dwarf marigolds, followed by sage. In the background are tall marigolds.

Tissues of flowering plants. The various organs of higher plants perform their activities with great efficiency because of the specialized tissues which form them. We will study these tissues more thoroughly when we discuss each of the plant organs in greater detail in the chapters to follow. However, before dealing with any individual organ, you should be familiar with the names of various tissues and the general functions of each. These are summarized as follows:

Epidermis (ep-ih-*der*-miss) — an outer protective layer which prevents loss of water, injury, and the entry of disease-causing organisms.

Cork — a waterproof covering of dead cells, especially in woody plants. It serves the same general purpose as an epidermis, but is more efficient.

Parenchyma (pah-*ren*-kih-ma) — a thin-walled, soft tissue of the type forming flower petals, leaf blades, and the cortex and pith regions of stems and roots. Food manufacture and storage of food and water are functions of parenchyma tissues.

Xylem (zy-lem) — a supporting and conducting tissue. Large cells called **vessels** and small cells called **tracheids** (*tray*-kee-ids) are thick-walled conducting tubes. Xylem fibers give strength, especially to stems and roots. This is the tissue which makes up the large area of a stem called *wood*.

Phloem (*flow*-em) — a tissue composed of long, slender cells for conduction and support. Phloem occupies the inner bark of trees.

Embryonic tissue — composed of small, active cells. During the growing season, embryonic tissues divide continuously and give rise to cells which mature into other plant tissues. Embryonic tissue at the tips of roots and in the buds of stems forms the tissues which result in growth in length. The cambium layer between the bark and the wood causes growth in diameter.

Fig. 10-9. Here are two biennial plants. On the left is the foxglove and on the right, canterbury bells. Name two biennial vegetables.

Herbaceous and woody plants. To a biologist, an herb is any plant with a soft stem which lasts for only one growing season. Garden vegetables and flowers, cereal grains, and many of our common weeds are herbaceous. In short, any plant which grows for one season and then dies to the ground is *herbaceous.*

Woody plants include trees, shrubs, and certain vines such as the wild grape, Virginia creeper, and poison ivy. In a woody stem, the conducting and supporting tissues form layers which are added to year after year. Growth of the stem continues each year from embryonic tissues in various growing points.

The life span of a seed plant varies from one season to many centuries. Those which live for only one season are called *annuals.* These plants, including the zinnia, marigold, bean, and pea, grow from a seed, mature, reproduce, and die in a single growing season.

Biennials (by-*eh*-nee-als) live two seasons. The first year they produce vegetative parts only. At the close of the first season, the stem dies down. Food reserves are stored in the root. The plant then grows during its second season and bears the flowers. When seeds are produced, it dies. Beets, carrots, and parsnips are biennial vegetables. Among the biennial garden flowers are the sweet William, digitalis (foxglove), and Canterbury bells.

Perennials live more than two seasons. In most cases, they form their vegetative organs the first year, but do not produce flowers until a season or more later. Herbaceous perennials die to the ground each year. The roots remain alive and new stems and leaves grow each season. Delphiniums, lilies, columbines, and daisies are herbaceous perennials. Woody perennials include the trees, shrubs, and many vines. Once perennials have started to flower, they usually continue season after season, if conditions for growth are good.

Fig. 10-10. Perennials, as the name implies, live for more than two seasons. Identify this perennial plant.

In Conclusion

What if the seed plants had not replaced most of the more primitive plants during the past ages? There would have been no cereal grains for breakfast foods and flour, no potatoes, tomatoes, lettuce, onions, radishes, and other vegetables in our stores. Could our civilization ever have developed in such plant surroundings?

You might debate this point. But one thing is certain. Our plant and animal industries, in fact, our very survival, is geared to the seed plants.

In the next chapter, we will start with the first root which grows from a seed. In other chapters, we will study the vegetative organs, then the reproductive organs of flowering plants. We will come to the seed again as the climax of reproduction.

Questions for Review

1. On what basis are the seed plants divided into two great classes, gymnosperms and angiosperms?

2. Explain why we speak of the ginkgo tree as a " living fossil."

3. Describe several uses made of conifers in yard plantings.

4. Name five well-known families of monocots and five well-known dicot families.

5. Name the three vegetative organs of a seed plant and describe briefly the functions of each organ.

6. List six specialized tissues of a seed plant.

7. (a) Distinguish between herbaceous and woody plants. (b) Give several examples of each type.

8. Discuss the life cycle of annual, biennial, and perennial seed plants.

Biologically Speaking

angiosperm	embryonic	parenchyma
annual	epidermis	perennial
biennial	gymnosperm	phloem
cork	herbaceous	woody
dicotyledons	monocotyledons	xylem

Applying Facts and Principles

1. Discuss possible reasons for the disappearance of most gymnosperms and the rise of angiosperms through past ages.

2. Discuss various ways in which high development of the organs of angiosperm plants has given them an advantage over other kinds of plants in the struggle for existence.

3. Many of our most beautiful garden flowers are annuals. Why are annual plants considered to be ideally suited to garden needs?

CHAPTER 11

Roots and Their Activities

Let's start our study of seed plants from the ground up. You'll find how much real activity takes place under the ground and how important this activity is to supply the needs of the plant. A great deal of activity also takes place above ground but the basis for this above-ground activity occurs under the ground. You will learn why the root is such an efficient anchor and why you have to tug so hard to pull up a mere dandelion or other weeds.

There are many different kinds of roots and each kind has its own function. To get a real understanding of the work of the root, we had better start in exploring its various regions and its tissues. We will begin this study with the first root of a young seedling as it enters the soil.

The origin of the root system. When a seed first begins to grow, two parts push out of the seed coats. The young shoot grows upward and soon it unfolds its first leaves. The first, or **primary root,** lengthens rapidly and quickly pushes its way down into the soil. After a short period of growth, **branch,** or **secondary roots,** begin to appear, first near the top of the primary root, and later farther down. As roots branch and rebranch, they develop the complete root system. (See Fig. 11-1.)

You have probably wondered how a root system compares in size with the stem and branches. Of course, there is not any definite rule since different kinds of plants vary in this respect. And, too, the size of the root system differs in various soil conditions. But you can estimate that the average land plant has about as much or more below ground as above ground.

Root systems. If the primary root continues to grow, it will remain the largest root of the root system. We re-

fer to such a root as a **taproot.** This main root, with its branching secondary roots, forms a **taproot system.** (See Fig. 11-2.) If the taproot is large, as in the case of the carrot, beet, radish, and parsnip, we term it **fleshy.** Fleshy taproots serve as underground storehouses for the food supply of the plant. For this reason, many of them are used for food by man.

Some taproots are very long and slender. The alfalfa root grows 15 feet or more into the soil. The root system of corn or bluegrass is quite different. In these plants, the primary root lives only a short time. Secondary roots may grow as a cluster at the base of the stem. We call these slender roots **fibrous roots.** They form a **diffuse root system** because of the characteristic spreading. While most diffuse root systems are composed of fibrous roots, a few plants have fleshy diffuse root systems. Among these are the dahlia and the sweet potato.

Often, you can determine the kind

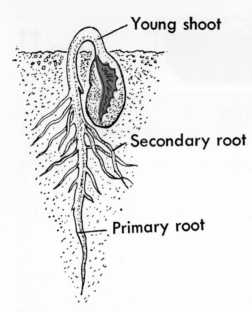

Fig. 11-1. New roots branch out from the primary root. They keep rebranching to form the complete root system. One of the chief functions of a root is to draw raw materials from the soil.

fact that plants live in so many different environments. The shallow roots of grasses are ideal for absorption of water and dissolved minerals from the rich topsoil of the prairies. During dry periods, spreading grass roots, clinging to the soil particles, act as soil binders against the sweeping winds. The shallow roots of cacti are ideal for desert conditions, where rainfall is low and very seasonal. When rain comes to the desert, cactus roots absorb water from near the surface over a wide area.

Taproots have advantages, too. They're ideal for anchorage. Furthermore, they go down far into the ground and can get at the deep water supplies. This accounts for the fact that alfalfa, with its long taproot, absorbs water after the grasses growing with it may have turned yellow and brown. It explains, also, why oak and hickory forests, with their deep roots, thrive on dry hillsides

of root system a plant will produce even in the seedling stage. Put some radish and oat seeds between moist blotters in a covered dish. Examine the root systems after a few days or a week. The radish will have a distinct taproot, with small secondary roots. This taproot continues to grow and will become the radish you eat. You may have difficulty in distinguishing the primary root and the large secondary roots of the oat seedlings. This primary root lives only a short time. Secondary roots form a diffuse root system.

The corn seedling is similar to the oat, except that its diffuse roots live only a week or so before they are replaced by roots which grow out from the base of the stem.

Taproots and diffuse roots — advantages of each. Variation in the form of root systems accounts partially for the

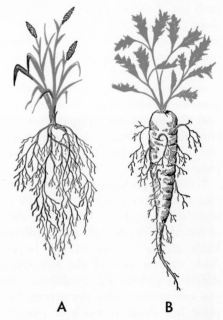

A   B

Fig. 11-2. Compare the fibrous root system of plant A with the taproot system of plant B. Which acts as the better soil binder?

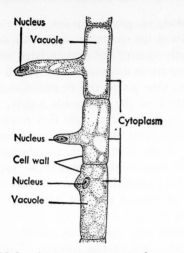

Fig. 11-3. An important part of a root is its tip and the root hairs just behind the tip. Root hairs develop best in **well-aired, moist** soil.

and why the date palm survives in dry, arid regions.

Young roots and root hairs. Roots of seedlings show another important characteristic of young roots. A short distance back of the tip, you can see strange, white, fuzzy growths extending from the surface of the root. These tiny **root hairs** are important in absorp-

tion. Root hairs are delicate projections of the outer cells or **epidermis** (ep-ih-*der*-miss) of the root. You shouldn't confuse them with secondary roots which, like primary roots, are composed of many cells. Root hairs are produced in a zone about one to two inches long. As the root moves downward, new root hairs form close to the tip and older ones wither away near the top of the region. Thus, they are constantly extending into new areas of soil as the young root pushes on. (See Fig. 11-3.)

Detailed structure of a root tip. Cut off a root half an inch or so back of the tip, slice it thinly lengthwise, and examine it with a microscope. You'll see the cells composing it and several important regions, too. These regions are: (1) *the root cap;* (2) *the embryonic region* (region of cell division); (3) the *elongation region;* and (4) the *maturation region.*

Regions of the young root. At the tip is the **root cap** which protects the delicate end. As the cap is pushed through the soil by the growing root behind it, its outer surface is torn away.

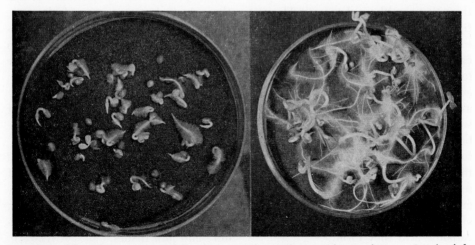

Fig. 11-4. The above photographs show radish seedlings with root hairs. On the left the roots are 48 hours old. On the right they are 96 hours old.

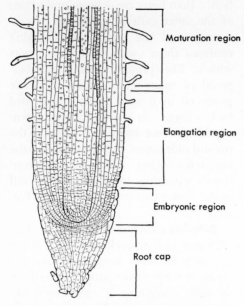

Maturation region

Elongation region

Embryonic region

Root cap

Fig. 11-5. This drawing shows a root enlarged, much as you would see it under a microscope. Notice the blunt, thimble-shaped root cap. It protects the delicate embryonic region.

The addition of new cells to the inner surface, however, keeps it in constant repair.

You may wonder at the fact that the delicate root tip can force its way through soil without damage. The root tip partly *pushes* its way and partly *dissolves* its way through soil. The gas, carbon dioxide, combines with water to form a weak acid called *carbonic acid*. Carbonic acid is familiar to you as the soda or " fizz " water used at the soda fountain. Root caps give off carbon dioxide into the soil water and so form carbonic acid. This, in turn, aids the progress of the young root by dissolving minerals in its path. As roots grow over smooth rocks, their pattern is often etched into the surface by the carbonic acid they form.

Immediately behind the cap, at the tip of the root proper, is the **embryonic**

region, or growing point of the root. Cells of the embryonic region are small, nearly square, and contain large nuclei. They are in a constant state of cell division, thus giving rise to new root cells.

Back of the embryonic region, cells gradually lengthen until they reach full length a considerable distance from the tip of the root. This lengthening of cells marks the **elongation region,** which causes the forward movement in the growth of the root tip. (See Fig. 11-5.)

After the cells have grown to full length, they change further. Cells on the surface give rise to root hairs, while those inside the root change somewhat as they become special tissues of the mature root. Modification of cells to form these special tissues marks the **maturation region** of the root.

Regions and tissues of a mature root. The tissues of a root are distinct under the microscope. If available, use a cross section especially prepared for microscopic examination. (See Fig. 11-6.) The **epidermis** shows as a single layer of brick-shaped cells. Under the epidermis are layers of rounded, loosely-packed cells, the **cortex.** This is the principal storage area of the root, and is several cells thick. The **endodermis** is a single layer of cells, often with thick walls, located at the inside edge of the cortex.

The **pericycle** is a layer of thin-walled cells lying at the outer edge of the central cylinder and just inside the endodermis.

The **central cylinder** is the principal conducting and strengthening region of the root. It is composed of *xylem* (zy-lem) and *phloem* (flow-em) tissues, and may contain *cambium* (kam-bee-um) and *pith* tissues.

The **xylem** is the *water-conducting tissue* because it is the path through

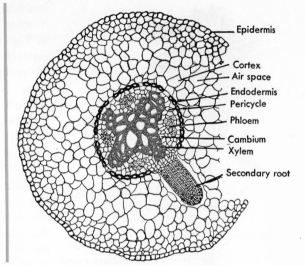

Fig. 11-6. This cross section of a buttercup root shows the regions and the tissues. Summarize the functions of each of the tissues.

Labels on figure: Epidermis · Cortex · Air space · Endodermis · Pericycle · Phloem · Cambium · Xylem · Secondary root

which water and soil minerals travel *upward* to the stem and leaves. The conducting portion of the xylem is composed of large, rounded, thick-walled cells. They are long, empty cells which resemble pipes. These cells live only a short time, but continue to serve as channels of conduction long after death. In addition, the xylem contains numerous smaller cells. These give great strength to the root. We commonly speak of the xylem tissues as *wood*.

The **phloem,** or *food-conducting tissue,* lies outside the xylem. If the xy-

SUMMARY OF ROOT TISSUES AND THEIR SPECIAL FUNCTIONS

TISSUE	FUNCTION
Epidermis	Absorption and protection
Root hairs	Outgrowths of epidermis which increase the absorption area
Cortex	Storage of food and water
Endodermis (boundary layer)	Separates cortex from central cylinder
Central cylinder	
Pericycle	Origin of secondary roots
Phloem	Conduction of manufactured food downward from the stem and leaves
Cambium	Increase in diameter of central cylinder
Xylem	Conduction of water and dissolved minerals upward to the stem and leaves

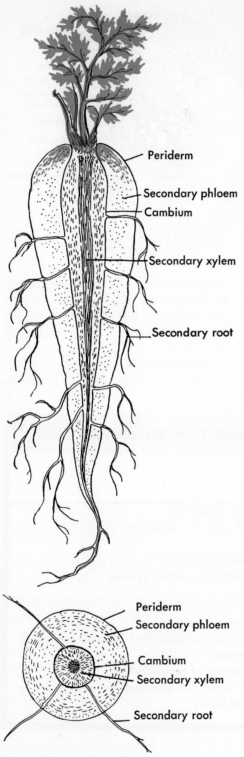

Periderm

Secondary phloem

Cambium

Secondary xylem

Secondary root

Periderm

Secondary phloem

Cambium

Secondary xylem

Secondary root

lem is arranged in the form of a cross as in some roots, like the buttercup shown in Fig. 11-6, you can find the phloem between the arms of the cross in rounded groups. Foods, produced in the stem and leaves, travel *downward* through the phloem cells.

Secondary thickening in the root. The primary tissues we have described do not increase as the root continues its growth. However, the cambium adds secondary xylem cells on its inner side and secondary phloem cells on its outer side by continuous cell division during the growing season. This produces a root like the carrot, shown in Fig. 11-7.

The outer edge is a corky layer, the **periderm**, which develops from the pericycle. Inside the periderm is a thick layer of phloem, most of which has been formed by the cambium. This is a food-conducting and storage region. The cambium appears as a line at the inner edge of the phloem. The center of the carrot is xylem, much of which has been formed by the cambium during secondary thickening. This is the water-conducting region of the carrot. Notice that the secondary roots extend from the xylem. This permits the flow of water and minerals into the main conducting vessels leading upward to the stem and leaves.

These same regions are shown in the cross section of the carrot in Fig. 11-7.

An old root, such as the root of a tree, contains many layers of xylem and phloem, formed by the cambium season after season. The outside of the root is covered with a thick layer of bark.

Fig. 11-7. You can see the same root regions in both the longitudinal and cross sections of a carrot. What kind of a root system does the carrot have?

Such a root is an efficient organ of conduction and anchorage, but no longer absorbs water.

Responses of roots to their surroundings. If you happen to plant a seed upside down, will the roots grow out of the soil? Is it mere chance that willow or poplar roots enter cracks in a sewer and clog it with a ball of roots? If a root growing downward strikes a rock, will the rock stop its progress indefinitely?

The various parts of a plant respond, rather slowly, to certain factors or **stimuli** in their environment. The automatic responses of a plant or any of its parts toward or away from a stimulus is called a **tropism** (*troh*-pizm). If the response is in the direction of, or *toward,* the stimulus, as when a root grows toward the earth, we call the response *positive.* On the other hand, a stem shows a *negative* response to the earth because it grows *away* from it. In

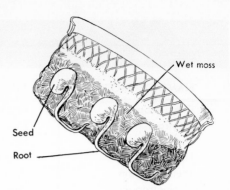

Fig. 11-9. This experiment shows that water is an even stronger stimulus than gravity. As you can see, the root is growing toward the wet moss. What do biologists call this type of response?

discussing tropisms, we must keep in mind the fact that they are automatic responses. A root doesn't grow into the soil " in order to find water." The root isn't aware of either soil or water, but its growth is influenced by both. If a stimulus causes more growth on one side of a root than on the other, the root will bend. It may bend toward the stimulus, or away from it, depending on the area of the root which is influenced most.

Geotropism. The gravity of the earth is a strong stimulus influencing root growth. It is more than sheer weight which causes the root to grow toward the stimulus of gravity. The stem is equally heavy and grows away from it. **Geotropism** (jee-*ot*-roh-pizm) directs the growth of the root toward the earth and its supplies of soil water and dissolved minerals. Without this important stimulus, roots would probably not grow deep enough to reach these necessary substances. Here is an interesting experiment.

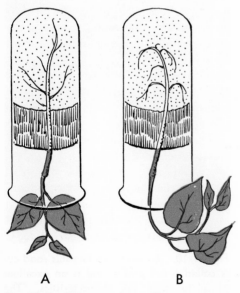

Fig. 11-8. This experiment illustrates geotropism. In A, the roots point upward. In B, the roots start to bend down and the stem turns upward.

A   B

Split a test tube cork to the middle and enlarge the center sufficiently to receive the stem of a well-started seedling. Slip the seedling through the

SUMMARY OF TROPISMS

NAME OF TROPISM	TYPE OF REACTION
Chemotropism	Response to chemicals, such as soil minerals
Geotropism	Response to gravity
Hydrotropism	Response to water
Phototropism	Response to light
Thermotropism	Response to heat
Thigmotropism	Response to pressure

split to the center opening with the roots turned toward the bottom of the tube. Fill the tube with water and insert the cork and seedling securely, as in Fig. 11-8. You'd better seal the cork with warm paraffin, too. Invert the tube so that the roots point upward. Make a record of the experiment at the beginning and note the time required for downward growth of the roots.

Hydrotropism. Water is a very strong stimulus, and may cause a root to grow toward it from a considerable distance. This response is **hydrotropism** (hy-*drot*-roh-pizm). (See Fig. 11-9.) It is shown in the vast number of fine roots which force their way into water pipes or spread through the moist topsoil. They grow in these directions in spite of the force of gravity which attracts them downward. The great response of the shallow roots of willows, cottonwoods, and elm trees makes them undesirable for planting near drains, sewers, or septic tanks.

You can show hydrotropism and the strength of water and gravity as stimuli in the following experiment. Make a basket of hardware cloth, or other large meshed wire similar to the one in Fig. 11-9. Fill the basket with moist peat moss or sawdust and plant seeds (lima beans are good) near the bottom. Tilt

the basket at an angle of about 45 degrees in a dark place or in a light-proof box. Why should the seeds be in a dark

Fig. 11-10. An exposure like this road cut is called a soil profile and is an excellent place to study soil characteristics. The dark layer of topsoil varies in thickness in different parts of the country. Some layers are only one or two inches, while others are thicker.

Fig. 11-11. Plants are adapted to different conditions in many ways. The bald cypress of the south, which grows in swamps, requires great quantities of water.

place? The roots will start downward at first as they respond to gravity. When they have penetrated through the sieve, however, they will turn back toward it in response to the water stimulus. The experiment illustrates a hydrotropic response and shows that the water in the moss, in this case, is a more powerful stimulus than gravity.

Root environments. In the discussion of *soil roots,* we need to consider the soil itself as a root environment. We need to know how it is formed, how it varies from place to place, and the critical relationship of the root to the soil.

Soil is a mass of rock particles of various sizes, formed through weathering, freezing, and thawing. The mineral portion of soil may be coarse sand, fine sand, or clay, depending on the size of the particles.

Through the ages, plants have enriched this mineral matter with the organic remains of their roots, stems, and leaves. These have become part of the soil through the process of decay. This organic matter, together with mineral matter, forms topsoil. The many bacteria, molds, and other soil microorganisms which live in topsoil are essential to its fertility.

The texture of soil refers to its physical composition. Texture refers to the size of soil particles and the amount of space between them. The average loam soil is said to contain spaces amounting to from one-third to one-half of its total volume. Spaces between soil particles are very important to the root, since they contain air and fill with water after rains. This allows the water to seep gradually to those areas in which roots are absorbing. As water seeps through the soil, it dissolves soil minerals and carries them to the root.

Organic matter in soil holds water. It swells and keeps the soil loose. This

Fig. 11-12. Although many roots grow downward into the ground, some plants, like the orchid, have roots that grow in the air. How do these aerial roots receive water?

explains why rich woods dirt is usually moist. Manure, leaf mold, and peat moss are excellent soil conditioners. We speak of them as **mulches.**

Loam soils have an ideal balance between mineral and organic matter for the majority of garden and crop plants. However, we cannot say that most plants live best in loam. Some plants thrive in heavy clay. Others require the almost pure organic soil of bogs, or loose, dry sand.

Aquatic roots are found on such plants as the duckweed and the water hyacinth. They are usually small and few in number and lack root hairs. They do not need extra surface on the epidermis for absorption in a water environment.

Cypress "knees" show an odd relationship both to water and to soil. Cypress trees grow in swamps and are rooted in water-covered soil. The curious "knees," shown in Fig. 11-11, form a ring around the tree above the

waterline. They seem to supply air to the submerged tissues of the roots.

Many plants in the tropics produce **aerial roots.** Tropical orchids live on trees and absorb water from the falling rain and from the very humid atmosphere (see Fig. 11-12). The debris which collects around the roots is enough to supply the mineral needs. Aerial roots have a thick, spongy cortex, making possible absorption from the atmosphere.

Adventitious roots. The roots we have discussed thus far have developed from the primary root or from one of its branches. However, in some plants roots develop from the stem or even from the leaves. These roots are **adventitious** (ad-ven-*tish*-us) as shown in Fig. 11-13.

You have probably noticed the circle of roots which grow from the joint of the corn plant just above the ground (see Fig. 11-13). These are a kind of adventitious root called **brace** or **prop roots.** These roots grow into the ground, and help the underground roots support the stem. If soil is piled around the stem, additional prop roots develop from the next joint above the soil line. Actually, all the roots of the corn plant are adventitious, since they come from the stem and not from the short-lived primary root.

Roots for propagation. In certain plants, if the stem lies in contact with the soil long enough, you'll see that roots will spring from the joints and produce new plants. You can start climbing roses by burying a portion of a stem until it has taken root. Raspberry bushes root from the stem in a similar way, except that the roots usually form at the tip of the stem. This process is called **tip layering.** (See Fig. 11-13.)

Some plants, like the begonia and sedums, can be propagated from leaf

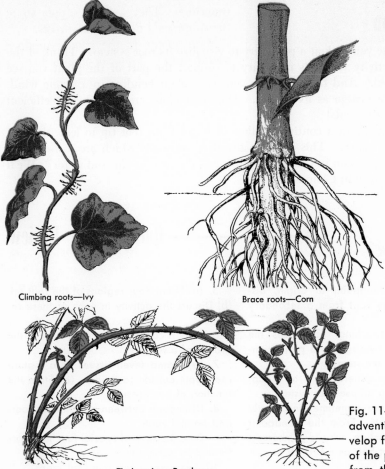

Climbing roots—Ivy

Brace roots—Corn

Tip layering—Raspberry

Fig. 11-13. All of these adventitious roots develop from another part of the plant rather than from the primary root.

cuttings placed in moist sand. Other examples of adventitious roots for propagation include the roots which form on pussy willow stems when cut and put in a container of water, and the roots which form on strawberry runners as they reach into new areas of the patch.

Climbing roots. Poison ivy, English ivy, and other vines produce clusters of roots along the stem. These roots cling to a wall or to some other support and hold the stem securely. Such plants also have ordinary soil roots which absorb water and dissolved minerals.

Direct uses we make of roots. We use roots indirectly when we use any part of a plant. However, there are many direct uses we can make of roots.

In many plants, the root is the principle reservoir for stored foods. The cortex is greatly thickened to receive the food reserves. We grow many of these plants as **root crops.** Among them are the carrot, beet, parsnip, radish, turnip, rutabaga, and sweet potato.

The roots of some plants contain valuable drugs used in making medicines. These medicinal plants include licorice, ginseng, rhubarb, marsh mallow, and sassafras. Other roots, such as the horse-radish, are used for seasoning. The madder and yellowwood tree produce dyes in their roots. At one time, these dyes were widely used.

In Conclusion

The next time you look at a plant, try to visualize its root system. Think of the underground activity which is necessary to support the part of the plant you see above the ground. And the next time you see a plant bending in a strong wind, think of the root system as its anchor. How marvelous are these highly efficient plant organs — the roots!

In order to maintain a continuous flow of water from root tip to leaf, the root must absorb soil water. This contains dissolved minerals which are so necessary for life processes to go on in the cells. How does the root get this soil water? We'll hear about that story in Chapter 12.

Questions for Review

1. From the standpoint of origin, distinguish a primary root from a secondary root.

2. Generally speaking, how does the root area of the average land plant compare with that of the stem?

3. Describe the general form of a taproot system and a diffuse root system.

4. Root hairs are sometimes incorrectly called branch roots. From the standpoint of origin and structure, why is it incorrect to speak of a root hair as a branch or secondary root?

5. (a) Name four regions of the root tip. (b) Discuss the activity in each of these regions.

6. Why is carbonic acid important to the growth of a root?

7. (a) Name seven tissues of a mature root, from outside to inside. (b) State the function of each tissue.

8. Distinguish between adventitious roots and normal roots.

9. Describe several special functions performed by adventitious roots.

10. List several common root crops.

Biologically Speaking

adventitious root	fleshy root	root cap
aerial root	geotropism	root hair
aquatic root	hydrotropism	root system
cambium	maturation region	secondary root
cortex	pericycle	taproot
elongation region	phloem	tip layering
embryonic region	primary root	tropism
endodermis	prop root	xylem
fibrous root		

 —————— **Applying Facts and Principles**

1. Oak and hickory trees thrive on dry ridges and hillsides. What kind of root system would you expect these trees to have?

2. A plant dug with a large ball of dirt has a far better chance of living than one taken out with the roots exposed, even though these roots aren't torn off. Why is this true?

3. Branch roots grow from the pericycle at the outer edge of the central cylinder. Why is the attachment of the branch root to the central cylinder extremely important?

4. Explain the importance of hydrotropism to the life of a plant.

5. Rose bushes should never be planted close to a hedge. Why?

CHAPTER 12

The Root—an Organ of Absorption

You know that a plant has a far better chance of living after transplanting if you move it with a large ball of soil. Do you know why? Some people think the large roots are very necessary and important. True, they anchor the plant but they do not absorb water and dissolved soil minerals. Absorption takes place near the tip of a root where it is no larger than a piece of string. Absorption also takes place in the ends of tiny branch roots. In these root tip areas the epidermis is young and active. Root hairs project into the soil and increase its absorbing surface greatly. These tiny feeding structures are torn off if you disturb the soil with which they are in contact. So when you dig up a plant and shake off the earth around it, you destroy many of these young root tips.

The cell membrane and absorption. All the substances which a cell's protoplast receives, and the waste materials it discharges, must pass through the plasma membrane of that cell. Therefore, it's not hard to see why the study of membranes and the passage of various substances is extremely important in biology. Keep in mind, however, that absorption applies to all living cells.

Biologists believe that cell membranes contain tiny pores through which substances pass. They have found further that cell membranes are *selective* in the passage of these substances. Some substances can enter. Others cannot because the membrane seems to reject them. Furthermore, chemical changes in the protoplast often determine what substances will pass through the membrane and in what quantity they will enter. A cell may absorb a certain substance for a time. Then, because of a change in the protoplast, the cell may reduce or stop further absorption of that substance.

Absorption is an extremely complicated process. Scientists still do not understand all of the factors involved. But we can study certain physical principles involved in absorption — principles which are in no sense limited to cells.

Diffusion, the spreading out of molecules through space. Let's visualize a substance as a mass of quivering molecules. These molecules bump into each other like a crowd of people at a bargain counter. Just as you want to escape from such a crowd and find space to move around in freely, so molecules tend to spread apart from each other. This spreading out of molecules in space is known as **diffusion.**

To illustrate diffusion, let's imagine that you open a bottle of peppermint oil in the corner of a closed room. (See Fig. 12-1.) Peppermint oil molecules are *concentrated* inside the bottle. This means that there are many of them packed close together in the bottle. As soon as you open the bottle they start

140

diffusing into the air. Soon you begin to smell peppermint across the room. As the process continues, the peppermint odor becomes stronger. More and more peppermint oil molecules are mingling with the molecules of gases that are in the air. Finally, when all the peppermint oil molecules are mixed equally with the air, diffusion stops. A state of **equilibrium** has been reached. If you could see the molecules, you would discover that the entire room, as well as the bottle of peppermint oil, contained a uniform mixture of peppermint oil and air.

According to the laws of diffusion, *two* things happened. Peppermint oil diffused from the bottle into the air, and air diffused into the peppermint oil bottle. Both movements were from a region of *greater* concentration to a region of *lesser* concentration. Diffusion continued until the concentration of air and peppermint oil was equal in all parts of the room.

Other familiar examples of diffusion. Solids and liquids, or liquids and other liquids, may diffuse as readily as gases *if they normally mix and do not repel each other.* Drop a cube of sugar into a glass of water. As the sugar dissolves, taste the water from time to time. You can taste the increase in the number of sugar molecules. Finally, the sugar will dissolve completely without any stirring. Sugar molecules diffused from a region of greater concentration (the lump) into a region of lesser concentration (the water). Meanwhile, water molecules diffused into the sugar. When equilibrium was reached, all parts of the water tasted equally sweet.

Diffusion through membranes. The study of diffusion becomes more complicated and more interesting when a membrane is involved. **Membranes** are thin materials such as cellophane, a portion

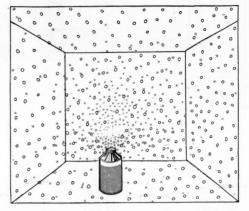

Fig. 12-1. When peppermint oil is released in the room, the molecules diffuse into the air until a state of equilibrium is reached.

of an animal bladder, a piece of parchment, or a piece of muslin. Membranes allow certain substances to pass through. The membrane is said to be **permeable** (*per*-mee-ah-bul) to the substance which passes through it.

Examine the apparatus shown in Fig. 12-2. You can set this up easily in the laboratory. A thistle tube (a funnel can be used) is fastened to a ring stand clamp. The lower end of the thistle tube is submerged in water. The bulb of the thistle tube is filled with molasses. A piece of muslin is tied tightly over the open end of the bulb.

Two things happen in this experiment. Water molecules diffuse from the jar, through the muslin, into the molasses in the thistle tube. At the same time, molasses molecules diffuse through the muslin into the water. You can see this happen over a period of a few hours. Finally, molasses and water molecules are equally distributed both inside and outside of the thistle tube. This is an **equilibrium.** Diffusion stops. Muslin is permeable to both water and molasses molecules.

Now we will repeat the experiment

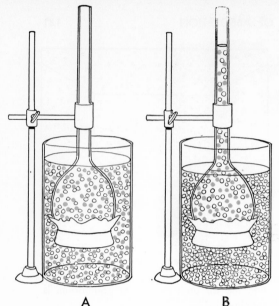

Fig. 12-2. This experiment shows diffusion: **A** water and molasses through a permeable membrane and **B** water through a semi-permeable membrane (osmosis).

exactly except for one item. Instead of muslin, we will use a piece of parchment or a piece of animal bladder to cover the thistle tube. Something quite different happens. This membrane is *permeable* to water. Water molecules pass back and forth through it. Most of the flow is into the molasses because water molecules are less concentrated there. Molasses molecules should diffuse into the water, but the membrane stops them, or at least interferes with their movement. We say that this membrane is **semi-permeable** (differentially permeable) because it is permeable to different substances in different degrees. As the experiment progresses, water and molasses rise in the thistle tube. Why? Molasses molecules can't come out, and water continues to come in. You can see that this builds up a pressure. If the water and molasses could not rise in the tube, the pressure would probably burst the membrane. Water continues to diffuse into the molasses until the weight of the liquid in

the tube causes enough pressure against the membrane to stop the flow.

Osmosis, a special type of diffusion. The experiment we just described illustrates **osmosis** (os-*moh*-sis), a kind of diffusion. Scientists do not agree on an exact definition of osmosis. They do agree that it is a form of diffusion and that the diffusion is through a semi-permeable membrane. But they do *not* agree on the substances which pass through the membrane during osmosis. Chemists and physicists refer to osmosis as the passage of a liquid, a gas, or a dissolved solid through a semi-permeable membrane. According to this definition, everything which passes into or out of a cell does so by osmosis.

Other scientists limit osmosis *to the passage of water alone.* They say that substances dissolved in water enter by diffusion and independently of water. Water is the medium in which molecules of dissolved substances reach the cell membrane. But at that point, the dissolved substances may be rejected by the membrane, while the water passes through. In line with the majority of biologists we will define *osmosis as the passage of water through a semi-permeable membrane.* The flow is from a region of *greater* concentration of water molecules to a region of *lesser* concentration of water molecules, according to the law of diffusion.

The root hair and the soil — an osmotic system. Think back to the osmosis experiment with the thistle tube. Now let's substitute a root hair for the thistle tube; the cell content for the molasses; a living plasma membrane for the membrane fastened over the mouth of the thistle tube; and for the jar of water, the water in the soil. (See Fig. 12-3.) Inside the cell, there are solutions of various substances dissolved in water. One of these is protoplasm, con-

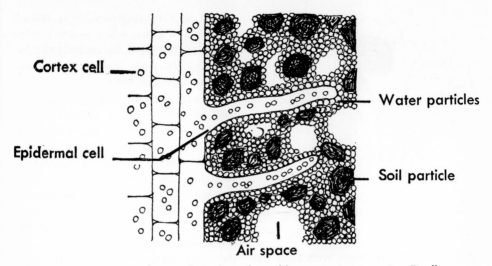

Fig. 12-3. Water enters the root hairs from the soil by successive osmosis. Finally, water and dissolved minerals move upward to the stem.

taining about 70 per cent of water. Cell vacuoles contain solutions of minerals, food materials, and other dissolved substances. The soil water also contains dissolved minerals, but *normally,* not as much as the cell content. In other words, the concentration of water molecules outside the cell is greater than inside. The soil water is separated from the cell content only by a thin, porous cell wall and the semipermeable plasma membrane. Can you predict what will happen? Water will diffuse from the soil into the root hair.

Successive osmosis. Now let's think of the whole root. The root hair is an outgrowth of an epidermal cell. Inside are many layers of cortex cells. When the epidermal cell takes in water, the concentration of water molecules becomes greater than that of the cortex cell lying against it. This cell draws water from the epidermal cell. As the water content in this cell increases, the next cortex cell receives water from it. As the second cortex cell takes water from the first, the first one takes water from the epidermal cell. The epidermal

cell, in turn, takes in more water from the soil through its root hair.

This diffusion of water from cell to cell continues to the xylem vessels in the central cylinder of the root. Here, water and dissolved minerals move upward to the stem. We call this cell-to-cell diffusion of water *successive osmosis.*

Turgor, the result of water pressure in cells. As water diffuses into a cell during osmosis, it builds up a pressure inside the cell. We call it *osmotic pressure.* It makes the cell firm, just as you can make a paper sack rigid by filling it with water. The cells, in turn, make the whole plant stiff and firm. We call this stiffness of plants, due to the presence of water in their cells, *turgor.* It is very important in supporting tender plants whose stems are not stiffened by woody fibers. Leaves and flowers are stiffened by cell turgor. When turgor is lost, they wilt.

When a plant is fully turgid, the pressure in its cells may be as great as 60 to 150 pounds per square inch. Fruits and vegetables often burst when

Fig. 12-4. Turgid cells enable a plant to push through cracks in cement sidewalks such as this one.

their cells can no longer withstand the pressure. Turgor permits the mushroom and delicate seedling to push through the hard ground. There are even cases where concrete has been cracked by the push of a growing plant, as in the case of the fern in Fig. 12-4.

Turgor in root cells creates root pressure. Pressure in root cells is maintained, or even increased, from outside to inside. Thus, when water reaches the xylem vessels of the central cylinder, it enters the pores of their thick walls with considerable force.

We can show the force of root pressure by cutting off a plant near the ground. Water runs out of the severed vessels. In plants such as grass, tomato, and strawberry, root pressure may be great enough to force water through the stem and out through the ends of leaf veins, where it appears as drops. We call this loss of excessive water *guttation* (gut-*tay*-shun). On the other hand, loss of water through a cut stem is called *bleeding.*

However, root pressure alone cannot supply all the force necessary to raise water through the stem. It could never push water to the top of a tree. In Chapter 13, you will study other forces which add pull to the push of root pressure.

Fig. 12-5. Guttation in these strawberry leaves is the result of root pressure which forces water through the stem and out through the leaf veins.

Osmosis " in reverse " — loss of turgor in cells. So far we have discussed only the entry of water into a cell during osmosis. Is water ever taken out of the cell? Yes, it is, and that occurs when the greater water-attracting solution is outside the cell.

To demonstrate " reverse osmosis " and loss of turgor, slice two pieces of potato. Put one in strong salt water and the other in fresh water. The slice in salt water soon becomes limp, while the slice in fresh water, which is the control, remains stiff and turgid. The control shows that slicing alone did not cause the limpness. The salt solution must have attracted water from the cells.

The collapse of cell protoplasm and loss of turgor due to the loss of water is called **plasmolysis** (plaz-*moll*-ih-sis). You can see this in Fig. 12-6. Temporary plasmolysis may be corrected by an intake of water. If the condition remains very long, the cell will die.

Now you can understand why salt kills grass. You can understand too why shipwrecked men die from drinking salt water. The cells of your mouth, throat, and stomach are just as subject to plasmolysis as are the cells of roots and leaves. Plasmolysis explains, also, why too heavy an application of strong fertilizers to the soil may kill the roots they contact. Fertilizers contain large quantities of various chemical salts.

Osmosis is a purely physical process. A cell has *no control over osmosis whatever*. Whether a cell takes in water, or loses it to its environment, depends on two critical factors: (1) concentration of water inside the cell; and (2) concentration of water outside the cell.

If water enters a cell, it is because the water concentration is less inside than outside. Concentration of water inside is related directly to the amount of dis-

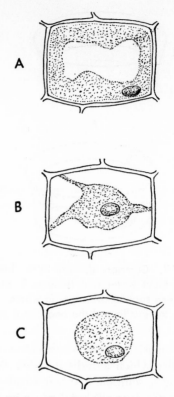

Fig. 12-6. The diagram above shows the result of plasmolysis, or loss of turgor. A. Turgid cell of a potato. B. Partially plasmolyzed cell. C. Completely plasmolyzed cell.

solved minerals and soluble food materials contained in solution in the vacuoles. The greater the amount of these dissolved substances, the less the concentration of water and, logically, the greater the water-attracting power of the cell solutions. Similarly, the lower the water content of protoplasm, the greater its water attraction.

Absorption through the forces of imbibition. Many organic substances, such as starch, gelatin, wood, and seed coats absorb large quantities of water. This causes them to swell. The absorption of water by a solid, resulting in swelling, is called **imbibition** (im-bih-*bish*-shun). Imbibition is different

A

B

Fig. 12-7. Compare the size of the beans in A without water and those in B which have been soaked overnight in water. To what is the swelling of the beans in B due?

from osmosis in that water enters the substance which absorbs it rather than entering a solution. When wood imbibes water, it swells because water molecules enter the wood substance.

When you first put a wooden boat in the water, it may leak for a time. Then as the wood imbibes water and swells, the cracks close and it stops leaking. A wooden shingle roof may be full of cracks during dry weather, but when a rain comes, the shingles swell and close the cracks. Another example is the swelling of dry beans when you put them to soak overnight before baking.

Absorption of minerals. Absorption by the root concerns not only the intake of water, but the entry of dissolved mineral substances as well. They pass through the membranes of root hairs in solution with water. Together with water, they move through the cortex to the inner tissues of the central cylinder where they are conducted to other parts of the plant.

The relation of dissolved minerals to water in the soil solution is very close. We might assume that they enter the root with water during osmosis and imbibition. Biologists have found evidence that mineral absorption may be independent of water intake. This phenomenon of mineral intake has been called **selective absorption.** It takes into account the variation of mineral content found in different plants even when they are grown under similar conditions of soil environment.

Broccoli has a high calcium content. But peas, growing under the same conditions in the same soil, will not have the same high calcium content because selective absorption is not as active in peas as in broccoli.

How rapidly do plants absorb soil minerals? A very graphic answer was given this question by a representative of the Oak Ridge Operations, United States Atomic Energy Commission. During an address on the use of radioisotopes in biology, the speaker produced two potted tomato plants. One was watered with distilled water, and the other with water containing a radioactive phosphate (a soil mineral). In less than 45 minutes, the water containing the radioactive phosphate was absorbed through the root hairs of the tomato plant and moved up into the leaves. This was proved by removing a leaf and testing it for the presence of radioactivity with a Geiger counter. The plant had shown no radioactivity at the beginning of the experiment. The control plant showed no radioactivity either before or after the experiment.

Mineral salts containing radioactive elements will enable biologists to learn more about absorption. The technique will show what minerals are absorbed by certain plants and what ones are rejected. It will also show the rate at which soil minerals enter roots.

In Conclusion

Now perhaps you can see why the transplanting process can be so hazardous for a plant. Unless great care is taken to keep a large ball of earth around roots, wilting will probably take place. The plant may even have the young areas of its root system so severely damaged by transplanting that it will never recover. Osmosis and absorption will therefore cease because they can occur only in these younger areas at the tips of roots.

The entire contact of the plant with its soil environment depends on a healthy, functioning root system. If this is upset drastically, the plant cannot survive.

The root, important though it is, is only one of several different plant organs. True, the average seed plant could not exist without its root system. But it would have just as much trouble living without its stem. Let's take a look at the stem in Chapter 13 and see what part it plays in the life of a seed plant. Why is the system just as important to the plant as the root?

Questions for Review

1. Give an illustration of diffusion of gases and explain what takes place.

2. Distinguish between a permeable and a semi-permeable membrane.

3. Define osmosis so as to distinguish it from other types of diffusion.

4. Explain how successive osmosis takes place in the cells of a root.

5. Discuss cell turgor; what it is, what causes it, and why it is important to cells.

6. Explain how turgor and root pressure assist in the movement of water from root to stem.

7. Describe the cause and result of loss of turgor in plant cells.

8. How do we know that mineral absorption is independent of water absorption in a root?

Biologically Speaking

absorption
bleeding
concentration
diffusion
guttation

imbibition
membrane
osmosis
osmotic system
permeable

plasmolysis
selective absorption
semi-permeable
successive osmosis
turgor

Applying Facts and Principles

1. A man spread a heavy application of fertilizer on his lawn and watered it well. A few days later, his grass turned brown. There were no chemical compounds in the

fertilizer which could poison the grass tops. What probably killed the grass?

2. In what respect is imbibition different from osmosis?

3. Discuss the use of radioactive sub-stances in the study of mineral absorption by roots.

4. Explain how manure, peat moss, compost (decayed vegetable matter), and other organic materials keep the soil moist.

Fig. 12-8. The Banyan tree is a member of the fig family, growing in India and tropical Africa. Its branches send out numerous adventitious roots that grow down to the soil and form " props " or additional trunks. A single tree may thus cover an area large enough to shelter several hundred people.

CHAPTER 13

Stems and Their Activities

You might think of a root as the plant's receiving department for soil water and minerals. The leaf is a factory where they are used in the production of foods. The stem is the supply line — a vital link between these organs. Through long conducting tubes of the stem tissues, a constant stream of water and dissolved minerals moves up to the leaves. Foods travel down through other tubes. *Conduction* is one of the chief activities of stems.

Equally important to the plant is the *production* and *display* of leaves and flowers. This is an important function of stems. In most plants, the leaves are so arranged on the stem that they receive sufficient light for the needs of the particular plant.

Food manufacture, usually associated with leaves, is an activity of the stem in many plants. Green tissues in the outer region of many stems greatly increase the food-producing regions of the plant.

Some stems serve as vaults for the *storage* of water and food reserves. The white potato plant sends most of its food reserves into the thick underground stems we dig as potatoes.

Herbaceous and woody stems. Those which are usually soft and green are **herbaceous** (her-*bay*-shus) stems. (See Fig. 13-1.) Some examples are the stems of tomatoes, beans, peas, corn, grasses, and lilies. Herbaceous stems lack the woody tissues which give strength to trees and shrubs. However, the stiffness of many herbaceous stems is due to cell turgor. If the stem loses water, it wilts. Most herbaceous stems grow very little in diameter and last only one season. In plants like the hollyhock, columbine, delphinium, and shasta daisy, the stem is herbaceous and annual, while the root is more woody and perennial. Both the root and the stem are annual in the marigold, zinnia, nasturtium, morning glory, tomato, bean, and pea.

Woody stems, on the other hand, are perennial. They grow in length, increase in diameter, and form branches season after season. The woody tissues of these stems give them great strength and allow them to reach much greater size than an herbaceous stem.

The external structure of a woody stem. The twig of a tree is an ideal subject for study of the external structure of a woody stem (see Fig. 13-2). In regions where trees shed their leaves during autumn, a dormant winter twig is especially suitable.

Buds are perhaps the most noticeable structures on the dormant stem. Each bud contains a growing point of the stem — a place from which a new stem, leaves, and flowers may develop. In cold climates, *winter buds* are pro-

Fig. 13-1. It is easy to cut flowers with herbaceous stems like this lily. Woody stems, on the other hand, are tough and you need shears to cut their tissues.

twig. We call this angle the **axil**. Lateral buds produced in the leaf axils are given the special name of **axillary buds**.

A **node** is the point at which leaves or branches are produced from a stem. The space between two nodes is called an **internode**. In examining several twigs, note that a single leaf, two leaves, or three or more leaves may develop from a node. If a winter twig has one leaf scar at each node, the leaves are **alternate**. If there are two leaf scars, the leaves are **opposite**. If three or more leaf scars are present at each node, the leaves are **whorled**.

tected by overlapping **bud scales** which completely enclose the tender growing point. These bud scales serve to protect the delicate tissues inside from drying out.

We classify buds further according to their position on the twig. The **terminal bud**, not present on all twigs, is located at the tip and contains the terminal growing point of the stem. Along the sides are lateral buds, from which branches may develop. They are usually smaller than terminal buds and usually different in shape.

At intervals along the twig, circular, oval, or shield-shaped **leaf scars** mark the point of attachment of leaf stalks from previous seasons. On the leaf scars, minute dots called **bundle scars** show the location of the conducting vessels which carried water and dissolved minerals into the leaf from the stem. These bundle scars are of a definite number and arrangement, depending on the species of plant.

You will note in examining the lateral buds that they are usually just above a leaf scar. When the leaf was attached to the twig, these buds were in an angle between the leaf stalk and the

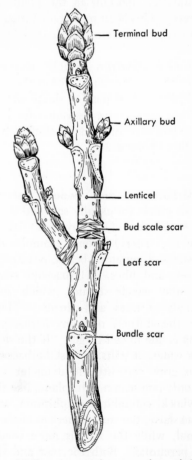

Fig. 13-2. A woody stem has definite characteristics. This buckeye twig shows the various parts of such a stem.

Fig. 13-3. The type of branching depends on bud arrangement. Opposite buds, as in the case of the Norway maple (left), produce opposite branches. Alternate buds produce alternate branches, as in the case of the hickory (right).

Along the internodes, especially on young twigs, you can see tiny pores called **lenticels** (*len*-ti-sels) opening through the bark. These let air enter and water escape from the twig, especially while it is young and active. In an old twig, they cease to function.

You can find other interesting structures on certain twigs. When terminal buds swell and drop their scales at the beginning of the growing season, a series of rings encircling the twig marks the place where the bud scales were fastened. These **bud-scale scars,** at intervals along a twig, show the exact location of the terminal bud during previous seasons. Thus, by starting at the present terminal bud and counting the sets of bud-scale scars along the twig, you can find the exact age of a twig.

Some twigs bear characteristic thorns which make them very easy to identify. These thorns may be either short and broad, long pointed, or branching. In some cases, thorns are outgrowths of the epidermis. They may also be modified branches. The thorns of hawthorn trees and the branching thorns of the honey locust are examples of stems modified into protective thorns. The thorns on a rose, however, are outgrowths of the epidermis.

Branching is due to bud arrangement. If a young tree has a strong terminal bud, and terminal buds of other years escape injury, the main stem will continue upward, forming a central shaft. Branches will grow from this as a result of the development of lateral buds. We class such trees, characterized by forming branches from a central shaft, as **excurrent.** (See Fig. 13-4.)

Excurrent branching is shown in the pine, fir, spruce, hemlock, redwood, and cypress. These trees, unless injured or diseased, have a perfect cone-shaped outline. A strong central shaft

Fig. 13-4. All the branches on these evergreen trees arise on the main stem or trunk. What are the advantages of excurrent branching?

rises to a point at the tip of the tree. Branches grow horizontally at regular intervals along the stem, decreasing in length from bottom to top. This difference in length is due to a difference in age, the oldest branches being located at the base, while the youngest are at the top. By counting the number of circles or whorls of branches along the trunk, you can tell the age of the tree fairly accurately.

Among the advantages of the excurrent type of branching are:

1. Small resistance to storms due to slender tops.

2. Branches which may bend downward and shed snow easily.

3. Pyramid shape allowing light to reach all branches to the base of the tree.

The willow, cottonwood, and elm have quite a different form of branching. These trees produce a single trunk which divides, usually rather low, to form several large branches. The effect is a spreading pattern of growth called

deliquescent (del-ih-*ques*-sent). (See Fig. 13-5.) This growth results when twigs lack a terminal bud, or when lateral buds form branches which equal or exceed growth from the terminal bud. In trees like the buckeye, horse chestnut, and magnolia, terminal buds develop flower clusters. Lateral buds form branches, resulting in a spreading, deliquescent pattern.

Branching form often determines the timber value of trees. Quite obviously, trees forming large, central shafts far exceed the spreading type in timber value. This characteristic growth of pine makes it ideal for lumber, while spruce and fir are fine for telephone poles.

In the case of the oak, walnut, hickory, maple, and other forest trees, long trunks develop under forest conditions, although the same trees branch more freely in open places. Foresters have found that the best timber trees are these types which are found growing in dense stands.

Fig. 13-5. This elm tree shows deliquescent branching because the branches arise from older branches and not all from the trunk.

How do stems grow? To show the way in which stems grow, let's assume that a tree is 30 feet high, one foot in diameter, and that the first branch is exactly six feet above the ground. After ten years, we return to the tree and find that the trunk is now 16 inches in diameter and 40 feet high. After this period of growth, how far is the first limb from the ground? The answer is *still six feet.* Growth in length has occurred at the tips of all the branches. The stem regions below the tips have not lengthened at all!

In plants, certain areas called **growing regions** are the only places where growth occurs. Only in these special areas can new tissues form as a result of cell division. Furthermore, the growing regions of the stem are of two distinct types: (1) those causing increase in length; and (2) those causing increase in diameter.

Stems grow in length by forming new tissues at their tips, or, in some cases, at the nodes. Such growing points were found, also, at the tips of roots. The growing area, or embryonic region, of the stem is much like the root, except that it is longer and not protected by a cap. The embryonic region of a stem is often several inches long, while the corresponding region of the root is only a small fraction of an inch long. As new tissues are produced at the stem tip, they continue to grow until they reach maximum size. Once they have matured they can never lengthen again. Growth in length is limited to the actively-dividing cells of the growing point.

Growth in diameter results from the

Fig. 13-6. The wood of hardwood trees is heavy, close-grained, and resistant. Note the tall, straight trunks of these forest trees due to their positive phototropic response.

activity of an entirely different region, located deep in the tissues of the stem. To discover this region, we must study in detail the regions and tissues which make up the stem.

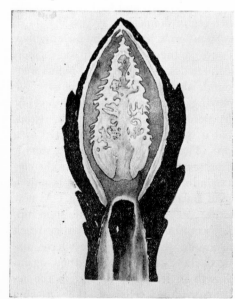

Fig. 13-7. This longitudinal section of a bud shows the terminal growing point.

The internal structure of woody stems. If you cut a branch or a trunk of a tree, you can see three distinct regions, as shown in Fig. 13-9. The outer region, or *bark,* is quite distinct from the large area of wood within. Usually, a core of *pith* occupies the center of the stem, although the pith of a large tree is often difficult to find because it is so very small in comparison with the large amount of wood. A fourth region, the *cambium,* lies between the bark and the wood and consists of a very thin, slimy layer of delicate tissue.

The wood in a stem frequently appears to be of two types. The outer area is usually light in color and consists of active, living tissue called **sapwood.** Sapwood is absolutely necessary for the tree to live. Next to the sapwood is a cylinder of darker wood called **heartwood.** This occupies the center of the stem and surrounds the cavity where the pith originally was. The tissues composing the heartwood are dead and often filled with gums or resins which give it a characteristic dark color. Heartwood is of no use to the tree except for support. However, it makes beautiful furniture.

Besides the rings you can see additional markings by examining a cross-section of a woody stem as, for example, the end of a log. The **pith rays** appear as lines radiating from the center to the outside of the wood like the spokes of a wheel. Some types of wood, such as oak, show especially prominent rays. **Annual rings** form circles through the wood, one outside the other, and mark each season's growth of wood. By counting the annual rings, you can find the age of a stem.

Fig. 13-8. By counting the annual rings of this cross section of a pine tree, you can find its age.

Bark — its structure and activity. The term **bark** includes much more than just the outer covering of a tree. It is a region of the stem, composed of several kinds of tissues.

A young twig is covered, for a time, by a thin epidermis which protects the young stem from injury and disease. Soon, however, the epidermis is replaced by a tissue called **cork**, which forms the outer covering we see on a branch or tree trunk. Cork is composed of dead cells arranged in layers and containing special substances which give it a characteristic waterproofing. The corky layer protects the stem from mechanical injury, from disease, and from loss of water.

As stems grow in diameter, the outer corky layer splits. Consequently, it is constantly renewed. New cork is produced by a special layer of cells called the **cork cambium.** The cells which compose the cork cambium divide frequently and add new cork on the inside as it is destroyed on the outside. The structure of the cork cells and the continual splitting of the cork layer due to the growth of the stems result in the characteristic appearance of tree trunks — scaly, peeling, grooved, fissured, or, in some cases, smooth. The cork tissue of a tree is often called the *outer bark* to distinguish it from other bark tissues within.

Inside the cork and cork cambium lie two other important bark tissues composing the *inner bark.* The outer one of these, the **cortex,** is composed of large thin-walled cells arranged like stones in a wall. In young stems, the cortex cells contain green chloroplasts and carry on food manufacture. As the stem matures and cork begins to form, this function ceases, and the cortex becomes an area of *food storage.*

Inside the cortex lies the innermost layer of the bark, called the **phloem** (*flow*-em). The phloem consists principally of large, thin-walled sieve tubes which conduct *food materials* dissolved in water. Since food materials usually come from the leaves, the phloem carries them *downward* toward the roots. In plants like wheat and rye, however, foods are conducted *upward* through the phloem to the heads of grain at the tip

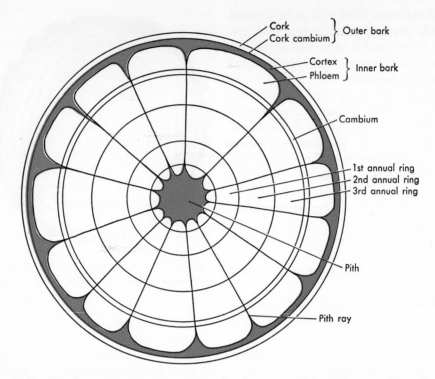

Fig. 13-9. This diagrammatic cross section of a three-year-old woody stem shows the internal arrangement of its tissues.

of the stem. Tough, thick-walled fibers, called **bast fibers,** may often be seen associated with the phloem tubes. These fibers give toughness to the bark.

Activities of the cambium. This small ring of active tissue between the bark and the wood is responsible for all increase in thickness of the stem.

During the spring and summer, the cambium is active in producing new cells by division. It forms new phloem tissues on its outside surface and new wood tissues on its inside surface. During one season of cambium activity, many more wood cells than phloem cells are formed. That is why the wood area of a tree is always much greater than its bark thickness.

The tissues composing wood. *Wood,* or **xylem** (zy-lem) tissues extend from

the cambium to the pith in the center of the stem. Wood consists of several kinds of cells. The largest of these are the **vessels** which appear in the stem as large, thick-walled tubes. Viewed from the ends in a cross section of wood, they are nearly round. If you cut a stem lengthwise, the vessels appear as long tubes arranged end to end forming continuous channels through the stem. Other wood cells called **tracheids** (*trake*-ee-ids) are often grouped among the vessels. Tracheids are smaller than vessels and are longer and more angular. The smallest wood cells are the **fibers,** which have extremely thick walls and very little cell activity.

Cells of the **pith rays** are quite different from the vessels, tracheids, and fibers. They are thin-walled, and form rows of two or three cells in width, and contain protoplasm and a large nucleus.

As woody stems increase in thickness, year after year, the wood formed by the cambium is arranged in layers. Frequently, the cambium produces two kinds of wood during the season: (1) *spring wood,* containing many large vessels mingled with tracheids and fibers; and (2) *summer wood,* containing few vessels and large numbers of fibers. This difference in texture between spring and summer wood results in layers which appear as the annual rings. The picture in Fig. 13-11 shows these.

The pith region of the stem. The central core of pith is scarcely noticeable in an old woody stem. In the young stem, however, the pith occupies a proportionally large area and serves as an important place of storage. Since pith isn't produced by the cambium, it never increases in size. Regardless of the size to which a tree may grow, its pith never increases beyond the amount present during the first year of growth.

Why does girdling kill a tree? The complete removal of a section of bark is called *girdling.* This may be done by various animals which chew on the bark such as rabbits, beavers, porcupines, or even horses. It can also be done by using an axe or other means (see Fig. 13-10).

It is not hard to see why the tree will eventually die. The reason is because food is no longer able to pass through the phloem from the leaves to the roots.

Movement of materials through the stem. Blood circulates through our

SUMMARY OF STRUCTURE AND ACTIVITIES OF A STEM

REGION	TISSUE	ACTIVITY
Bark	Epidermis (only on young stems)	Protection
	Cork	Protection
	Cork cambium	Production of cork
	Cortex	Storage and food manufacture
	Phloem tubes	Conduction of food usually downward
	Bast fibers	Strengthen bark
Cambium	Cambium cells only	Formation of phloem, xylem (wood), and rays
Wood	Xylem vessels	Conduction of water and minerals upward
	Tracheids	Conduction and strengthening of wood
	Xylem fibers	Supporting tissues
	Pith rays	Conduction laterally
Pith	Pith	Storage

bodies due to the pressure maintained in the blood vessels by the pumping action of the heart. Plants have no such pump, yet are able to carry water and dissolved minerals hundreds of feet high. The flow of food materials through the phloem cells of the bark is not difficult to understand, since the flow is downward. Likewise, the movement of materials across the stem through the ray cells is quite understandable since only short distances are involved. But the rise of water and dissolved minerals through the wood vessels and tracheids *against* the force of gravity certainly involve powerful forces.

Biologists have not agreed entirely as to what these forces are, but we can explain several factors which may account for upward conduction.

Root pressure forces water into the

Fig. 13-10. Completely removing a section of bark on a tree is called girdling. The tree eventually dies because food can no longer pass through the phloem from the leaves to the roots.

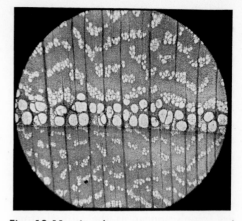

Fig. 13-11. In what ways are spring and summer wood different?

stem with considerable force and is one of the factors. A second factor called **capillarity** is another force. We can illustrate capillarity by placing a small glass tube or soda straw in a glass of water, as in Fig. 13-12. The level in the tube will be higher than in the glass. Water is attracted by the walls of the tube and rises above the level in the glass. The smaller the tube the higher the level that will be reached. Capillarity acts in the stem by drawing water upward along the walls of the vessels and tracheids.

Leaves constantly lose water due to evaporation from their surfaces into the air. This loss of water from the leaf results in an **evaporation pull** which, in turn, lifts water through the plant. Water is held in continuous columns through the vessels of the leaves, stem, and roots. As it is removed from above by evaporation, the entire column is pulled up. We can further account for this rise by the **cohesion** of water in the vessels. Water clings together throughout the vessels and may be lifted as an entire column. This action is like drawing on a soda straw which lifts an entire column of liquid and causes more to enter at the lower end.

Plant propagation by means of stems. While conduction, support, and storage are the most outstanding functions of a stem, *propagation,* or multiplication of plants by stems, is another function. Propagation may occur either naturally or artificially.

Grafting consists of bringing into close contact the cambium layer of a live, dormant twig and the cambium layer of the tree on which it is to grow. We can accomplish this by tapering the end of the twig or *scion* (*sy*-on) to be used and inserting it into a slit prepared in the rooted branch or **stock** which is to receive the graft. Such a graft can be successful *only if the cambiums of scion and stock are brought into contact with each other.* Grafting is successful only when stems of the same species or closely related species are united. We can't graft an apple twig to an oak tree, but we can graft several varieties of apple trees onto a single apple stock.

Budding is similar to grafting except that a *bud* rather than a twig is united with the stock. (See Fig. 13-13.) In budding, a vigorous bud is selected and removed with a piece of bark surround-

Fig. 13-13. These drawings show the different methods of grafting. Top row: cleft grafting; center row: whip grafting; bottom row: budding.

ing it. The bud is united with the stock by slipping the piece of bark under the bark of the stock, which has been loosened by a T-shaped cut. In this way, the cambiums of scion and stock are united. In both budding and grafting, the wound resulting from the operation should be covered with wax to prevent the entrance of bacteria and the different kinds of rotting fungi.

Pruning woody plants. We call the cutting of surplus branches of trees and shrubs **pruning.** We do this for several reasons. (1) We may wish the plant to conform to a certain shape. (2) We may want the plant to produce more fruit rather than so many leaves. (3) We want a transplanted tree or shrub to recover quickly. Thus, we reduce the number of branches and the resulting leaves so there will be only a small loss of water. (4) We want

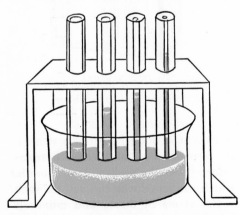

Fig. 13-12. This experiment with glass tubes illustrates capillarity. The force of capillarity draws water upward through the xylem vessels in the stem of plants in the same way.

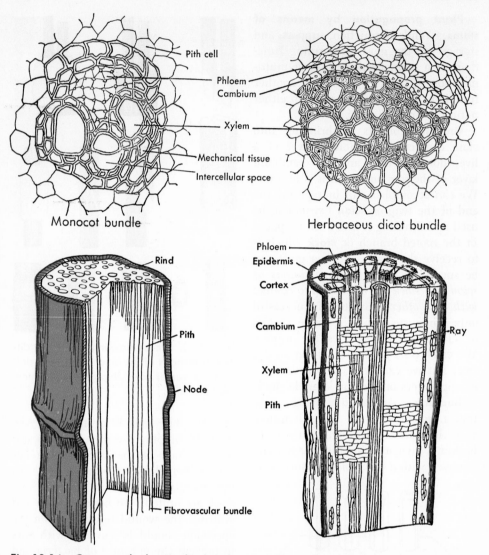

Fig. 13-14. Compare the longitudinal and cross sections of a typical monocot stem (corn) and herbaceous dicot stem (bean). Note that monocots lack a cambium.

our plant to be healthy so we cut off all dead or decaying branches.

As a rule, it is better to prune in the winter when the sap is not rising. Then the cut ends will not "bleed" and lose the food-bearing sap.

The structure of an herbaceous stem. Herbaceous stems differ from woody stems chiefly in having much less xylem (woody) and phloem tissue. These two occur in most herbaceous stems in the form of long strands called **fibrovascular** (fy-broh-*vass*-kyoo-lar) **bundles** which run lengthwise through the stem.

The stems of dicots and monocots. We can classify herbaceous stems, according to structure, in two types: (1) the *dicot,* represented by the tomato, buttercup, bean, and other plants with broad leaves and soft stems; and (2)

Fig. 13-15. Creeping stems, like this ivy, grow in open places where they do not have to compete with other plants for light.

the *monocot,* including iris, orchids, lilies, and grasses and sedges. The leaves of monocots are mostly narrow and have parallel veins. Corn is a typical monocot. (See Fig. 13-14.)

The herbaceous dicot stem. If you section the stem of an herbaceous dicot plant (your teacher will tell you a good one to use in your community), you'll see several distinct regions. The outer layer of the stem is a thin *epidermis* which serves for protection. Inside the epidermis is a layer of *cortex,* composed of loosely-packed cells containing chlorophyll. These manufacture as well as store food. Within the cortex, the *fibrovascular bundles* occupy a ring-shaped zone. These bundles contain xylem and phloem tissues. In some species the bundles form a continuous ring. In others, the ring is separated by broad *pith rays.*

Many herbaceous dicot stems develop a cambium in the form of a thin layer which runs through the ring of the bundle cylinder. The cambium separates the phloem in the outer portion of the bundle from the xylem tissues within. The activity of the cambium in producing new phloem and xylem cells results in an increase in the diameter of the stem. However, the herbaceous dicot stem dies during the winter so the growth in diameter of the stem is only for one season.

The structure of a monocot stem. If you cut a section across a corn stem, you will find the tissues very differently arranged from those in the dicot stem.

The outer covering is a **rind** composed of thick-walled, hard cells. It functions to support the plant and to protect the other stem tissues. The bulk of the stem consists of a pith whose cells have thin walls. Through the pith you will see numerous fibrovascular bundles which are *scattered* at random, rather than being arranged in a ring.

Fig. 13-16. Because they cannot stand erect, climbing stems must have some support like a fence.

We say that monocot stems have *scattered bundles* while dicots have their *bundles in a ring*.

Monocots lack a cambium. Monocots usually grow in diameter only until their cells have reached a maximum size. This is why they are generally long and slender as in the iris, orchids, lilies, grasses, and sedges. Their leaves are enclosed in sheaths which wrap around the stems from one node to the next lower one.

Aerial stems. We classify a stem which grows above the ground as **aerial**. Such stems range in length from a fraction of an inch to the towering trunk of a forest tree. In general, we group aerial stems as: (1) shortened; (2) creeping; (3) climbing; and (4) erect.

1. *Shortened stems.* **Shortened stems** are aerial but they are so reduced in size that they frequently seem to be lacking entirely. For this reason, the dandelion, primrose, and carrot are often called *stemless,* although anyone

referring to them as such has failed to notice the short, disk-shaped stem growing just above the root.

2. *Creeping stems.* The **creeping stem,** like the shortened stem, remains close to the ground, but its leaves spread much more widely as a result of its length. Plants with creeping stems often form patches or communities of plants all connected by runners, as their stems are often called. (See Fig. 13-15.) The creeping stem is weak and slender. Lacking woody tissues for support, it must grow along the surface of the ground. Like plants with shortened stems, creeping plants need open places where they are not forced to compete for light with taller plants.

3. *Climbing stems.* As a rule, **climbing stems** are slender and very long. Like creepers, they lack enough woody tissue to stand erect, and so are curiously modified in raising their leaves to light by clinging to supports.

The pole bean, sweet potato, and

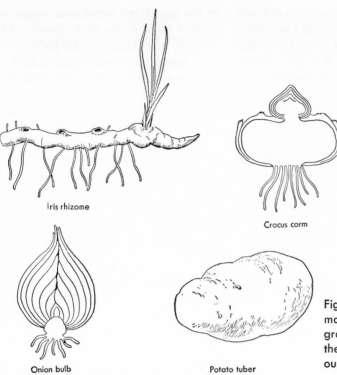

Iris rhizome

Crocus corm

Onion bulb

Potato tuber

Fig. 13-17. Although you may not think of stems as growing under the ground, these drawings show various types that do.

morning glory lift themselves into the air by *twining* around an object with encircling growth of the stem. On the other hand, the grape and the cucumber produce **tendrils** which are really modified stems. These tendrils serve as a means of grasping a support and holding the stem securely. The pea plant climbs by tendrils which develop from the tips of leaves. The tip of the tendril grows unequally on different sides, causing it to swing through the air in circles as it grows. Thus, it can reach anything within the radius of its swing, often several inches.

4. *Erect stems.* We call a stem **erect** which stands above the ground with no attachments to an object. Such stems may range from a few inches to several hundred feet high. They may be herbaceous or woody.

Underground stems. Would you think to look for a stem in the ground?

Probably you wouldn't, but you are familiar with several kinds of **underground stems.** You may not think of them as stems because of their unusual location.

You can't dig a clump of iris or lily-of-the-valley without noticing the thick, fleshy underground stem which creeps horizontally close to the surface. This rootlike stem is a **rhizome** (*ry*-zome). If you examine a rhizome closely, you'll see buds which develop at the nodes and produce leaves and flowers. The nodes are separated by internodes. On the lower side, nodes give rise to clusters of roots. Rhizomes may be thick and fleshy and filled with food, or slender as in the quack grass and other grasses.

Tubers are enlarged tips of rhizomes which are swollen with stored food. The white potato is an example. A tuber, like other stems, has nodes at which buds or " eyes " develop. Internodes separate the "eyes." Each bud may form an aerial shoot and reproduce the plant. You plant potatoes by cutting "seed" potatoes into pieces, each with several "eyes," and putting them into the ground.

A **bulb** is a large underground bud. It has thick leaves and a stem which is reduced to a small disk. Cut an onion lengthwise and notice the small stem at the base. The leaves grow in compact layers. Roots grow from the lower side. Tucked away in the center is a flower bud. This will grow through the leaves at the top of the aerial stem when the bulb is planted the next season. The daffodil is an example of a bulb.

A **corm** is different from a bulb in that most of it is stem covered with thin scales. One or more shoots develop from buds on the top. Roots grow from the lower side. The gladiolus and crocus are examples of corms.

Gardeners often speak of any underground stem as a "bulb." Lilies, daffodils, and tulips produce true bulbs. Crocuses, gladioli, and elephant ears form corms.

In Conclusion

Had you ever thought of the forces necessary to raise columns of water a hundred feet or more through the vessels and tracheids of a tree? Had you wondered how a tree trunk could support tons of branches and leaves in a wind? Did you know that stems do not grow all over but only at growing points?

A stem is a remarkable organ — a jack of many trades. In the next chapter, we will study the leaf. Here, marvelous chemical processes lay the foundation for the entire living world. A chemist who would duplicate these processes in the laboratory would achieve one of the greatest scientific triumphs of our age.

Questions for Review

1. Name five specialized activities of stems.

2. (a) Distinguish between herbaceous and woody stems. (b) Give examples.

3. From what danger does a bud protect the growing point of a twig during the winter season?

4. Explain how the branching pattern of a tree is determined by the arrangement of buds.

5. Distinguish between sapwood and heartwood in regard to appearance and use to the tree.

6. Name four tissues found in the bark regions of a woody stem and list the function of each tissue.

7. In what direction are water, minerals, and dissolved foods moved through the rays of a stem?

8. In many stems, spring wood is easily distinguished from summer wood. Describe the difference in structure in these types of wood.

9. Explain how the cambium causes increase in the diameter of a woody stem.

10. What two tissues of a stem must be united if a graft is successful?

11. List several reasons for pruning a woody plant.

12. What three tissues form the fibrovascular bundles of herbaceous stems?

13. How can an herbaceous dicot stem

be distinguished from a monocot stem by the arrangement of its fibrovascular bundles?

14. Name five underground stems and give an example of a plant producing each type.

Biologically Speaking

aerial stem	deliquescent	root pressure
annual ring	epidermis	sapwood
axil	excurrent	scion
axillary bud	fiber	sieve tube
bark	fibrovascular bundle	spring wood
bast fiber	grafting	stock
bud	growing region	summer wood
bud-scale scar	heartwood	tendril
budding	herbaceous	terminal bud
bulb	internode	tracheid
bundle scar	lateral bud	tuber
cambium	leaf scar	vessel
cohesion	lenticel	whorled
conduction	node	winter bud
cork	phloem	wood
cork cambium	pith	woody stem
corm	pith rays	xylem
cortex	rhizome	

Applying Facts and Principles

1. Why are forest-grown timber trees more valuable than the same species grown in open places?

2. Compare the way in which a tree grows with the growth of your body.

3. Rabbits, beavers, horses, and deer often chew the bark of young trees. If they girdle the tree, it usually dies within a few weeks or months. Explain.

4. When the leaves of a tree drop off in the fall, much of the upward movement of water and soil minerals through the stem ceases. Explain why.

5. Most plants with shortened stems grow in open fields or prairies. Why?

6. Pruning is usually done in winter but some plants react better when pruned in the spring. Why?

CHAPTER 14

Leaves and Their Activities

Early one morning, a transcontinental bus was passing through a southwestern Indian village. One of the passengers happened to notice an old Indian sitting quietly on the roof of his house facing the east, awaiting the first rays of the morning sun. For centuries, his ancestors had observed this primitive sun worship.

To the Indian the rising sun meant another day of growth for his crops and more food for himself and his animals. Without the sun, he would have nothing. So in his own own way, he gave thanks each morning.

We owe our life to the energy of the sun. We owe it to leaves, too, for the leaf is the plant organ where the energy from sunlight is locked into organic compounds. In this chapter, you will explore the food factories of a leaf. You will follow water and minerals into the leaf and trace the stream of foods out of the leaf to places of storage.

External features of a leaf. A typical leaf consists of a thin green portion, the **blade.** The blade is strengthened by a framework of veins. **Veins** are really fibrovascular bundles which enter the blade, much as blood vessels branch and rebranch in reaching all the tissues of our bodies. In addition to strengthening the blade, they carry water, dissolved minerals, and food materials between the leaf and the stem.

Usually the blade is attached to the stem by a stalk or **petiole** (*pet*-ee-ohl). At its base, the petiole joins the stem at a node. Veins, in turn, connect with the petiole at its upper end. Some leaves have no petiole. Instead, the blade fastens directly to the stem by the veins. Leaves of this type are called **sessile** (*sess*-ill).

What is venation? We call the arrangement of veins through the leaf blade **venation.** In most leaves, the *principal veins* tend to follow one of

three general patterns. The maple leaf shows an arrangement in which several large veins branch out from the tip of the petiole much the way your fingers extend from your hand. This first pattern is called **palmate venation.**

Other leaves, like the willow and elm, have a single, large vein called a *midrib,* extending through the center of the blade from the petiole to the leaf tip. Smaller veins branch from the midrib and run to the margins. This second pattern of venation, resembling the structure of a feather, is called **pinnate venation.**

Certain plants, like the grasses, lilies, and iris, have several large veins running *parallel* from the base of the leaf to the tip. This third pattern is called **parallel venation.**

Some leaf forms. The outline of a leaf depends somewhat on the arrangement of its veins. If the veins are parallel, they are usually long and slen-

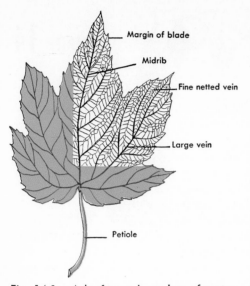

Fig. 14-1. A leaf must have lots of water for its food-making. The veins serve as pipelines. The petiole brings water into the leaf from the stem.

der. The forms of the leaves are almost as varied as the kinds of plants; some having regular or *entire* edges (lily), others *notched* (elm), *lobed* (maple), or *finely divided* (carrot).

Where the blade of the leaf, even though greatly indented, is in one piece, it is called a **simple** leaf. There are many leaves, however, where the blade is divided into three or more parts. In such a case, we say the leaf is **compound** and each separate part of the blade is called a **leaflet.** Where the leaflets radiate from a common point as in the clover and strawberry, the leaf is **palmately compound.** When the leaflets are arranged opposite each other or alternate on the sides of a single midrib, as in the pea, the leaf is **pinnately compound.**

In the case of certain leaves, it may

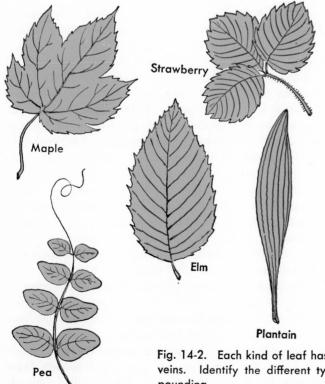

Fig. 14-2. Each kind of leaf has a definite arrangement of veins. Identify the different types of venation and compounding.

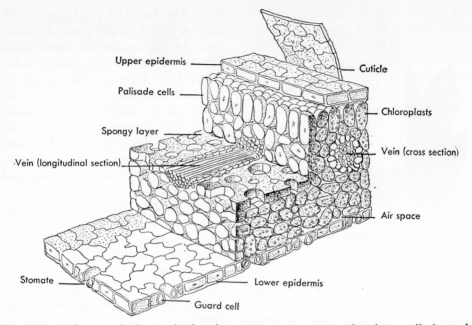

Fig. 14-3. When you look at a leaf under a microscope, you realize how well-planned a food factory it is. What is the function of each tissue?

be difficult to tell whether the part is a leaflet of a compound leaf or the blade of a simple leaf.

Internal structure of leaves. If you cut across the blade of a leaf and study it with a microscope, you will see these tissues: (1) *the upper epidermis;* (2) *the palisade layer;* (3) *the spongy layer;* and (4) *the lower epidermis.*

The **upper epidermis** usually consists of a single layer of cells. Often this layer is very irregular as seen from above, but the cells are brick-shaped when viewed in cross section. The function of the upper epidermis is to prevent loss of water. It is sometimes covered by a waxy, transparent layer called the **cuticle,** as in ivy, cabbage, and most leaves whose upper surfaces appear shiny. This layer prevents the evaporation of water from inside the leaf, and protects the tissues beneath.

The palisade layer. Just below the upper epidermis is the **palisade layer.**

It consists of long narrow cells arranged endwise at right angles to the surface of the leaf. (See Fig. 14-3.)

As you look at the palisades, you'll see many bodies called chloroplasts (*kloh-roh*-plasts), which occur in the area of cytoplasm. **Chloroplasts** contain the important green pigment or coloring matter, **chlorophyll** (*kloh*-roh-fill). This remarkable green substance enables the plant to manufacture food.

Chlorophyll is extremely sensitive to light. Since light is essential to food formation, chloroplasts must be exposed to it. But light also destroys chlorophyll. The shape of the palisade cells meets this critical light situation by allowing the chloroplasts to receive intense light in the upper regions, and to escape from light somewhat in the lower portion of the cells.

The spongy layer of the leaf. Under the palisade layer is a **spongy layer,** which consists of thin-walled cells and air spaces. It is penetrated in all directions by large and small veins. The spongy cells are rounded, irregular, loosely-packed, thin-walled, and full of protoplasm. They also have chlorophyll. However, their chloroplasts are fewer and lighter in color than those of the palisade cells. In the cells of the spongy layer, as in the palisade layer, food-making and other leaf functions are carried on. They also give off water to the air spaces.

The **air spaces** are usually large, irregular cavities among the spongy cells. They are connected with each other and open through the lower epidermis by way of the **stomates** (*stoh*-mates). They receive water vapor from the spongy cells and pass it out through these openings. They also let oxygen and carbon dioxide pass to all the cells of the spongy layer.

The **veins,** containing xylem and phloem tubes and fibers, are scattered through the spongy layer. They transport water and foodstuffs and support the blade of the leaf.

The lower epidermis of the leaf. The lower epidermis usually has only one layer of cells. Through it many stomates open. These regulate the passage of air and water vapor to and from the inside of the leaf. (See Fig. 14-4.)

The stomates. Stomates are small slitlike pores, about one-twentieth as wide as the thickness of this paper. On each side of the pore is an oval **guard cell** containing chloroplasts. The guard cells regulate the opening and closing of the stomates. Influenced by warmth and sunlight, as well as by other factors, the stomates open when there is an excess of water to be passed off. They close in a drought. The function of the stomates is threefold: (1) regulating the giving off of water vapor; (2) admitting carbon dioxide used in mak-

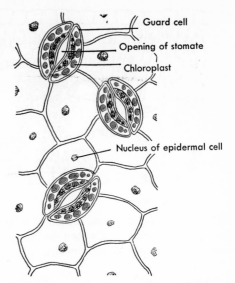

Fig. 14-4. Countless numbers of tiny air holes called stomates are found in the lower epidermis of the leaf. Their function is to take in air and to give off water vapor and waste gases.

ing sugar and setting free oxygen, the leftover product of food manufacture; and (3) admitting oxygen for respiration, and giving off carbon dioxide formed by respiration.

However, stomates would not be of much use if it were not for the many air spaces in the spongy tissues into which they open. By means of these air spaces, all parts have access to air for sugar making, respiration, and other functions. The number of stomates varies from 60,000 to 450,000 per square inch. There are usually more stomates on the lower surface than on the upper. Floating leaves have all their stomates on the upper surface. In vertical leaves, they are about evenly distributed.

Chlorophyll, the green coloring matter of plants. This is the most important part of the leaf. Practically the whole function of the other parts is in exposing the chlorophyll to light and in

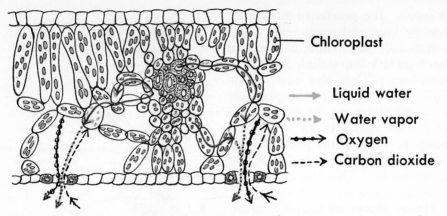

Fig. 14-5. Above is a cross section of a leaf showing the movement of water and gases during photosynthesis. Oxygen and some water vapor leave the leaf through the stomates, while carbon dioxide enters.

providing it with materials on which to work. Chlorophyll is a complex substance composed of carbon, hydrogen, oxygen, nitrogen, and magnesium. Its action is aided by small amounts of iron compounds.

A mystery of plant life. Nature has gradually unfolded her truths to the ever-searching scientist. But with all his knowledge and skill, he has yet to discover the workings of a basic chemical process which occurs in nature all about him. Every green leaf performs this strange activity during the course of every day. We call it *photosynthesis* (foh-toh-*sin*-thee-sis). We understand what happens, but can't explain how it goes on. The reason scientists can't duplicate photosynthesis is the association of the process with life. It is a function of a *living green cell*. However, only certain cells are capable of photosynthesis because it requires *chlorophyll*. All living plant cells containing chloroplasts with active chlorophyll can carry on photosynthesis.

Chlorophyll, the agent of photosynthesis. Often chemists find that two substances put together react only when a third substance is added. But the third substance does not enter into the reaction — its presence merely causes the reaction. Such a substance is called a *catalyst* (*kat*-ah-list). Chlorophyll bears much the same relation to photosynthesis. It serves as a catalyst or agent without actually entering into the reaction which occurs.

You can remove chlorophyll from a leaf easily by merely heating it in alcohol or some other solvent. You might even assume that you can use this catalyst in the laboratory and carry on photosynthesis artificially. But you cannot because photosynthesis seems to need a living cell to operate successfully.

Besides chlorophyll, chloroplasts contain substances called *enzymes* (*en*-zymes) which are important to photosynthesis. Enzymes serve as catalysts and, together with chlorophyll, cause the chemical reaction of photosynthesis without actually entering into the process.

Raw materials for photosynthesis. From what substances are paper, wood, coal, oil, sugar, starch, and thousands of other organic compounds formed? The answer is very simple — carbon dioxide and water. These two abundant inorganic compounds are the only materials necessary for photosynthesis.

Plant roots absorb *water* from the soil and carry it through the stem to the leaves. *Carbon dioxide* enters with air through the stomates and is removed in the leaf tissues. In living chloroplasts, these two substances are combined chemically, by means of chlorophyll, to form a compound quite different from either.

The energy factor in photosynthesis. Carbon dioxide, water, and chlorophyll alone cannot result in photosynthesis. One extremely important factor is still missing. The product which they form must contain *energy*. This energy must be absorbed by living cells as *light*. The sun is the source of light in nature and is, therefore, the source of energy for photosynthesis. Direct sunlight is not necessary, however. Plants may use artificial light in the process. You can grow plants indoors with nothing but artificial light, if it is adequate.

Photosynthesis becomes even more wonderful when you consider that it involves two changes. One is a **chemical change** during which carbon dioxide and water unite to form a new product. The other is an **energy change**. *Radiant energy* (light rays), which is quite useless in supporting life, is converted into *chemical energy*. It is locked into the product and is released in the body of a plant or animal as energy for life.

The product of photosynthesis. We now have all the four requirements for photosynthesis: (1) a living cell with chloroplasts; (2) carbon dioxide; (3) water; and (4) light energy. The result of this chemical reaction is *sugar,* an organic compound. Sugar forms in the chloroplasts of active cells during the daylight hours. Since sugar is soluble in water, it dissolves as it is formed in the water of the cells. This explains

why we can't see it when we look at green cells under a microscope.

Most plants immediately change the sugar which is formed from photosynthesis into *starch*. Others change it to oil. Onion cells show large numbers of oil droplets scattered through the cells. In this case, sugar is converted into an oil which gives the characteristic odor to onions.

The original or *simple sugar* formed during photosynthesis may be changed to many other products in plants of different kinds. Woody plants, like trees, convert some of the sugar into *cellulose* which is used in forming the woody cell walls of the xylem. Sugar cane, sugar beets, and sugar maples form a complex type of sugar called *double sugar* because two parts of simple sugar are used to form one part of double sugar.

Literally thousands of organic compounds may be traced back to photosynthesis. Green tissue alone can link the inorganic world with the organic world in the making of simple sugar.

The waste product. When carbon dioxide and water unite to form sugar, some of the *oxygen* which they both contain is left over. Oxygen thus becomes a *waste product,* though it is in no sense waste. In fact, the oxygen is as important as the sugar! It passes out of the leaves by way of the stomates into the air. Here it is taken in by all living things during respiration. Much of the oxygen we use during respiration originally passes through leaf stomates following its release from photosynthesis.

Radioactive carbon and photosynthesis. The element carbon may be the key which will unlock many of the present mysteries of photosynthesis. Recent atomic research has isolated a radioactive form of carbon, known as **carbon 14.** Scientists can detect carbon in this

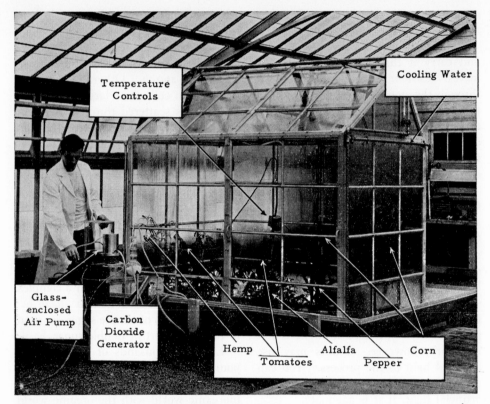

Fig. 14-6. This research scientist is growing plants in an environment containing radio-active carbon dioxide. He will later trace the path of the gas through the plant in an attempt to see how and where it is used by the plant.

form quite readily with a Geiger counter. Thus, carbon 14 serves as a tracer element.

In the use of radioactive carbon in biological research, carbon 14 is combined with oxygen to form a " tell-tale " carbon dioxide. The carbon dioxide is admitted to a closed chamber in which green plants are growing. The plants absorb this special carbon dioxide and use it in the production of sugar containing radioactive carbon. Further food production within the plant may yield fats and oils and proteins, all containing radioactive carbon which can be traced with a Geiger counter. This development in biological research is

extremely important in the study of photosynthesis. It is also helpful in the study of the uses of plant and animal foods. (See Fig. 14-6.)

Photosynthesis — a definition. We can condense this discussion of photosynthesis into one brief definition as follows:

Photosynthesis is the process by which certain living plant cells combine carbon dioxide, water, and light energy, in the presence of chlorophyll, to form sugar and release oxygen as a waste product.

We may state it even more simply in a chemical equation, showing the amount of each substance involved and

Fig. 14-7. These drawings of a geranium leaf illustrate the starch test. The leaf on the left shows natural green and white areas before being treated with iodine. The leaf on the right, after treating with iodine, shows the blue-black color only in those parts of the leaf which were green.

the proportions of the elements included in each as follows:

6CO₂ + 6H₂O + energy
(carbon   (water)   (light)
dioxide)

$$\longrightarrow \quad \textbf{C}_6\textbf{H}_{12}\textbf{O}_6 + \textbf{6O}_2$$
(sugar)   (oxygen)

This equation means that six molecules of carbon dioxide and six molecules of water combine, with energy included, to form one molecule of sugar with six molecules (twelve atoms) of oxygen left over. The sugar contains stored energy which is later released in the body of a plant or animal cell.

An experiment to show that green plants produce starch (photosynthesis). You can take leaves from active green plants, scald them to kill the protoplasm and to release the chlorophyll, and then boil them in alcohol to remove the green color. (*CAUTION: Do not use a flame near alcohol. Use only an electric plate.*) If you test them with iodine, a dark blue color results, proving that starch is present in the leaves. The chlorophyll had to be removed so that

this blue could be seen. To prove that it is *made there* by the action of light on the leaf requires further experiment. Sugar is formed before the starch, but it remains in solution and its presence is not so easy to prove.

To show that chlorophyll is necessary, you can treat a leaf from a green-and-white-leaved geranium as shown in Fig. 14-7. You will find little starch in the white portions. How do the cells of the white area get food?

To show that light is necessary, areas of an active leaf are covered with corks pinned through on both sides. After a few days the covered portions will not yield the starch test, while the exposed parts will still do so. Another proof of the same thing is to keep a plant entirely in the dark, as a check experiment, and when it has become pale, test for starch, which will be lacking. Of course, in both experiments you should use the same kind of plant, under the same conditions except the light as a control.

An experiment to show that green plants produce oxygen. Oxygen is the waste product of photosynthesis, given

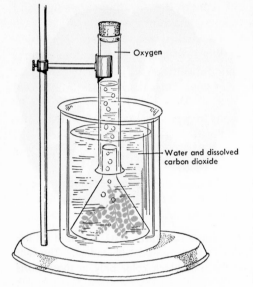

Fig. 14-8. In this experiment, you can see the oxygen bubbles rising in the tube from the green plants at the bottom of the funnel. How can you prove this is oxygen?

off when sugar is made. Since it is easier to collect a gas over water, a water plant is good for this experiment, but all green plants carry on the same process.

A water plant (such as *Vallisneria, Sagittaria, Elodea,* or *Myriophyllum*) is submerged under a glass funnel whose stem is covered with a glass tube. The tube is corked at one end, filled with water and inverted (see Fig. 14-8). If you set the apparatus in the sun, bubbles of gas will rise in the funnel and collect in the tube. Before removing the cork to make a test for the gas which is collecting in the funnel, lower the tube so that the water in it is on the same level as that in the jar. This will prevent a downward rush of water in the tube when the cork is removed. Otherwise, the air would be sucked in from the top and the gas thus diluted. Test this gas by lowering a glowing splint in the funnel. It will burst into flame and show

the presence of oxygen. If carbon dioxide is dissolved in the water, the process will go on much faster because carbon dioxide is one of the materials used in photosynthesis, and that in the jar is soon exhausted.

Another similar experiment ought to be set up in the dark to prove again that light is the source of energy for this important process.

To prove that the oxygen did not come from the water, another check could be used with the apparatus the same but without a plant; in which case no oxygen would be produced. How would this prove anything?

Conditions for photosynthesis. The rate of photosynthesis depends on several important factors both inside the plant and in its surroundings. Probably the most critical internal factor is the condition of the food-making cells. The chlorophyll content of their chloroplasts is related directly to the general condition of the plant as well as to the environment which supplies water, light, and the proper minerals for chlorophyll manufacture. In addition to these requirements for the making of chlorophyll, other factors of the environment are essential for photosynthesis to take place.

Water is necessary both as a material for the process and to maintain healthy cells capable of food manufacture. The *carbon dioxide* content of the atmosphere is another critical factor since the gas serves likewise as an essential material. *Light* serves a double role as the energy source for the process and as a requirement for chlorophyll formation.

Temperature is an extremely critical factor since it affects cell activity. Summer temperatures, ranging from 80° to 90° F., are ideal for photosynthesis. As the temperature drops, the process slows down. It stops altogether near the freezing point. Likewise, a rise in temperature above 100° F. slows down the enzymes involved. This lowers the rate of photosynthesis accordingly.

Photosynthesis supplies the basic needs for all life, both plant and animal. The most direct importance of photosynthesis is food production. Sugar, the direct product, is an essential food. From this basic substance, plants and animals build other food substances including starches, fats, oils, proteins, and vitamins. They all contain the energy from photosynthesis and are related directly to the activity of green plant tissues.

Energy from fuels. Our modern civilization runs on power — power obtained largely from natural fuels. One of man's earliest achievements was the use of fire from wood. Wood contains stored energy taken originally from the sun during photosynthesis. We start a chemical breakdown of wood by igniting it and thus releasing this stored sunshine as heat and light energy. Wood has served for ages as a simple source

of energy for heating, cooking, and fueling machines.

As civilization advanced, other fuels were discovered to supply more complicated machines. Plant remains of past ages were unearthed in the form of coal and oil deposits. The sunshine of millions of years ago, still locked inside the molecules of these substances, serves as the most efficient energy supply for modern civilization.

Storage and translocation of foods. During a bright warm day, photosynthesis forms sugar in leaf cells much more rapidly than the plant can remove it to other parts. As a result, most leaves convert the sugar to starch either immediately or soon after it is formed. As the day's food manufacture progresses, starch grains become more and more abundant. About the middle of the afternoon, the starch content reaches its peak.

In the evening, light is reduced and photosynthesis slows down. It stops almost entirely at night but may continue slightly on a clear, bright, moonlit night. Through the night, the stored starch is

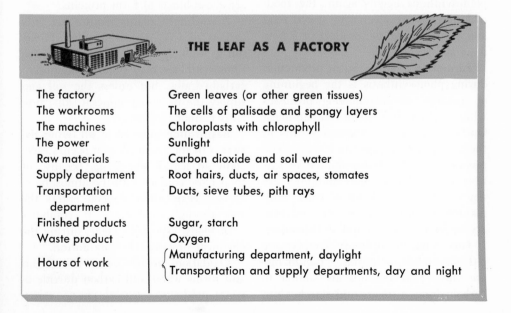

THE LEAF AS A FACTORY

The factory	Green leaves (or other green tissues)
The workrooms	The cells of palisade and spongy layers
The machines	Chloroplasts with chlorophyll
The power	Sunlight
Raw materials	Carbon dioxide and soil water
Supply department	Root hairs, ducts, air spaces, stomates
Transportation department	Ducts, sieve tubes, pith rays
Finished products	Sugar, starch
Waste product	Oxygen
Hours of work	{ Manufacturing department, daylight { Transportation and supply departments, day and night

Fig. 14-9. This engine is being filled with diesel oil. It operates as a result of the release of energy from the oil.

digested in the cells and forms sugar which dissolves in water. The **translocation** or movement of the sugar solution through the veins into the stem continues all night. At daybreak, when photosynthesis begins again, the food-making cells are cleared of stored food and are ready for the product of a new day's activity.

Formation of fats. Sugar production during photosynthesis is the beginning of a series of food-making processes which occur in both plants and animals. One such group of processes results in the formation of *fats* and *oils*. The process is by no means limited to leaf tissues since light and chlorophyll are not necessary. All living cells, both plant and animal, possess the " machinery " necessary for fat and oil formation.

Fats occur at ordinary temperature either as solids or liquids. Liquid fats are oils. Fats and oils are similar to carbohydrates (sugars and starches) in that they contain the same elements: (1) carbon; (2) hydrogen; and (3) oxygen. Other elements are sometimes present in fats which do not occur in carbohydrates. Fats are formed largely as storage products and are used later as energy foods. Many plants like soybeans, castor beans, cotton, flax, wheat, and others store oils in their seeds which serve as important articles of commerce. Animals too change carbohydrates to fats and store them under the skin and in other regions of the body.

Formation of proteins. They are necessary for growth and for the repair of tissues. They contain stored energy from photosynthesis, and were produced from sugar.

Proteins are complex substances. They contain carbon, hydrogen, and oxygen. They also contain nitrogen and sulfur, and often, but not always, phosphorus. These last three elements enter the plant from the soil as dissolved mineral salts. During complicated chemical reactions, these mineral salts are broken down in the cells of the plant and together with carbohydrates are recombined to form proteins.

Accordingly, plants require not only carbon dioxide and water, but fertile soil as well, in order to form proteins. Photosynthesis may produce abundant carbohydrates, but unless the soil can supply the necessary mineral salts, proteins cannot be formed.

Respiration goes on in all living tissues. In the green plant it occurs especially in leaves and stems because of their close contact with the atmosphere. During **respiration,** oxygen enters the leaf through stomates. It combines with foods, especially sugar, during the chemical process called **oxidation.**

Oxidation breaks down the sugar, and forms water and carbon dioxide as waste products, releasing energy stored in the sugar molecules. The carbon dioxide and water which originally composed the sugar are released as waste products. The energy is used by the cells to perform their life activities. We can summarize respiration as follows:

Sugar + oxygen ——→ water + carbon dioxide + energy

Chemically, respiration may be shown as follows:

$$C_6H_{12}O_6 + 6O_2 \longrightarrow$$
(sugar)   (oxygen)

$$6H_2O + 6CO_2 + energy$$
(water)   (carbon dioxide)

You will note that respiration is the *exact opposite* of photosynthesis.

Photosynthesis and respiration are by no means balanced in the plant. Since photosynthesis is limited to the daylight hours, it occurs more rapidly than respiration. Respiration, on the other hand, takes place during both day and night. Furthermore, a plant normally builds up a much greater supply of carbohydrates than it needs. Biolo-

gists estimate that a corn plant uses only about one-fourth of its total food supply during a growing season.

During daylight, the water and carbon dioxide released from oxidation supply only a fraction of the needs of photosynthesis. Likewise, oxygen is released during food-making in much greater quantity than is needed for respiration. During the day, then, leaves take in carbon dioxide and release oxygen through their stomates. At night, when respiration alone takes place, oxygen enters the leaf and carbon dioxide is given off.

Plant and animal respiration are essentially the same. Both types of organisms exchange gases between the body and atmosphere. Respiration supplies oxygen for oxidation and removes carbon dioxide as a waste product. Animals and man need more energy for body activity than plants, so their *rate* of respiration is greater than that of plants. Animals and man *breathe* by means of muscular processes. But breathing is *not* respiration and you should not confuse the two. Breathing is merely the means by which animals and man take in oxygen and give off car-

COMPARISON OF PHOTOSYNTHESIS AND RESPIRATION

PHOTOSYNTHESIS	RESPIRATION
Constructive process	Destructive process
Food accumulated	Food broken down (oxidized)
Energy from sun stored in sugar	Energy released
Carbon dioxide taken in	Carbon dioxide given off
Oxygen given off	Oxygen taken in
Complex compounds formed	Simple compounds formed
Produces sugar, starch, etc.	Produces CO_2 and H_2O
Goes on only in light	Goes on day and night
Only in presence of chlorophyll	In all cells

bon dioxide. Plants have no lungs or other organs for breathing, and so take in and give off these gases only by means of stomates in leaves or lenticels in stems.

Transpiration in plants. During the growing season, a plant conducts a continuous stream of water up through its roots and stem into the leaves. This flow of water carries dissolved minerals which are used in the manufacture of proteins, chlorophyll, and other products. Some water is used for maintaining cell turgor, and some for photosynthesis. With all of its uses, however, much more water is absorbed than the plant can use. Accordingly, the excess escapes from the plant through the leaves.

During the process known as **transpiration** (trans-peer-*ay*-shun), water passes from the spaces of the spongy areas through the stomates and into the air as a vapor. While leaves primarily are concerned with transpiration, other plant parts may likewise pass water vapor into the atmosphere.

The control of transpiration. Transpiration is more than evaporation. We see this when we note the difference in the *rate* at which it occurs under different conditions. The rate of transpiration is controlled *to a limited extent* by the opening of the stomates. This opening is, in turn, controlled by the shape of their guard cells. When the guard cells change shape, the size of the opening between them also changes. When the guard cells are full of water, they swell outward and spread the opening. Then water escapes rapidly. But when they contain little water, they shrink and reduce further water loss. A closed stomate slows up but does not entirely stop transpiration.

The opening and closing of leaf sto-

Fig. 14-10. Water flows into leaves day and night. It evaporates and escapes into the air through the stomates. On the right you see a plant that is wilted because of excess transpiration on a hot day and the loss of turgor in the cells.

mates are influenced to a great extent by external factors. Light, humidity of the air, and temperature affect the guard cells and, hence, the escape of water vapor.

That leaves cannot entirely stop transpiration, even with their stomates closed, is clearly shown in the wilting which frequently occurs on hot days. Such wilting ceases in the evening when the atmosphere cools and absorption makes up the water deficiency. Transpiration is especially dangerous to plants after transplanting. Removing some of their leaves reduces the evaporation of water vapor from the leaves. Fig. 14-11 illustrates an experiment to show that plants give off water vapor.

Leaves in relation to light. No factor of the physical environment has so great an influence on the leaf as light. As a source of energy necessary for food manufacture, light has a direct bearing on the nutrition of the entire plant. The supply of food depends on the extent to which a plant displays its leaves to light.

The critical relationship between a

SUMMARY OF LEAF ACTIVITIES

PROCESS	CENTER OF ACTIVITY	APPARATUS	MATERIALS REQUIRED	PRODUCT	BY-PRODUCT
Photosynthesis	Palisade and spongy cells (cortex of green stems)	Chlorophyll Enzymes	Water Carbon dioxide	Sugar (may be changed to starch)	Oxygen
Digestion	All living cells	Protoplasm Enzymes	Starch, oils, fats, proteins	Simple sugars, fatty acids and glycerin, amino acids	
Fat formation	All living cells	Protoplasm	C, H, and O	Fats and oils	
Protein formation	All living cells	Protoplasm	C, H, and O from carbohydrates; N, S, and P from minerals	Proteins	
Respiration	All living cells	Protoplasm	Foods (especially carbohydrates) and oxygen	Energy	Carbon dioxide and water
Translocation	Leaf cells and veins	Water as a conducting medium	Sugar (dissolved in water)		
Transpiration	Leaf epidermis	Leaf spaces (spongy layer) and stomates	Water	Water vapor	

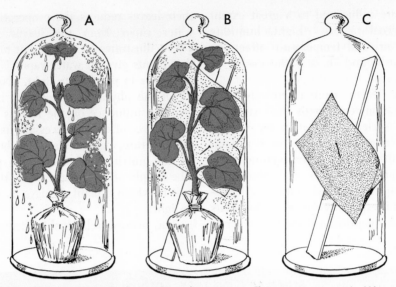

Fig. 14-11. This experiment shows that plants give off water vapor. A. Water vapor has condensed on the walls of the jar. B. Water vapor turns the cobalt paper pink in 15 minutes. C. Check experiment shows that water vapor in the air is not enough to change the color of the paper.

leaf and light is shown in the influence of light on leaf area. In places of reduced light, for example the inside or lower branches of a tree, leaves tend to be larger than those at the tips of branches or at the top where abundant light strikes the leaves.

Light influences leaf growth further in the make-up of the internal tissues. Leaves exposed to bright light usually develop one or more layers of compact palisade cells on the upper side. They also have many cells in the spongy layer. Leaves which are shaded have loosely arranged palisade cells, or may lack them entirely. They have fewer spongy cells than leaves growing in bright light.

The arrangement of leaves in respect to light. Leaves are arranged on the stem in a way which will expose each to the most light. Each leaf is pro-

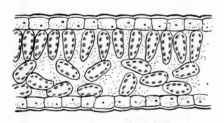

Leaf in shade

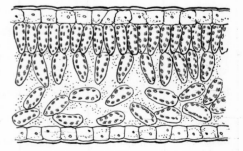

Leaf in sunlight

Fig. 14-12. Compare these cross section drawings of a leaf grown in the shade and that of a leaf grown in sunlight.

duced at a different angle on the stem. For example, two leaves arranged in a north-south direction will alternate with leaves arranged in an east-west direction. Thus, one leaf does not shade another growing from the node under it.

The general arrangement of leaves on the stem tends to put each in the best position to get light. Any rigid placing of leaves would not be very effective among plants which must compete with one another for light. Individual leaves can adjust the position of their blades by a bending of the petiole. The bending is due to the fact that the cells away from the light are stimulated to grow faster than those facing the light. This response to light by plants is called **phototropism** (foh-*tot*-roh-pizm).

Effects of moisture on leaves. Like light, moisture affects the size and growth of leaves. In regions of heavy rainfall and moist atmospheric conditions, leaves are usually large. As rainfall decreases and air becomes drier, leaves tend to become smaller. In extremely dry places, plants may have hardly any leaves at all, as in the cactus where leaves are reduced to mere spines.

Fig. 14-14. Here you see a Venus' flytrap leaf. Note the action as it captures the insect.

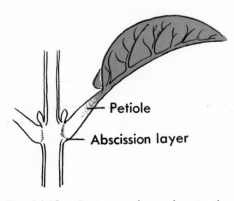

Fig. 14-13. During cool weather in the autumn, the walls of the abscission layer disintegrate and cause the leaf to drop from the stem.

Leaf coloration. Biologists explain the glorious change in the color of leaves in the autumn on the basis of light, temperature, and moisture.

During the late spring and summer, leaves are green because chlorophyll is present in the chloroplasts. During the growing season, chlorophyll is constantly destroyed by light, but is replaced just as quickly by the activity of the leaf cells.

In addition to chlorophyll, the chloroplasts also contain **xanthophyll** (zan-thoh-fill) which is a yellow pigment, and **carotene** (*kar*-oh-teen), an orange pigment. Chlorophyll masks these two other pigments so we hardly know they exist.

With the coming of fall, the temperature is apt to drop below the point necessary for chlorophyll formation. Light destroys the remaining chlorophyll, then the previously hidden yellow and orange pigments begin to appear.

The cool weather and increase in air moisture also produce a red pigment **anthocyanin** (an-tho-*sy*-an-in) in many leaves. This red pigment does not form in the chloroplasts, but in the cell sap in vacuoles of the leaf cells. It is formed from food materials. This accounts for the red appearance of leaves of many woody plants during the cool spring and fall season.

Brown coloration results from the death of leaf tissues and the production of *tannic acid* within the leaf.

The falling of leaves from their branches. The natural fall of leaves is caused by an **abscission** (ab-*sis*-shun) **layer** consisting of two rows of cells near the base of the petiole. These cells are joined firmly together during the growing season. When cold weather comes, their walls disintegrate so that the slightest jarring or gust of wind will loosen the petiole from the stem, causing the leaf to drop from its position.

While evergreen trees do not shed all their leaves at any one time, new leaves usually appear during the spring and replace those of the previous season.

Special leaf modifications. Leaves frequently may be reduced to mere **tendrils,** or the skeleton of veins, or they may develop as thorns. Some plants like *Sedum* have leaves thickened with stored food and water. These may even reproduce the plant. Perhaps the most curious adaptation of leaves is found in the tubular, vase-like leaves of the *pitcher plant* which form living flytraps. *Venus' Flytrap* has leaves which form strange " double jawed " traps for catching small insects. (See Fig. 14-14.)

These insectivorous plants secrete special enzymes that digest the small insects which their leaves trap. They are the only plants able to do this.

In Conclusion

With the leaf, we complete our study of the vegetative organs of a seed plant. Most of the activities of the root and stem serve to supply the leaf with materials and conditions for the many vital processes which are carried on by the leaves.

At the end of a season of activity, many plants shed their leaves. New, active leaves take up their work the following growing season. Even the evergreen plants lose their old leaves and grow new ones at regular intervals. Thus, the food factories of seed plants remain young and active.

In the next chapter, we begin the study of reproductive parts of a plant with the flower. We will follow the reproductive process from flower to fruit and seed. We shall complete the reproductive cycle with the development of the new plant.

Questions for Review

1. Why is it important that leaf blades in most cases be thin and broad?

2. Name two important functions of leaf veins.

3. Distinguish dicot and monocot leaves on the basis of vein structure.

4. Name the tissues of a leaf from top to bottom.

5. Why are the numerous spaces in the spongy layer necessary for leaf activity?

6. Discuss the location, structure, and function of the stomates of a leaf.

7. Explain the role of chlorophyll in photosynthesis.

8. Why is light necessary for photosynthesis?

9. Name several fuels which can be traced back to photosynthesis.

10. Explain why soil minerals are necessary for protein formation in green plants.

11. Compare photosynthesis and respiration in regard to substances necessary for the processes, waste products formed, and energy changes.

12. Explain how the rate of transpiration varies with the water content of a plant and conditions of the atmosphere.

13. Discuss the relation of leaf area and size to atmospheric moisture.

14. Why do various pigments appear in leaves during the fall season?

Biologically Speaking

abscission layer
blade
catalyst
chlorophyll
chloroplast
compound leaf
cuticle
enzyme
guard cell
leaflet

lower epidermis
midrib
netted veins
palisade layer
palmate venation
parallel veins
petiole
photosynthesis
phototropism
pinnate venation

sessile
simple leaf
spongy layer
stipule
stomate
translocation
transpiration
upper epidermis
vein
venation

Applying Facts and Principles

1. Most of the cells of a leaf have thin walls. Why is this important to the activities of a leaf?

2. The duplication of photosynthesis in the laboratory, independent of a green plant, would be one of the greatest scientific advances of all time. Do you think it will ever be done? Why, or why not?

3. If photosynthesis did not occur at a much greater rate than respiration in a plant, there would be no animal life. Explain why this is true.

4. Do you agree or disagree with the belief that plants should be removed from a sick room at night? Explain your opinion.

5. A nurseryman planted a tree in full leaf during the month of June. After planting, he pruned back the branches and removed many of the leaves. Why did this give the tree a far better chance to survive?

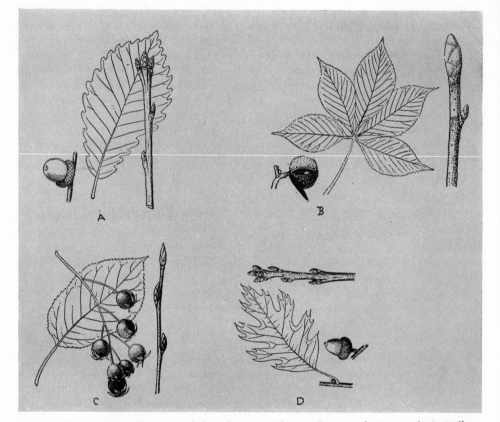

Fig. 14-15. The above leaves and their fruits are the: A. Swamp chestnut oak; B. Yellow buckeye; C. Serviceberry; D. Northern red oak. What kind of venation is represented by each?

CHAPTER 15

Flowers and Reproduction

Flowers are among the most beautiful creations of nature. But to the plants producing them, flowers are more than beautiful creations. A flower is a specialized organ which reproduces the species. It exists only a short time and then parts of it develop into the fruit. The fruit contains the seeds which, in turn, produce a new generation of plants.

In this chapter you will learn the parts of a flower and the role that each part plays in reproduction. You will discover that bright petals are not a necessary part of the flower and that many plants around you bear small, inconspicuous flowers.

The structure of a flower. A *flower* is really a modified branch in which the leaves are extremely altered to form the parts of the flower. A typical flower, such as the geranium, apple blossom, snapdragon, sweet pea, or petunia, has four sets of parts. (See Fig. 15-1.) These parts grow from a special flower stalk or **peduncle** (*peh*-dunk-al), the end or tip of which is the **receptacle**. The outer ring of floral parts consists of several green leaflike structures called **sepals** (*see*-pals). Together, the sepals form the **calyx** (*kay*-liks). The sepals cover and protect the rest of the flower in the bud stage. They also help in supporting the other parts when the bud opens.

Inside the calyx is the **corolla** (*kor-ol*-luh) which consists usually of one or more rows of petals. These are often, but not always, brightly-colored. The calyx and corolla frequently attract insects, as we shall see later. They may also help to protect the inner parts.

In certain flowers, both the calyx and corolla are the same color. You may miss the fact that both parts are present.

Reproduction is concerned directly with two kinds of **essential parts:** (1) the *stamens* (*stay*-mens); and (2) the *pistil,* located in the center of the flower. Each **stamen** consists of a slender stalk, or **filament,** supporting a knoblike sac called an **anther.** The anther produces yellow or reddish powdery grains called **pollen** (*pah*-len) which play an important part in reproduction.

The **pistil** occupies the very center of the flower. (See Fig. 15-1.) It consists of a sticky knob at the top, called a **stigma**, a slender stalk, or **style**, which supports the stigma, and a swollen base, or **ovary,** which is joined to the receptacle of the flower stalk. Inside the ovary are the **ovules** which will later become seeds. The ovules are attached to the ovary either at its base, or along the side walls, or to a special stalk running lengthwise from the base of the ovary to the base of the style. Ovules may number from one to several hundred, depending on the kind of flower.

Types of flowers. A flower which contains all four main parts: (1) *calyx;* (2) *corolla;* (3) *stamens;* and (4) *pis-*

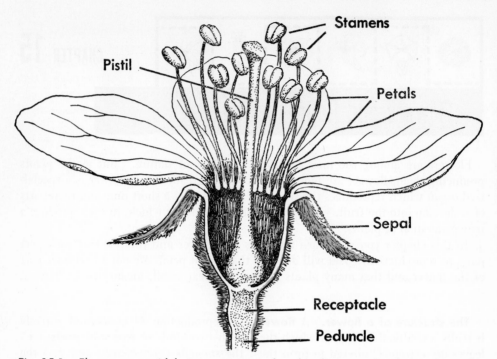

Fig. 15-1. Flowers vary widely in appearance, but this diagram of a flower shows the typical structure.

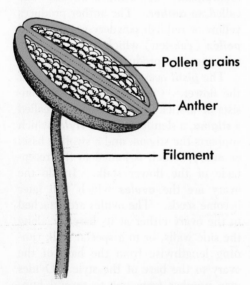

Fig. 15-2. The anther and its stalk which is called the filament make up the stamen. Pollen grains are produced inside the anther.

til is **complete** (cherry, rose, lily). If one or more of these parts is missing, the flower is **incomplete.** Where the stamens and pistil are both present in the same flower, even though the sepals and petals are missing, the flower is **perfect** (wild ginger and maple). If either the stamens or pistil is missing, the flower is **imperfect,** although other parts may be present (pussy willow, cottonwood, alder, corn).

Many of our common trees, like the willow, cottonwood, birch, and alder, produce imperfect flowers. Therefore, you'll find two kinds of flowers present. One kind contains only stamens so you can see why we call them **staminate flowers.** The yellow pussy willows in early spring are usually staminate flowers of the willow.

Some plants bear these imperfect flowers on separate plants — that is,

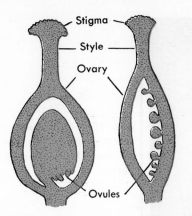

Stigma

Style

Ovary

Ovules

Fig. 15-3. The stigma receives pollen grains. Each develops a tube which grows down through the pistil to the ovary. There the sperm nuclei fertilize the egg cells. The ovules then develop into seeds. On the left is a peach; on the right a pea.

staminate flowers on one plant and pistillate on another. We call these plants **dioecious** (dy-*ee*-shus), as in the wil-

low, cottonwood, white campion, and meadow rue. Other plants produce both kinds of imperfect flowers on the same plant, as in corn. Here the pistillate flowers form on the ear and the staminate flowers compose the tassel. Plants of this type are **monoecious** (mon-*ee*-shus). The corn, birch, alder, and squash and walnut are good examples.

Flowers of monocots and dicots are different. You can easily distinguish a monocot stem from a dicot stem by the arrangement of tissues. Also the venation of the leaves is different. Therefore, it is not surprising that the flowers of these two great groups differ. A **monocot flower,** such as a lily, a tulip, or an iris, has flower parts in threes or in multiples of three, such as six. A lily has three sepals (colored like the petals), three petals inside the sepals

Fig. 15-4. The flowers of the walnut are imperfect. These photographs of the walnut show staminate flowers (left) and pistillate flowers (right).

Fig. 15-5. The tulip, a monocot flower, has flower parts in multiples of three.

and usually the same color, six stamens, and a pistil with a three-part stigma and three chambers in the ovary.

Flowers of **dicot plants** usually have their parts in fours or fives, or in multiples of these numbers. You will find such an arrangement in the buttercup, rose, columbine, and other dicot flowers. The magnolia is one of few dicot flowers with parts in threes or sixes.

Of course, not all flowers follow this pattern of threes or sixes for monocots and fours and fives for dicots. There are exceptions, as stated above, for the magnolia. But in general, the patterns are characteristics for **those** groups.

Fig. 15-6. The columbine, a dicot flower, has its parts in fives, or multiples of fives.

Fig. 15-7. The sunflower is composed of two kinds of flowers, ray and disk. Those on the outside are ray flowers, while those in the center are disk.

What are composite flowers? Did you know that a daisy, a zinnia, a sunflower, a dandelion, or a cosmos is not a single flower, but a whole flower cluster? These plants belong to the composite family of dicots. They form a flower cluster known as a *head.*

The sunflower, and many other composites, have two kinds of flowers forming the head. The so-called petals around the outside are individual *ray flowers.* Their petals serve to attract insects, but they do not produce seeds. *Disk flowers* fill the center of the head. These flowers are small and lack petals. Each disk flower develops a small, dry fruit.

The entire head of the dandelion is made up of ray flowers. Each has a petal and will produce a tiny seed which will leave the head on a parachute.

The anther and pollen formation. Pollen grains develop in four pollen sacs in each anther. If you cut an anther from a large stamen as the lily or tulip, you will see the sac quite clearly with a hand lens.

When the pollen is ripe, the sacs open as the anther splits. The grains are then exposed to wind, water, or insects.

Pollen grains vary in size, shape, and texture. Some are rough, while others are smooth (see Fig. 15-9).

Each grain consists of cytoplasm and two nuclei, one the *tube nucleus* and the other the *generative nucleus.*

Structure of an ovule. The formation of pollen in the flower is only half the story of reproduction. The other half concerns the *ovules* which develop in the ovary at the base of the pistil early in the formation of the flower.

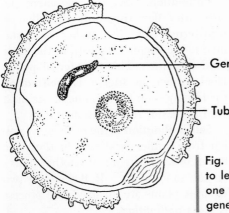

Generative nucleus

Tube nucleus

Fig. 15-8. The pollen grain, when ripe and ready to leave the anther, contains one generative and one tube nucleus. As the pollen tube grows, the generative nucleus divides into two sperm nuclei.

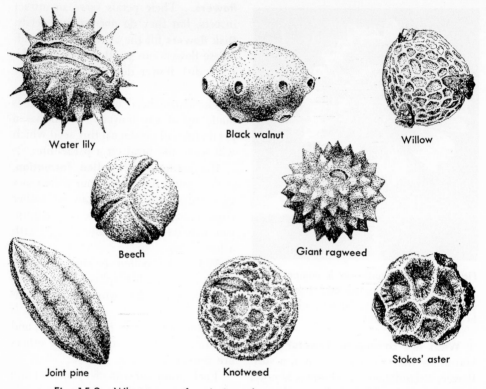

Fig. 15-9. What types of variations do you see in these pollen grains?

A pistil sectioned lengthwise shows the **stigma** at the tip, the slender **style** and a swollen **ovary** at the base, in which are one or more ovules. For the sake of simplicity in studying the detailed structure of an ovule, we'll use an ovary containing a single ovule, like the peach. Many flowers produce ovaries with numerous ovules, like the bean, pea, orange, apple, and melon.

The ovule is attached to the ovary wall by a slender stalk through which nourishment reaches the ovule during its development. The walls of the ovule are in two layers. A tiny pore, or **micropyle** (*mike*-roh-pile), leads through the walls on the lower side to the interior of the ovule. Inside the walls is an oval area, the embryo sac, containing eight nuclei. Three of these nuclei are at each end of the *embryo sac* (see Fig.

15-10). The two others are near the middle and are the *polar nuclei* which unite before fertilization and form one endosperm nucleus. The egg, or female reproductive cell, is the large nucleus in the bottom of the embryo sac near the micropyle.

Pollination. Seed development occurs after flowering only if pollen is transferred from the anther of a stamen to the stigma of a pistil of the same kind of plant. This transfer of pollen from anther to stigma is **pollination** (*pol*-lin-ay-shun). It is one of the most vital phases of reproduction.

Self-pollination is the transfer of pollen from anther to stigma in the same flower or to the stigma of another flower on the same plant. If flowers on two separate plants are involved, the process is **cross-pollination.**

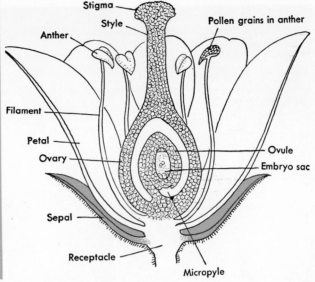

Fig. 15-10. The peach produces a single ovule. This sectioned pistil shows its parts.

The transfer of pollen from one plant to another in cross-pollination requires an outside agent. The chief ones are: *insects, wind,* or *water*. Curious adaptations of different kinds of flowers are frequently necessary to accomplish pollination by these outside sources.

Adaptations for pollination. Chief among the *insect pollinators* are bees. But moths, butterflies, and certain kinds of flies visit flowers regularly and in so doing carry on cross-pollination.

Insects come to the flower to obtain the sweet nectar which is secreted deep in the flower from special glands at the base of the petals. Bees swallow nectar into a special honey stomach where it is mixed with saliva and converted into honey. When they return to the hive, the bees deposit the honey in six-sided cells of the comb and use it later as food.

The plump hairy body of the bee makes it an ideal pollinator. To reach the nectar glands, located at the base of the flower, the bee must rub its hairy body against the anthers. These are usually located near the opening of the flower. When the insect visits the next

flower, some of the pollen is sure to rub against the sticky stigma of the pistil as a new supply is brushed off the stamen.

Brightly-colored petals and sweet odors aid insects in locating flowers. Nectar guides in some flowers may be brightly-colored stripes located on the petals.

We must include at least one bird in

Fig. 15-11. This bee is entering flowers of the western anemone. Why are bees ideal pollinators of plants?

Fig. 15-12. The flowers of wind-pollinated plants, like this maple, usually appear in dense clusters near the ends of branches.

discussing agents of pollination. Tiny hummingbirds feed on nectar of certain flowers. Their long bills and equally long tongues reach down to the nectar glands while the bird hovers over the flower.

The flowers of wind-pollinated plants are much less striking than are those pollinated by insects. They are usually borne in dense clusters near the ends of branches. As a rule, petals are lacking and the flowers seldom have any nectar. Frequently, the stamens are long and produce enormous quantities of pollen. The pistils are also long and the stigmas

are large and often sticky to catch pollen grains that are blown about by the wind. Pines, cottonwood, willow, walnut, corn, oats, and other wind-pollinated plants literally fill the air with pollen when their stamens are ripe.

Natural prevention of self-pollination. While not always the case, a great many plants form better seed as a result of cross-pollination than self-pollination. Accordingly, nature has provided various means of avoiding self-pollination in certain plants. Imperfect flowers on separate plants are a guarantee of cross-pollination. Likewise, imperfect flowers on the same plant, as in the corn, usually result in cross-pollination. This is because pollen is carried by the wind from the tassel to the ear of another plant.

The shape of many perfect flowers like the sweet pea and iris is irregular. The pollen can hardly get to the pistil of the same flower except by accident, but is almost certain to be crossed when the flowers are visited by insects. Often the stamens and pistil mature at different times in the same flower, so when the pollen is ripe the pistil has not matured sufficiently to receive it, or the reverse. Sometimes plants have two different types of flowers. One has long stamens and a short pistil, the other has a long pistil and short stamens.

Growth of the pollen tube and fertilization. As a result of pollination, the pollen grains reach the stigma of the pistil. Once a grain lands there, it begins to form a long pollen tube which grows through the surface of the stigma and the soft tissue of the style and reaches the micropyle of the ovule. Then it enters through this thin tissue

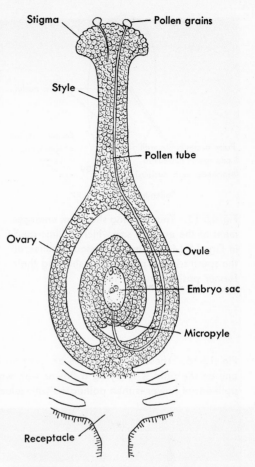

Fig. 15-14. Fertilization is about to occur in this flower. Note the pollen tube growing down the style.

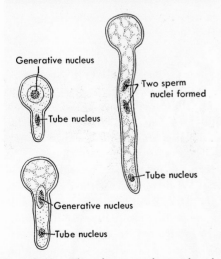

Fig. 15-13. This drawing shows the development of a pollen tube. Note the formation of the various nuclei.

of the embryo sac, and the tip end dissolves.

Now let's go back to the pollen grain at the time it was released from the anther. Then, it had two nuclei. One was the *generative nucleus*. The other was the *tube nucleus*. While the pollen tube pushes down into the style, the tube nucleus stays down near the tip of the tube. The generative nucleus divides and forms two **sperm nuclei**. These are the male reproductive nuclei. When the tube reaches the embryo sac in the ovule, these nuclei are discharged from the tip end.

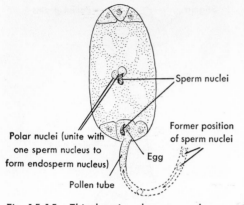

Sperm nuclei

Polar nuclei (unite with
one sperm nucleus to
form endosperm nucleus)

Former position
of sperm nuclei

Egg

Pollen tube

Fig. 15-15. This drawing shows an enlargement of the embryo sac which is illustrated in Fig. 15-14. Note the dotted outlines of the sperms in the pollen tube showing their former position in that tube.

One sperm unites with the two polar nuclei and forms the *endosperm nucleus*. The other sperm unites with the egg. This union of sperm and egg is called **fertilization**. The fertilized egg then becomes a **zygote** (zy-goat). After it is formed, it begins to grow inside the embryo sac of the ovule. It then becomes a young embryo plant enclosed in the seed.

The seed is merely another name of the ovule after fertilization has occurred. Each ovule needs one pollen grain to fertilize its egg. Those flowers which have large numbers of ovules like beans, peas, melons, and others, have to have an equally large number of pollen grains on their stigma if fertilization is to succeed.

After fertilization, the flower has

Fig. 15-16. These two biologists are preparing a lettuce plant for cross pollination. The one on the right is spraying a flower with water to remove all the original pollen. This pollen-free flower is then pollinated with selected pollen.

served its purpose. The sepals and petals fall away (sometimes, though, the sepals remain as part of the fruit), the stamens wither, and only the ovary in the pistil remains. The ovary contains the seed or seeds inside. It develops into the fruit which ripens, and at its maturity the seeds escape and begin to grow into new plants.

Artificial pollination. By controlling pollination, a plant breeder can make scientific crosses and produce new and improved varieties of plants. There are several ways of preventing natural self-pollination occurring before artificial pollination can be carried out. One method is the removal of the stamens of a flower before the pollen is mature. Another is to cover the flower with a sack. To prevent pollen from other plants reaching the pistil, that is, to prevent cross-pollination, the flower may be covered with a sack after the stamens have been removed.

The breeder then selects the plants he wants to use as parents and transfers pollen from the stamens of one to the pistil of the other.

Pollen allergy. To many, pollen isn't a pleasant subject to discuss because of an allergy we commonly refer to as *hay fever* or *rose fever*. The content of certain pollen grains causes swelling, irritation, and itching of the membranes of the eyes, nose, and throat, in some people. The *spring type* of pollen allergy is usually due to tree pollens. Grasses and plantain are usually responsible for the *summer type*. The *fall type,* most common of pollen allergies, is usually due to ragweed. The fall type usually starts about mid-August and lasts until frost.

Pollen allergies are nearly always caused by wind-carried pollen. Many people associate goldenrod with hay fever. However, doctors have found

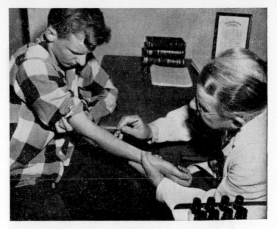

Fig. 15-17. By injecting various pollens in his patient's skin, this doctor is trying to find out to which ones he is allergic.

that the usual cause is ragweed growing with the goldenrod. The pollen grains of goldenrod are waxy and are not easily carried by wind.

An attack of seasonal hay fever usually begins and ends on about the same day each year. This shows that weather variations from year to year have little effect on the time plants bear their pollen. In many cities, pollen counts of the air are reported in the daily newspapers.

In treating hay fever the doctor first finds out which pollen or pollens are involved. This is done with a series of skin tests. Extracts from various pollens present in the air during the patient's allergy are put in scratches in the skin, or they may be injected under the skin with a hypodermic needle. If the patient is sensitive to a particular pollen, a raised area which itches violently appears. Having found out the kind of pollen involved, the doctor can give a series of hypodermic injections or " shots " containing the pollen substance in increasing strength. Usually this brings at least partial relief. Various drugs, including *antihistamines* (antee-*his*-tah-meens), which shrink swollen membranes, may bring temporary

Fig. 15-18. The lady's slipper, so-called because of its resemblance to a slipper, grows wild in certain sections of the country. It is quite rare and you can prevent its extermination by not picking it.

relief. However, these should be used *only under a doctor's care*.

Our native flowers. All around you, native plants of the roadside, field, forest, and pond bear their flowers in an almost continuous succession from early spring until fall. In many sections of the country, the spring flowers of a woodland transform the forest floor into a flower garden for several weeks. Violets, buttercups, triliums, anemones, spring beauty, hepaticas, crowfoot, and squirrel corn are among these early spring flowers. Later, plants of the field and roadside add their color to the landscape.

Among the most beautiful of all flower gardens is the Alpine meadow in summer. High above timber line in the great mountain ranges, the rocky slopes lose their snow in early summer and are transformed into a garden of unsurpassed beauty.

Many think of a desert as dry and colorless. But during the period when cacti and other desert plants bloom, the reds and pinks and yellows of desert flowers make it a place of great beauty.

The beauty of our wild flowers has led to the extermination of many. In every region there are plants which need protection. If you happen to find one, admire it in its native haunt, but don't pick it or dig it up. Perhaps future generations will have more of these interesting and unusual plants because you spared them.

In Conclusion

With fertilization completed, the flower has served its purpose. The petals and stamens wither. The ovary of the pistil grows rapidly and matures into the fruit. Inside the ovary, each ovule grows into a seed, containing an embryo plant and a food supply.

In the next chapter, you will follow the development of the fruit and seed. You'll probably have to change your idea of what a fruit really is.

Within the protective covering of seed coats, tiny plants may float through the air or ride long distances on the fur of an animal. This is nature's method of spreading plants to new locations.

Questions for Review

1. The sepals and petals of a flower are often spoken of as " accessory parts " because they do not function directly in reproduction. What purpose do they serve?

2. Name the essential parts of a flower which function directly in reproduction.

3. Both dioecious and monoecious plants bear imperfect flowers. Distinguish between these two kinds of plants and give an example of each.

4. Explain how you can distinguish a monocot flower from a flower of a dicot plant on the basis of number of floral parts.

5. The head of a composite flower, such as the sunflower or dandelion, is not a single flower but a flower cluster. Explain the structure of a composite flower.

6. (a) Describe the structure of an ovule at the time of fertilization and locate the eight nuclei of the embryo sac. (b) Explain how the number of nuclei is reduced to seven just before fertilization.

7. Name three agents of pollination.

8. Discuss some characteristics of insect pollinated flowers which serve as devices for attraction.

9. Describe various ways in which certain plants avoid self-pollination.

10. Distinguish the various types of hay fever and name a plant responsible for each type.

Biologically Speaking

allergy	filament	pollen sac
anther	generative nucleus	pollen tube
calyx	imperfect flower	pollination
complete flower	incomplete flower	ray flower
corolla	micropyle	receptacle
cross-pollination	monoecious	self-pollination
dioecious	ovary	sepal
disk flower	ovule	sperm
egg	peduncle	stamen
embryo	perfect flower	staminate flower
embryo sac	petal	stigma
endosperm nucleus	pistil	style
essential parts	pistillate flower	tube nucleus
fertilization	pollen grain	zygote

Applying Facts and Principles

1. Most seed plants produce huge quantities of pollen grains. In proportion to the amount of pollen produced the number of ovules is very small. Why?

2. If the weather is rainy and cold during the apple blossom season, the apple crop will probably be greatly reduced even though the weather isn't cold enough to

injure the flower parts. Give possible reasons for this.

3. Most wind-pollinated trees flower in the early spring. What reason can you give for this?

4. Explain why the flowers grown in gardens and those bought from a florist are much less apt to cause pollen allergy than those growing wild.

5. Explain why you might find an unusual plant along a highway or a railroad track.

Fig. 15-19. Mountain laurel, an eastern and central North American shrub, is greatly admired for its beauty. For that reason, it is rapidly becoming extinct. Many states have passed a law prohibiting the picking of its exquisite blooms.

CHAPTER 16

Fruits and Seeds

A forest of mighty trees is a beautiful sight, but when you consider that at one time you could have carried nearly a whole forest in your pocket, the processes involved in its growth seem even more wonderful. Yes, "great oaks from little acorns grow," and a seed no larger than a pea produces the pine.

This chapter begins with the withering flower and ends with a new plant established in new surroundings and leading its own life. Before the seed pushes its root into the soil or sends up its shoot, it may have traveled many miles from the parent plant. Vegetation moves by scattering seeds. Once a seed has sprouted, the plant must live or die where it happens to grow because it no longer has the ability to move; it is securely rooted in its new surroundings. While many seeds lodge in unfavorable surroundings, a few sprout in ideal places and although the mortality of seeds and seedlings is high, enough survive to carry on the species year after year.

From flower to fruit and seed. Fertilization brings a sudden end to the work of the flower. As the sepals, petals, and stamens wither, a group of special hormones force the plant to pour its full energies into the development of the ovary and the ovules inside. After a few weeks, the ovary and its contents ripen. In many plants other nearby parts, such as the receptacle or the calyx, enlarge and become part of the fruit so that we can define a *fruit* as a *ripened ovary, with or without associated parts*. A seed, on the other hand, is a matured ovule which is enclosed in the fruit.

A fruit need not be fleshy, like an apple, a peach, or an orange. A kernel of corn, a hickory nut, a bean pod with its beans, a sticky burr of burdock, and a cucumber or pumpkin are just as much fruits as the fleshy, juicy type. So you must change your idea of a fruit from the grocery store meaning to that of a biologist.

The relation of fruits and seeds. Let's remember one important fact about seeds: the new plant grows from a seed, not from a fruit. But the fruit is highly important because it encloses the seed and protects it from water-loss, disease, insect attack, and other dangers while it is developing. Later the fruit serves as a device for distributing the seeds. The fruit may be a tempting meal for a bird or another animal or it may serve as a parachute or a wing for dispersal through the air. In some cases, a fruit bursts open and throws the seeds out when it ripens or it may develop specialized devices for clinging to the fur of animals or the feathers of birds in order to leave its original home. Later in this chapter we will discuss more fully the ways in which fruits and seeds are dispersed.

199

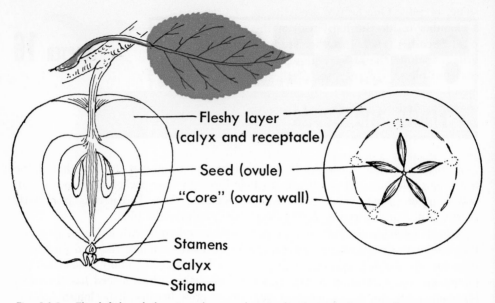

Fig. 16-1. The left-hand drawing shows a longitudinal view of an apple, a pome type of fruit. The right drawing is a cross sectional view of the same fruit.

Structure of typical fruits. Fruits, like the flowers from which they develop, vary greatly in structure. The apple is especially interesting because it involves more than the ovary and

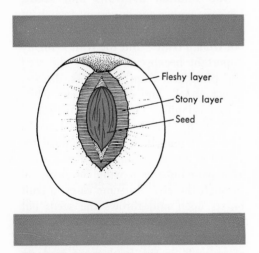

Fig. 16-2. The drawing above shows a longitudinal view of the peach. Note that it consists of two layers. Which is the part you eat? Compare this type of fruit with the apple in Fig. 16-1.

ovules in its development. Have you ever noticed a swollen region in the stem of an apple blossom or a rose just below the sepals? This is the **receptacle.** The ovary is located in this swollen region, below the petals and sepals and as the apple develops, the receptacle enlarges and becomes part of the fruit. The ovary wall is the edge of the papery core and the ovules develop into the seeds which lie in the chambers of the core. Examine the sectioned apple in Fig. 16-1 and find the various parts we have described. At the end opposite the stem, you can see the calyx of the apple blossom, the dried stamens, and the stigma of the pistil. We refer to a fruit of this type as a **pome.** Other pome fruits include the pear and the quince.

The peach is another type of fruit which we classify as a **drupe** because the ovary wall ripens in two layers — an outer fleshy layer and a hard inner layer. The outer layer is the part you eat while the inner layer forms the stone, or pit. One or two seeds lie in a chamber inside the hard wall of the pit. (See Fig. 16-2.) Other kinds of drupes include the cherry, plum, apricot, and olive. In the case of the almond, for example, we discard the worthless fleshy portion, open the pit, and eat the seed.

The bean is a type of many-seeded fruit known as a **legume.** Most of a bean pod is a greatly enlarged ovary wall. The pointed end is the style and sometimes the stigma remains as a tiny knob on the end of the style. At the stem end, you can see the calyx of the bean blossom. The string is a fibrovascular bundle which brings food and water to the attached seeds. The small undeveloped beans you sometimes find in a pod are shriveled ovules which were not fertilized. As the bean ripens, the pod dries out and splits open. The seeds loosen from their stalks and fall out. This type of fruit is produced only by one large family called *Leguminoseae* (leh-gume-in-*oh*-see-ee). Included in this, besides the beans and peas, are the clovers, alfalfas, soybeans, redbuds, locusts, Kentucky coffee-trees, and many others.

Classification of fruits. In classifying various kinds of fruits, we divide them first into *fleshy* and *dry* fruits. You are familiar with such fleshy fruits as the apple, pear, cherry, banana, tomato, and gooseberry. Fruits which become dry when they are ripe include the various legumes, iris and poppy capsules, hickory nuts, acorns, and the winged fruits of the maple, ash, and elm.

We classify dry fruits further as: (1) **dehiscent** (dee-*hiss*-sent) — those which split along definite seams when ripe; and (2) **indehiscent** (in-dee-*hiss*-sent) — those which do not open along definite seams when ripe. The bean,

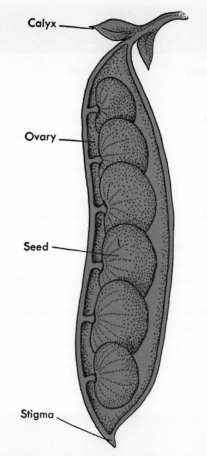

Fig. 16-3. The lima bean is a type of dry fruit called a legume.

milkweed pod, lily, and iris capsules are dehiscent fruits. The acorn and winged fruits of maple, ash, and elm are typical indehiscent fruits.

The table on page 202 shows a classification of some of the more common types of fruits.

How seeds are dispersed. When seeds mature, they must be carried from the parent plant by some means or other. If they fall to the ground close by, the parent plant will be surrounded by struggling seedlings and few of these will have much chance of survival. Nature avoids this waste by attempting to scatter seeds as far as possible from the

CLASSIFICATION OF FRUITS

TYPE	STRUCTURE	EXAMPLES
	FLESHY FRUITS	
Pome	Ovary forms a papery core containing seeds. Outer fleshy layer developed from calyx and receptacle	Apple, quince, pear
Drupe	Ovary ripens into two layers. Outer layer fleshy; inner layer hard, forming stone or pit, enclosing one or more seeds	Plum, cherry, peach, olive
Berry	Entire ovary fleshy and often juicy. Thin-skinned and containing numerous seeds	Tomato, grape, gooseberry
Modified berry	Like berry, but with tough covering	Orange, lemon, cucumber
Aggregate fruit	Compound fruit composed of many tiny drupes clustered on single receptacle	Raspberry, blackberry
Accessory fruit	Edible portion formed from enlarged receptacle. Fruits small and hard; scattered over surface of receptacle	Strawberry
Multiple fruit	Compound fruit formed from several flowers in a cluster	Mulberry, pineapple
	DRY FRUITS (DEHISCENT)	
Pod	Ovary wall thin, fruit single-chambered, containing many seeds. Splits along one or two lines when ripe	Bean, pea, milkweed
Capsule	Ovary containing several chambers and many seeds; splits open when mature	Poppy, iris, cotton, lily
	DRY FRUITS (INDEHISCENT)	
Nut	Hard ovary wall enclosing a single seed	Hickory nut, acorn, pecan
Grain	Thin ovary wall fastened firmly to single seed	Corn, wheat, oats
Achene	Similar to grain but with ovary wall separating from seed	Sunflower, dandelion
Winged fruit or samara	Similar to achene but with prominent wing attached to ovary wall	Maple, ash, elm

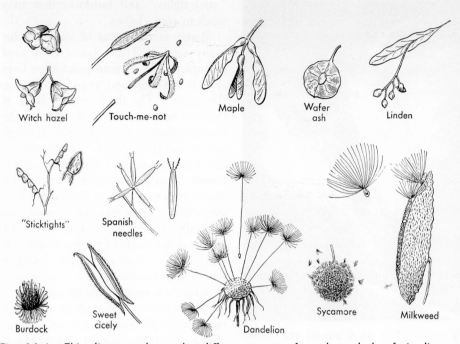

Witch hazel   Touch-me-not   Maple   Wafer ash   Linden

"Sticktights"   Spanish needles   Sycamore   Milkweed

Burdock   Sweet cicely   Dandelion

Fig. 16-4. This diagram shows the different types of seeds and the fruit dispersal mechanisms.

parent plant, a process we refer to as **seed dispersal.** (See Fig. 16-4.)

Sometimes only the seed is transported, but often the entire fruit is carried to a new location. In some cases, seed dispersal is a mechanical process, while in other cases an outside agent, such as the wind, water, a bird, or some other animal, is involved. We will consider some of the methods by which fruits and seeds travel from the parent plant.

Pod fruits, like the bean and pea, often twist as they ripen as a result of changes in the amount of moisture in the air. This causes a strain on the pod so that it bursts open suddenly and with enough force to throw the seeds some distance from the parent plant. Another interesting example of *mechanical dispersal* of seeds is the fruit of the *garden balsam,* or *touch-me-not.* When

the fruits of this plant are ripe, they open upon the slightest touch and curl upward violently with the result that the seeds may be thrown several feet. Capsules, like the poppy, do not split open along the sides, but holes form around the top as they ripen. They resemble salt shakers and as the fruit sways back and forth on a long and flexible stem in the breeze, seeds sift out.

The *wind* is the agent of dispersal for many fruits and seeds. When the milkweed pod splits open, the wind empties the pod of its seeds and each, equipped with a miniature parachute, is carried to a new location. You've probably blown the fluff off of a dandelion or a thistle head. The fruits of these plants often travel long distances on their tiny tufts. In the spring, the cottonwood tree fills the air as spring breezes empty its catkins of cottony tufted seeds. The

Fig. 16-5. The wind carries the tufted seeds of the milkweed fruit great distances. The capsule opens when the seeds are ripe.

winged seeds of maple, ash, elm, and pine whirl in the air like tiny propellers and are scattered to quite a distance from the place where they develop.

The delicious flesh of the apple, grape, or cherry is a sort of biological bribe. Birds and other animals feed on the fruits and scatter the seeds. Often the seeds pass through the digestive tract of an animal unharmed because their cellulose covers cannot be digested and are deposited far from the parent plant. Did you know that many walnut and hickory trees are planted by squirrels?

Animals aid in fruit and seed dispersal in another way. Many plants produce fruits with stickers or spines which cling to the fur of animals. You have probably aided plants in seed dispersal when you sat down after a hike in the fall to pick off the " beggar's-lice,"

" stick-tights," and burdocks that have stuck to your clothes.

Water is the agent of dispersal for many seeds. The coconut is a good example. The coconut palm often lives close to the shore and drops its fruit into the water. The thick, stringy husk of the coconut is waterproof. When the seed germinates, a sprout pushes through one of the three " eyes " on the end of the hard covering. Grasslike plants, known as sedges, are among some other plants which may drop their fruits into the water. They, like the coconut, are generally found along the shores of oceans or the banks of rivers and streams where their seeds may have found a foot-hold on the land.

What is a seed? We defined a seed as a matured ovule and as the final product of plant reproduction. Actually, a **seed** contains a tiny, living plant, the *embryo* (*em*-bree-oh), and *stored* food. This food will nourish the young plant from the time it starts to grow until it can produce its own food by photosynthesis. The regions in which food is stored may vary with different seeds. In some seeds, food is stored in thick " seed leaves," known as **cotyledons** (kot-ee-*lee*-donz), which are not true leaves because they develop as a part of the seed.

You may have seen thick cotyledons on the stems of such young plants as the green bean or lima bean shortly after they have pushed through the garden soil. They are located below the true leaves and last for only a few days before they wither and fall off. The number of cotyledons in the seed serves as the basis for the classification of the Angiosperms. Monocot plants have only one cotyledon in their seeds, while dicot plants have two.

Not all seeds have the same kind of food stored in the cotyledons. A grain of corn, for example, has its starchy food stored in a tissue known as *endosperm* while the cotyledon contains oils and proteins. This tissue, filling much of the corn seed, develops from the endosperm nucleus after it unites with one of the two sperms during fertilization. On the other hand, the major part of the bean seed is made up of the two cotyledons which store a large amount of starch as well as proteins and oil. Some seeds have a large endosperm, while others have a very small endosperm or none at all. One of the latter is the bean.

Seed coats cover the seed and protect it from drying out and from other dangers before it germinates. Usually, there are two seed coats, but some seeds have only one. The outer coat is usually tough and thick. The inner coat is much thinner.

Structure of a bean. This familiar seed is usually kidney-shaped. (See Fig. 16-7.) The outer seed coat, the *testa,* is smooth and may be white, brown, red, or other colors, depending on the species. An oval scar on the concave side, the **hilum** (*hy*-lum), marks the place where the bean was attached to the wall of the pod. Near one end of the point of attachment is a tiny pore, the **micropyle** (*mike*-roh-pile). The pollen tube grew through this tiny opening in the wall of the ovule just before fertilization. The inner seed coat of a bean is a thin, white tissue which is difficult to separate from the testa. Both of these coats have developed from the wall of the ovule.

If you soak a dried bean and remove the seed coats, the cotyledons will separate easily, the water having entered through the micropyle. Note that the cotyledons fill the space within the seed coats and that they are thick and fleshy and not at all leaflike. Abundant food

Fig. 16-6. Water is the agent of dispersal for the coconut palm. The ripe coconut may float thousands of miles in the ocean currents and lodge on the beach of a distant island.

is stored in them in the form of starch, protein, and oil.

Lying between the cotyledons are the other parts of the embryo plant. A fingerlike projection fits into a protective pocket of the seed coats. This is the **hypocotyl** (hy-poh-*kot*-il). It will grow into the lower part of the stem and the roots of the plant, and you can see that the cotyledons are attached to its upper end.

The **plumule** (*ploo*-mule) joins the upper end of the hypocotyl. It consists of two tiny leaves, folded over each other and between them lies the minute bud that will later form the plant's terminal bud as the plumule develops into the shoot. The location of the cotyledons is important to the seedling. Both the hypocotyl and the plumule will grow rapidly when the seed germinates and the cotyledons, located between them, supply nourishment to both.

Structure of the corn kernel. Each corn grain is really a complete fruit, and therefore it corresponds to the bean pod and its contents rather than to the in-

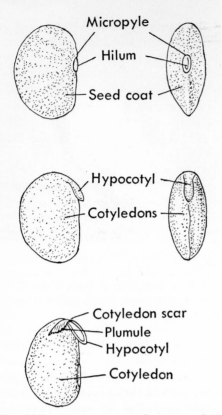

Fig. 16-7. Here you see drawings which show the external and internal appearance and structure of the bean.

dividual bean seed. However, there is only one seed in each grain and it completely fills the fruit, the outer coat of the kernel having been formed from the flower's ovary wall. A very thin inner seed coat is fastened tightly to the outer one and is only one cell layer thick. It developed from the wall of the ovule.

The *micropyle* is covered by the fruit coat but there is an obvious *point of attachment* of the corn fruit to the cob. This corresponds to the stalk of the bean's flower and is the pathway through which the developing fruit received its nourishment.

On one side of a grain of corn you can see a light-colored, oval area which marks the location of the embryo. This

is faintly visible through the fruit coat. Near the top of the kernel, on the same side as the embryo, you will find a tiny point, the **silk scar,** where the corn silk was attached.

If you cut a grain of corn lengthwise through the region of the embryo, you can see the internal parts clearly, especially if you put a drop of an iodine solution on the cut surface. The *endosperm* fills much of the seed (see Fig. 16-8). This part of the seed developed from the endosperm nucleus after fertilization. The endosperm contains sugar, starch, and will turn blue when treated with iodine. This indicates that there is a large quantity of starch present. The embryo, however, will turn yellow showing that it contains

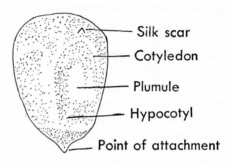

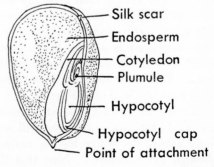

Fig. 16-8. Compare this external and internal structure of the corn grain with the bean seed in Fig. 16-7.

considerable protein. Sweet corn stores sugar in the endosperm, but field corn stores starch which accounts for the fact that we eat the garden variety and not the other.

The embryo, consisting of the hypocotyl, plumule, and cotyledon, lies on one side of the corn grain. The hypocotyl points downward, toward the point of attachment and is surrounded by a protective cap. The plumule is also protected by a sheath or cap. The leaves of the plumule are rolled, not folded as they are in the bean, into a compact " spear," which pushes easily through the soil when the seed germinates.

The corn has only one cotyledon which partly surrounds both the hypocotyl and the plumule and lies against the endosperm. During germination, the cotyledon absorbs and digests food from the endosperm, besides furnishing some of its own, and supplies it to the growing seedling. Notice that in the corn grain most of the energy-producing food is stored outside the embryo rather than in the cotyledon, as we found in the case of the bean.

Dormancy in seeds. Many seeds go through a rest period before they germinate. This rest period, or *dormant state,* may be a few weeks, an entire season, or last for years. Many plants bear seeds in the fall and these seeds are normally dormant throughout the winter in the colder regions but germinate during the following spring or summer.

Drought, cold, and heat are all enemies of the tiny plant although it is enclosed in protective seed and fruit coats. When, however, conditions are favorable for growth of a particular seed, the period of dormancy ends and **germination,** or sprouting, begins.

While some seeds may lie dormant for several years and still remain alive, there is a limit to the length of this period. Some seeds may live for almost 100 years in a dormant state and then germinate when conditions become satisfactory. On the other hand, some seeds, like the maple, germinate almost immediately after falling from the tree with the result that you frequently see a large number of young maples starting to grow under the parent tree in the late spring.

COMPARISON OF TYPICAL DICOTYLEDONOUS AND MONOCOTYLEDONOUS SEEDS

BEAN	CORN
Has testa with hilum and micropyle plainly visible	Hilum and micropyle covered by a three-layered fruit coat. The true seed coat lies inside of it
Two cotyledons	One cotyledon
Large embryo	Small embryo
No endosperm	Large endosperm
Plumule fairly large	Plumule rather small
Plumule leaves folded	Plumule leaves rolled
The fruit is a pod, with several seeds	The fruit is a single grain, with one seed

Fig. 16-9. The maple seed germinates almost immediately after falling from the parent tree. Note how many maple seedlings occur in this typical forest scene.

In the case of annuals growing in colder climates, seeds are the only form in which the plants can survive the winter months. The period of dormancy normally extends from one growing season to the next. The seeds of many perennials, likewise, lie dormant through the winter months and germinate the following spring or summer. In many cases, cold weather increases the percentage of seeds that germinate the following spring. Foresters have found this to be true in the case of the seeds of the tulip tree, or yellow poplar.

The ability of seeds to germinate after dormancy is called **viability** (vy-ah-*bill*-ih-tee). Seed viability depends on the conditions during dormancy and on the amount of food stored in the cotyledons and endosperm. Cool, dry places are ideal for storing seeds, while warmth and moisture lower viability.

Commercial seed growers run viability tests and mark the results on various lots of seeds they sell. If you check the reported viability test, you can find out the percentage of germination you can expect. If a lot of seeds has a viability of 92 percent, you can expect 92 seedlings from each 100 seeds you plant. Remember, however, that viability may vary since only a relatively few representative samples were used in each test.

Conditions for germination. For germination, most seeds require at least three conditions. These are: (1) *moisture;* (2) *the correct temperature;* and (3) *oxygen.* The amount of each of these required varies greatly with different kinds of plants.

Seeds of many water plants germinate under water where there is plenty of moisture, a quite even temperature, and oxygen dissolved in the water. The seeds of most land plants, while they need moisture, cannot germinate under water. They require less moisture, an extreme example being the desert plants where the dew supplies sufficient water for this process.

Before a seed germinates, it usually absorbs considerable water. This causes the seed to swell and soften its seed coats, but too much moisture, especially if it is warm, during the growing season encourages the growth of fungi which may cause the seeds to decay.

The temperature at which seeds germinate best is also variable. A maple seed can germinate on a cake of ice, but growth will be slow and survival very uncertain under these conditions. Others, like corn, require much higher temperatures, with a range of between 60° and 80° F. being the most suitable for the majority of seeds.

During germination, the tissues of a seedling are dividing very actively.

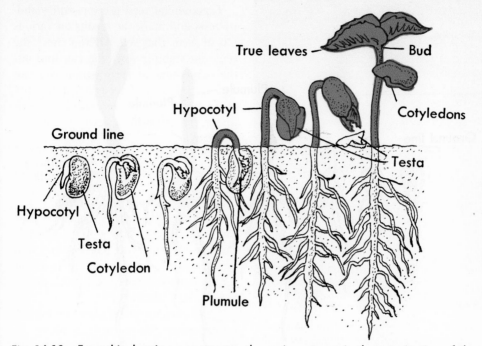

Fig. 16-10. From this drawing, you can see the various stages in the germination of the bean. The second, third, and fourth stages have been drawn with one cotyledon removed in order to show the growing plumule.

This increased activity requires a much higher rate of respiration than that of an older plant and you can see, therefore, why the oxygen supply to a seedling is critical. That is the reason the soil in a garden should be loose and the seeds planted sufficiently near the surface to give them an ample supply of oxygen.

Food changes during germination. Much of the food stored in the cotyledons or endosperm of a seed is starch. The plant changes this to sugar by the action of an enzyme known as *diastase* (*dy*-ah-stase) and the cells of the embryo absorb it. This change accounts for the sweetish flavor of sprouting seeds and explains why sugar is extracted from sprouting grain (malt) or why soybean sprouts are sometimes used in cooking.

Germination of the seed and growth of the seedling. The manner in which the seed germinates and the seedling establishes itself varies in different kinds of plants and in the location of the seed during germination. If the seed is lying on the surface, the hypocotyl must penetrate the soil from above, and the plumule will grow freely upward. If, on the other hand, the seed is completely buried, the plumule must grow through the soil and unfold its leaves above the surface while the hypocotyl grows downward. We'll follow the stages in the germination of a bean seed and a grain of corn and see how this is accomplished.

Fig. 16-10 shows the stages in the germination of a bean. After the bean has absorbed water and softened its seed coats, the hypocotyl grows out through

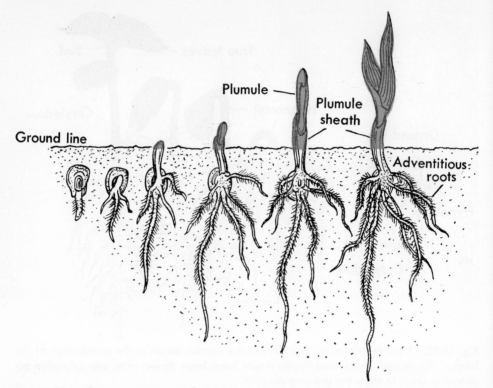

Fig. 16-11. Above you can see the stages in the germination of the corn seed. Note that neither the hypocotyl nor the cotyledon of a corn grain grows above ground as in the case of the bean.

the micropyle of the seed coat. The *lower part* of the hypocotyl grows downward and forms the primary root of the seedling, while the *upper part* is growing upward and forming an arch which pushes its way to the surface. After the hypocotyl arch appears above the ground, it straightens out and lifts the cotyledons upward. The cotyledons turn outward and release the plumule which grows upward forming the **shoot**, and the minute leaves unfold forming the first true leaves of the plant.

The stem lengthens rapidly, developing more leaves, the small bud which was between the plumule leaves of the seed becoming the terminal bud of the plant. The cotyledons remain attached to the stem for a time, below the true

leaves. But as the plant becomes better able to supply its own food by photosynthesis they wither, and finally fall off.

The corn embryo also takes in water after it has been planted and pushes its hypocotyl through the softened fruit and seed coats. This forms a temporary primary root which is soon replaced by branch roots that develop from the bottom of the stem. The leaves of the plumule which are tightly rolled and are encased in a sheath penetrate the surface of the soil. After reaching the surface, the leaves unroll and the stem continues its growth upward forming the cornstalk. Neither the hypocotyl nor the cotyledon of a corn grain grows above the surface of the soil as was the case in the germination of the bean.

Fig. 16-12. Wheat has become a most important cereal food throughout the world. What different kinds of wheat are grown?

You need not worry about a root growing upward and a shoot entering the soil if you happen to plant a seed upside down. The lower part of the hypocotyl has a strong *positive* response to gravity, and the plumule an equally strong *negative* response.

Seeds as food — cereal grains. Of all the plant parts used for food by man, seeds are the most important, and among them the cereal grains easily take first place.

These cereals are the fruits of various cultivated grasses and include wheat, corn, rice, rye, barley, and oats.

They are the most important group of foodstuffs used by man and other animals. Cereal grains contain very little water, hence farmers can store them in cribs, bins, and elevators for considerable periods without spoilage. All are rich in starch. Some, like wheat, contain much protein, and others, like corn, are rich in oil.

The protein of wheat, **gluten,** makes a flour that is good for baking and yields a light loaf which no other grain will form.

All cereals, especially if the whole grain is used, supply such essential elements as phosphorus, sulfur, potassium, calcium, magnesium, and sodium. They are easily cultivated, ripen quickly, and yield plentifully if grown in proper soil. The history of cereals is the history of the human race. Wheat dates back to the early Egyptians and corn to the North American Indians. Rice has been cultivated by the Chinese for more than four thousand years.

Cultivation of cereal grains. *Wheat* is the most important cereal food both in Europe and in America. The United States leads other nations in its production. Our wheat producing lands are the " bread basket " of the nation, extending through much of the Middle West. Several kinds of wheat, requiring quite different conditions for growth, are grown in different regions.

Fig. 16-13. As you can see, the soybean has many uses, both as a food and also in industry.

North Dakota, South Dakota, and parts of Minnesota are the centers of *spring wheat* production and have made cities, such as Minneapolis, the milling centers of the nation. The rich soils and bright sunshine of these northern prairie states are ideal for varieties of spring wheat which is planted in the spring and harvested in the autumn. Wheat of this type produces a hard seed with abundant gluten, making it ideal for flour.

The *winter wheat* area occupies a belt farther south and more extensive. Here the grain is planted in the fall and harvested in late summer of the next year. Although grown in many other states, the principal winter wheat belt includes Ohio, Indiana, Illinois, Iowa, Missouri, Nebraska, Kansas, and Oklahoma. A third important type of wheat called *durum,* or hard wheat, is grown still farther west in the states of the Great Plains.

Corn is another important crop of the Middle West. Although corn is grown in two thirds of the states, the area of heaviest production occupies a belt extending from western Ohio through Indiana, Illinois, Iowa, Missouri, and Nebraska. Almost all of the corn now planted is hybrid corn. The hybrid field varieties are used for flour and animal food. The hybrid garden varieties give a larger yield and are better for home freezing and canning than the older varieties.

Rice probably feeds more people in the world than any other grain. It is the chief cereal of India and China. In this country it is grown in some parts of Louisiana, Texas, Arkansas, and California. Rice requires warm semi-aquatic conditions and so must be grown in low-lying regions or areas which can be flooded readily.

Oats are important items in the diet of livestock, both as a grain and as fodder. The ripened stalks and leaves of oats, together with wheat stalks, are used as straw. By various mechanical processes, such as rolling, oats are prepared for human use as an important cereal food.

Barley and *rye* also are grown as crops in many sections of the nation. Barley is widely used in preparing various food products as well as for fodder and malt, while the use of rye to the baking industry is well known.

Legume fruits. Next in importance to the cereal grains are the legumes, which include the bean, pea, soybean, and peanut. Legumes are rich in protein, starch, and oil, and, like the cereals, may be stored in the dry form. *Bush beans, pole beans,* and *lima beans* are important crops in gardens of all sizes. *Peas,* too, are an important crop in the spring garden. Both as fresh vegetables and as material for the cannery, peas are indeed an important food.

Soybeans are rapidly becoming a major crop, due to the development of many new uses for their seeds. Aside from the use of soybeans as food for man and animals, various commercial uses have been developed. As a source of material for plastics, soybeans have found their way into the manufacture of automobile parts, radios, and other products of industry.

In the sandy soils of the southeastern coastal states, the *peanut* is grown extensively. Its greatest use is for food after the nuts have been roasted and crushed into peanut butter. Peanut oil is also extracted for food and industrial uses. In the region where peanuts are grown extensively, the leaves and stems of the plant are used for animal food much as clover is used.

Nuts. While larger and richer in protein and oil than cereals, *nuts* are used less for food because the crop takes so long to mature, requires so much space to grow, and is too bulky to store.

For the most part, the walnuts, chestnuts, and hickory nuts of commerce are gathered from native places. In many places, however, English walnut and pecan (species of hickory) trees are cultivated as crops.

In Conclusion

When you consider what a seed contains, it is really quite a remarkable thing. It is a tiny plant, packaged for shipment, and provided with the food it needs to get started. It is the stage in which plants can be moved to claim new places. Whether the new environment will be good or poor and whether the embryo plant will ever grow out of its covering is all a matter of chance. Far more seeds are lost than germinate. But nature allows for this in the great abundance of seeds produced.

Had you ever thought how this over-production of seeds affects your life? How much of your daily diet comes from seeds? Think of the flour we make from cereal grains and all of the beans, peas, and corn you eat. Think of the breakfast food. Seeds receive the richest food stores of the plant. No wonder they are basic foods of the animal world. And since plants produce so many more than are needed, we can supply our food needs and still have enough left to establish other generations of plants.

Questions for Review

1. Explain the relation between the flower and the fruit.

2. Name several ways in which the fruit serves the seeds which it encloses.

3. Explain how the apple flower, as well as the stem, is involved in the formation of the apple fruit.

4. Using the peach or plum as an example, describe the structure of a stone fruit.

5. Dry fruits may be either dehiscent or indehiscent. On what basis do we divide them into these two groups?

6. What method of seed dispersal is shown in pod fruits which twist and open suddenly?

7. (a) Give several examples of fruits which are dispersed by the wind. (b) Explain how they are modified for this type of dispersal.

8. Describe modifications of fruits for dispersal by animals.

9. What purpose do cotyledons serve?

10. Describe the parts of a bean embryo.

11. Name three conditions required for seed germination.

12. How does the young shoot of the corn plant force its way through the soil in which it grows?

Biologically Speaking

cotyledon	fruit	pod
dehiscent	germination	pome
diastase	hilum	seed
dispersal	hypocotyl	seed coat
dormancy	indehiscent	seedling
drupe	legume	silk scar
embryo	micropyle	testa
endosperm	plumule	viability

Applying Facts and Principles

1. A seed will not germinate until it has enough water to soften the seed coats. How is this an automatic safeguard against germination during unfavorable conditions?

2. Explain why seeds planted in heavy clay soil or set too deep may germinate very slowly, if at all.

3. Food is stored in many seeds as starch. During germination, the starch is changed to sugar by the action of the enzyme, diastase. Why is this change necessary?

4. Certain weeds are often more common in some areas than in others. Why?

Research On Your Own

1. Examine the staminate cones of a pine or other conifer. These are the pollen-producing cones which appear for a short time in the spring. At other seasons, you can buy them from biological supply companies. Dust some pollen on a microscope slide and examine it under high power. If you can get pollen from several genera, study the variations in the kinds of conifer pollen.

2. Make a list of common garden flowers and classify them as annuals, biennials, or perennials.

3. Cut a blotter or a piece of paper towel to fit the bottom of a covered dish (a Petri dish is good). Wet the blotter and drain off the excess water. Lay three radish seeds on the blotter, spacing them well apart. Cover the dish and set it in the dark. Repeat,

using corn, peas, or beans. Examine the dishes daily for a week. Study the growth of the primary root and the formation of secondary roots and root hairs. Your observations might include measurements or drawings of the seedlings.

4. Cut a carrot lengthwise and crosswise and find the epidermis, cortex, endodermis-pericycle line, and central cylinder in both sections. Record your observations in a drawing. Additional fleshy roots, such as a radish, parsnip, turnip, and beet, might be used for comparison with the carrot. Notice especially the origin of the secondary roots. You can pry the central cylinder out of the carrot cut lengthwise and see the secondary roots which have grown through the cortex.

5. Cut several slices of potato or cucumber. Put some of them into a dish of water. Put others into a dish containing salt water (strong solution). After five or ten minutes, examine the slices in both dishes. Explain your results.

6. Count out ten prunes. Select an average prune and measure its length and width. Weigh the ten prunes and record the weight. Put them into a dish of water and allow them to soak overnight. On the following day, measure the length and width of an average-sized prune. Drain all the water from them and weigh them. Record the increase in size and weight of water imbibed.

7. Collect twigs from 20 different trees of your region. Classify them to genus (maple, ash, oak, etc.), using a tree book giving twig characteristics. Mount your twigs on a piece of cardboard with the name given under each one.

8. Extract some chlorophyll from a leaf by grinding it up and placing it in warm alcohol. Put one tube of extracted chlorophyll in bright light and another in a dark place. Examine the tubes after two or three days and explain your results.

9. Pick a vigorous leaf from a plant as you come to school in the morning (plantain, which grows in most lawns, is good). Extract the chlorophyll with alcohol and test the leaf for the presence of starch with iodine. In the late afternoon, take another leaf from the same plant. Repeat the test and explain the results. This experiment must be performed on a sunny day.

10. Wet two pieces of muslin, burlap, or other cloth about one foot wide and three feet long. Select 100 seeds of the same kind. Lay them out in rows, spaced well apart, on one piece of cloth. When the seeds are arranged, lay the other piece of cloth over them. Then, roll the two pieces loosely. This is a "rag doll tester" used in viability tests. Keep the cloth roll moistened for several days. When the seeds have germinated, unroll the cloths and count the number of seeds which have sprouted. Since we used 100 seeds, the number which sprout will be the percentage of viability.

More About Biology

Asch, John. THE STORY OF PLANTS. G. P. Putnam's Sons, New York. 1949

Buff, Mary. BIG TREE. The Viking Press, Inc., New York. 1946

Collingwood, G. H. KNOWING YOUR TREES. The American Forestry Association, Washington, D.C. 1947

Dickinson, Alice. THE FIRST BOOK OF PLANTS. E. Franklin Watts, Inc., New York. 1953

Jacques, H. E. PLANT FAMILIES AND HOW TO KNOW THEM. Wm. C. Brown Co., Dubuque. 1948

Jensen, Lloyd B. MAN'S FOOD. Garrard Press, Champaign, Ill. 1953

Kieran, John. AN INTRODUCTION TO

TREES. Hanover House, Garden City, New York. 1954

Kumlien, L. L. THE FRIENDLY EVER-GREENS. Rev. Ed., Rinehart and Co., Inc., New York. 1954

Lane, Ferdinand C. THE STORY OF TREES. Doubleday and Co., Inc., Garden City, New York. 1952

Lucas, Jeanette May. FIRST THE FLOWER AND THEN THE FRUIT. J. B. Lippincott Co., Philadelphia. 1942

Lucas, Jeanette May. INDIAN HARVEST: WILD FOOD PLANTS OF AMERICA. J. B. Lippincott Co., Philadelphia. 1945

Peattie, Donald Culross. A NATURAL HISTORY OF TREES OF EASTERN AND CENTRAL NORTH AMERICA. Houghton Mifflin Co., Boston. 1950

Peattie, Donald Culross. A NATURAL HISTORY OF WESTERN TREES. Houghton Mifflin Co., Boston. 1953

Quinn, Vernon. STORIES AND LEGENDS OF GARDEN FLOWERS. Frederick A. Stokes Co., New York. 1939

Robbins, Wilfred William and Ramaley, Francis. PLANTS USEFUL TO MAN. 2nd Ed. P. Blakiston's Sons and Co., Philadelphia. 1937

Schery, Robert W. PLANTS FOR MAN. Prentice-Hall, Inc., New York. 1952

Sherman, Henry Clapp. FOOD PRODUCTS. 4th Ed. The Macmillan Co., New York. 1948

Zim, Herbert Spencer. FLOWERS; A GUIDE TO THE FAMILIAR AMERICAN WILDFLOWERS. Simon and Schuster, Inc., New York. 1950

Zim, Herbert S. and Martin, Alexander C. TREES: A GUIDE TO FAMILIAR AMERICAN TREES. Simon and Schuster, Inc., New York. 1952

UNIT 4

Flowerless Plants

Having found out how complex plants can be, you will soon discover how simple some can be. A single bacterium one ten-thousandth of an inch or less in diameter is a complete plant. Other lowly plants live as long threadlike strands of cells without any organs such as roots, stems, or leaves.

The flowerless plants include the ferns and their relatives, mosses and liverworts, and the vast number of plants we class as algae and fungi.

In the study of flowerless plants, you will deal with a wide variety of plant bodies, some large and some small, and some simple and others complex. But size and complexity are no indicators of importance to us. Bacteria, perhaps the lowliest of all plants, can invade our bodies and cause disease, and destroy our food supplies. Yet, certain forms are essential to soil fertility, food processing, and industrial processes.

This Unit will acquaint you with plant life from bacteria to ferns.

CHAPTER 17

Algae—the Simplest Green Plants

It is hard to imagine a plant without flowers, yet that is the type to which we now turn our attention in this Unit. The flowerless plants are simple organisms although they are not always small. There seems little doubt that some of them were the first living things on the earth.

The first phylum of the three which we shall discuss in this Unit is called *Thallophyta* (*thal*-oh-fyta). It consists of two main divisions, the *algae* (*al*-jee), [sing. alga (*al*-gah)], those which possess chlorophyll, and the *fungi* (*fun*-jye), [sing. fungus (*fun*-gus)], which lack this green substance and are therefore unable to make their own food.

The algae make up the first large group in the Thallophyta. They lack roots, stems, and leaves but unlike the fungi, they all have chlorophyll. Algae vary tremendously in size. Some are microscopic. Others, like the giant kelps, may be several hundred feet long. Yet, even so large a plant as this is really just a mass of similar cells. It lives no more efficiently than an alga only a fraction of its size.

Many scientists are anxiously searching for a more abundant source of food to feed the growing population of the world. Only recently, however, has man been able to harvest in commercial quantities a crop which has supported for ages almost all life in the oceans and streams. The name of this possible new food supply for mankind is the *algae*.

Classification of algae. If you have ever noticed the shores of ponds, lakes, and smaller bodies of water such as roadside ditches, you have undoubtedly seen the greenish, gray, or yellow-brown scum which often occurs on the surface. If you have tried to pick it up, you know that it is slimy, stringy, or sometimes tough. This scum may include many different kinds of algae. Other green algae cover the rocks in a rapids with green, hairlike tufts or give an entire stagnant body of water a deep green color, due to the presence of literally millions of tiny algal cells. The Red Sea is so named because of the color given it by algae which is found

growing there at certain seasonal times of the year.

Biologists recognize about 30,000 different species of algae. All of them are primarily classified on the basis of their color. In many cases, they contain *pigments* in addition to chlorophyll. This fact makes it easy to group them into various classes as the table on page 219 shows.

Characteristics of algae. The cells of algae contain *chlorophyll* and can therefore manufacture food by photosynthesis just as flowering plants do. They carry on all the life processes and in every way are independent organisms. They absorb the water and car-

SOME GROUPS OF ALGAE

1. **Cyanophyceae** (sy-an-oh-*fy*-sih-ee).   Blue-green.
Examples: *Nostoc* and *Oscillatoria*.   (Fresh-water and salt-water.)
2. **Chlorophyceae** (klor-oh-*fy*-sih-ee).   Green.
Examples: *Protococcus, Spirogyra, Ulothrix, Zygnema, Vaucheria, Hydrodictyon, Oedogonium, Cladophora,* desmids.   (Fresh-water, salt-water, and land.)
3. **Chrysophyceae** (kry-soh-*fy*-sih-ee).   Golden-brown.
Example: diatoms. (Fresh-water and salt-water.)
4. **Phaeophyceae** (fay-oh-*fy*-sih-ee).   Brown.
Examples: *Fucus* and kelps.   (Salt-water.)
5. **Rhodophyceae** (roh-doh-*fy*-sih-ee).   Red.   (Mostly salt-water.)

bon dioxide necessary for photosynthesis either from the air or the fresh or salt water in which they live.   The light energy is likewise absorbed by their cells from the sun's rays, since they live in regions where these penetrate.

Fission, or simple splitting of a cell into two parts, is the one method of reproduction of certain of these primitive plants.

Other forms produce *eggs* and *sperms* which unite to form a fertilized egg or *zygote*.   Many types likewise produce **spores** which are specialized reproductive cells.   Spores are capable of growing into a new plant directly without uniting with another cell, as in the case of eggs and sperms.   Some spores are provided with whiplike appendages which enable them to swim about for a considerable time before coming to rest and growing into a new plant.   Other spores surround themselves with a thick wall.   When the pond or other body of water dries up during a hot summer, they become dormant, resting over the unfavorable period.

Algae reproduce by one or more of these methods.   All carry on cell division, but many form eggs and sperms under certain conditions and, at other times, reproduce by means of spores.

Fig. 17-1.   Algae, once only a source of food for fish and other water animals, have now become edible for humans as well.   Here are some candies and cookies made from certain algae.

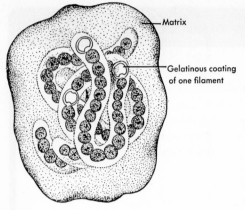

Fig. 17-2. If you examine *Nostoc* under a microscope, you will see that the cells are arranged in colonies in the form of a string of beads. The colony is held together by a slimy mass of gelatinous material called a matrix.

We call reproduction by spores **asexual,** since no union of eggs and sperms is involved. *Sexual reproduction* by sperms and eggs, on the other hand, involves the union of two cells. Some of the more advanced forms reproduce by both methods. One stage alternates or leads into the next.

Many algae spend their entire lives as solitary cells. Each time a cell divides, the two cells separate into two *one-celled organisms.* Others live in **colonies,** consisting of two or more cells attached to each other. When attached to each other, however, each cell in the colony actually leads an independent life. They don't depend on one another as do the cells of a root or leaf of a higher plant. The pond scum which you pick up out of the water consists of thousands of colonies of individual one-celled algae. Some of these colonies comprise long threadlike groups called **filaments.** Others consist of globular or spherical colonies comprising thousands of individual algal cells surrounded by a jellylike substance which protects them

from heat, cold, and other unfavorable climatic conditions. This jellylike substance is characteristic of many of the algae, both fresh- and salt-water forms. It accounts for the slimy texture which makes them hard to grasp in the water.

Blue-green algae. These are all one-celled plants and usually exist in colonies. Some are in filaments, while others consist of masses of a slimy material in which the cells are embedded. Blue-green algae live in almost every roadside ditch, pond, and stream. Together with the viruses and bacteria they are supposed to be the most primitive of plants. Perhaps they are the descendants of the earliest forms of life.

These blue-green algae are one constant problem in drinking water and swimming pools. Their presence often gives water a foul odor, characteristic of stagnant streams during the summer months. For these reasons, biologists very carefully check the content of blue-green algae in sources of water for drinking and swimming.

Nostoc, a typical blue-green alga. Of the common blue-green algae, one of the most curious is *Nostoc* (*nosstock*). You'll find it in mud and sand, usually just at the point where the ripples from the pond or lake hit the shoreline. It looks much like a mass of greenish or blackish jelly. Actually, the jellylike substance is secreted by thousands of *Nostoc* cells, arranged in filamentous colonies (see Fig. 17-2). Try crushing a portion of one of these gelatinous masses on a clean glass slide and examine it under the microscope. The plants will look like small, round cells, arranged like a string of beads. Each cell is a complete plant which manufactures its own food and carries on all the life processes.

Nostoc reproduces by *fission.* When a cell divides, it splits into two equal parts each of which becomes a new plant. These two cells may divide again into two more cells each. The chain then becomes longer and longer.

Nostoc produces no spores. As in all the blue-greens, it has no organized nucleus in the cell. The chlorophyll is scattered throughout the cytoplasm rather than being in chloroplasts.

All blue-green algae are simple, and in many respects they resemble *Nostoc*. One blue-green, called *Oscillatoria* (os-sill-ah-*tor*-ee-ah), is composed of narrow disk-shaped cells arranged end to end in a filament (see Fig. 17-3). Filaments of *Oscillatoria* sway back and forth in the water. Recently, scientists have discovered the ability of *Oscillatoria* to remove oily wastes from water around refineries.

Green algae. Green algae vary from one-celled forms to species composed of many cells. Some grow in salt water, but the great majority occur in fresh water. Some are on land, especially on rocks and tree trunks. Some, to the wonder of the scientists, live in extremely high temperatures.

The cells of green algae show much advance over the simple cells of blue-greens. Each has an organized nucleus

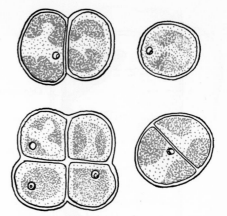

Fig. 17-4. The round cells of the green alga, *Protococcus*, may occur singly or in colonies of two or four.

and one or more chloroplasts containing chlorophyll. They range in color from bright grass-green to yellowish-green.

Protococcus, a common green alga. *Protococcus* (pro-toh-*cock*-us) is one of the commonest green algae. You all know it, although you may not have realized that it is an alga. It grows on trunks of trees. During dry weather you seldom see it, but in wet weather it is very much in evidence. Usually, it is common on the north side of tree trunks because that side is more sheltered from the sun.

The plant body (see Fig. 17-4) is composed of a single round or oval cell. Each cell contains a nucleus and one large chloroplast. *Protococcus* cells live in colonies like *Nostoc,* but are not embedded in a jellylike secretion. Nor are the colonies in chains, but comprise two, four, or six cells which are grouped together in small cubes, often two cells on the top and two on the bottom. These colonies are formed as a result of ordinary cell division.

Protococcus cells are so tiny that millions are required to cover a few square inches of bark. They may be carried from tree to tree by birds and by the

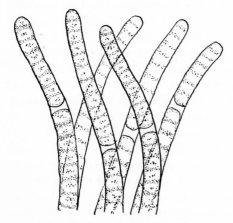

Fig. 17-3. *Oscillatoria,* another blue-green alga, has narrow, disk-shaped cells.

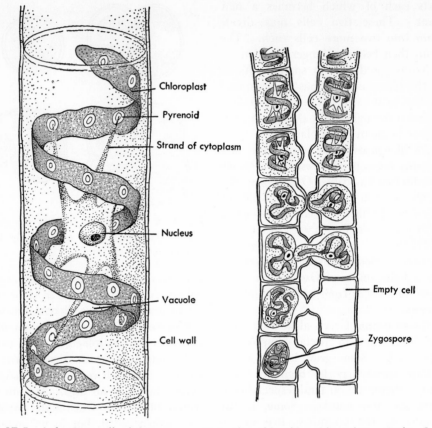

Fig. 17-5. Left: One cell of *Spirogyra*. Note the ribbonlike chloroplast. Right: Conjugation in *Spirogyra*. The filaments are lined up parallel with each other and you can see the various stages of this process of reproduction.

wind during dry weather. Since *Protococcus* is a green plant, it requires no nourishment from the tree.

Spirogyra, a filamentous green alga. *Spirogyra* (spy-ro-*jy*-rah) is one of the many threadlike or filamentous green algae you find in fresh water. These masses of green threads cover large areas during the spring and fall and make the water in which they grow appear to be a brilliant green. The filaments are unbranched and range from a few inches to a foot or so long. They are slimy because of a thin jellylike sheath which coats each strand. Under a microscope, a thread of *Spirogyra* looks like a series of transparent cells, arranged end to end like tank cars in a train. (See Fig. 17-5.)

Each cell has one or more spiral bands arranged like a ribbon. This is the *chloroplast*, containing chlorophyll. In the center of each cell is a large nucleus suspended in a vacuole by strands of cytoplasm which radiate to the cell walls. On the ribbonlike chloroplasts are small protein bodies surrounded by a layer of starch, called **pyrenoids** (py-ree-noids). Like other green algae, *Spirogyra* makes its own food by photosynthesis. The excess oxygen, released in the process, causes the mass of green

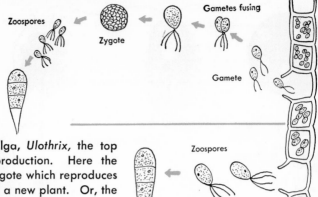

Fig. 17-6. In this green alga, *Ulothrix*, the top drawing shows sexual reproduction. Here the gametes fuse and form a zygote which reproduces zoospores. These grow into a new plant. Or, the parent plant may reproduce asexually by forming zoospores which grow into a new plant (bottom drawing).

threads to float to the surface. You can see such floating masses during the afternoon on a bright day. When photosynthesis stops during the night, oxygen gradually escapes from the cells, causing the threads to settle back into the water.

Reproduction of Spirogyra. *Spirogyra* reproduces in two ways, and is therefore more complex than either *Nostoc* or *Protococcus*. The first, and most common method, is by ordinary cell division. Its cells divide crosswise, and in doing so add to the length of the filament. A *Spirogyra* filament seldom becomes more than a foot long because water currents, moving fish, and other outside forces continually break it into small pieces. This does no harm to the plant because each cell lives independently and can reproduce the filament.

The most curious method of reproduction occurs when weather conditions are unfavorable for normal growth. It is called **conjugation** (kon-ju-*gay*-shun) and may be seen in material collected during the hot summer days when the pond or stream may dry up. Conjugation also occurs in the autumn when the growing season ends.

Conjugation involves two filaments of *Spirogyra*. The filaments line up parallel to each other and a small knob grows out from each cell on its inner side, as shown in Fig. 17-5. Each knob grows until it touches the knob of the cell across from it in the parallel filament. A ladderlike structure results because the knobs of the cells in one filament touch those directly across from them in the other filament. Then the tips of the knobs dissolve and form a passageway between the two cells. Through this passageway the contents of one cell flow into the other cell. The materials of the two cells unite and form an oval mass of protoplasm which quickly becomes surrounded by a thick, heavy wall. This is called a **zygospore** (*zy*-go-spore).

When conjugation is completed, one of the two parallel filaments contains only empty cells while the other contains only zygospores. The thick wall surrounding these spores enables them to withstand severe weather conditions such as excessive heat, dryness, and freezing. Such conditions would soon kill ordinary filaments of *Spirogyra*.

The zygospores fall to the bottom of the stream or pond as soon as the cell

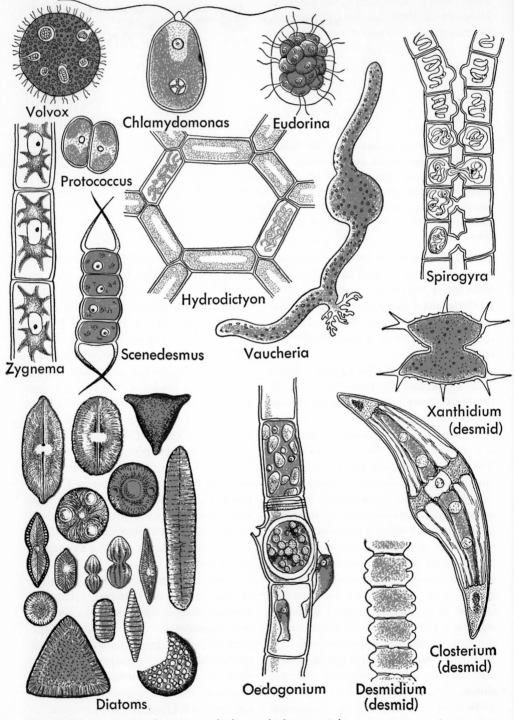

Volvox

Chlamydomonas

Eudorina

Spirogyra

Protococcus

Hydrodictyon

Zygnema

Scenedesmus

Vaucheria

Xanthidium
(desmid)

Diatoms

Oedogonium

Desmidium
(desmid)

Closterium
(desmid)

Fig. 17-7. Here are a few types of algae which you might see among specimens you bring to class.

walls which hold them disintegrate. They remain there for long periods until favorable environment conditions appear. Then, each grows into a new *Spirogyra* cell which, by the usual process of cell division, develops into a new filament. The more complicated life history of *Ulothrix* is diagramed in Fig. 17-6 on page 223.

Flagellates. If you examine many cultures of green algae, you're almost sure to find certain one-celled forms which will immediately attract your attention. Among these will be flagellates which have one or more slender whips of protoplasm. By means of these little whips they propel themselves through the water. Usually the whip of flagellum is invisible, but you can see the tiny green cells moving about rapidly. The term *flagellate* is commonly used to include a variety of these free-swimming algae. It is not the name of any particular group or kind of algae. Many flagellates are green algae, while others can be considered as animals and will be studied later.

Diatoms are common in both fresh and salt water. They are one-celled, free-floating algae varying from rectangular, round, triangular, or oval to spindle-shaped or boat-shaped forms. They are sometimes green but more often golden brown. They all contain chlorophyll in their cells. The products of their photosynthesis are chiefly oils, instead of carbohydrates. One authority believes that they account for 90% of all the photosynthesis occuring in salt water plants. Their walls contain small amounts of *silicon* and *manganese*. The wall is in two sections or valves, one fitting over the other like the top and bottom of a pillbox.

The shells of diatoms are pretty not only because of their shapes, but also because of the many fine lines which

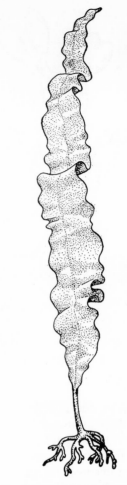

Fig. 17-8. Brown algae include the largest as well as many small algae. Here is one of the kelps, brown algae which are attached to rocks near shore.

form intricate and beautiful designs on their walls (see Fig. 17-7). When they die, they fall to the bottom of the pond, stream, or ocean and may form deposits of *diatomaceous* (dy-ah-tom-*ay*-shus) *earth*. In California and other parts of the world, these deposits are thick. They are mined and sold as ingredients in various scouring powders, or used in various commercial processes.

Red and brown algae. These are mostly salt-water forms, commonly

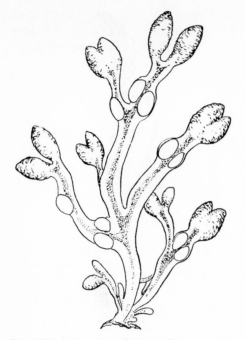

Fig. 17-9. *Fucus* is a brown alga growing on rocks at the water line along the Atlantic Coast.

known as seaweeds. They vary from small threadlike forms, such as some of the red algae, to the giant species of the Pacific Ocean kelps. They usually live in shallow water near the shore, where light can reach them but some of the reds live in deeper water. These red algae grow attached to solid objects on the bottom or may grow in mud or sand. Because they vary so much as to structure and reproduction, and are often difficult to get, we cannot study any one type. A brown alga, called *Fucus,* is a favorite for study because it is so common along a seacoast. (See Fig. 17-9.) You may find it, however, as the packing around oysters, lobsters, and other seafoods which are shipped from the coast to your town.

Economic importance of the algae. The algae are the chief source for much of the animal life in environments where they occur. Although many small fish live entirely on algae, one large species of mammals, a whale, also exists primarily on them. Too, algae are a good source of the oxygen in the water, and that is necessary for aquatic life.

The use of marine algae as soil fertilizers has long been known. If seaweeds are mixed with the soil, they not only add organic matter to it but also replenish the salts which land-growing plants have removed. Thus algae will return iodine to the soil. Iodine is a chemical element necessary for animal well-being.

While useful in certain parts of the world in the preparation of soups, gelatins, and other foods, we are more likely to find algae as a part of our ice cream. They are added to keep it smooth. They are used as a stabilizer in chocolate milk, or as a thickener in salad dressings. *Agar-agar* is produced from algae in the Indian Ocean and is used in large quantities in hospitals and laboratories as a base for culture medium for bacteria. The list of other industrial uses of algal preparations ranges from cosmetics to leather-finishing.

An interesting new discovery is the mass-culture of algae in plastic tubes or tanks. By continually pumping the algae solution and supplying it with all the best conditions for photosynthesis, such as light, water, and carbon dioxide, the algae multiply rapidly. Periodically, some algae are strained out, dried, and then made ready for use as flour in baking or as a thickening in foods such as soup.

Some algae can do harm. They may become poisonous when they die, and thus pollute the water. This not only makes the water unfit for humans, but also for fish and other water life. Great care is taken in fish hatcheries to prevent this "weediness." A very weak solution of copper sulfate put in the water will kill blue-green algae. The treatment, however, is not recommended for home aquaria because there is considerable danger of overdosing.

Fig. 17-10.   This red alga is about its actual size.   As you see it in sea water, the dainty filaments look like bits of dark red lace.

In Conclusion

Algae belong to the phylum Thallophyta and are the simplest green plants. Diatoms constitute a smaller group, while flagellates are examples of several groups which swim about by flagella.

Algae carry on cell division.   This results in new individuals in the case of one-celled forms, and enlargement of the colonies in those forms which grow attached to each other.   Certain algae reproduce by conjugation.   Others form spores which are able to withstand severe environmental conditions.

Algae are economically important, not only as plants which contaminate water, but also as sources of fertilizer, food for fish, and as a possible major source of food for humans. From the lowly algae which make their own food, we turn next to plants which depend on other organisms for their food. The bacteria will occupy our attention for a while and we will see how they are both harmful and helpful to man.

Questions for Review

1. (a) What are the chief classes of algae? (b) Give an example of each.

2. Why do we class all the algae as independent plants?

3. What is the essential difference between sexual reproduction and asexual reproduction?

4. Of what economic importance are the blue-green algae?

5. In what respect is *Protococcus* an exception to the usual rule among green algae?

6. Describe a typical filament of *Spirogyra*.

7. (a) Describe conjugation in *Spirogyra*. (b) Is it a type of sexual reproduction?

8. In what ways are some of the green algae different from each other?

9. What is distinctive about the structure of diatoms?

10. In what ways are the flagellates different from other algae?

11. Describe the typical habitat of red and brown algae.

12. In what ways are the algae important to man?

13. How is diatomaceous earth formed and for what is it used?

Biologically Speaking

algae	egg	pigment
asexual reproduction	filament	pyrenoid
colony	fission	sexual reproduction
conjugation	flagellate	sperms
diatom	flagellum	zygospore
diatomaceous earth	matrix	zygote

Applying Facts and Principles

1. There are some obstacles to the full-scale production of algae for human food. Economically, what are they in their production and in their use as food?

2. Why do you suppose there is disagreement as to the classification of the flagellates?

3. How can such a flexible plant as the brown algae, *Fucus,* grow to a huge size and still exist close to the surface of the water?

4. (a) Why is copper sulfate ineffective when used in salt-water swimming pools? (b) Why is it so effective in fresh-water?

CHAPTER 18

Bacteria—Beneficial and Harmful Plants

When bacteria were first discovered, they were thought to be extremely small animals. Later, however, they were found to be members of the plant kingdom and are usually classed with the fungi. *Bacteria* are simple organisms consisting of one tiny cell. Each cell is composed of a thin cell wall enclosing a mass of living protoplasm.

Bacteria range in size from about one ten-thousandth to one fifty-thousandth of an inch in diameter, barely visible under the high power of a standard microscope. Special microscopes providing a magnification of at least one thousand diameters are necessary for the study of most forms.

Bacteria are found almost everywhere. They live in the air, in water, in food, in the soil, and in the bodies of plants and animals. They are by far the most widespread form of life. It is fortunate that most of the bacteria are harmless, for we would have little chance to escape them. In fact, perhaps one of our chief problems in life is to learn how to live *with* bacteria.

The importance of bacteria. We have heard so much about disease-producing bacteria that we are inclined to think of all of them as being harmful organisms. Fortunately, however, this is not the case. In fact, many kinds of bacteria are absolutely necessary to our lives. According to their importance, we can classify bacteria in three general groups as follows: (1) harmless bacteria; (2) beneficial bacteria; and (3) bacteria which produce disease.

The *harmless bacteria* compose by far the largest group. They live in the air, in water, and even in our bodies and yet do no particular damage. The second group, the *beneficial bacteria,* also live all round us. They carry on activities which are of a definite value and, in some cases, necessary to our lives. Only a small number of organisms are *disease-producing,* or *pathogenic* (path-oh-*jen*-

ick). These invade the bodies of plants, animals, and man with serious effects. Their activities cause disease and sometimes death. We shall study them in detail in Unit 8.

While a few bacteria live on inorganic compounds in springs and streams, most are dependent organisms and need an organic host. The parasitic forms invade a living host, and may or may not cause disease. For instance, some bacteria live in the intestinal tract and are necessary for its proper functioning.

Many other bacteria live as *saprophytes* on nonliving organic matter. They may be beneficial or harmful, depending on the kind of substance on which they live and on the nature of their activities.

Forms of bacteria. While they vary considerably in size, we can classify the thousands of forms known to science in

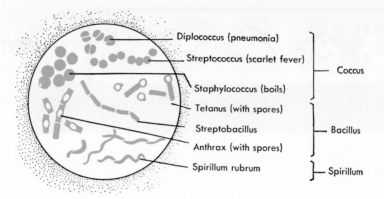

Fig. 18-1. This diagram shows the typical shapes of three important groups of bacteria.

three relatively simple groups. (See Fig. 18-1.) These groups are based entirely on the individual shapes of the cells as follows: (1) *coccus* forms — round; (2) *bacillus* forms — oblong or rod-shaped; and (3) *spirillum* forms — spiral-shaped and curved.

Many *coccus* and *bacillus* forms form clusters or colonies of cells which are as characteristic as the shape of the individual cells. For example, many coccus bacteria live in pairs. The bacteriologist can look for this characteristic in determining the presence of pneumonia organisms in sputum. Other coccus bacteria form clusters or chains resembling a string of beads. Bacillus, or rod-shaped bacteria, may likewise exist in colonies. The most common bacillus grouping is in chains, resembling a string of sausages. These groups of bacteria are classified as follows:

1. Diplococcus (*dip*-loh-cock-us) — pairs of round cells, or two-celled filaments.

2. Staphylococcus (*staff*-ee-loh-cock-us) — clusters of round cells.

3. Streptococcus (*strep*-toh-cock-us) — strings or chains of round cells.

4. Streptobacillus (*strep*-toh-bass-*sill*-us) — strings or chains of rod-shaped cells.

The shape and microscopic arrangement of cells help us to classify bacteria. But you cannot ever identify any bacterium solely by its shape. *Streptococcus,* for example, is a form of round-celled bacteria with the cells attached in chains. To many people, the term *streptococcus* refers to blood poisoning or to a severe throat infection. True, both of these diseases are caused by a streptococcus form. But other organisms of the streptococcus type cause milk to sour and eggs to rot. Similarly, a rod form may cause typhoid, another may produce diphtheria, while others live in the soil and are essential to soil fertility.

Structure of bacteria. Bacteria are single cells with protoplasts which have a simple appearance. They have nuclear material but seldom can you see a well-defined nucleus. The wall of a bacterium is important in its life activities. This is because the wall determines the method of movement of the bacterium, its ability to stick to its host cell, and to some extent its ability to withstand virus enemies.

Many of the rod and spiral forms can move about by means of a long outgrowth of the cell called a **flagellum** (fla-*jel*-um). Some have a single flagel-

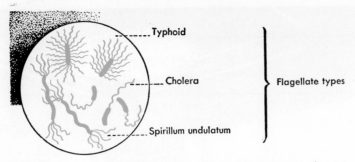

Typhoid

Cholera

} Flagellate types

Spirillum undulatum

Fig. 18-2. Many bacteria, such as these above, are able to move about in liquids by means of slender threads of protoplasm called flagella.

lum at the end of the cell, while others have numerous flagella extending over the cell wall. The flagella move back and forth in a liquid environment and thus propel the bacteria like tiny oars.

Multiplication of bacteria. Bacteria multiply by dividing. They accomplish this apparent mathematical impossibility by the simple method of cell division. When a cell reaches maturity, it merely separates into two cells by forming a wall through the middle. Since a complete organism consists of only one cell, the division of a cell into two parts results in two organisms. Neither cell would be considered the parent cell. Both are young, small, and capable of further enlargement.

One of the most amazing things about bacterial reproduction is the rate at which it may occur. Under ideal conditions, a cell may reach maturity and divide every 20 minutes. This may not seem alarming until you calculate the results. When you consider that a single bacterium under these ideal growth conditions would form a mass weighing 7,000 tons in three days, bacterial multiplication becomes much more significant.

Such rapid increase accounts for the fact that an invisible bacterium growing on a source of food can produce a large, visible colony in a day or two.

If a portion of the colony is examined under the microscope, you'll see literally billions of bacteria. Fortunately, this rate of division of bacterial cells continues for only a limited time. As the mass of cells becomes larger and larger, the bacteria themselves begin to interfere with each other. Poisonous waste products accumulate, and food supplies often fail to reach many cells in the mass. As a result, cell division ceases and the bacteria become inactive. Over a three-day period, growth is extremely rapid during the first day, much reduced during the second day, and usually ceases during the third.

Spore formation in the bacteria. Many kinds of bacteria, especially the bacillus or rod-shaped types, may change their appearance to protect themselves during unfavorable periods. Each cell may draw its content into a spherical mass which becomes surrounded with a thick protective wall. This special body is called a **spore.** Since a single cell produces only one spore, the total number of bacteria is not increased. Spore formation is not a method of reproduction in the case of bacteria.

Bacterial spores can endure almost unbelievable conditions. They may dry out completely and remain in a dormant condition for years. During the spore stage they may be carried far and

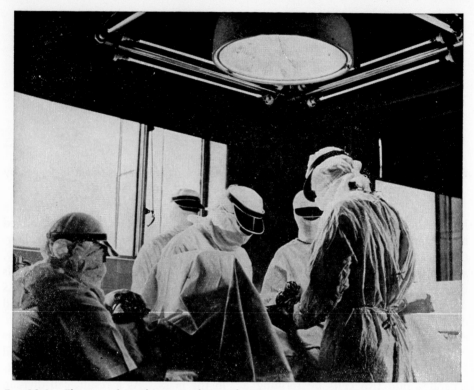

Fig. 18-3. The use of sterilamps in this modern operating room of a large hospital retards the growth of bacteria.

wide by various means. Some of these spores even resist boiling water. But when they are subjected to live steam under 15 pound pressure for 15 or 20 minutes, they invariably die. Steam sterilizers are the most effective way of getting rid of them.

When a spore falls on a suitable host, the resting period ends, and a new cell develops. By rapid division, the new host may soon support tremendous numbers of bacteria, all having come from the single spore. Spore-forming bacteria are especially dangerous in a hospital. Tetanus, (see Fig. 18-1), more commonly known as lockjaw, is caused by a spore-forming bacillus organism.

Conditions for growth. *Warmth* is essential to bacterial activity although coldness does not destroy the cells. It merely causes them to cease activity and enter a dormant period. While bacteria vary in their heat requirements, most pathogenic forms grow best at a temperature of 98.6° F. (37° C.), or ordinary body temperature. *Moisture* is a second growth requirement for bacteria. Prolonged dryness will not kill most bacteria, but like low temperatures, it may produce a period of dormancy.

Darkness is an extremely essential requirement in the growth of bacteria. Exposure to light retards growth considerably and sunlight, containing ultraviolet rays, kills many forms. Sunlight does not, however, injure spores. Cold storage and packaging of foods in dehydrated (water removed) form are examples of using low temperatures and dryness for preservation.

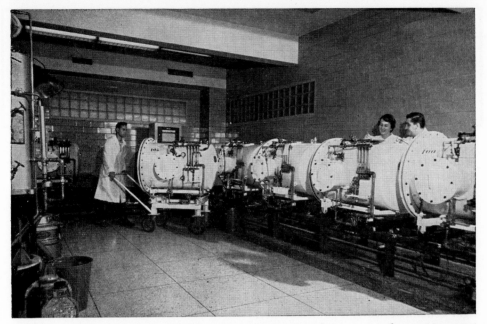

Fig. 18-4. This scene is taken at Notre Dame University where a germ-free environment is kept for all experimental animals. Thus bacterial contamination is prevented in these germ-free cages.

Bacteria have many fascinating ways of obtaining their food. Most bacteria must live on organic compounds, either from living or nonliving material. Their ability to live on a variety of organic materials, useless to so many other forms of life, is due to secretion by bacteria of powerful substances called *enzymes*. The action of these enzymes kills other living matter and it breaks up dead organic matter. It is one reason for the importance of bacteria to all other forms of life. The waste products which bacteria secrete also help to produce the harmful as well as the beneficial work of the bacteria.

Some forms of bacteria, however, are unusual in the fungus world. These forms do not depend on living organisms or organic matter. They are capable of changing inorganic compounds into living matter and obtaining energy from them. The iron, sulfur, and ni- trogen bacteria in this group obtain their food and energy from simple compounds without any outside energy source such as sunlight. Deposits of iron ore are thought to represent the work of countless iron-fixing bacteria over many, many years. The results of this bacterial action can be seen in many streams with an orange scum on the rocks. Many people know this indicates the presence of iron in the water.

Bacteria in relation to air. Oxygen is another important factor controlling the growth and activity of bacteria. Some forms require oxygen from the atmosphere for their activity and can't grow in air-tight places. Bacteria of this type are **aerobic** (air-*robe*-ick). Other forms are just the opposite and can't grow in free oxygen. These **an- aerobic** (an-air-*robe*-ick) bacteria get oxygen as a result of certain chemical reactions they produce on the host.

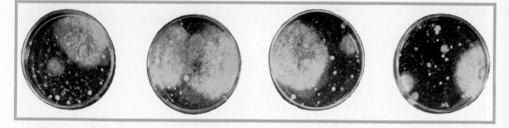

Fig. 18-5. These Petri dishes show exposures to bacteria in the air of a cow barn. They were made without the use of sterilamps and indicate contamination of the air by floating bacteria.

Many types of anaerobic bacteria can live in the air only as spores. While less numerous than aerobic forms, anaerobic bacteria are abundant in the soil and in decaying organic matter. They occasionally become active in food products which have been packed in airtight containers without sufficient sterilization during processing. The tetanus organism is a good example of an anaerobe which causes human disease.

Laboratory culture of bacteria. While bacteria exist nearly everywhere, they are grown in the laboratory under carefully controlled conditions.

Growth of bacteria in artificially prepared cultures is essential not only to provide organisms for study, but also as a means of identifying them. While useful, the size, shape, and other structural characteristics are not sufficient to classify a form of bacterium. The bacteriologist must grow the organism in question in various kinds of cultures and observe its effect on a culture medium before he can make a positive identification.

This culture medium should provide the food substance from which the organisms obtain nourishment. It may be gelatinous materials, such as *agar-agar* (*ah*-gar-*ah*-gar), or gelatin to which protein, sugars, and other nutrients have been added. Broths and sugar solutions, or solid substances of various sorts,

are also used. Certain disease bacteria require the addition of blood to the medium.

Cultures are frequently prepared in shallow glass dishes called *Petri* (*pee-tree*) *dishes* or in culture tubes plugged with cotton. After the medium has been added to the container, it is *sterilized* to destroy any bacteria which may have entered during preparation. The cultures are then handled carefully to prevent exposure of the sterile media to outside sources of bacteria.

The next step in the culturing process is called **inoculation** (in-nock-ku-*lay*-shun). It consists of the addition of bacteria from a known source to the sterile medium. Bacteria may be added by touching an object to the medium, adding a small quantity of liquid containing bacteria, or by transferring organisms from another source to the culture by means of a sterile inoculating needle.

After inoculation, the bacteria which have been added are invisible in the culture. But after two or three days of **incubation,** during which the organisms are provided with warmth, moisture, and darkness, the individual cells have multiplied to form millions. The bacteria are now visible in colonies. The bacteriologist notes carefully the shape, size, and color of these colonies in each kind of culture he uses. Such items are important factors in the identification of bacteria. From the colonies, he makes *smears* by spreading a thin film of bacteria on a clean glass slide. After thorough drying and flaming to kill the organisms, a stain is added to make the bacteria more visible under the microscope. If an examination of living cells is necessary, they may be added to a small drop of sterile water.

Beneficial activities of bacteria. When we consider the beneficial activities of some bacteria, we quickly change our impressions of at least a few of them. The study of the beneficial forms is an extensive one. However, the following are some of the ways in which bacteria are useful: (1) bacteria in the food industry; (2) bacteria in other industries; and (3) bacteria in the soil.

Bacteria in the food industry. We may or may not consider the souring of milk as a beneficial activity. But this process is essential to the dairy industry in making butter and cheese. In the case of cheese-making, bacteria are necessary in acid formation and in the coagulation of milk protein from which the cheese is made. Certain kinds of aged or ripened cheeses, such as Swiss, Limburger, and Liederkranz, owe their distinctive flavors to bacterial action during the ripening period. Milk sours as a result of the activity of several kinds of organisms which digest the milk sugar (*lactose*) and form *lactic acid*.

Another group of souring or fermenting bacteria lives in fruit juices, where they occur associated with *yeasts*. Yeast cells break down the sugar in the fruit juice and form alcohol, after which acetic acid bacteria convert the alcohol into vinegar. Colonies of these beneficial bacteria grow in vinegar jars, are called "mother of vinegar."

Bacteria in other industries. The finest grade of linen fibers comes from flax plants. The plants are tied in bun-

dles and put in water. Bacteria enter the stems and gradually destroy the stem tissues. This action, called **retting,** loosens the phloem fibers from the other tissues. These are then removed and used to make linen threads.

The tobacco industry uses bacterial action in the curing process. Stalks and leaves of the tobacco plant are harvested and hung in special curing barns where sweating occurs at cool temperatures. Bacteria invade the moist leaves and cause fermentation, resulting in special flavors.

The tanning industry, likewise, makes use of bacteria in the processing of leather and animal hides. During tanning, bacteria attack the hides and make them pliable.

Fig. 18-6. Note the contrast between the corn on the left and that on the right. The corn on the left was planted following a four-year growth of Lespedeza (a legume plant) on the soil. That on the right was planted to row crops of cotton and corn, for the same period.

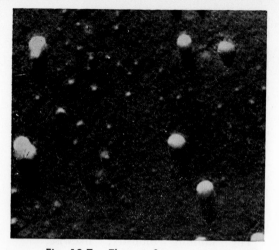

Fig. 18-7. These influenza virus particles can be seen with the help of an electron microscope.

In the dairy industry, bacteria help to produce **ensilage** (*en*-si-lij), a fermented fodder fed to cattle. A special type of structure called a *silo* (*sy*-lo) is filled with shredded corn stalks and leaves which are fermented by souring bacteria. Fermenting not only preserves the ensilage but adds acid, which is of the greatest value in the diet of dairy cattle.

Bacteria in the soil. Without soil bacteria, few plants could get their necessary soil elements. These bacteria form a vital link in the constructive and destructive processes which constitute the chemical cycles of living things. You learned that plants remove mineral compounds containing nitrogen, phosphorus, potassium, and sulfur from the soil and use them in the formation of complex organic compounds. Thus, these essential soil materials are temporarily " lost " from the soil, but will be replaced on the death of the organism. Before these elements can be used again, the complex compounds composing the organism must be returned to simpler forms. Undecomposed plant and animal remains are not usable by other plants. Therefore, before these elements can be used again, the compounds of which the organism was composed must be returned to simpler forms. Review pages 69–71 where we discussed the nitrogen cycle.

Farmers make use of the activity of these soil bacteria in the practice of *crop rotation*. After growing crops of corn, wheat, or other cereals for several years, the soil usually becomes deficient in nitrates. Accordingly, clover, alfalfa, lespedeza, or some other legume crop is grown to introduce nitrogen-fixing bacteria into the soil. During a single season, these organisms may produce enough nitrates to supply other crops for several years. The clover or alfalfa is usually plowed under and increases the supply of available nitrates.

Harmful bacteria. One of the most harmful activities of bacteria is the spoilage of food. Certain bacteria produce poisonous substances, or toxins, during the breakdown of foods which may cause illness or death if eaten. In other cases, the food may simply be rendered unfit for use.

Milk may be freed of most dangerous bacteria by **pasteurization** (pass-tur-i-*say*-shun), which means heating to a temperature of from 140° to 150° F. for a period of 30 minutes, and then cooling quickly.

Most of us have the wrong idea as to what pasteurization really does. It doesn't completely sterilize the milk. It merely destroys the large majority of bacteria that are present, including those that might be capable of causing infectious diseases. Even though pasteurization delays souring milk, the container must still be closed to prevent any of the souring organisms in the air from entering. The milk must be kept cool to keep those which are already present from multiplying.

Some close relatives of the bacteria. In the early 20th century, while study-

Fig. 18-8. The live polio virus in the culture field is made harmless by the addition of formaldehyde in the processing of polio vaccine in a commercial laboratory. This is one of several steps designed to insure the safety of the vaccine.

ing a strange disease called Rocky Mountain spotted fever, scientists discovered in the blood of the victims tiny, rod-shaped organisms. Although resembling bacteria in form, they are smaller, are able to live only in a living host, and are carried only by insects, spiders, and their relatives. The organisms were named **Rickettsiae** (rick-ett-see-eye) after Dr. Howard Ricketts who did a great deal of work with them. More and more diseases throughout the world, such as the mysterious " Q " fever, have been found to have the Rick-

ettsiae as their cause. They seem to stand midway between bacteria and the smallest of all living matter, the viruses. Fig. 18-7 shows an influenza virus.

What are viruses? Biologists are still trying to discover the nature of one group of organisms, the **viruses** (*vy*-russ-sez) which behave like bacteria in some ways but are invisible except under the powerful electron microscope. These tiny forms of life, if they are alive, are so small that they pass through fine clay filters used to separate bacteria from solutions in which they grow. The whole study of viruses is labeled **virology** (vy-*rah*-loh-jee).

Besides their extremely small size, there are other differences between the viruses and the bacteria. They cannot grow in anything *except living cells*. Thus, the only laboratory media used in their culture are living animals and plants, tissue cultures of living cells, and chick embryos. They do not reproduce in the same way as bacteria, but their exact method of reproduction is still under study. Each virus may be a single protein molecule in combination with a nucleic acid molecule. Or it may possibly be a single hereditary particle known as the *gene* (*jean*). Viruses have a way of changing their characteristics, just at the moment the researcher believes he has accurately described a pure culture.

Dr. Wendell Stanley of the Rockefeller Institute discovered a startling fact about the viruses in 1935 which earned him a Nobel Prize. In the case of a virus causing a disease of tobacco plants, he found that the virus could be crystallized into a nonliving form. He actually could store it on a laboratory shelf. But when the crystals were injected into a healthy tobacco plant, the plant became diseased. The virus crystals had been transformed from a nonliving form into an active living organism. Scientists are now actively exploring that mysterious gulf between living and nonliving matter. The viruses seem to shuttle back and forth.

Many problems persist for the virologist. The known virus diseases, such as polio, smallpox, yellow fever, and influenza have resisted many ingenious techniques for their cure. But a few new discoveries, such as the *Salk vaccine* for polio, indicate that our knowledge of the virus may not be so limited. Why do these organisms change as they grow and reproduce? How do they reproduce? Will viruses prove to be the chief enemy of bacteria? The fascinating fields of bacteriology and virology, which are so closely related, are one of the active frontiers of modern biological study.

In Conclusion

One of the most important groups of fungi are the microscopic bacteria found almost everywhere. Close relatives of the bacteria are the Rickettsiae and the viruses.

Bacteria multiply very rapidly. Most of them require specific conditions of environment with a definite food supply.

Certain kinds are beneficial in food processing and other industrial activity. Bacteria cause great harm in the spoilage of food and as causative agents of disease.

But all bacteria, with few exceptions, are examples of the fungi in every sense of the term. The other members of the group known as fungi will be described in the next chapter.

Questions for Review

1. Why are bacteria classified as fungi?
2. Where are bacteria found?
3. Name the three groups of bacteria according to their importance to man and to their various activities.
4. What are three groups of bacteria according to their shape?
5. Describe some of the ways in which bacteria are joined to form colonies.
6. Describe an individual bacterium.
7. How do you explain the apparent mathematical impossibility " bacteria multiply by dividing "?
8. What is a bacterial spore?
9. What conditions are necessary for bacterial growth?
10. What is the difference between aerobic and anaerobic bacteria?
11. Name four general ways in which bacteria are beneficial to man.
12. Why are bacteria which change nitrogen compounds important to man?

Biologically Speaking

aerobic
anaerobic
bacillus
bacteria
bacteriology
coccus
culture medium

ensilage
flagellum
incubation
inoculation
microbiology
pasteurization
pathogenic

Petri dish
retting
Rickettsiae
spirillum
spore
virology
viruses

Applying Facts and Principles

1. Discuss the problems a bacteriologist has in identifying a bacterium.
2. On the basis of what you know about bacterial characteristics, describe as many ways as you can of killing bacteria.
3. What reasons can you give for bacteria being the first living things on the earth? Or, do you think perhaps the viruses may have been first?
4. What reasons can you give for the reduced rate of growth of a mass of bacteria after two or three days?

CHAPTER 19

Fungi—Notorious Thallophytes

Each of us has had some contact with the fungi. We eat fungi like the mushroom; we also eat the products of fungus activity like certain cheeses, and the citric acid found in many soft drinks; we use such drugs as penicillin and other antibiotics which come from fungi; and some people even have fungi growing on their bodies in the form of " athlete's foot," or ringworm. But this is only a brief survey.

There is no escaping the fungi. Most of them either affect us harmfully or beneficially. Indeed, this is a notorious group, but do not forget that many are beneficial.

What are the fungi? As you have already learned *fungi* lack true roots, stems, and leaves. This is one trait which puts them in the Thallophytes. Also, the fungi are similar in another way. *They lack chlorophyll and therefore cannot produce their own food supply.* This fact puts them in a separate group from the algae. But this does not mean they're different in form. The fact is that some fungi resemble the algae more than they do the rest of the fungi.

How the fungi obtain food. Fungi depend on other living organisms or other organic matter for their food, either directly or indirectly, and therefore live in direct competition with man and the other animals. In other words, the fungi are either *parasitic* or *saprophytic.* All the fungi must have some source of carbohydrates, protein, or fat to exist. Quite often the type of food must be a very specific kind because some fungi produce enzymes which will only break down that particular type food. Other fungi have powerful enzymes to break down a variety of foods.

The fungi cannot move around, so their problem of obtaining food is solved in two ways: (1) some secrete enzymes capable of acting on materials on which most organisms could not exist; and (2) some reproduce by forming spores in such huge numbers that they reach the majority of places where food is available.

Classification of the fungi. Although based on visible structures primarily, the classification system of the fungi indicates that the biologists, too, are often puzzled by this group. The main classes of this group are listed in the table on page 241 if you wish to find out more about them.

The mushroom, a typical fungus plant. *Mushrooms* are among the largest of the fungi and are also the best known. We find them in orchards, fields, and woodlands, and popping up suddenly on the lawn after a warm spring or autumn rain.

The familiar mushroom is a *reproductive structure* and represents only a portion of the complete mushroom plant. The *vegetative part* consists of a tangled mass of colorless, cobwebby threads of **hyphae** (*hy*-fee) [sing. hypha (hy-fah)] penetrating the soil. The entire mass of hyphae comprising the whole mushroom plant is the **mycelium** (my-*see*-lee-um). The hyphae of the mushroom resemble filaments of algae, except for the fact that *they lack chlorophyll.* They penetrate large areas of the soil, wood, bark, or other host material in which they grow. They get nourishment from organic matter which they absorb through the thin hypha wall. This food is carried by means of the flowing protoplasm to all parts of the mycelium or plant body. The hyphae secrete *digestive enzymes* which penetrate the source of food and break down the organic materials of which it is composed. While the reproductive structure of the mushroom lives only for a short time, the mycelium may live on for many years, gradually penetrating more and more of the food-producing area.

Reproductive structure of the mushroom. The familiar mushroom has a reproductive structure consisting of a

Fig. 19-1. The puffball is a fungus plant that produces spores in clublike clusters. Some puffballs grow to be more than two feet in diameter.

great number of hyphae, tightly packed together. It has a stalk or **stipe** which supports an umbrella-shaped **cap.** While pushing up through the soil the cap is folded downward around the stipe to form a hard knoblike structure. After forcing its way through the soil, the cap opens out, leaving a ring, or **annulus** (*an*-yule-us), around the stipe marking the point where the rim of the cap and the stipe were joined.

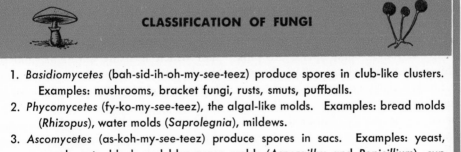

CLASSIFICATION OF FUNGI

1. *Basidiomycetes* (bah-sid-ih-oh-my-*see*-teez) produce spores in club-like clusters. Examples: mushrooms, bracket fungi, rusts, smuts, puffballs.
2. *Phycomycetes* (fy-ko-my-*see*-teez), the algal-like molds. Examples: bread molds (*Rhizopus*), water molds (*Saprolegnia*), mildews.
3. *Ascomycetes* (as-koh-my-*see*-teez) produce spores in sacs. Examples: yeast, morels, rots, black and blue-green molds (*Aspergillus* and *Penicillium*), cup fungi.
4. *Deuteromycetes* (doo-ter-oh-my-*see*-teez), the imperfect fungi that fit into no particular class. Cause " athlete's foot," ringworm, and other diseases.
5. *Myxomycetes* (mik-soh-my-*see*-teez), the slime molds.
6. *Schizomycetes* (skiz-oh-my-*see*-teez), the bacteria.
7. *Lichenes* (ly-kee-neez), algae and fungi combination. Examples: reindeer moss, (*Cladonia*).

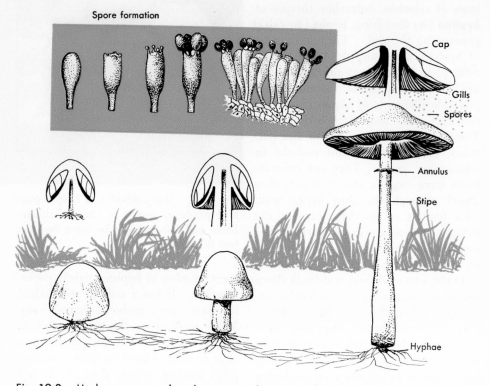

Fig. 19-2. Mushrooms reproduce by means of spores. This drawing shows stages in the development of the mushroom.

Most mushrooms bear numerous platelike **gills** on the lower side of the cap, radiating out from the stipe like wheel spokes. Outside and around each gill small structures produce spores in groups of four. Some spores are pink while others are white, yellow, brown, or black. Each mushroom produces a huge quantity of spores, usually estimated to be several hundred million. These asexual spores drop from the gills when mature and may be carried to a new location by animals or by the wind. Each spore is capable of forming a new mushroom plant if its new environment is favorable for growth. However, most spores fail to reach a suitable location and die without developing a new mycelium. Otherwise, the entire earth would soon be covered with mushrooms.

Food problems of fungi. The way in which fungi grow indicates a great deal about their food problems. Many of them tend to grow in circles. This is true of molds, or ringworm on the skin which is really a fungus, and of the beautiful " fairy ring " mushroom. In the case of the " fairy ring " shown in Fig. 19-3, one original mushroom developed its mycelium in order to digest the organic matter available at that spot. As the mycelium expanded into the unused organic matter in the soil around it, new mushrooms would be produced periodically at the outer edge of this growing ring of mycelium. As the food supply in the interior of the circle was used, the circle kept growing larger and larger.

You may see the same growth prin-

Fig. 19-3. What causes these mushrooms to grow in this " fairy ring "?

ciple if you notice the growth of a mold in a culture dish. The circle will grow larger, and that means the newest, most active part of the mold is on the outer edge of the colony. The oldest, dying portion is always in the very center.

Poisonous and edible mushrooms. The word " toadstool," frequently used as a popular term for poisonous mushrooms, is false. While many people claim to have methods of distinguishing edible from poisonous varieties, experts tell us there is no rule or sign which can be used to distinguish the two types. Frequently, some of the most harmless-looking forms are poisonous and produce severe, or in some cases, even fatal effects if eaten. The only safe advice which can be given is to leave them alone unless you know exactly which forms are edible and which forms are poisonous.

Puffballs. These resemble mushrooms except that the reproductive structure never opens to discharge the spores. It merely dries and the spores are then exposed to the air. Puffballs are round or pear-shaped growths, usually white in color. Nearly all species are edible if collected before the spores mature. Large ones weighing several pounds are fairly common.

Bracket fungi. *Bracket fungi* are the familiar shelf-like growths you see on the stumps or trunks of trees. They may be either parasites, doing great harm to living trees, or saprophytes, living on dead wood. They are the most destructive of the wood-rotting fungi. The mycelium of the bracket fungus penetrates the woody tissue of the host and causes it to disintegrate internally. The shelf-like reproductive body is telltale evidence of the damage which is occurring within the host. They are woody in texture when old and remain attached to the host year after year. New spore-producing hyphae form on

Fig. 19-4. The morel (left) is highly prized as an edible fungus belonging to the Ascomycetes group. The "death angel" (right) is a poisonous mushroom belonging to the Basidiomycetes group.

the underside of the shelf, forming layers or rings of growth. Spores are discharged through tiny pores located on the underside of the shelf-like growth.

Fig. 19-5. Bracket fungi like that shown below may grow on living tree trunks or on fallen logs in the forest.

Molds. We use the term **mold** for numerous kinds of fungus plants which grow on wood, paper, leather, and various other sources of food. Some cause heavy damage to food supplies in storage. Yet, this group has many very beneficial forms, too.

Molds thrive in dark, moist places. While warmth stimulates the growth of many forms, others grow well at temperatures near the freezing point. This great range in growing temperature causes serious difficulty in cold storage plants.

One of the commonest of molds is *bread mold* **Rhizopus** which frequently invades breadboxes. One tiny spore is enough to start a cottony growth on a piece of bread. Before long the bread is completely covered by the mold. Each tiny thread is a hypha. The tangled mass of hyphae make up the mycelium. A portion of a bread mold viewed with a lens reveals several distinct kinds of hyphae composing the mycelium. Those which spread over the surface of the food source are **stolons.** At intervals along the stolons, clusters of tiny rootlike hyphae called **rhizoids** (*ry*-zoids) penetrate the food source and serve as absorbing structures.

Rhizoids produce digestive enzymes which dissolve the starch and sugar contained in the bread. These materials are then absorbed into the plant body of the mold. The characteristic odor and color spots which mold produces in bread are due to these enzymes and to other products formed during action of the mold on the food source.

After a few days of growth, tiny black spots appear among the mold threads. Each black spot is a spore case, or **sporangium** (spor-*an*-jee-um), which is produced at the tip of a special hypha called an **ascending hypha.** Under the microscope, each sporangium appears as a thin-walled sac containing millions of spores. At maturity, the sporangium covering breaks open and the spores are discharged into the air. Like spores of mushrooms, each spore may form a new mold mycelium if it happens to fall on a piece of bread, leather, paper, or any other suitable food source.

Blue and green molds (*Penicillium* and *Aspergillus*) form the familiar powdery growth on oranges, lemons, and other citrus fruits. The powdery substance consists of spores in tremendous numbers which form at the tips of hyphae. The mycelia of these molds are deeply embedded in the tissues of the food source. In addition to citrus fruits, these molds may live on meat and other food products.

In this group of molds we find several of the most valuable of all fungus plants. Several species of one of the blue molds, called *Penicillium,* are used in the processing of fine-flavored cheeses. Cheese manufacturers carefully grow these molds and add them to the cheeses at a certain point in processing. During the aging period, the mycelium of the mold grows through the cheese and, by chemical activity, forms substances which add distinctive flavors.

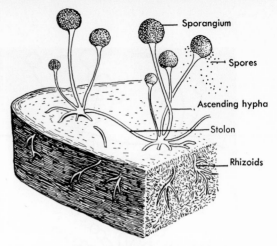

Fig. 19-6. This is what bread mold looks like when greatly magnified. You can see the mold plant with its rootlike threads and its raised spore cases.

Among the more popular mold cheeses are Roquefort and Camembert. Both are cheeses in which *Penicillium* molds are used.

Today, however, *Penicillium* means much more than an organism for the flavoring of cheese. We associate it with one of the most notable medical advances of our time, the discovery of the wonder drug, **penicillin** (pen-ih-*sill*-in).

Penicillin, the drug, is a secretion of some of the *Penicillium* species, formed during normal digestive activity of the mold. The powerful effects of penicillin in checking the growth of certain kinds of bacteria were known to science before 1940. But it remained for Sir Alexander Fleming in England to recognize the full importance of this. In a few years, industrial concerns perfected methods for large-scale production of penicillin. Today, entire factories are devoted to producing it.

Mildews. *Mildews* are the white or grayish powdery patches which appear on the leaves of lilacs, roses, potatoes, onions, grapes, and some nonliving matter like leather and cloth. Some types

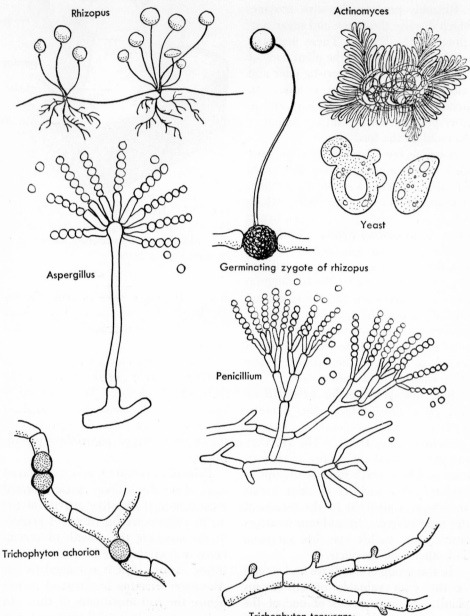

Rhizopus

Actinomyces

Aspergillus

Yeast

Germinating zygote of rhizopus

Penicillium

Trichophyton achorion

Trichophyton tonsurans

Fig. 19-7. Above is a microscopic drawing of various types of fungi. What character-istic do all fungi have in common?

of mildews form their mycelia on the outer surface and send rootlike branches into the epidermal cells. In these cells the mycelia absorb nourishment doing considerable damage to the plant. Oth-er types of mildews attack materials in damp, dark basements, producing a musty odor. They even are thought to cause some discoloration of paint on houses.

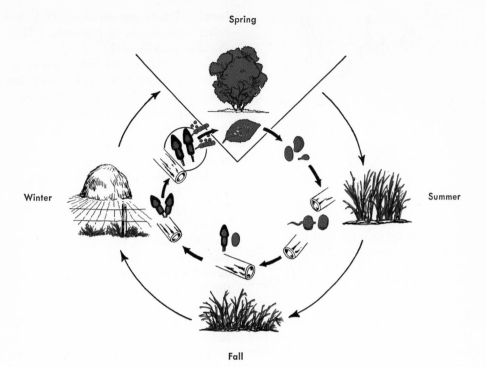

Fig. 19-8. The barberry plant and wheat or related grass plants are the two hosts responsible for stem rust of wheat and other grains. Follow the stages from spring to winter in this life cycle of stem rust.

Rusts. Several types of *rusts* are among the most destructive plant parasites. There are 250 known forms of grain rusts which attack wheat, oats, barley, and other cereals. They cause millions of dollars of damage annually to these crops. There are two stages of the parasite on grains, a red-spore stage and a black-spore stage. The red stage gives the fungus disease its name. You can easily spot a field of wheat which is heavily infected by its characteristic reddish color.

The *red stage* appears on the stem and leaves of the wheat plant in the spring. Tiny blisters appear along the stem and leaf surfaces where the internal mycelium of the mold grows to the surface to discharge spores. These red spores are carried to other wheat plants by the wind and thus may spread the infection rapidly.

During the late summer and early fall, when the wheat is mature, a second kind of spore called the *black stage* is produced from the same pustules. These spores cannot reinfect wheat but form a stage which infects the wild barberry (not the cultivated Japanese barberry). This infection occurs in the spring of the following year, after some complicated changes have taken place between the wheat and barberry stage. Infections in the form of tiny cups on the lower surface of the barberry leaves produce spores which are wind-borne. These spores return to the wheat plant and infect it during the spring growth of a new crop. Both hosts, the wheat and barberry, are absolutely necessary

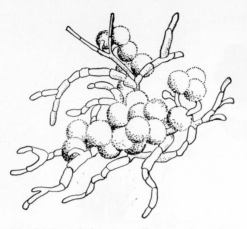

Fig. 19-9. A lichen is really two plants living together: an algae and a fungus. The fungus is a mass of colorless filaments depending for their food on the green algae.

for the life cycle of wheat rust to be completed. Consequently, wheat rust can be controlled by getting rid of the wild barberry plant.

Another rust, the *white pine blister rust,* causes severe damage to this valuable timber tree. Like the wheat rust, this rust infects two hosts: (1) the white pine; and (2) the wild currant.

Smuts. *Smuts,* like rusts, are parasites which do great damage, especially to cereal grains. One type infects wheat and barley, while another causes extensive damage to corn. Smut spores infect the plants while young and, within a few weeks, show as a moist black swelling on the leaves or stem. Corn smut often affects the ears and appears as large swellings containing millions of black powdery spores. These spores may infect other plants or may remain dormant until spring. Then they germinate, forming hyphae which produce another kind of spores. These spores then infect new host plants. Only by burning infected plants can the smut be controlled.

Yeasts are among the well-known

fungi. Yeasts are all one-celled, and either saprophytes or parasites. Their shape is usually oval.

Commercial yeasts exist mostly on dilute sugar solutions which they ferment, forming *alcohol* and *carbon dioxide.* This fermentation of sugar makes yeast very important to two industries. Commercial alcohol manufacturers use yeasts to ferment various carbohydrate mashes. Bakers, on the other hand, use yeast to form carbon dioxide in dough. Yeast " works " in the dough and forms bubbles of carbon dioxide. These bubbles swell during baking and make the loaf light. This gas, as well as the alcohol which is formed, is driven off in the baking process.

Yeast cells reproduce very rapidly if kept warm and moist and supplied with sugar or starch for food. Buds develop on each parent cell and soon become full-sized cells which again reproduce, the process resulting in long chains of attached cells. Wild yeasts live in the air and ferment fruit sugars of various sorts. The familiar commercial cake of yeast is a mass of yeast cells held together by starch which will serve as food when they start to grow. The yeast cells remain inactive as long as the cakes are kept cool, but begin active fermentation when they become warm and moist.

Lichens. *Lichens* (*like*-ens) are an example of a community relationship of plants, for they are not one plant, but two. They consist of certain types of algae held in a mass of colorless filaments of fungi. The fungus is dependent on the alga for the food which it manufactures through photosynthesis. Although the alga is, in a sense, a " slave," it is protected and kept moist by the fungus filaments, and is thus able to grow in exposed positions on rocks and trees, where it could not exist alone. This is a good example of **symbiosis,** a

Fig. 19-10. Lichens are common fungi found in many parts of the world. You can find them on tree trunks, as shown here, or on rocks and stones.

relationship in which two organisms live together with mutual benefit.

Lichens are abundant on the tops of mountains, along rocky seacoasts, and in the treeless Arctic regions. You'll also find them on rocks and dead trees in open fields and woods. A widespread lichen, Cladonia, is so valuable as food for reindeer that it is commonly called *reindeer moss.*

In Conclusion

The fungi are a group of Thallophytes lacking chlorophyll. Fungi must grow on a source of organic materials because they have no chlorophyll and thus cannot make their own food. This may be either living or nonliving. If the food source is living material, the fungus is a parasite. If the source is nonliving, the fungus is a saprophyte.

Among the most important groups of fungi are mushrooms, bracket fungi, molds, mildews, rusts, smuts, blights, yeasts, bacteria, and the curious combinations of an alga and a fungus called lichens.

Fungi may be beneficial or harmful, depending on their source of food. Among the valuable fungi are certain of the mushrooms, some of the molds, and yeasts. Certain molds, mildews, rusts, smuts, blight-causing organisms are among the most destructive plants in the entire plant kingdom.

In the next group of plants, we shall examine some members which are more like the familiar land plants of the field, woods, and garden. These, the mosses and ferns, show many advances over the simple plant bodies of the algae and fungi.

Questions for Review

1. What one characteristic do all fungi have in common?

2. How do fungi digest their food externally?

3. Describe the mycelium of a typical fungus.

4. Describe the structure of a common mushroom.

5. Explain how bread may become innoculated with bread mold even though there may be no mold growing close by it.

6. How do rust fungi cause extensive damage to cereal crops?

7. What are some ways in which fungi have been and are important to man?

8. How does a lichen show symbiosis?

9. In what ways is the process of fermentation important to man?

10. In what environments would you expect to find lichens?

Biologically Speaking

annulus	host	saprophyte
antibiotic	hypha	sporangium
cap	lichen	spore
enzyme	mycelium	stipe
fungi	parasite	stolon
gill	rhizoid	symbiosis

Applying Facts and Principles

1. Parasitic organisms tend to grow only on specific hosts under specific conditions. What type of structures and what type of food-getting characteristics do fungi have which make this true?

2. Why do electrical equipment manufacturers find it necessary to search for and use anti-fungi materials?

3. What property of molds do you suppose make them such effective bacteria killers?

4. Why is meat usually aged before being sold?

5. Why does animal feed enriched with antibiotics have such a beneficial effect on animals using it?

CHAPTER 20

The Mosses and the Ferns

At one time the mosses and ferns were probably the most common form of plant life on the earth. Their importance now is due not so much to their presence today but to the remains of their ancient relatives. Ancient green plants stored up the energy from the sun which shone on the earth millions of years ago. Now this energy is released when we burn their remains as coal or oil.

Still another reason for our attention to these plants is the fact that their reproductive cycle is somewhat more complicated than that of the majority of the Thallophytes. Mosses and ferns help us understand the process of seed formation in the modern seed plants.

The Bryophytes. The *Bryophytes* (*bry*-oh-fytes) consist of two main groups of plants, the mosses and the liverworts. They are found in every section of the world, ranging from great extremes in temperature and altitude. They probably were the first plants to live exclusively on the land. However, some members of the group still live in water. Together with lichens they serve as soil builders. Gradually they wear away large rocks by acid secretions.

No Bryophyte plant is very large. Although they live on land, these plants have no structures which can carry water to their leaves very efficiently. Nor do they have true roots, so they cannot absorb much water from the soil. Thus, the Bryophytes, while showing a more complicated reproductive cycle, do not have the cell specialization for water movement on a large scale. This is necessary for a large land plant to live.

Mosses. You have seen mosses growing in cracks in shaded sidewalks, on moist ground under trees, or in clumps in deep woods. What looks like a tuft or carpet is, actually, a compact clump of moss plants. Each plant has its tiny stem with a cluster of leaves encircling it. If you pull one of these tiny plants from the soil, you will find a group of rhizoids growing from the base of the stem. Mosses do not have true roots, but the rhizoids serve the purpose by anchoring the plant and by absorbing some water and dissolved minerals from the soil. Mosses do, however, have stemlike and leaflike structures.

Life cycle of the moss. The moss plant which we commonly see is only one phase of the life cycle. If you examine the diagram in Fig. 20-1, you will notice that each moss plant goes through a reproductive cycle in which an asexual, spore-producing stage forms a sexual gamete-producing stage. This, then, in turn, forms the spore stage again. A type of reproductive cycle like this illustrates *alternation of generations.* Putting it another way, the

251

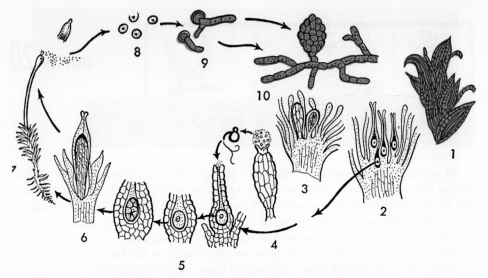

Fig. 20-1. Life cycle of the moss. Stages 1-4 show the female (2) and male (3, 4) gametophyte plants. After fertilization of an egg by a sperm, the sporophyte generation (6, 7) grow out of the top of the female plant. Spores (8) form in the sporangium at the top of the sporophyte and, when mature, fall to the ground and give rise to a new generation of gametophyte plants (9, 10).

sporophyte (*spore*-oh-fite) plant (spore-producing) alternates with a gametophyte (ga-*met*-oh-fite) plant (gamete-producing).

Some Thallophytes and all of the other plants, including the seed-producers, show an alternation of generations. When we study heredity, we shall see a further significance of this reproductive cycle of alternation of generations.

At the tips of the leafy stems of the mosses, and entirely hidden by the leaves, are many *reproductive organs*. Some species bear both male and female organs on the same plant. Other species have the male organs on one plant and the female organs on another. Inside the male organs, we find sperms which are the male sex cells, or gametes. A **gamete** is any sex cell. Sperms are discharged from the male organs and swim to the female organs. Usually dew provides enough moisture for this.

Inside each female organ is an egg. This is the female sex cell, or gamete. One sperm enters the neck of the female organ and unites with an egg. The union of sperm and egg is called *fertilization* and results in the formation of a *zygote* (zy-goat). This entire process is part of the gametophyte or sexual stage of the life cycle.

Fertilization starts the sporophyte, or asexual phase, of the cycle. The zygote always remains in the female organ. Soon it begins to grow and produces a slender stalk which grows up and out of the leafy shoot of the plant. The top of the stalk swells and becomes a large mass of tissue called a **capsule** which is covered with a thin hood. Inside the capsule are many microscopic *spores*. These are asexual. That is, they are neither definitely male or female. When the spores are ripe, the hood falls off, the capsule opens, and the spores escape. They are carried off by the

Fig. 20-2. You often see the sporophyte stage of a moss plant with its delicate capsules on slender stalks growing from the leafy gametophyte.

wind and when they fall on the ground, they begin to grow, provided environmental conditions are right. The sporophyte stage has ended and the gametophyte stage begins.

Each spore produces a small threadlike structure called a **protonema** (proh-toh-*nee*-mah). All the cells that make up the protonema have chlorophyll and can make their own food. Their resemblance to algae is startling and caused many scientists to class them as close relatives of the algae. Some threads of the protonema produce short buds which grow into a new moss plant. Other threads enter the ground and become the rhizoids. Thus, a new moss plant is formed and this gametophyte plant will soon form sex cells. The gametophyte phase produces gametes and the sporophyte produces spores.

Economic importance of the mosses. The **sphagnum** (*sfag*-num), or peat-forming mosses, are the most widely used. Sphagnum grows in small lakes and bogs, where it forms floating mats. These mats increase in size and thickness each year as generation after generation occupies the surface of the mat. Plants of previous years decompose slowly, settle to the bottom, and form peat. In time, the growth of sphagnum mats in a lake may close the water entirely, causing the lake to enter the bog stage. Eventually, what was once a thriving, open lake may become a deep deposit of brownish-black peat. Large sphagnum mats are often invaded by larger plants: rushes, grasses, shrubs, and even trees.

Sphagnum is valuable to nurserymen because of its absorbent qualities.

Fig. 20-3. Peat moss or sphagnum grows in swampy places. These mosses have considerable commercial use.

It holds water like cotton, and is used for packing the roots of plants to prevent their drying out during shipment. This same absorbent quality of sphagnum makes it valuable to the gardener as a *mulch*. It can be worked into the soil or placed on the surface to make the soil loose and to hold water.

Decayed sphagnum moss or peat is valuable also as a fuel. The slow decay and compression of decaying sphagnum moss in a lake is an early stage in the formation of coal. Before peat is used as a fuel it must be removed from deep layers. Then it must be compressed further, dried, and finally is ready to be burned. Peat as fuel is very important in regions where it's plentiful and where coal is scarce or costly.

Other mosses are important to us as pioneer plants in rocky areas. The small amount of soil which collects in cracks on the bare surfaces of cliffs and ledges is sufficient to support moss plants. The rhizoids secrete substances which break down rocks gradually and thus form more soil. As mosses die and

Fig. 20-4. This is a clump of *Marchantia* plants, another member of the phylum, Bryophyta.

Fig. 20-5. The Carboniferous forest probably looked like this. The most abundant plants are representatives of the tree ferns.

decompose season after season, they form enough soil to anchor the roots of larger plants.

The liverworts. Much less familiar than mosses are their relatives, the *liverworts*. These curious plants grow in wet places, often along the banks of streams, around the outlet of a spring, or on rocky ledges. They look like thin, leathery leaves laid flat against the ground. One of the common liverworts resembles a thin tongue with Y-shaped branches at the tip. Under ideal conditions, a clump of liverworts may cover considerable area. Male and female sex organs are formed in curious umbrella-like structures which rise about an inch above the flat plant body. A liverwort in such a condition is interesting to find and will reward your careful search in moist habitats.

The odd name of the liverworts goes back to an ancient theory which said that the shape of a plant indicated what it was good for in the way of medicine. Since these plants resemble tiny livers, they were thought to be good for liver trouble and were used to treat it.

A common liverwort, *Marchantia* (mar-*kan*-shih-ah), appears in Fig. 20-4.

Pteridophytes — ferns and their relatives. To have appreciated the Pteridophytes (*ter*-ih-doh-fites) fully, we should have lived millions of years ago during the age in which they were in their glory. Then, they were not limited to a few places in the woods, or swamp, or hillside, or flower pot. They formed large forests which covered the wet, marshy land common at that time. Ferns much like those of today flourished during this past age. Tree ferns 30 to 40 feet high were also abundant.

Fig. 20-6. Ferns are delicate, beautiful plants, often found in moist, shady woods among rocks and cliffs.

Although no man ever saw these great forests of ferns, today we are reaping the benefits of their existence. During this age, referred to as the Carboniferous period, great layers of fern remains accumulated in the swampy areas where they grew. Later, the movements of the earth compressed these layers into

layers of coal. It has been estimated that it took 300 feet of compressed vegetation to form 20 feet of coal. When we consider what coal has meant to industry, we might almost conclude that the high civilization of modern America has sprung from the Pteridophyte vegetation of millions of years ago.

Most of us are familiar with ferns as clumps of plants with graceful, deeply-cut leaves. In all but the few remaining tree ferns of the tropics, the stems are underground, creeping horizontally just below the surface. These underground stems, called **rhizomes** (*ry*-zomes), bear clusters of true roots which spread through the ground in anchoring the plant and in absorbing water and dissolved minerals.

Life cycle of the fern. The fern you find in the shaded woods or growing as a potted plant is the sporophyte stage of the life cycle. (See Fig. 20-7.)

When the familiar fern leaves are mature, small dots called **sori** (*sor*-eye) [sing. *sorus*] appear on the lower side.

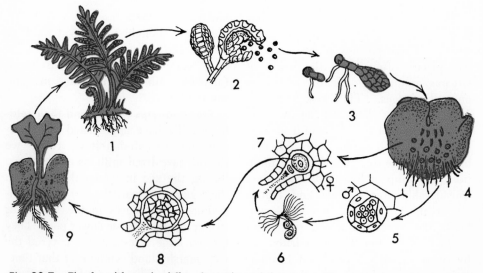

Fig. 20-7. The fern life cycle differs from that of the moss. The sporophyte (stages 1–2) is the plant you see above ground. The gametophyte (stages 3–9) develops on the ground and is seldom seen because it is so small.

Christmas fern   Interrupted fern   Bracken fern

Sensitive fern   Maidenhair fern

Fig. 20-8. Note how the location of the sori with their sporangia differs with various kinds of ferns.

The sori differ in shape and location in different kinds of ferns. Some people become alarmed when sori appear and remove them carefully, thinking the fern is diseased.

Each sorus contains a cluster of helmet-shaped **sporangia** (spor-*an*-jee-ah) [sing. *sporangium*], each of which contains numerous *spores*. Each sporangium is attached to the sorus by a short stalk. Since the fern leaf bears sporangia and spores, it corresponds to the stalk and capsule of the moss.

When the spores are mature, the sporangium bursts open and releases them. Air currents carry them to new locations. If a spore falls in a moist place, it begins to grow.

The spore gives rise to a short filament of cells with rhizoids. The second, or the gametophyte stage, of the fern life cycle has begun. This stage

at first resembles the protonema of a moss. However, unlike the moss, the filament broadens at the tip and becomes a flat, heart-shaped structure called a **prothallus** (pro-*thal*-us). When fully grown, the prothallus is one-

Fig. 20-9. The horsetail rush (*Equisetum*) is a relative of the fern.

Fig. 20-10. Club mosses are another relative of the ferns. Too many of them are used at Christmas time. They are rapidly becoming extinct in some areas and care should be taken to preserve them.

quarter to one-half inch in diameter. The flat prothallus is green and clings close to the ground, held by a cluster of rhizoids which form on the underside at the rounded or lower end of the "heart." It will be an interesting project for you to try to raise some fern prothalli.

The male sex organs containing sperms develop among the rhizoids. Several female sex organs form near the notch at the upper end of the prothallus. Each one contains an egg. In most ferns, the eggs and sperms mature at different times. Thus, when sperms escape, they swim in the film of dew to another prothallus. When a sperm fertilizes an egg, a zygote is produced. This marks the end of the gametophyte stage and the beginning of the sporophyte stage. It is interesting to note that this prothallus stage of a fern corresponds to the familiar leafy-shoot stage of the moss.

Immediately after fertilization, the zygote grows into a young fern plant. Soon, the young fern becomes established with a root, a leaf, and a stem. The stem bears additional leaves and the familiar fern clump results. Thus the sporophyte is the most conspicuous part of the life cycle of the fern.

Relatives of the fern. Closely related to the ferns are two groups of plants, fairly common in some localities. The *horsetails,* or scouring rushes, are often seen in wet places or around the margins of lakes. They appear as slender, dark-green, rodlike stems bearing light-colored cones at their tips. The leaves are reduced to small scalelike structures growing in circles around the stem at regularly spaced intervals.

Club mosses resemble true mosses

only in general appearance and constitute another group of the fern relatives. These plants bear curious club-shaped reproductive structures at the tops of certain of their branches. You can find them in rich, damp woods, or creeping along the rocky slopes of mountains.

Like the ferns, both horsetails and club mosses are now merely remnants of the once flourishing age of Pteridophytes. At that time they were the size of trees. You can still see some of their remains in the form of leaf or stem imprints in coal.

In Conclusion

The two intermediate plant phyla between the Thallophytes and the Spermatophytes are the Bryophytes and Pteridophytes. They both show a complicated life cycle in which one spore-producing stage, the sporophyte, produces a gamete-producing stage, the gametophyte, in an alternation of generations.

The Bryophytes have the mosses as their chief representatives and the Pteridophytes, the ferns. The fact that these plants once covered the earth is important to man today because of the coal they formed millions of years ago.

This survey of the plant kingdom has shown us the simpler, flowerless, less-noticed forms of plant life. In the next Unit we will discuss the animals which have no backbones. They too will prove to be an important and interesting collection of living organisms.

Questions for Review

1. In what way does the water-carrying characteristic of the Bryophytes prevent them from growing into large plants?

2. Describe briefly the two phases in the life history of the moss.

3. Explain what is meant by alternation of generations.

4. What process separates the gametophyte from the sporophyte generation?

5. Describe briefly the formation of a peat bog.

6. In what ways are the mosses important to man?

7. Describe coal formation.

8. List the various structures in the order of their appearance in the life cycle of the fern.

9. Describe the way in which the fern produces its spores.

10. In what ways are the gametophyte and the sporophyte generations of the fern connected with each other?

Biologically Speaking

alternation of generations	gametophyte	rhizoids
Bryophyte	peat	rhizomes
capsule	prothallus	sorus
fertilized egg	protonema	sphagnum
gamete	Pteridophyte	sporophyte

Applying Facts and Principles

1. Why do you suppose that seldom do we find more than one sporophyte growing from a single leafy stalk of moss, although that stalk usually carries more than one female sex organ?

2. What reasons can you give for the Pteridophytes dying out as the common plants in the world? Refer to the Carboniferous period.

3. Compare the sporophyte plant of a moss and a fern and explain in what ways the fern is more advanced.

4. List various ways in which the fern is better suited to life on land than the moss.

Research On Your Own

1. Make a collection of algae from the ponds, streams, or seashore in your vicinity. Try to identify them. Most algae can be cultured in an aquarium or in large glass jars. Frequent inspection may show some of the specimens in different reproductive stages.

2. In an aquarium which has chiefly one-celled algae, try to strain the water through a fine-mesh cloth. Dry the resulting material in an oven. Then add it, using sterile techniques, to a sterile jar of water and add a dropper of water containing protozoa. Test the water periodically to determine the growth of the protozoa. Keep a control jar which has not had the algae material added.

3. Scrape some of the white " tartar " from your teeth and smear the material on the slide. Pass the slide through a flame many times, and then place several drops of stain (methylene blue will do) on it. Let the slide stand for a few minutes, then wash it by allowing water to run over it, and let it stand to dry. Examine under the microscope. Make a careful and complete record of what you have done and observed.

4. Prepare some culture dishes and inoculate them with bacteria or expose them to some source of bacteria, such as air. However, when inoculating some of the dishes, have an ultraviolet or a " sun " lamp shining on the dish. What type of growth do you find in the dishes after incubation?

5. Moisten a piece of bread and expose it to the air for about 30 minutes. Put it in a covered dish and keep it in a warm, dark place. After a few days, a growth of mold should appear. Observe it closely. Inspect a part of it under the microscope.

6. Sow some moss or fern spores on a layer of damp, moist soil to produce gametophyte plants. Keep the soil covered. The spores from several fern species may be obtained from a local greenhouse.

7. Using a special agar medium, molds can be cultivated in Petri dishes and test tubes if the same procedures are used as shown in the chapter on Bacteria. Various places for obtaining specimens are soil, air, infected skin, and molded food materials.

8. Add various quantities of an antibiotic to the food supply of animals, being sure to keep some other animals of the same kind as controls. Observe any change in weight, appearance, and general vitality of the test animals.

9. Fern spores can be planted on agar media in Petri dishes. Prothallia should then develop. The surface of the agar should be kept moist.

More About Biology

Christensen, Clyde M. *COMMON EDIBLE MUSHROOMS*. The University of Minnesota Press, Minneapolis. 1943

Christensen, Clyde M. *THE MOLDS AND MAN*. The University of Minnesota Press, Minneapolis. 1951

Conrad, Henry S. *HOW TO KNOW THE MOSSES*. William C. Brown Co., Dubuque. 1944

Durand, Herbert. *FIELD BOOK OF COMMON FERNS*. Rev. Ed. G. P. Putnam's Sons, New York. 1949

Eberson, Frederick. *MICROBES MILITANT*. The Ronald Press Co., New York. 1948

Hausman, Leon. *BEGINNERS' GUIDE TO FRESH–WATER LIFE*. G. P. Putnam's New York. 1950

Hylander, Clarence. *SEA AND SHORE*. The Macmillan Co., New York. 1950

Jacques, H. E. *PLANT FAMILIES AND HOW TO KNOW THEM*. William C. Brown Co., Dubuque. 1948

Lewis, Lucia Z. *THE FIRST BOOK OF MICROBES*. E. Franklin Watts, Inc., New York. 1954

Morgan, Ann Haven. *FIELDBOOK OF PONDS AND STREAMS*. G. P. Putnam's Sons, New York. 1930

Needham, James and Needham, Paul R. *A GUIDE TO THE STUDY OF FRESH–WATER BIOLOGY*. Comstock Co., Ithaca. 1938

Parker, Bertha Morris. *DEPENDENT PLANTS*. Row, Peterson Co., Evanston, Ill. 1944

Rahn, Otto. *MICROBES OF MERIT*. The Ronald Press Co., New York. 1945

Reed, Maxwell W. and Bronson, Wilfred S. *THE SEA FOR SAM*. Harcourt, Brace and Co., New York. 1935

Schwartz, Julius. *THROUGH THE MAGNIFYING GLASS: LITTLE THINGS MAKE A BIG DIFFERENCE*. Whittlesey House (McGraw-Hill), New York. 1954

Selsam, Millicent. *MICROBES AT WORK*. William Morrow and Co., New York. 1953

Shatz, Albert. *THE STORY OF MICROBES*. Harper and Brothers, New York. 1952

Thomas, William S. *FIELDBOOK OF COMMON GILLED MUSHROOMS*. G. P. Putnam's Sons, New York. 1928

Tressler, Donald K. *THE WEALTH OF THE SEA*. The Century Co., New York. 1937

Wedberg, Stanley E. *MICROBES AND YOU*. The Macmillan Co., New York. 1954

Zim, Herbert S. *PLANTS*. Harcourt, Brace and Co., New York. 1947

The cinnamon fern, shown here, is one of our most beautiful native ferns. The green fronds are large, varying from 2 to 4 feet high, depending on the environment, but do not bear any sporangia. The cinnamon-colored sporangia occur on nongreen fronds which arise from the underground stem and look like brown plumes. You can see these spore-bearing fronds in the center of the photograph surrounded by the green fronds on the outside.

Simpler Forms of Animal Life

It is amazing how much biology you can study in a single drop of water. And this is the place we will begin the study of animal life in this Unit. A pond or stream or roadside ditch teems with tiny organisms strangely different from the animals of the larger world of life. You can see animals which spring from a stalk and those which dart about with thousands of tiny hairlike oars; cannibals and victims of cannibals.

Leaving these tiny creatures, you will explore the animal life of shallow ocean stretches, with their jellyfish and corals, sponges and starfish. These creatures, together with the various kinds of worms, clams, oysters, snails, octopus, crayfish, lobsters, spiders, insects, and a host of others are classified as invertebrates.

Several chapters in this Unit are devoted to insects. Included here will be many " old friends " you have seen in your garden or flower beds. When you consider the enormous number of insects and the harm and good they do, you realize the need for becoming well-acquainted with this group of invertebrates.

CHAPTER 21

Microscopic Animal Life

Having become acquainted with some of the Thallophytes which compose the vegetation of the microscopic world of life, we now turn our attention to the animals in this society of tiny living things.

While these organisms are the simplest animals, if their life activities are examined, you may conclude that they are not so simple. Their bodies consist of a single animal cell living a solitary existence, yet these bodies are capable of performing all the processes of life. Protoplasm becomes even more striking when we see one of these tiny-celled creatures without any specialized organs moving about, taking in food, throwing off waste products, and reproducing at regular intervals. Biologists call these one-celled animals *Protozoa* (*pro*-toh-zo-a), which means, literally, " first animals." They are well-named, for they are probably the beginning of all animal life — animal life in its most primitive form.

Plants, animals, and basic forms of life. You know that plant life and animal life are basically similar because plants and animals are composed of a universal substance, protoplasm. Yet there are some differences between the two types. Plant cells usually have cell walls and chlorophyll which animal cells seldom have. Plants are usually anchored, while animals usually move around a great deal. A plant commonly grows at certain growing tips, the buds on a stem, and the tips of the roots. Animal growth is not, on the other hand, usually confined to these areas. Animal protoplasm usually shows more sensitivity to stimuli than plant cells. But notice that all these differences are *not* hard and fast divisions. This may be better illustrated by our " V " diagram.

Let us visualize all life as a " V," with plant life representing one side of the " V " and animal life the other (see Fig. 21-1). At the top of the plant side, we find the seed plants, with complex tissues and specialized organs, such as leaves, stems, and roots. As we follow the line downward, plants become more and more simple, until we arrive at the primitive algae and fungi at the base of the line.

The complex animals, like horses, cattle, and man, are found at the top of the other side of the " V." These organisms, like higher plants, are extremely specialized and have complex organs such as muscles, hearts, and brains. They're quite unlike the higher plants, and are widely separated from them. But farther down the animal kingdom we find the simpler creatures, tending to have much more in common with plant life. At the bottom of the " V " we find those forms which contain characteristics of both plants and animals.

Classification of the Protozoa. At the extreme bottom of the animal king-

Fig. 21-1. By following this " V of life " chart you will get a better idea of the relationship of animal and plant groups.

dom, we find one-celled animals known as the *Protozoa*. This phylum may be organized into four main classes in which the animals included are different primarily in their method of locomotion.

Euglena, plant or animal? This organism lives in fresh-water ponds and streams where it is often so abundant that the water appears a brilliant green.

Under the microscope, *Euglena* appears as a spindle or pear-shaped cell which swims about freely. The front, or **anterior end,** is rounded, while the

rear, or **posterior end,** is usually pointed. (See Fig. 21-2.) Movement is accomplished in two characteristic ways. The organism swims by means of a long whip, or *flagellum,* which is attached to the anterior end and is nearly as long as its one-celled body. The flagellum is held straight in front and the tip of it rotates, pulling the organism rapidly through the water.

Another type of movement is accomplished by a gradual change in shape of the entire cell. The posterior portion

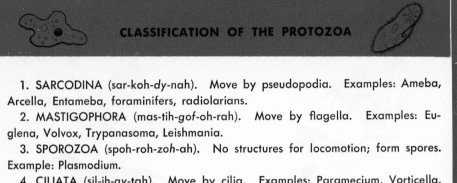

CLASSIFICATION OF THE PROTOZOA

1. SARCODINA (sar-koh-dy-nah). Move by pseudopodia. Examples: Ameba, Arcella, Entameba, foraminifers, radiolarians.
2. MASTIGOPHORA (mas-tih-gof-oh-rah). Move by flagella. Examples: Euglena, Volvox, Trypanasoma, Leishmania.
3. SPOROZOA (spoh-roh-zoh-ah). No structures for locomotion; form spores. Example: Plasmodium.
4. CILIATA (sil-ih-ay-tah). Move by cilia. Examples: Paramecium, Vorticella, Stentor.

of the body is drawn forward, causing the cell to assume a rounded form, after which the anterior portion is extended, thus pushing the cell forward. This type of movement is so characteristic of

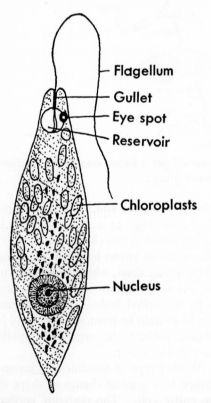

Fig. 21-2. Is *Euglena* plant or animal?

Euglena we call it **euglenoid movement**.

The internal features of *Euglena* show an interesting combination of plant and animal characteristics. The outer covering is a thin, flexible membrane like the membranes of typical animal cells. At the anterior end of the cell is a **gullet** opening which leads to an enlarged **reservoir**. The gullet and reservoir closely resemble similar structures found in distinctly animal relatives of *Euglena*. Near the gullet is a very noticeable red **eyespot**. This tiny bit of specialized protoplasm is especially sensitive to light and serves to direct the organisms to bright areas in its habitat. Near the center of the mass of cytoplasm is a large *nucleus*.

Perhaps the most striking plant characteristic of *Euglena* is the presence of numerous oval *chloroplasts* which are scattered through the cytoplasm. These bodies contain *chlorophyll*. Most species of *Euglena* carry on photosynthesis and live independently of any outside source of food. Some species eat bacteria. When some *Euglena* lose their chlorophyll, they begin to absorb dissolved organic matter from the water in which they live. Food materials pass through the cell membrane in a way

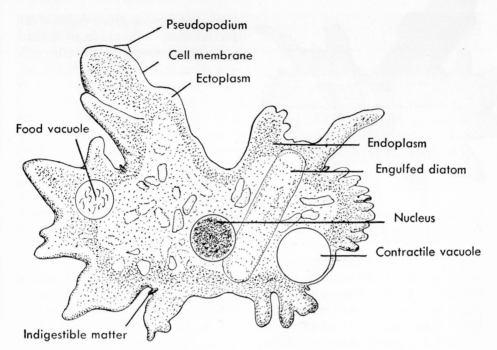

Fig. 21-3. This drawing shows the detailed structure of an *Ameba* cell.

characteristic of animal cells. Thus, these organisms live as green plants in the presence of light but assume a form of animal nutrition when light is not available.

Euglena multiply rapidly under ideal conditions by cell division. A mature organism splits lengthwise, forming two new cells. Thus, a few *Euglena* may give rise to teeming millions within a few days, if conditions for growth are favorable.

Ameba, a mass of living jelly. Living or animated jelly is the best description of this organism, the most primitive of true animals. At first you may overlook *Ameba* (*am*-ee-bah) as a particle of nonliving matter, for it bears little resemblance to other members of the animal kingdom. But the fact that this tiny blob of grayish jelly moves of its own accord, consumes food, and grows in size puts it immediately in the realm of animal life. (See Fig. 21-3.)

Amebae are barely visible to the naked eye when mounted on a microscope slide or confined in a small glass dish. To collect the organisms in their native haunts, take samples of the slime at the bottom of streams and ponds and from the surface of the leaves of aquatic plants.

Under the microscope, an Ameba appears as an irregular mass of jellylike protoplasm surrounded by a thin membrane. When the animal is active, its cytoplasm exhibits a constant flowing motion. This moving cytoplasm presses against the thin cell membrane resulting in numerous projections called *false feet*, or **pseudopodia** (soo-doh-*poh*-dee-ah). The cytoplasm is of two types: (1) an outer, thin layer of watery **ectoplasm** (*eck*-toh-plazm); and (2) an inner area of **endoplasm** (*end*-oh-plazm) which resembles gray jelly with pepper sprinkled through it. The *nucleus* is a large, spherical mass of protoplasm,

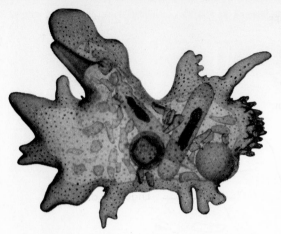

Fig. 21-4. An *Ameba* looks something like this when you see it under a microscope.

somewhat bronze-colored, and changing its position continually with the flowing cytoplasm. Scattered through the cytoplasm are numerous food particles contained in tiny cavities, or **vacuoles.**

Another vacuole expands slowly, forming a large, clear bubble and then contracts suddenly, forcing its contents out through the cell membrane and disappearing. This is the **contractile vacuole** which collects water from the cytoplasm and discharges it through the outer membrane.

How Ameba digests food. Ameba gets food by extending pseudopods and actually flowing around each particle. As a food particle enters the cytoplasm, it is surrounded by a thin membrane and is thus enclosed in a vacuole.

Digestion is accomplished by means of enzymes formed by the cytoplasm which pass into the vacuole and act on the food substances. Digested food is absorbed by the cytoplasm, where it may be oxidized to release energy or assimilated to form additional protoplasm. Undigested particles remain in the vacuole and pass out of the cell at any point in the membrane. Oxygen is absorbed directly from the water and enters the protoplasm over the entire surface of the membrane. Thus, the

Ameba cell shows a certain degree of cell specialization. It carries on all its functions without associating with other cells — a thing that the cells of higher animals and man cannot do since each of these is dependent on the other.

Sensitivity in Ameba. The response of Ameba to conditions around it is a good example of the sensitivity of protoplasm. It has no eyes, yet it is sensitive to light and seeks areas of darkness or dim light. It has no nerve endings such as we associate with the sense of touch, but reacts to jarring. It moves away from the objects with which it comes in contact in the water.

You can see how it responds to food by placing small amounts of food in a culture. Watch how the *Ameba* cells flock to the place where the food is located. Mere chance doesn't cause this to happen. The food, perhaps by a chemical attraction, acts as a stimulus to the cells. Unfavorable conditions, such as dryness or cold, cause some species of *Ameba* to become inactive and to withdraw into a rounded mass. When favorable conditions return, the organisms resume activity.

Reproduction in Ameba. In the presence of aboundant food and ideal conditions for growth, *Ameba* rapidly reaches maximum size. Reproduction occurs when the mass or volume of protoplasm has become so great that the membrane surface cannot supply enough food and oxygen, and remove waste. *Reproduction* is accomplished by division of the mature cells of the *Ameba* into two smaller organisms. The nucleus divides first, forming two similar portions which move to opposite ends of the cell. The rest of the protoplasm then separates gradually, forming two distinct masses. Each has a nucleus and is capable of independent life and growth.

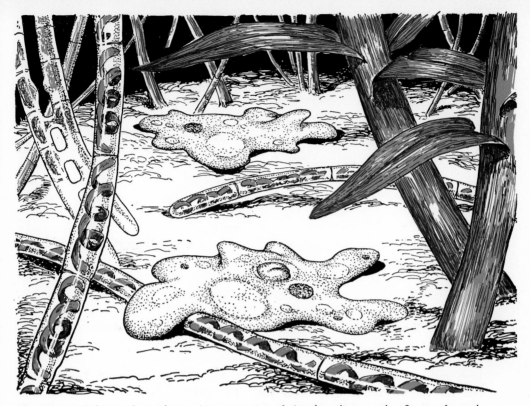

Fig. 21-5. Habitat of *Amebae*. Many species of *Amebae* live on the floors of ponds among the algae and other fresh-water plants.

Paramecium, a complex protozoan. *Paramecium* (par-ah-*mee*-see-um) lives in stagnant water where it often forms a scum on the surface. You can easily cultivate it in the laboratory by making a *hay infusion*. Put some boiled timothy hay or leaves in distilled water. Then add a portion of pond water containing *Paramecium* cells, or the contents of a commercially prepared *Paramecium* culture. Set the infusion in a warm place in the laboratory for several days. The liquid will soon be teeming with various kinds of Protozoa (if pond water is used) and great numbers of saprophytic bacteria which live on the hay.

Paramecium is shaped like the sole of a shoe. (See Fig. 21-8.) It doesn't change its shape as *Ameba* does, but it is by no means rigid. It often bends around an object it happens to meet when swimming. The form of the cell is maintained by a thickened cell membrane called a **pellicle** (*pell*-ih-kal) surrounding the protoplasm.

Perhaps, the most striking characteristic of this one-celled animal is its rapid movement. When you put it on a microscope slide, it appears to swim rapidly through the thin film of water between the slide and cover glass. Its actual rate of movement is quite slow — about 3 inches per minute; but the microscope magnifies the speed to the same extent it does the object. A few strands of cotton or filaments or algae serve as effective barricades in preparing a slide for examination of these fast-moving organisms. They move by tiny, hairlike **cilia** (*sil*-ih-ah), which project through minute openings in the cell membrane. These cilia are arranged in

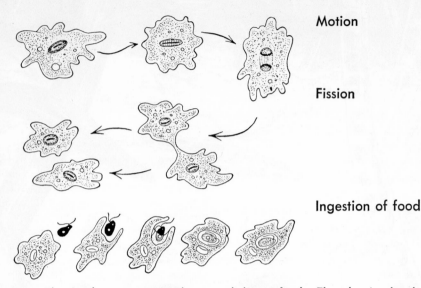

Motion

Fission

Ingestion of food

Fig. 21-6. The *Ameba* moves, reproduces, and digests food. Thus the *Ameba* shows a certain degree of cell specialization.

rows and are lashed through the water like tiny oars. While they cover the entire cell, they're most easily seen along the edges of the organism.

Another striking feature of *Paramecium* is a deep **oral groove** along one side of the cell. This depressed area is lined with long cilia which cause the animal to rotate around its long axis as it swims through the water. *Paramecium* has a definite *anterior end* which is rounded, and a more pointed *posterior end* — a perfect design in streamlining. The oral groove runs from the anterior end toward the posterior end. At its lower end, the oral groove forms a narrow gullet which leads into the cell's endoplasm. The bottom of the groove is called the **mouth cavity,** and marks the point at which food enters the gullet. The oral groove is lined with cilia which lash inward toward the gullet. The action of the cilia and the forward movement of the organism force food particles into the gullet, from which they enter the cell protoplasm in the form of food vacuoles.

Internal structure of Paramecium. The internal structure of the cell illustrates a high degree of specialization of protoplasm. Like *Ameba,* the cytoplasm of *Paramecium* is in a constant state of motion. In *Paramecium,* however, the flow is confined by the outer membrane and follows a circular course around the cell. Food vacuoles circulate with the cytoplasm, digestion occurring in the vacuoles during the process. Undigested food passes to a special opening through the pellicle called the **anal** (*ay*-nal) **spot.** This tiny opening, quite difficult to see, is located near the posterior end of the cell.

The **contractile vacuoles** are two in number and have a definite location, one near either end of the cell. Surrounding each vacuole are numerous **canals** which radiate from the central cavity into the cytoplasm. The canals enlarge as they fill with water, after which their content is passed to the central cavity and excreted at the surface through a tiny opening.

As in the *Ameba,* the contractile

vacuoles of *Paramecium* serve as a means of removing excess water that has entered by osmosis. Since the protoplasm of the cell contains many substances such as salts, sugars, and proteins, water will pass through the semipermeable *pellicle*. Unless there were some means of getting rid of this excess water, the cell would swell and burst.

Reproduction in Paramecium. The organism posesses two different nuclei which are located near the center of the cell. A *large nucleus,* or **macronucleus** (mak-roh-*new*-klee-us), regulates the normal activity of the cell. Near the large nucleus is a *small nucleus,* or **micronucleus** (mike-roh-*new*-klee-us), which functions during reproduction.

Reproduction may involve two distinct processes: (1) *fission;* and (2) *conjugation.* **Fission** involves the separation of a cell in two parts in a way similar to the reproduction of *Ameba.* Both nuclei elongate and pull apart, half of each moving to either end of the cell. Following division of the two nuclei, a constriction forms through the center of the cell.

The lower portion of the oral groove and the gullet remain with the lower daughter cell. The upper daughter cell soon forms these two parts again by means of regeneration. **Regeneration** is the ability of cells and entire organisms to form new parts. Fission may occur several times a day under ideal conditions, but usually conjugation occurs after a limited number of divisions.

During **conjugation,** two *Paramecium* cells unite by joining together in the region of the mouth cavity. Their cell membranes become quite thin at the point where the two cells join. Complicated divisions occur in the micronucleus, resulting in the formation of numerous particles of nuclear material. An exchange of particles of the micro-

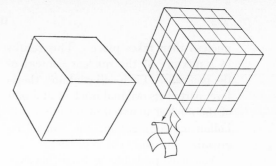

Fig. 21-7. The cube on the left and the one on the right have the same volume. If you could measure the surface exposed on the six faces of the left cube, you would find it to be only a small fraction of the total surface area of the 64 small cubes on the right. This volume-surface relation in cells is critical. A large cell increases the surface without increasing the volume of protoplasm by cell division.

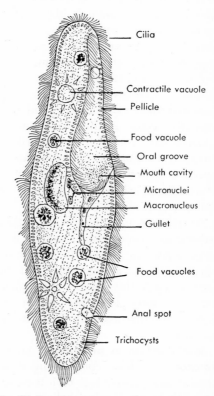

Cilia

Contractile vacuole

Pellicle

Food vacuole

Oral groove

Mouth cavity

Micronuclei

Macronucleus

Gullet

Food vacuoles

Anal spot

Trichocysts

Fig. 21-8. Here you see the structure of a *Paramecium* cell. Compare it with *Ameba* in Fig. 21-3.

nucleus then takes place. This results in a mixture of the nuclear content of the two cells. Each cell contains, therefore, part of its original nucleus and part of the nuclear material of the other cell. Following conjugation, the nuclei reorganize and the cells separate.

You have probably realized that conjugation is not actually reproduction because no new individuals are formed. Rather, for some species, it is a revitalizing of the cells. It increases their vitality and makes them better able to continue their reproduction by fission. It is like conjugation in *Spirogyra* in some ways, but differs chiefly in that no zygospores are formed.

Sensitivity in Paramecium. The reactions of *Paramecium* cells to conditions around them are remarkable, considering that this animal, like *Ameba,* has no specialized sense organs. Except when feeding, the cells swim constantly, bumping into objects, reversing, and moving around them in a trial-and-error fashion. Excessive heat and cold, chemicals, the lack of oxygen, and food substances cause definite reactions in *Paramecium.* One of the most striking sensitivity reactions occurs when the organism is molested by enemies and at certain times when it is feeding on smaller organisms.

Special protoplasmic threads, called **trichocysts** (*trik*-oh-sists), which normally appear as minute lines just inside the pellicle, are exploded into the water through tiny pores. The trichocysts are quite long and, when exploded, give the organism a bristly appearance.

Specialization of protoplasm in the Protozoa. *Euglena, Ameba,* and *Paramecium* were selected as typical examples of Protozoa. Biologists have found about 20,000 different species of this group. They are all one-celled animals

ranging from simple creatures like *Ameba* to complex organisms like *Paramecium.* The progression through these organisms from simple to complex forms shows the increasing specialization of protoplasm. Different degrees of specialization are especially well illustrated in a comparison of the structure and activity of *Ameba* and *Paramecium.*

Economic importance of the Protozoa. Many of the Protozoa lead a rather unimportant existence in freshwater ponds and streams. Certain of their number, however, are of great economic importance. They are a source of food for larger animals and form part of the food chain of a pond.

Some Protozoa, notably the ones living in salt water, secrete a hard wall made of *calcium* (*kal*-see-um) or *silicon* (*sil*-ih-kon). This may appear as the elaborately beautiful organisms. Members of this group, called the *foramini-*

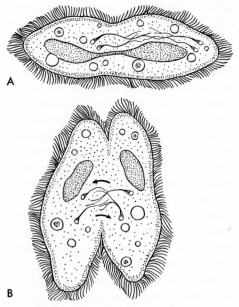

Fig. 21-9. Reproduction in *Paramecium* may be carried on by one of two methods as shown above. A. Dividing cell, or fission. B. Conjugating pair of cells.

COMPARISON OF AMEBA AND PARAMECIUM

	AMEBA	PARAMECIUM
Form	Variable	Constant
Locomotion	Pseudopodia	Cilia
Speed	Slow	Rapid
Food-getting	Pseudopodia surrounding food	Cilia; oral groove
Food taken in	At any point on membrane	Through gullet
Respiration	Contact with dissolved oxygen in water; over cell surface	Same
Excretion	Contractile vacuole, variable	Two contractile vacuoles, constant
Sensation	Responds to light, heat, contact, moisture, etc.	Same
Reproduction	Fission	Fission; conjugation

fers (for-a-*min*-ih-fers), are responsible for the formation of many of the limestone and chalk deposits throughout the world. As they die, their miniature skeletons fall to the bottom of the sea, and there, with billions of others, form a muddy deposit. If, as the earth's surface changes, this is dried out, it will become a hard deposit.

The action of the Protozoa in the intestines of some animals in digesting certain foods is a good illustration of a symbiotic relationship. In cattle they play such a role, and in the intestines of termites, the Protozoa are chiefly responsible for digesting the woody material they eat.

Pathogenic types of Protozoa. There are many animal organisms beside the bacteria and the fungi which are parasitic on animals.

When the disease-producing Protozoa are studied, many people are surprised to find that the great majority of humans and most animals are infected with some type of Protozoa. In man and most animals, the favorite place for

these infections is the intestine. There a flourishing collection of these animals can be found. If you examine the intestinal contents of a freshly-killed animal under the microscope, you will probably see a great many Protozoa. In the intestine, they live on food material there. Some may invade the intestinal wall to show up later in the blood stream and finally lodge in some other part of the body.

Some biologists disagree as to the precise classification of the *spirochetes* (*spy*-ro-keets). They twist and turn like Protozoa, but in many other respects they resemble bacteria. The list of diseases for which they are responsible include some of the most vicious, widespread, and difficult to cure maladies which afflict mankind. One of the venereal diseases called *syphilis* and a very common tropical disease, *yaws*, are on this list.

Many local and international health organizations are waging a determined battle to reduce the amount of these diseases in the world.

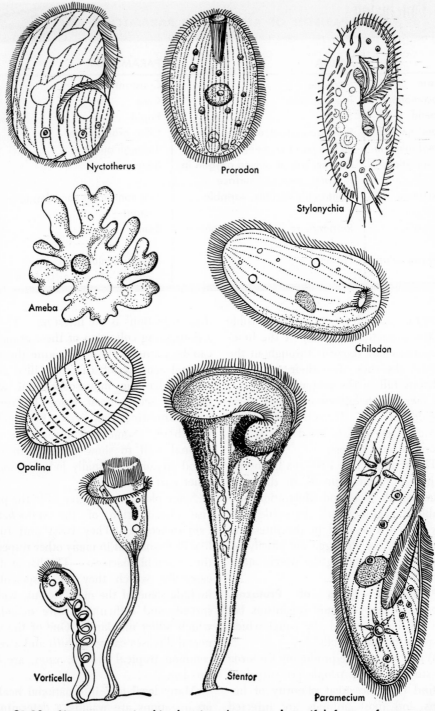

Fig. 21-10. You can see in this drawing the many beautiful forms of some typical Protozoa.

In Conclusion

Protozoa, the simplest forms of animal life, are one-celled animals which function as complete organisms. *Euglena* is a connecting link between the plant and animal kingdoms, since it has certain characteristics of both groups.

Ameba represents a simple form of animal life. This shapeless mass of living protoplasm lacks the specialization of other protozoan cells, yet in its primitive way, performs all of the processes of life. *Paramecium,* on the other hand, illustrates a high degree of specialization.

A great economic importance of the protozoans is found in those forms which live as parasites in the bodies of man and animals, and which cause disease.

The next chapter will introduce us to some other very interesting animals, but they are made up of many cells rather than one cell. They are more complex than the Protozoa.

Questions for Review

1. Why do the plant and animal kingdoms form an imaginary " V " rather than two parallel lines?

2. (a) What are the chief classes of Protozoa? (b) Give an example of each.

3. List the characteristics of *Euglena* which tend to make it an animal and those which tend to make it a plant.

4. Why is *Ameba* even more simple than *Euglena* and other Protozoa?

5. Describe the way in which *Ameba* obtains its food.

6. Describe motion in *Ameba*.

7. Describe the specialized structures which are present in *Paramecium* which were not found in *Ameba*.

8. (a) Explain how *Paramecium* cells multiply. (b) How are they rejuvenated?

9. Describe various ways in which *Paramecium* shows sensitivity.

10. Mention several ways in which Protozoa are of economic importance to man.

11. Name some of the pathogenic types of Protozoa and the diseases they cause.

Biologically Speaking

anal spot	eyespot	oral groove
anterior	fission	pellicle
cilia	food vacuole	posterior
conjugation	foraminifers	Protozoa
contractile vacuole	gullet	pseudopodia
ectoplasm	macronucleus	regeneration
endoplasm	micronucleus	spirochetes
euglenoid movement	mouth cavity	trichocysts

 ——————— **Applying Facts and Principles**

1. In what ways are the Protozoa important parts of the plant and animal population of a pond?

2. Biologists frequently say that understanding the life processes of a single protozoan will enable them to understand the life processes of complicated organisms like man. Explain why this is probably true.

3. What useful functions could certain Protozoa perform in the human intestine?

4. What reasons can you give for the fact that *Paramecium* has two contractile vacuoles rather than one, as in *Ameba*?

5. What reasons can you give for the fact that Protozoa reach a certain maximum size and then divide but never exceed this microscopic size?

CHAPTER 22

Sponges and Coelenterates

Looking back on the Protozoa you will agree that after all is said and done, theirs is a fairly simple type of animal life. Their body consists of only one cell which performs all the necessary life activities.

Now we come to the second large subdivision of the animal kingdom, the *Metazoa*. This group contains all those animals whose bodies consist of more than one cell. But we must remember one important fact. Regardless of how many cells any animal has when it is mature, it began life as a one-celled organism. During its early hours when it was merely a fertilized egg it was no bigger than a protozoan. The difference between a protozoan and a metazoan animal is merely that the protozoan never increases in the number of its cells.

Division of labor. When cells live in close association with other cells, as they do in the body of a metazoan animal, there must be some division of labor. The story of Robinson Crusoe will show you what we mean.

After Crusoe's ship was wrecked, he found himself alone on an island. He had to catch and prepare his food. He had to make his clothes and shoes. He had to build his house and protect himself from any enemies that might be present. Even though he learned how to do all these things, he could not devote enough time to any one job to excel in it. He was like a protozoan, where one cell must perform all its activities without the aid of any other cells.

Now, if there had been ten men shipwrecked with Crusoe, each could have specialized in a job. One man could have hunted food, while another was building a house or making clothes for the group. They could have formed a small society with much greater efficiency than Crusoe's simple, solitary existence. An increase in numbers allows for what we call **division of labor**. This takes place in the many-celled organisms like the metazoan animals. Cells become specialists in performing certain functions for the benefit of all the cells.

The modification of a cell to perform a specialized activity is known as **adaptation**. The more perfectly a plant or animal is adapted to its environment, the better its chance to survive. As we study metazoan animals, from the more simple ones to those which are more complex, we will find increasing cell specialization. As a result of this specialization, the animal is better able to adjust to its environment. Cell specialization is carried to the highest degree in the *vertebrates*, the subphylum to which man belongs (see Appendix, in back of book). **Vertebrates** are all metazoan animals which have a backbone. **Invertebrates** are all metazoan animals which do not have a backbone.

Fig. 22-1. This underwater view shows several forms of animal life, including sponges and corals. Why do we speak of these animals as simple metazoa?

Interdependence of cells. Division of labor and cell adaptation result in the dependence of cells on each other. This vital relationship is **interdependence**. The man who devotes his life solely to one task is liable to lose the ability to do other necessary things. He depends on other specialists for help in these phases of his life. When cells are specialized for one activity, they become dependent on other cells for other activities. The *Ameba* can live independently in a pond. But a muscle, nerve, or bone cell removed from your body cannot live independently.

Some metazoan phyla. We will take a look at eight phyla of metazoans. The table on page 279 will give you a summary of the most important of these phyla.

The Porifera. The first metazoan phylum, the *Porifera* (poh-*rif*-er-ah),

consists of creatures which really are just one step beyond a colony of independent cells. Their cells show considerable independence, yet sufficient interdependence to classify them as real metazoans.

The animals in this phylum are called **sponges.** Most sponges live in the ocean attached to rocks or other objects, or to the ocean bottom. A few species live in fresh-water lakes and streams. They may be dome-shaped like a cup, a cone, or a cylinder, and may vary in size from a pinhead to over six feet in length. The living sponge may vary in color from white, gray, brown, red, orange, yellow, to black. Were it not for its skeleton, the sponge would be a shapeless mass of animal matter.

Sponge skeletons vary in form and composition, depending on the kind of sponge. Some are composed of numer-

SUMMARY OF IMPORTANT METAZOAN GROUPS

PHYLUM	DEGREE OF SPECIALIZATION	REPRESENTATIVES
Porifera (Sponges)	Cells in two layers, penetrated by numerous canals. Slight specialization for food-getting, digestion, and reproduction	Salt-water and fresh-water sponges
Coelenterata	Cells in two layers around a central cavity. More specialized than sponges. Capable of movement and defense	Jellyfish, *Hydra*, coral polyps, sea anemone
Platyhelminthes (Flatworms)	Cells in three layers; various organ systems; many parasitic. Bodies flattened and unsegmented	*Planaria*, flukes, tapeworms
Nemathelminthes (Roundworms)	Round, unsegmented bodies; various organ systems; many parasitic	*Ascaris*, pinworms, *Trichinella*, hookworm, vinegar eel, "horsehair snake"
Rotifera	"Wheel animals" with rows of cilia around mouth; well-developed digestive system	Rotifers
Annelida (Segmented worms)	Body divided into segments; organs well-developed	Earthworm, leech, sea worm, *Tubifex*
Arthropoda	Segmented bodies, 3 or more pairs of jointed appendages; external skeleton, well-developed ventral nervous systems; all senses present	Lobster, crayfish, crab, insects, spiders, ticks, centipedes, millepedes
Mollusca	Mantle and muscular foot present; soft bodies with or without a protective shell	Clam, oyster, scallop, snail, slug, squid, octopus
Echinodermata	Radially symmetrical, spiny skinned, highly complex organs; true nerves	Starfish, brittle star, sea urchin, sand dollar, sea cucumber, crinoids
Chordata (Subphylum Vertebrata)	Animals having a backbone; internal and external specialization; brain; varied locomotion, never more than two pairs of limbs	Fish, amphibia, reptiles, birds, mammals (including man)

Fig. 22-2. After being dried and bleached, bath sponges are ready for commercial use.

the openings of *canals* which penetrate the layers of cells. They lead to larger internal canals or to a large central cavity, the **gastral cavity**. Moving flagella of the collar cells of the inner layer create a current, which draws water in through the pores in the sides and forces it out through an opening usually at the top. A tremendous amount of water passes through the canals of a sponge to supply food and oxygen to the cells and to carry away their waste products.

Sponges reproduce in several ways. They may grow buds, usually near the base at the point of attachment. The bud enlarges on the parent sponge for a time, then breaks off and lives independently. Sexual reproduction also occurs as a result of the formation of eggs and sperms.

ous hard **spicules** (*spike*-yules) of lime or silicon. The material used in the formation of the spicules is extracted from the water by the sponge cells. Other sponges, like the bath sponge, produce a more pliable and leathered skeleton composed of spongin fibers. **Spongin** is a secretion of the cells. When we use a sponge to clean a car or for bathing, we are using this material.

The sponge body consists of two layers of cells with a jellylike substance between them. The outer layer of cells can be compared to the skin of higher animals because it is protective. Some of the cells comprising the inner layer have curious collars with flagella projecting through them. These flagellate cells set up currents in the water and draw food into the sponge's body. Strange wandering cells, resembling *Ameba,* move through the jellylike substance between the layers.

Numerous **pores** are located in the body wall of the sponge. This accounts for the name *Porifera.* The pores are

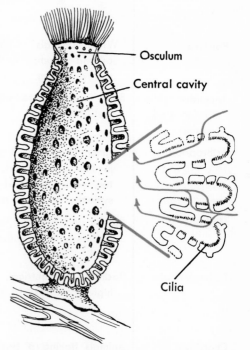

Osculum

Central cavity

Cilia

Fig. 22-3. Water continually enters the sponge through the minute pores in its body, as shown by the arrows above. The water is forced out through the opening (osculum) at the top.

Fig. 22-4. One of the most beautiful coelenterates is the sea anemone which resembles a brightly-colored flower. It is easily seen in tide pools on rocky shores.

Sponge growers multiply sponges by cutting them in many pieces and sowing the pieces in special sponge beds. Each piece then *regenerates* a new sponge. To **regenerate** means to produce or form a new organism. This method of reproduction is used because it is faster than budding would be.

Sponges are collected by divers or by the use of drag hooks. The animals are then piled on shore or hung in the rigging of the boat until the flesh has decayed. The remaining spongin skeletons are then washed, dried, sorted, and sometimes bleached. They are then ready for market.

Famous sponge fishing grounds include the Mediterranean and Red Seas, the waters around the West Indies, and Tarpon Springs, Florida.

The coelenterates. Strange indeed are the pulsating jellyfish which bob around in the ocean currents, dangling long, stringy tentacles under a floating, inflated sac. Also in this phylum, as well as the jellyfish, are such animals as the hydroids, corals, sea fans, sea anemones, and Portuguese man-of-war. Some are very beautiful to see and others are so tiny as to be almost invisible. Some live in fresh water, but many of them live in salt water environments. Some live deep in the sea and others can exist only near the shore in shallow water.

Hydra. One of the most common fresh-water coelenterates is a small animal called *Hydra*. *Hydra* is attached to plants and other objects in quiet ponds and streams. There are many

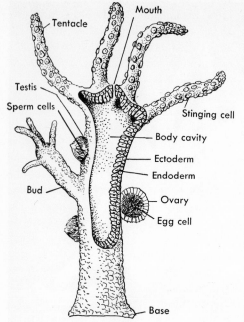

Tentacle
Mouth
Testis
Sperm cells
Stinging cell
Body cavity
Ectoderm
Endoderm
Bud
Ovary
Egg cell
Base

Fig. 22-5. This drawing of a *Hydra* shows the internal and external structures. It consists of two layers of cells with a jellylike material between the two layers.

species, which may be white, brown, or green. The tubular body expands or shrinks from an inch to less than an eighth of an inch as the animal seeks food.

The body of *Hydra* consists of two layers of cells. We call the outer layer the **ectoderm** and the inner layer the **endoderm**. Like the sponge, *Hydra* has a layer of jellylike substance between the cell layers. The animal attaches itself to plants or other objects by means of a **basal disk**. It may leave one place of attachment and float or move to another, or secrete a bubble at the base and float to the surface upside down. Hydra moves also in a peculiar somersaulting fashion as shown in Fig. 22-6.

A circular mouth at the end of the body opposite the basal disk leads to a large, internal **gastrovascular cavity.** Water in this cavity comes in contact with the inner layer of cells. The *mouth* is surrounded by a ring of six to ten movable **tentacles.** They are hollow, and this cavity connects with the gastrovascular cavity. This may be considered the beginning of a digestive system.

Numerous **stinging cells** or **capsules** are scattered over the surface of the tentacles. When a victim comes in contact with the tentacles of *Hydra,* the stinging capsules explode and pierce the victim's body surface with tiny hollow spines. The poison the cell contains paralyzes the prey immediately. The *Hydra* tentacles then carry the victim to the mouth, where it is thrust into the gastrovascular cavity. Digestion then occurs in the cavity and undigested food and cell wastes are forced out of the cavity through the mouth.

Reproduction of Hydra. *Hydra* reproduces by forming **buds.** A bud appears first as a knob growing out from the side of the adult and later develops tentacles. After a period of growth, it separates from the parent and lives independently. This is *asexual reproduc-*

Fig. 22-6. The *Hydra* moves by a kind of somersaulting. It bends over, attaches its tentacles to the bottom, loosens its base, swings the base over the mouth, and attaches it to the bottom. After loosening the tentacles, it repeats the process.

Fig. 22-7. The mouth of the jellyfish is at the end of the long trumpet-shaped stalk which you see above.

tion. *Sexual reproduction* usually occurs in autumn. The eggs are produced along the body wall in little swellings called **ovaries** (*oh*-vah-rees). The sperm cells are formed in similar structures called **testes** (*tes*-tees).

After fertilization, the zygote grows into a spherical, many-celled structure which produces a hard, protective cover. In this stage, it leaves the parent animal and goes through a rest period before forming a new *Hydra*. Like the sponge, *Hydra* has the remarkable power of regeneration. If an animal is cut into pieces, each piece will regenerate the missing parts and become a whole animal again.

The behavior of Hydra. This shows an advance of coelenterates over the more primitive sponge. If you touch a tentacle of an extended *Hydra* with a needle, all the tentacles and the body contract suddenly. Apparently, the ir-

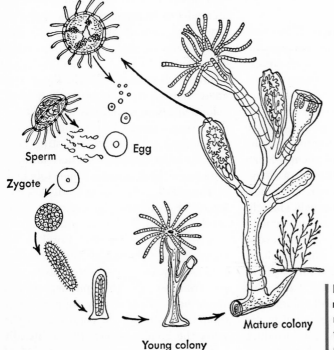

Sperm

Egg

Zygote

Young colony

Mature colony

Fig. 22-8. *Obelia* is the name of a genus of colonial coelenterates. Note that in this life history eggs and sperms are produced.

Fig. 22-9. Corals are strikingly beautiful in their varied forms and colors. The solid limy structure is the result of the life activities of many individual animals, the polyps.

ritation of one tentacle is sent to other cells through a series of nerve cells called the **nerve net.** This net lies in the middle layer of the body. The contraction itself is accomplished by slender fibers lying in the ectoderm, and these can be compared to the muscle cells of higher animals. *Hydra* has no real nervous system such as higher animals have and it has no brain.

The jellyfish. These creatures have earned the respect of swimmers who may come in contact with them. Some species have been found with a diameter of seven feet and with a tentacle spread of 100 feet. Strangely enough, many show an alternation of generations. In one stage of the life cycle, gametes are formed. The fertilized eggs then develop into a strange, plant-like colony of individuals. On this structure are formed the individual jellyfish by budding. These jellyfish are the sexual stages, that is, they produce either eggs or sperms. Following fer-

tilization, the eggs develop into free-swimming stages. When these mature, they settle on some base and reproduce asexually by budding to form a new colony. Fig. 22-8 shows the complete life cycle of one of these colonial coelenterates.

One well-known jellyfish, the Portuguese man-of-war, is really a floating colony of animals that has the ability of delivering a severe and poisonous sting. The poison comes from the sting cells found on the tentacles. These animals are extremely dangerous when touched.

The coral. This is the only coelenterate of economic importance. The coral is a small, flowerlike animal a fraction of an inch in length. Coral, as we know it, is a deposit of lime removed from sea water. The tiny polyps project from pores in the lime deposit. A single mass of coral may support many thousand animals. A coral reef represents the combined activity of literally billions of them over a long period of

Fig. 22-10. The drawings above show the three different kinds of coral reefs. Left: the marginal type growing around an island. Center: the barrier reef widely separated from the water. Right: an atoll with an open lagoon.

time. Coral reefs are most common in the warm, shallow oceans. Reefs may be: (1) the *marginal* type, close to the beach; (2) the *barrier* type, forming a ring around an island with a wide stretch of water between the beach and the reef; or (3) in the form of a ring with an open lagoon in the center, called an *atoll* (*at*-ol). See Fig. 22-10.

The Great Barrier Reef off the north-ern coast of Australia extends about 1,100 miles parallel to the coast. It is about 50 miles wide. Certainly, the military experience of World War II and during the atomic and hydrogen bomb tests in the South Pacific has shown us the vast extent of the coral formations there. We soon discovered its useful-ness in the construction of airstrips and roads.

In Conclusion

The sponges, simplest of the metazoan animals, represent a step above the pro-tozoans in complexity. These curious colonies of cells pump the sea into their bodies and force out water through a central cavity. The corals, jellyfish, and *Hydra,* representing the coelenterates, are slightly more complex. Here, two layers of cells form a tubular body. You might regard these simple creatures as nature's first effort to produce an animal with tissues.

Proceeding through invertebrate phyla in the next chapter, we will consider three groups of animals classed as worms. However, their elongated bodies are about the only thing the various worms have in common. Still more complicated than the highest worms are the starfish and its relatives and the clam and other mollusks. You may be surprised at the complex internal structure of the members of these invertebrate phyla.

Questions for Review

1. What principal characteristic distin-guishes the protozoans from metazoan?

2. How does increase in number of cells in a metazoan permit division of labor?

3. What is the chief difference between the invertebrates and the vertebrates?

4. Describe the usual habitat of the sponges and coelenterates.

5. What evidence is there for saying sponge cells are interdependent?

6. Describe the movement of water through a sponge and what uses the sponge makes of the water.

7. Give examples of regeneration in the sponges and coelenterates.

8. How does *Hydra* catch its food? How does *Hydra* move?

9. How is *Hydra* more sensitive than the sponges?

10. (a) Describe the formation of a coral reef. (b) What are three types of coral reefs?

 **Biologically Speaking**

adaptation	endoderm	regeneration
atoll	gastrovascular cavity	spicules
basal disk	independence	spongin
buds	interdependence	tentacles
division of labor	invertebrate	testes
ectoderm	ovaries	vertebrate

 **Applying Facts and Principles**

1. In what ways is the "division of labor" idea shown in modern civilization?

2. Some scientists believe there are several ways in which a metazoan organism is really more than merely the sum of its specialized cells. Explain.

3. Why is it essential that a jellyfish be hollow?

4. How do you suppose the alternation of generations in the jellyfish is similar to the life cycles of plants?

5. How do you account for the fact that some sponges, when exposed briefly to air and promptly returned to water, die?

6. Why is the sponge considered the most primitive form of metazoan life?

CHAPTER 23

Observing Worms, Echinoderms, and Mollusks

When you think of a worm, you probably visualize a lowly, crawling animal — possibly the " night crawler " you put on your hook when you go fishing. This " night crawler " is a true worm. However, it is only one kind of worm and totally different from the members of two other invertebrate phyla which contain other kinds. Some worms have hardly any internal systems. Others, like the earthworm, have " hearts " and blood vessels, brain and nerve cords, and many other well-developed organs.

How are worms important to us? The earthworm renders a highly valuable service in moving soil and adding to its fertility. Other worms of an entirely different kind are dangerous parasites in man as well as in other animals.

When is a worm not a worm? Many animals which resemble worms in general form — caterpillars and grubs, for example — are not worms at all. These are immature moths, butterflies, or beetles. When you finish this chapter, you will have a much better idea of what a biologist terms a " worm."

The starfish, its relatives, and the clam and other mollusks are more complex organisms than one would think. Thus, biologists do not always agree on how to place these two phyla of invertebrates properly in the animal kingdom.

The flatworms. The least complex phylum of worms is the *Platyhelminthes* (plat-ee-hel-*min*-theez), or flatworms. These flat-bodied animals have the usual two layers of cells, *endoderm* and *ectoderm* which you saw in the coelenterate group. In addition, the flatworms have a middle layer called the **mesoderm.** All the organs and tissues of the body develop from these three layers of cells. This will also be true in all the other animals we shall study. It is true, too, of man. The flatworms consist of three classes: (1) *fresh-water forms;* (2) *flukes;* and (3) *tapeworms.*

Fresh-water flatworms. *Planaria* is a common fresh-water flatworm (see Fig. 23-1) which is found on sticks and under stones in streams or ponds. It is one-quarter to one-half an inch long and roughly resembles an Indian spearhead in its shape. At the anterior end are two prominent *eyespots.* The *mouth* is on the lower side, near the center of the body, and at the end of a projecting tube.

Planaria are attracted to a piece of raw liver placed in a pond or stream. After a few hours these tiny animals gather. Their feeding habits make them scavengers, cleaning up dead organic matter in the water. They also feed on small water animals. One of the remarkable characteristics of this animal is its ability to regenerate after you have cut it. It can be cut into six pieces, and each piece will form new parts to produce six complete worms.

287

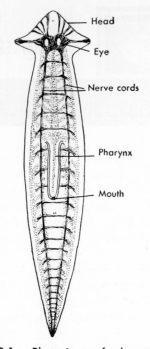

Fig. 23-1. Planaria, a fresh-water flat-worm, has a definite head, with eyes and other sense organs. Note the location of the mouth.

Flukes. *Flukes* are dangerous parasites in many animals, including man.

The flukes have complicated life histories, usually involving a snail and one or more other hosts. The *sheep-liver fluke* lives as an adult in the gall bladder of the sheep. Eggs pass from the gall bladder to the intestine and, if they fall in water, they hatch into a larva which enters the body of a particular kind of snail. In the snail, the larvae pass through several stages during which they increase in number by asexual reproduction. They then leave the snail, crawl upon blades of grass along water, and form a cyst. If a sheep eats this cyst within ten days after it has been formed, the fluke enters the sheep's liver and the cycle starts over again. (See Fig. 23-2.)

The widespread condition of human fluke infections in the world is not confined just to the Orient where they are the most common. Blood flukes are still common in certain areas. One type causes a " swimmers' itch " along the shores of some of the lakes in northern United States. In almost all cases, however, the best control of flukes is to eliminate one of the hosts in its life

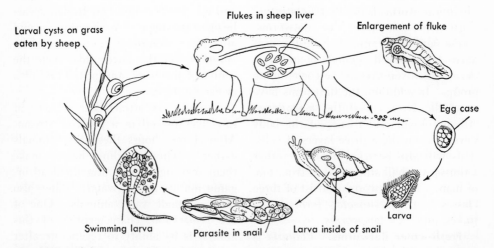

Fig. 23-2. Flukes are parasitic flatworms. Here you see the life cycle of the sheep liver fluke as it passes from the body of the sheep, to the snail, and then to the grass which the sheep eats.

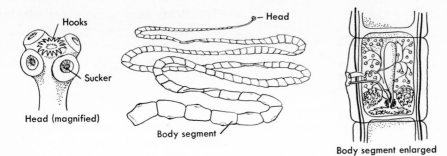

Fig. 23-3. This is the way one species of tapeworm looks. Inspection of meat has greatly reduced the number of tapeworm victims. However, it is best to avoid eating meat that is not cooked thoroughly.

cycle. Usually this is a snail of some particular species.

Tapeworms. The *tapeworm* is the best-known of the parasitic flatworms. An adult tapeworm has a flat, ribbonlike body and is grayish white in color. (See Fig. 23-3.) The very small knob-shaped head is equipped with **suckers** and, in certain species, with a ring of **hooks.** Below the slender neck are an indefinite number of nearly square sections, extending to a length of as much as 30 feet. Since new proglottids are formed at the head end, the oldest and largest sections are on the posterior end. The **proglottids** are essentially masses of reproductive organs. The worms are hermaphroditic, that is, having both male and female organs, and eggs formed in a proglottid are fertilized there. When the eggs mature, the proglottids break off and may be eaten by some animal such as a pig, cow, or fish.

Tapeworms enter the human body in a resting or **cyst** (*sist*) stage in the flesh of hogs, cattle, or fish. Each cyst contains a fully developed tapeworm head. In the human intestine, the head is released from the cyst and attaches itself to the intestinal wall. The worm grows by adding new segments. Digested food is absorbed directly into the segments, thus robbing the host of needed nourishment. As segments containing eggs pass from the intestine with body waste, they may be eaten by hogs or cattle. In the body of the pig, cow, or fish, the eggs form young worms called *larvae* which burrow into the muscles and form cysts. The cycle is repeated when man eats the improperly cooked flesh containing the cysts.

You will notice that in each case of the disease-producing worms, infection is spread and picked up through poor sanitary conditions. The fertilized eggs of the worms are given off with the intestinal wastes, the **feces** (*fee*-sees). When eggs are eaten by animals, the infection is spread.

Roundworms. A second phylum of worms, the roundworms, or **Nemathelminthes** (nem-uh-thel-*min*-thez), is famous for certain of its parasitic members. Here we find the *hookworms* and their allies. When you consider that over one-third of the human race is infected with parasitic roundworms, their importance can hardly be overestimated. Harmless roundworms include the *vinegar eel* and " horsehair snake," and the very numerous beneficial soil nematodes. Roundworms are long and slender and pointed at one or both ends. They have no body divisions or segments and thus

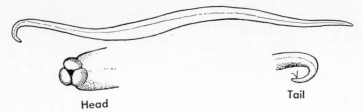

Head   **Tail**

Fig. 23-4. *Ascaris*, a roundworm, usually lives in the intestines of animals or man. There it does little harm unless it goes into the body tissues.

differ from round-bodied worms like the earthworm.

The *nematodes* (*nem*-ah-todes) are still more complex than the flatworms. Their digestive system is a distinct tube or cylinder housed in a long, wormlike body which is also a tube. This enables the animal to take in food through one opening, the mouth, digest it as it passes through the canal and remove the usable parts. The undigested material is eliminated through another opening, the **anus** (*ay*-nus). In the case of the *Hydra,* one opening, the mouth, was used for both food entrance and the elimination of undigested substances. This arrangement of a tube within a tube, however, makes necessary some sort of transportation system within the body. Digested food must be carried to all the cells of the body. Oxygen must also be transported to the interior cells. A circulating fluid, blood, therefore takes care of this new problem in metazoan body-organization. The roundworms are the simplest animals to have both a distinct digestive system and circulatory system.

Ascaris is a large roundworm which lives in the intestine of pigs, horses, and sometimes man. Females are larger than males, and may reach a length of nearly 12 inches. After the eggs have been fertilized, they pass from the intestine with body waste. (See Fig. 23-4.)

The *Trichina worm* (Trichinella) is one of the most dangerous of the parasitic roundworms. It is estimated that over one-fourth of the population of the United States suffer from this infection. It passes its first stage in the pig, dog, rat, or cat as a cyst in the muscles. If man eats pork that is insufficiently cooked, the cyst dissolves in the intestine and releases a worm. The worms reproduce in the intestine and produce larvae, as many as 10,000 being produced from a single worm. The larvae bore through the intestine wall and enter the blood stream. Later they leave the blood vessels and enter the body tissues. This produces the painful disease known as **trichinosis** (trih-kin-*oh*-sis). One method of prevention of this disease is to feed hogs only cooked garbage. But the best way to prevent this disease and other parasitic worm infections is to cook all meat thoroughly.

The *hookworm* of the southern states and all semi-tropical and tropical regions is a serious health menace. Larvae develop in the soil and enter the body by boring through the skin of the feet. Next they enter the blood vessels and travel through the heart to the vessels of the lungs. In the lungs, they enter the air passages and travel through the windpipe to the throat. They are swallowed and pass through the stomach to the intestine, where they attach themselves to the wall by means of hooks. In the human intestine the larvae grow to adult worms. The worms suck blood from the vessels in the intestine wall.

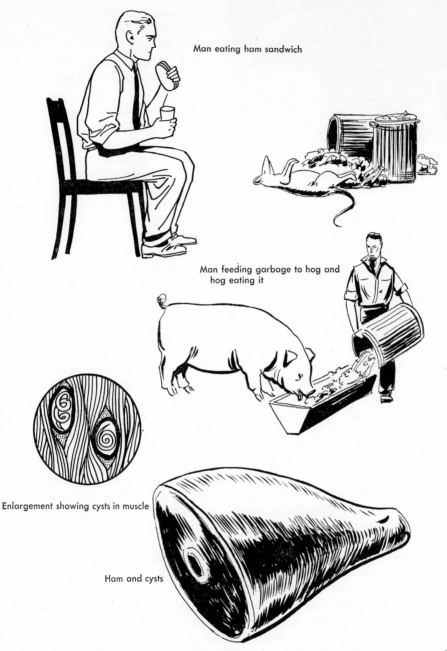

Man eating ham sandwich

Man feeding garbage to hog and hog eating it

Enlargement showing cysts in muscle

Ham and cysts

Fig. 23-5. The trichina worm life cycle is shown here. Trichina infection in man results from eating infected ham or pork that is insufficiently cooked.

Fig. 23-6. This is an unusual photograph of two earthworms. The one on the left is beginning to burrow into the soil.

Loss of blood lowers the victim's vitality by producing anemia. Excretions produced by the worms poison the victim and produce the characteristic laziness. Thus a typical hookworm victim may be quite shiftless and his growth may be retarded, although the latter is not always true. In the intestine, the worms reproduce, the fertilized eggs leaving in the fecal wastes. If these happen to lodge in warm, moist soil, they develop into minute larvae which can enter through cracks in the feet and eventually return to the intestine. Thus, three factors are responsible for the spread of this disease: (1) improper disposal of sewage; (2) warm soil; and (3) going barefoot. Public health agencies have done a remarkable job in reducing the number of cases in the southern United States.

Segmented worms. These worms are the most advanced of the worms in body structure. They belong to a phylum called **Annelida** (an-*nell*-ih-dah). Most segmented worms live in the ocean, although some live in fresh water and others, including the common earthworm, live in the soil. The segmentation characteristic is also found in two of the most complicated phyla which we will study. The annelids seem to be in a half-way spot between the very simple Protozoa and the highly complicated vertebrates. For this reason, and the fact that they are rather common, many biologists study them closely. They are, in a limited sense, a typical invertebrate. (See Figs. 23-7 and 23-8.)

If you examine a common earthworm, you will notice immediately that its body consists of many rings or segments. Furthermore, you'll see that the front, or *anterior end,* is more pointed and darker than the *posterior end.* There is no separate head, nor are there any visible sense organs. The *mouth* is on the anterior end and is crescent-shaped, lying below a *prostomium* (pro-*stow*-mih-um), which is a kind of upper lip. The vertical slit at the posterior end is the opening of the intestine, or **anus.** The segments are often numbered by biologists, starting with the segment containing the mouth as number one in order to locate definitely any special structure. On segments 32–39 there is a conspicuous swelling called the **clitellum** (klih-*tell*-um). It is involved in the animal's reproduction.

Four pairs of bristles, or **setae** (*see*-tee), project from the under surface and sides of each segment except the first and the last. The setae assist in movement and in clinging to the walls of its burrow, as those who hunt " night crawlers " can testify.

The earthworm moves by burying its anterior setae into the soil, then shortening its body by a powerful set of longitudinal muscles which stretch from anterior to posterior ends. The worm then sinks its posterior setae into the soil, withdraws its anterior setae, and makes itself longer. It does this by constricting the circular muscles which are found around the body at each segment. This makes the worm thin but long.

As you study this animal, you will notice that it not only consists of many

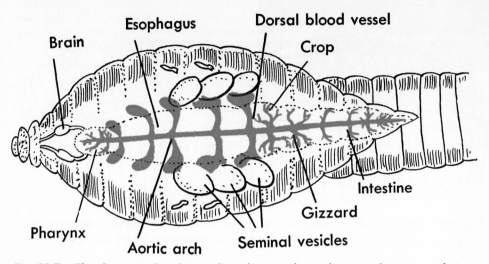

Fig. 23-7. The diagram of a dissected earthworm above shows its digestive and circulatory systems.

cells, but many kinds of specialized cells. These specialized cells, or *tissues,* are organized into larger structures called **organs.** The earthworm is so arranged that a whole series of organs takes care of some fundamental body process. These are called **systems.** Thus we can study in the earthworm the digestive, circulatory, nervous, and reproductive systems.

Digestive system of the earthworm. Below the prostomium is the mouth of the earthworm. There are no jaws or teeth, but it sucks in food (soil) by its muscular **pharynx** (*fahr*-inks). The food particles pass through a long **esophagus** (ee-*sof*-ah-gus) into a round organ called the **crop.** This acts as a temporary storage-place for food. From the crop the food is forced into a very muscular organ called the **gizzard.** There, by rhythmical contractions, the food is ground up by grains of sand rubbing the food particles. In the intestine which stretches from segment 19 to the end of the worm, complete digestion takes place. Enzymes break down the food chemically, and the blood which circu-

lates through the intestine walls absorbs it.

The digestive system of the earthworm takes up most of the room in the interior of the animal. Its organs are complex. The earthworm consumes large quantities of soil which contain organic matter. The useless inorganic matter passes through the system largely unchanged and is deposited on the surface of the ground in the form of *casts.* This method of feeding loosens and enriches the soil and is of great importance to soil fertility.

Circulatory system of the earthworm. As food is digested, the blood in the cir-

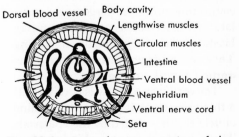

Fig. 23-8. From this cross section of the earthworm, you can see the structure of one segment.

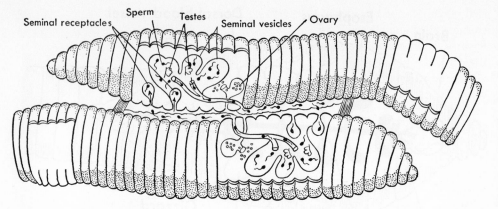

Fig. 23-9. These two worms are exchanging sperms. They are traveling from the semi-nal vesicles of one worm to the seminal receptacles of the other.

culatory system picks it up for distribution to all cells of the body. The body structure of the sponge was so arranged that each cell was responsible for obtaining its own food. But in higher animals greater specialization of cells is necessary to support the activities of a large organism. The transportation or distribution material is a circulating fluid called *blood*. In the wall of the intestine it picks up the digested food.

The blood then moves through a series of closed tubes, or vessels. It flows forward to the *anterior* (front) end on the *dorsal* (top) side and moves toward the *posterior* (back) end through a *ventral* (bottom) blood vessel. Small tubes connect the dorsal and ventral vessels throughout the animal except in segments 7–10. There, the five connecting tubes are large and muscular. By alternate contraction and relaxation, they keep the blood flowing. They are not true hearts, but are called **aortic** (a-*or*-tik) **arches.**

The earthworm's body is covered with a thin skin which is protected by a slimy cuticle that is secreted by the epidermis. Through this the worm absorbs oxygen and gives off carbon dioxide. But this process cannot take place if the cuticle is destroyed. Thus, drying in the sun will kill the worm, as will too much water which dissolves the cuticle.

Carbon dioxide and nitrogen containing waste materials from the cell activities are picked up by the blood and then removed to the outside of the body by little tubes. There are two such structures per segment, and each corresponds to one of the tiny tubes which make up the kidneys of the higher animals. These are the **nephridia** (ne-*frid*-ih-ah).

Nervous system. The nervous system coordinates the movements of the animal and sends impulses received from sense organs to certain parts of the body. In the earthworm, there is a very small brain or nerve center in segment 3. Two nerves form a connecting collar around the pharynx and join to become a long ventral nerve cord. There are enlargements called **ganglia** (*gang*-glee-ah), or nerve centers, in each segment. Two pairs of nerves in turn branch from each ganglion. One pair between each. The earthworm has no eyes or ears, but, nevertheless, it is sensitive to light and sound. Certain cells in the skin are sensitive to these stimuli, and the impulse is carried quickly to the muscles of the earthworm. How quickly they can react to a flash of light at night when you hunt them for the next day's fishing!

Reproduction in the earthworm is complex. Each worm forms both eggs and sperms. However, the eggs of one worm can be fertilized only by sperms from another worm. The eggs are formed in the ovaries and are given off through openings in the ventral side. Sperms are given off through similar openings. In Fig. 23-9, you will see **seminal vesicles** (*ves*-ih-kals) which store the sperms of that earthworm, and **seminal receptacles** which hold sperms from another worm. After mating, the clitellum secretes a slime band in which are deposited the eggs and sperms. Fertilization occurs in the slime band. This dries to form a cocoon in which the young worms develop for a time. Then they break out of the cocoon and crawl out into the soil.

The study of the earthworm will be rewarding if you will carefully study its organization and structures. Find out how each performs its functions and how they all depend on one another. You will see then how a common invertebrate animal has an organization and activities which are quite similar to yours in many respects.

The leech is another segmented worm. It is also called a bloodsucker and is found in streams and ponds. It is an external parasite on fish and other aquatic animals, but may attach itself to your skin while you are swimming or wading in a stream or lake.

Mollusks. These animals are often called *shellfish.* It is not a good name because they are not fish, and many mollusks live on land, and quite a few lack shells. The phylum name **Mollusca** (mol-*luss*-kah) refers to the soft body of these animals.

Fig. 23-10. The leech is a parasitic animal.

Bivalve mollusks have two valves or shells connected by a hinge. Common bivalves include clams, oysters, and scallops.

The clam is a more complex animal than those of you who dig it out of its shells realize. Within the shells is the **mantle.** Actually, this mantle forms the shells from lime, taken from the water. A clam moves slowly by means of a muscular hatchet-shaped *foot* which it pushes out between the shells when no enemies are around. The vital organs are located above the foot.

Water enters the animal's body through an opening called the **ventral siphon.** The water in the clam follows a circular path from the siphon forward along the bottom of the shell, around the front of the body, and out by means of the **dorsal siphon.** In its path, the water flows over the gills, which lie on

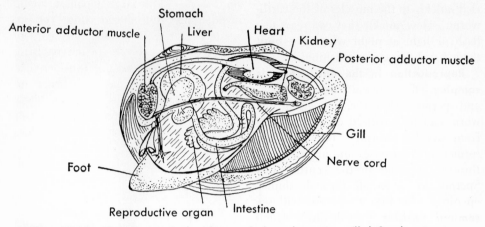

Fig. 23-11. This diagram of a dissected clam shows its well-defined systems.

both sides of the foot. There, oxygen and carbon dioxide are exchanged by the animal's respiratory system. Waste products are poured into the water by the kidney just before it leaves by the dorsal siphon. During the passage of the water through the clam's body, it goes through the digestive organs. Here the food materials — mostly microscopic animals and plants — are collected and digested.

The clam buries itself partially in mud or sand with the " head end " down. The posterior end, with the siphons, remains above the sand or mud line in open water. Strong posterior and anterior muscles close the shell halves. If the diagram in Fig. 23-11 is examined closely, you will see that what seems to be a shapeless animal has an intricate body. There is a well-developed nervous system with several large ganglia. An elaborate circulatory system is present with colorless blood.

The mantle forms the shell and its mother-of-pearl lining. When a grain of sand lodges between the shell and the mantle, the mantle becomes irritated and secretes layers of pearl around it. The most valuable pearls are produced in an oyster (not the edible species) which lives only in tropical seas. Pearl buttons are cut from the shells of clams.

Oysters, scallops, and marine clams are valuable food delicacies. With modern freezing methods, they can be purchased at any season in any part of the country.

Univalve mollusks, or gastropods (*gas*-troh-pods), have only one shell. Land and water snails, conches, and abalones (ab-ah-*loh*-neez) are examples. The snail carries its house on its back at a " snail's pace " of about ten feet per hour. The flat, muscular foot secretes

Fig. 23-12. Land snails are gastropods that feed mostly on leaves.

Fig. 23-13. The slug, another land gastropod, does not have an external shell. Because it eats plant leaves, it is an unwelcome sight to gardeners.

slime on which it travels in rhythmic waves. The eyes of land snails are situated on the tips of two tentacles. When touched, the snail draws in these tentacles as the toe of a stocking vanishes when you turn it inside out.

Many snails are vegetarians and feed on leaves. The large Japanese snail, accidentally introduced into certain western states, is a dangerous garden pest. Certain species of larger land snails are edible and are considered a delicacy. However, as we learned in the last chapter, snails are often hosts in the life cycles of parasitic worms.

The *slug* looks like a snail which has lost its shell. They come out at night, leaving silver trails of slime behind them. Slugs eat plant leaves and cause considerable damage.

Valveless mollusks, or **cephalopods** (*sef*-ah-low-pods) have no external shells but do have internal ones. They also have tentacles which project from their heads and which are used for walking and for food-getting. This group includes the octopus, squid, cuttlefish, and chambered nautilus. The giant squid is probably the largest of all the invertebrates, sometimes weighing as much as two tons. Accounts of bat-

Fig. 23-14. The octopus is a cephalopod with an internal shell. It moves by pulling itself over the rocks with its arms.

Fig. 23-15. The squid is one of the most highly developed of the invertebrates. The shell of the animal is internal and consists of a thin, horny plate.

tles between whales and giant squid have enlivened the tales of the sea for many years. However, the octopus has the worse reputation of the two. This is probably undeserved. One species may possibly be dangerous to man, but there are not enough proven accounts of loss of life to be definite on this point. Some of the squid have luminescent or-gans, the function of which is still un-certain.

Echinoderms. The starfish, brittle star, sea urchin, and sand dollar are common examples of the phylum *Echinodermata* (eh-ky-no-*dur*-mah-tah). They have a hard shell-like body coating which is covered with spines which may be long (sea urchin) or very short (sand

Fig. 23-16. Although the body of the starfish seems to be quite rigid, it is capable of a considerable amount of bending and twisting. In these two photographs above, you can see both the dorsal and ventral views.

dollar). The starfish is not a fish, in spite of its name. When alive, the five, or rarely six, **rays** which radiate from a central disk are movable. In a groove on the lower side of each ray, there are rows of **tube feet.** They are part of what we call a **water vascular system.** The tube feet are connected to canals which lead through each ray to a circular canal in the central disk. This canal has an opening to the surface on the dorsal side. When the starfish presses the tube feet against an object and forces water out of the canals, the feet grip firmly by means of suction. Return of water to the canals releases the grip.

The starfish uses the water vascular system in opening the shells of clams and oysters, its principal food. The body arches over the prey with the rays bent downward. The shells of the clam or oyster are gripped firmly by the tube feet, and a steady pull is exerted at the same time. This pull is exerted in opposite directions so that eventually the muscles that close the shell of

Fig. 23-17. Here you see a starfish eating a small fish. The starfish turns the lower part of its stomach inside out and extends it through the mouth.

the prey tire, and the halves of the shell separate. At this point, the starfish pushes out its stomach from a small opening in the center of the lower side. The stomach, turned inside out, enters the shell and digests the body of the clam or oyster, leaving only the shell. Although starfish have extensive skele-

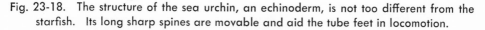

Fig. 23-18. The structure of the sea urchin, an echinoderm, is not too different from the starfish. Its long sharp spines are movable and aid the tube feet in locomotion.

tons, they are quite flexible and can bend easily around an oyster.

Oystermen are on constant lookout for starfish in clam or oyster beds. An active, adult starfish can destroy eight to twelve oysters a day. Formerly, men tore starfish to pieces thinking that they were destroying these pests. Actually, they were multiplying their troubles, for a starfish ray, with a portion of the cen- tral disk, can *regenerate* and become an entire new starfish.

Each echinoderm has a type of body arrangement which is radial or built like spokes of a wheel growing out from a center. The variety which this may take is easily shown in the starfish, the thick-bodied *sea cucumber,* and the flowerlike *sea lily.* This is called **radial symmetry.**

In Conclusion

This chapter has taken you through a large part of the animal kingdom. You have studied animal life in a wide variety of forms. You have discovered how an animal can degenerate and live as a parasite, depending on the body activities of a host organism. Perhaps it was surprising to find that a relative of a dangerous parasite, like the fluke, could live harmlessly in a stream and that a relative of the earthworm is a bloodsucker. In the study of echinoderms and mollusks, you investigated some of the most prominent members of the animal society of the shallow seas and tide pools.

In the chapters to follow, we will continue the study of invertebrates with a phylum which, if numbers count, is the most important of all invertebrate groups. Here, we find such well-known animals as the insects, the crayfish and lobster, the spider, and scores of others.

 Questions for Review

1. Why do we classify the various worms into three separate phyla?
2. What is the significance of the three layers of cells found in flatworms?
3. In what ways are the flatworms more complex than the sponges and coelenterates?
4. How does the trichina worm reach the human body?
5. How does an earthworm move?
6. Trace a particle of food through the digestive system of the earthworm, naming the organs through which it passes.

7. What characteristics of the echinoderms distinguish them from other invertebrate animals?
8. Describe the movement of the starfish.
9. How does the water vascular system assist the starfish in eating?
10. What is the chief characteristic of the mollusks?
11. Describe the path of water through a clam.
12. How does an oyster form a pearl in its shell? Do all oysters form gem pearls used in jewelry?

Biologically Speaking

anus	ganglion	seminal receptacle
aortic arch	gill	seminal vesicle
bivalve mollusk	gizzard	seta
clitellum	intestine	shellfish
crop	larva	sucker
cyst	mantle	tube foot
dorsal siphon	mesoderm	univalve mollusk
esophagus	pharynx	valveless mollusk
feces	radial symmetry	ventral siphon
foot	ray	water vascular system

Applying Facts and Principles

1. Symptoms of tapeworm infestation include loss of weight and general tiredness. Account for these conditions.

2. Discuss several measures which are important in the control of diseases caused by parasitic worms.

3. Serious trichinosis can become a hopeless disease. Why is it almost impossible to treat?

4. Discuss regeneration in the starfish.

5. Shells of mollusks are frequently ground up and used as fertilizer. What are some of the substances these shells may add to the soil?

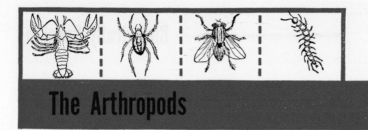

CHAPTER 24

The Arthropods

The large phylum **Arthropoda** (commonly called the arthropods) outnumbers all other kinds of animal life. Like knights of old, these invertebrates wear a suit of protective armor, completely covering the softer internal body parts.

The hard outer covering, or **exoskeleton,** is one of their most striking characteristics. But their name refers to their jointed feet (*Arthros* = joint; *-poda* = feet).

Arthropods thrive in nearly all environments in widely varied forms. Few living creatures are more widely distributed than the insects, one of the groups of animals included in this phylum. In addition to insects, we also find in this group such familiar animals as spiders, centipedes, millepedes, crayfish, crabs, and lobsters.

Some characteristics of arthropods. To the casual observer, the graceful butterfly has little in common with the crayfish lurking under a rock in a stream. But careful study of these quite different animals will show that they have much in common. The characteristics which make the butterfly similar in structure to the crayfish also relate these creatures to spiders, scorpions, and centipedes. The biologist includes among these points of similarity the following characteristics:

1. Jointed appendages, which include legs and other body outgrowths.

2. An exoskeleton of **chitin** (*ky*-tin), which serves as an external skeleton instead of the internal support of bones that we have.

3. A segmented body, which refers to distinct sections or segments into which the exoskeleton is divided.

4. A dorsal heart; that is, it is located above the digestive system.

5. A ventral nervous system, with the principal nerves running below the digestive system.

There are five classes of arthropods. In the classification of the arthropods, such widely varied forms as butterflies and crayfish, spiders and centipedes are segregated into separate groups called *classes.* This large phylum is commonly divided into five smaller classes of related arthropods as shown on page 303.

Each of these classes has all the fundamental characteristics of arthropods, and, in addition, certain characteristics of the class to which it belongs. For example, the Crustacea have two pairs of antennae, or feelers, on the front of the body, two distinct body regions, five or more pairs of legs, a chitinous exoskeleton which contains lime, and have structures called *gills* for respiration. The Insecta, on the other hand, have one pair of antennae, a body composed of three parts, three pairs of legs, and an exoskeleton composed of *chitin* lacking lime. They respire by means of air tubes called **tracheae** (*tray*-kee-ee).

The arthropods show a great advance over other animals already studied. Worms, especially the earthworm,

CLASSES OF ARTHROPODS

CLASS	EXAMPLES
1. Crustacea (crus-*tay*-she-ah)	Crayfish, lobsters, crabs, shrimps, and others
2. Chilopoda (ky-*loh*-poh-da)	Centipedes
3. Diplopoda (dip-*loh*-poh-da)	Millepedes
4. Insecta (in-*seck*-tah)	All insects
5. Arachnida (ah-*rack*-nid-ah)	Spiders, scorpions, ticks, and mites

show a high degree of specialization of body parts and the presence of specialized internal organs. In our study of the Crustacea as typical arthropods, we will deal with animals such as the crayfish, lobster, and crab, which are adapted for aquatic life. Division of labor among their various organs is carried to an even higher point than we found in the earthworm. All of this specialization has resulted in an efficient animal, very well-adapted to our present world. The segmented body is, of course, common to both the arthropods and the annelid worms. The ventral nervous system first appeared in the worms. How many other features of similarity can you discover between the arthropods and the other invertebrates?

The crayfish is a typical crustacean. The crayfish is large, easy to observe, characteristic of arthropods in its structure, and easily obtained in nearly all rivers, lakes, and streams when lime is present in the water.

The body is covered with a dark-gray, limy exoskeleton which is divided into two regions. The first of these regions, called the **cephalothorax** (sef-al-oh-*thor*-ax), includes the head and a second region, the thorax. These are separate in many arthropods. The cephalothorax is covered by a hard plate

or shell known as the **carapace** (*kar*-ah-pace). Attached to the rear of the cephalothorax is a second distinct body region, the **abdomen,** which is composed of seven movable segments.

It may seem strange to find the skeleton on the outside of the body of an animal. Whether internal or external, however, skeletons serve the same purpose. They give the body form, protect delicate internal organs, and aid in mo-

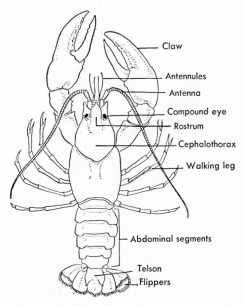

Fig. 24-1. The above diagram shows the dorsal view of the crayfish, a typical crustacean.

Labels: Claw, Antennules, Antenna, Compound eye, Rostrum, Cephalothorax, Walking leg, Abdominal segments, Telson, Flippers

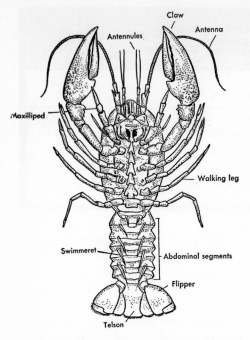

Fig. 24-2. Here you see a ventral view of the crayfish. The two pairs of antennae are a distinguishing characteristic of crustaceans. What homologous organs does the crayfish have?

tion by serving as attachments for muscles.

The Crustacea, with their armor-plated bodies, are among the best protected arthropods. This protective cover extends even over the legs, which may be bent only at special joints. The heavy carapace, covering the head and thorax, gives special protection to these vital regions of the body. It is like a plate of armor, but is even more efficient, for it is a shield far lighter than a warrior ever carried. Not only is the exoskeleton of the crayfish strong, light, and flexible, but its color blends with that of the surroundings so that it escapes the notice of enemies (protective coloration).

The front of the carapace extends forward in a protective beak, the **ros-**

trum (*ros*-trum). On either side of the rostrum are the eyes. These are set on short movable stalks and are composed of numerous lenses. For this reason, we speak of these eyes as **compound eyes.**

The head appendages of the crayfish. Beginning at the *anterior* (head) *end,* we come first to the small feelers, or **antennules,** and then the large feelers, or **antennae,** at whose base open tubes from excretory organs, known as **green glands.** Then come the **mandibles** (*man*-dih-bils) or true jaws, and two pairs of **maxillae** (max-*ill*-ee), or little jaws, which aid in chewing the food. The jaws work from side to side and not up and down, because they are merely leglike appendages adapted for chewing and so continue to have a horizontal motion, as do the legs.

The appendages on the thorax of the crayfish. The first appendages of the thorax are three pairs of **maxillipeds** (max-*ill*-ih-peds), or jaw feet. Their function is to hold food during chewing. Next come the large claws, obviously for protection and food-getting, then two pairs of legs with tiny pincers at the tip, and two more pairs with a claw. These four pairs of legs are concerned mainly with walking. Attached to the maxillipeds, to the eight legs, and to the large claws are feathery **gills** which extend up under the carapace into the gill chambers.

The abdominal appendages of the crayfish. The appendages of the abdomen are called **swimmerets** and are small on the first five segments. They are used by the female as an attachment for her eggs in the process of reproduction. The sixth swimmeret is enormously developed into a wide fin or **flipper,** located at the extreme posterior (rear end) part of the body. The appendage of the seventh segment is lack-

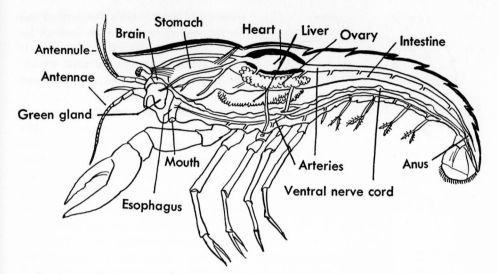

Fig. 24-3.   This is a side view of a female crayfish showing the main body parts.

ing, and the segment itself is reduced to a flat, triangular part called the **telson.** The sixth and seventh segments together form a powerful organ for backward locomotion, for they can be whipped forward by the strong muscles of the abdomen, making the animal shoot backward at high speed.

What are homologous organs? When we find organs (either in the same or different animals) which were developed from the same part — that is, whose origin and structure are similar, allowing for certain modifications — we call them **homologous** (ho-*mol*-oh-gus) **organs.** The antennae and claws of the crayfish are homologous to the swimmerets. Likewise the arm of man is homologous to the foreleg of the horse, even though the functions of the arm and foreleg are so different.

Analogous (an-*al*-oh-gus) means similar in function. We might say that the gills of the crayfish and the lungs of man are analogous because both perform the function of respiration, but we cannot say they are homologous. The gills are developed from the legs, while

the lungs are outgrowths of the throat. Their structure is quite different.

The internal structure of the crayfish. Internally there is a considerable degree of specialization. (See Fig. 24-3.) The *digestive system* and its glands occupy a large part of the cephalothorax. There are three toothlike structures in the *stomach* which grind up the food. A well-developed *circulatory system* and a muscular *heart* mark an advance in the adaptations of the crayfish over lower animals. However, the blood flows in an open system. This means that it goes from large arteries through spaces *around* the organs instead of a continuous system of tubes. The excretory organs, called **green glands,** and fairly well-developed reproductive organs are also present. The *nervous system,* though similar to that in worms, is much more specialized. The senses of touch and smell, located in the antennae, maxillae, and maxillipeds, are acute. The eyes are on movable stalks and are compound, each consisting of numerous lenses, but the sight is probably not keen. "Ear" sacs are located at the

Fig. 24-4. The gills of the crayfish are attached to the walking legs. They move in the water with every motion of the legs and thus insure a constant supply of water over the gills.

base of the antennules and probably aid in balancing. Hearing is poorly developed, but the sense of taste is well-developed.

While these sense organs do not seem very efficient, enormous advance can be seen when we compare the crayfish with the earthworm. The worm probably feels only touch and vibrations carried by the land or water through the body wall, with a possibility of chemical and heat or light sensations in the region of the head. Since the degree in which an animal can get in touch with its environment marks the stage of its advancement, the Crustacea far excel the worms in development.

How the crayfish moves. The function of locomotion is taken care of by the tail flipper which drives the crayfish swiftly backward. Further, by means of the four pairs of walking legs, the crayfish can travel backwards, forwards, and sideways. All are operated by powerful muscles, assisted by the exoskeleton.

The crayfish's adaptations for protection. These consist of the exoskeleton with its color and spines, the powerful jaws, and the claws which are used to attack an enemy. In addition, the animal possesses fairly keen senses, and a nervous system to guide its actions. Thus, a speedy escape is possible from an approaching foe.

How the crayfish respires. Respiration in Protozoa is accomplished by the contact of the cell with dissolved oxygen in the water; in the worm through the body wall with oxygen in the air. In the crayfish, as in all Crustacea, we find **gills.** These are especially developed organs for the exchange of oxygen and carbon dioxide between the animal and its environment. These gills are thin-walled to allow for the passage of gases. They are provided with many blood vessels to receive oxygen and to carry it to all cells, and also to liberate carbon dioxide.

The gills are arranged to insure a constant flow of fresh water over them. They move in the water with every motion of the leg or maxillipeds. The gills are protected by the carapace, which extends over them and forms a chamber. This chamber can hold moisture for some time, thus keeping the animal alive when it is removed from the water.

The food on which the crayfish lives. The crayfish eats many different kinds of food. If plant food is available, it eats that. It prefers animal food, however, and doesn't seem to object if the animal has been dead a long time!

The crayfish's history. Frequently, you'll find crayfish during the spring months with curious berrylike structures attached to the swimmerets on the lower side of the abdomen. These are the females, and the curious berrylike structures are *eggs*. The eggs number about 100. They are fertilized at the time they are laid by *sperms* which have been stored in small sacs on the lower side of the female's body since the mating which occurred the previous fall. The eggs generally hatch in about six to eight weeks, depending on the temperature and other conditions of the water. During the interval between laying and hatching, they remain securely fastened to the swimmerets. When first hatched the young are quite different in appearance from the adult. During a series of changes called **molts,** they become more like their parents in form.

How molting takes place. From the time of hatching until adult size molting occurs at increasingly long intervals. After that the animals usually molt about once or twice a year.

This molting, which consists in shedding the exoskeleton, is a direct result of having the hard parts of the body on the outside. Animals which have an exoskeleton cannot grow larger unless they shed their armor. When the crayfish is ready to molt, the lime is partly absorbed from the skeleton, the carapace splits across the back, water is withdrawn from the tissues, which causes them to shrink, and the animal literally humps itself out of its former skeleton. It also leaves behind the lining of its stomach and its teeth. Immediately following this process, water is absorbed and growth proceeds very rapidly. The lime is replaced in the new and larger armor. Usually the later molts take place quickly and in hidden locations. The animal is totally helpless and a prey to all sorts of enemies while growing its new suit.

The regeneration of lost parts. In molting or in battle with enemies, it often happens that appendages are lost or injured. In the latter case, the limb is voluntarily shed between the second and third segments. A double membrane prevents much loss of blood, and a whole new appendage is developed to replace the injured member. This is another example of regeneration.

Crustacea at home. Many of you have doubtless more than once pulled up a crayfish firmly attached to the bait on your fishline. It is one of the most common inhabitants of many streams and ponds where lime is dissolved in the water, and you can see it at nearly any

Fig. 24-5. Except for a few minor details, the structure of the lobster, shown above, is very similar to the crayfish.

time of the day or night searching for food. Since it eagerly consumes dead organisms in any condition, it is considered of benefit as a scavenger. In certain parts of the country, especially in the Mississippi River basin, crayfish cause extensive damage by making holes in earthen dams and levees and by burrowing in fields, thus destroying cotton and corn crops.

Another crustacean is the little *pill bug,* one of the *sow bugs,* which is always found under stones and logs in moist places. When sufficiently alarmed, it will roll into a little ball, thinly armored by gray overlapping plates.

There are many other crustaceans such as the lobster, crab, prawn, shrimp, and the barnacle. The latter shows its relationship to the other crustaceans only when young.

Economic importance of the Crustacea. Many Crustacea are of great economic importance to man. The *lobster,* the big brother of the crayfish, in-

Fig. 24-6. This lobster is capturing a crab in its pincers. In what ways are these two animals similar?

habits the cool waters of the Atlantic Coast from the Carolinas to Labrador. Lobster fishing is an important industry in many of the New England states, especially along the coast of Maine. In summer, the lobsters come into the shallow water close to the shore where they live among submerged rocks.

Another kind of lobster, the *spiny lobster,* lives in warmer regions of the ocean along the coasts of Florida, California, and the West Indies. This species lacks the large pincers of its northern cousin. The extremely long antennae are as characteristic of the spiny lobster as are the prominent spines which cover the front part of the body.

The *blue crab* ranks next to the lobster as a table delicacy. These animals live in the shallow grassy ocean bays where they move about in search of decaying matter or any kind of animal they can catch. The body of the crab differs from the lobster in being short and broad rather than elongated. The abdomen is much reduced in size and folds under the broad cephalothorax. Large pincers serve as organs of defense and food-getting. " Soft-shelled " crabs are merely edible crabs which are captured immediately following a molt. In a few days, these table delicacies form a hard shell again. The name *blue crab* comes from the fact that the feet are blue in color.

A discussion of Crustacea as items of food would be incomplete without mention of the *shrimp.* These creatures resemble other Crustacea in general form, but are distinct in having five pairs of walking legs and a much enlarged and highly muscular abdomen. They are fast swimmers, moving backward in true crustacean fashion. When alarmed, they bury themselves in the sand along the bottom and thrust out their eyes and antennae to keep in touch with their surroundings.

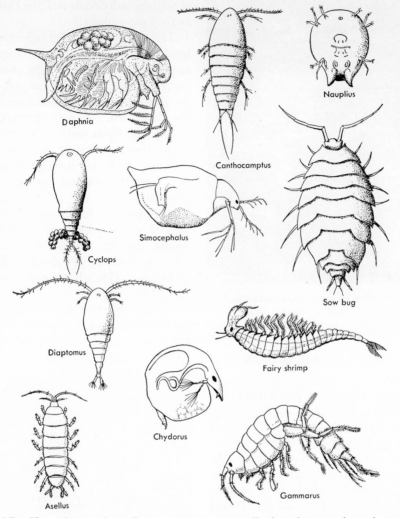

Daphnia

Nauplius

Canthocamptus

Cyclops

Simocephalus

Diaptomus

Sow bug

Fairy shrimp

Chydorus

Asellus

Gammarus

Fig. 24-7. These forms of small crustaceans are usually found in ponds and streams or in moist places on land. What characteristics do they have in common?

The shrimp industry is very important in the Gulf Coast states, as well as in California. Louisiana, Texas, and California supply much of the shrimp for inland markets.

Many forms of minute crustacea thrive in the waters of inland ponds and lakes. The small size of many of these forms brings them into contact with the microscopic Protozoa of these communities. The strange-appearing *Cyclops,* with its large, single eye, the

Daphnia or water flea, with its jerky movement, and the peculiar "back-swimming" fairy shrimp appear in swarms in certain bodies of fresh water during rather unpredictable periods. They serve as food for small fish and are a much sought item by owners of aquariums.

The barnacles which attach themselves to the hulls of ships and other structures in salt water cause great damage. A great number on a ship's hull

Fig. 24-8. Barnacles are crustaceans, too. They live attached to rocks, ships, and bodies of certain large salt-water animals.

may reduce its speed by as much as 20 per cent.

Spiders and other arachnids. Unfortunately, *spiders* are one of several groups of valuable animals whose reputations have been spoiled by a few undesirable members. With a few exceptions, spiders are extremely valuable because of their destruction of harmful insects. They belong to the class **Arachnida** (ar-*rack*-nid-dah).

Some kinds of spiders, called orb weavers, spin elaborate webs of tiny silken threads which are an engineering feat to behold. The web serves as a trap to capture flying insects. When a victim becomes entangled in the sticky threads of the web, the spider races out of its hiding place along the margin. It then bites its prey, thereby poisoning it. When the insect has become somewhat quieter, the spider binds it securely in a case of threads spun around the victim as the spider turns it over and over. Other spiders do not spin webs, but live as solitary individuals stalking their prey as they roam about.

The spider somewhat resembles an insect but differs in several important respects. The legs are eight instead of six in number, and the head and thorax are joined to form a cephalothorax as in the Crustacea. A pair of greatly enlarged **mandibles** serve as poison fangs. These fangs are hollow and have small openings in the tip through which poison may be injected into the prey. They then suck the juices from their victim's body. On the tip of the abdomen of many spiders are several **spinnerets,** through which tiny strands of silk pass from the silk glands within the abdomen. This silk is used in making the spider's web.

Among the most famous spiders are the *tarantula,* or banana spider, the *black widow,* famous for its very poisonous bite, and the *trap door spider* of the western desert regions.

With spiders are grouped many other forms of related animal life. *Scorpions,* found in southern and southwestern United States and in all tropical countries, are provided with a long segmented abdomen terminating in a venomous " stinger." The sting of a scorpion, while painful, is seldom fatal to

Fig. 24-9. Although many people think of the spider as an insect, it belongs to the arachnid family. It has eight legs instead of the six found in the insect.

man. Campers have found them annoying in that they like to crawl in empty shoes during the day to escape bright light. Scorpions live solitary lives except when mating, after which the female often turns upon her mate and devours him. The young are brought forth alive and spend the early part of their existence riding on the mother's back.

The *harvestman,* or *daddy longlegs,* is one of the most useful of the arachnids since it feeds almost entirely on plant lice. They lead a strictly solitary life, traveling through the fields in search of their prey.

Mites and *ticks* are among the more

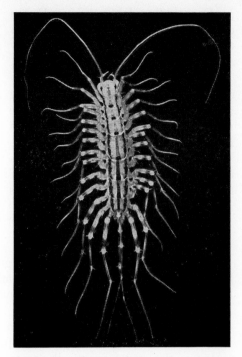

Fig. 24-11. The centipede is an arthropod with a long trunk and many legs.

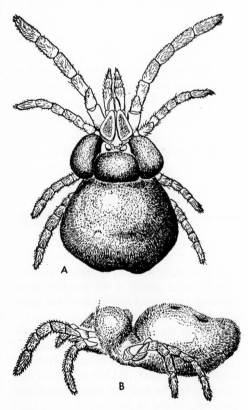

Fig. 24-10. The chigger can cause great discomfort. This drawing is magnified over 100 times. There are eight legs, as in all arachnids.

notorious arachnids, causing considerable damage to man and other animals. They live mostly as parasites on the surface of the bodies of chickens, dogs, cattle, man, and other animals. Some forms, like the Rocky Mountain tick, carry disease. The Texas-fever tick causes an annual loss of more than $50,000,000 to cattle raisers.

Harvest mites, or *chiggers,* are immature stages of mites which attach themselves to the surface of the skin and insert a beak through which they withdraw blood. They are almost microscopic in size and give no warning of their presence until a swollen area causes great itching and discomfort. After a few days, the sore becomes covered with a scab and disappears.

Arthropods with many legs — the Chilopoda and Diplopoda. We have all wondered how a centipede (*sen*-tihpeed) or millepede (*mil*-eh-peed) can operate so many legs and not get them tangled in each other. It is certainly an excellent example of coordination. These curious wormlike arthropods are often seen racing away with a rippling sort of motion when their hiding place under a log, stone, or piece of rubbish has suddenly been disturbed.

Centipedes, which belong to the class Chilopoda, have bodies composed of numerous segments each of which bears a pair of legs. The millepedes, or thousand-leggers, belong to the class Diplopoda. They have two pairs of legs attached to each segment. Millepedes are frequently slow moving and are likely to roll into a ball when disturbed. Centipedes, on the other hand, are fast moving and difficult to capture. In tropical countries, centipedes may measure 12 inches long and their bite may be quite poisonous. Some have as high as 173 pairs of legs, but 35 is about average.

In Conclusion

The arthropods are the largest single group of animals, containing more different forms than all other animal groups combined. The insects comprise by far the largest group of arthropods, which include, in addition to insects, the crustaceans, arachnids, chilopods, and diplopods.

All of these classes are similar in possessing, among other characteristics, exoskeletons, containing chitin, jointed appendages, and segmented bodies.

Among the most economically important arthropods are the crustaceans, which include the lobster, crab, shrimp, and other numerous minute inhabitants of pond water. The most famous arachnids are spiders which for the most part are extremely beneficial animals. Other arachnids are the harvestmen, scorpions, chiggers, ticks, and mites.

In the next three chapters, we will consider the insects, the most abundant group of arthropods.

Questions for Review

1. What are three external characteristics of an arthropod which distinguish it from other animals?

2. (a) What are the five principal classes of arthropods? (b) Give an example of each.

3. In what ways are the arthropods similar to the earthworm?

4. What are some advantages and disadvantages of an exoskeleton?

5. What are the main parts of the crayfish skeleton?

6. How do the gills in the crayfish carry on the process of respiration?

7. How does the crayfish reproduce?

8. To what stimuli is the crayfish sensitive and what structures assist in the process?

9. What three crustaceans are important to man because of their food value?

10. (a) Why are most spiders extremely beneficial animals? (b) What reasons can you give for the fact that many people are genuinely afraid of arachnids?

11. What other animals besides the spiders are classified as arachnids?

12. What is the outstanding characteristic of a centipede?

Biologically Speaking

abdomen	chitin	maxillipeds
analogous organs	compound eyes	molting
antennae	exoskeleton	omnivorous
antennules	flipper	rostrum
appendage	gills	spinnerets
arachnid	green glands	swimmerets
arthropod	homologous organs	telson
carapace	mandibles	thorax
cephalothorax	maxillae	tracheae

Applying Facts and Principles

1. Why is it especially important for an armored animal like the crayfish to have long antennae?

2. In which of the following localities do you think the crayfish would be likely to produce weaker exoskeletons: in waters flowing through limestone rock or in waters flowing through granite? Explain.

3. From your knowledge of the activity of crayfish, explain the meaning of the expression, " crawfishing."

4. What advantage is it for the young crayfish to cling to the adult's swimmerets until after the second molting?

5. In terms of molting of the crayfish, explain each of the following common fisherman's terms: " soft craw," " peeler," and " hard craw."

CHAPTER 25

Insects—a Representative Study

Most of us want to get out the spray gun when we think of insects. And it is true that many of them are our enemies. The flies, mosquitoes, and hundreds more do great harm to man and his activities. However, the praying mantis, ladybug, bee, silk moth, and many other insects are helpful. Certainly the class Insecta is the most numerous, both as to genera and individuals, of the great phylum Arthropoda.

Insects differ greatly. The common cockroach is one of the few animals on earth which still looks about the same as its ancestors many millions of years ago. The life cycle of some insects, such as the butterfly, is still a marvel of which scientists make an intensive study. Some insects can remain alive in a vacuum, and then surprisingly stay alive when the vacuum is suddenly ended. One species lays its eggs in hot water springs which are ordinarily at a temperature of 120° F. There is even one kind of beetle which can bore through a lead cable!

How to recognize an insect. Some people speak of any small flying or crawling animal as a " bug." They are wrong on two counts! First, a true bug is a member of only one division of insects. Second, what some people call a bug may be another type of insect, or even a spider or a centipede. These, of course, are not insects at all.

Insects include that division of the arthropods which have three separate body regions: (1) a head; (2) a thorax; and (3) an abdomen. They also have one pair of antennae, three pairs of legs, usually two pairs of wings, and breathing tubes called *tracheae* (*tray*-kee-ee). There are about twice as many kinds of insects as all the other living animals combined. More than 675,000 species of insects have already been recorded. Experts regard this as not more than half of all insects in existence! Not only are there many kinds

of insects, but each kind produces thousands of individuals, like the locusts and May flies, whose swarms may darken the sky. Their struggle for existence is terrific, and without special adaptations they would not have survived.

The insects possess a high degree of specialization. Mouth parts are adapted for different kinds of food, legs and wings are wonderfully developed for swift locomotion, and the internal structure is complicated. Some are adapted for aquatic life, some take refuge by burrowing, some live in colonies like bees and ants, while others fight their battles alone. Some have become swift in running, leaping, or flying, while others have no highly developed adaptations and may be dying out.

The grasshopper. We shall study the grasshopper as a representative of this class because it is so widely distributed. (See Fig. 25-1.) The grasshop-

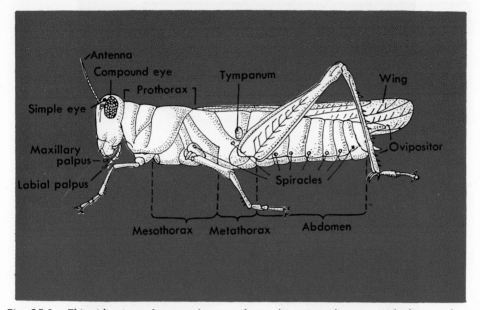

Fig. 25-1. This side view of a grasshopper shows the external parts. Which parts form the head? Note that here the thorax is divided into three sections.

per belongs to one of the eight more common orders of insects called **Orthoptera** (or-*thop*-ter-ah). This name means " straight-winged " and refers to the narrowly folded wings, held straight along the body when not actually used in flight.

As in all arthropods, the skeleton is external, but it differs from the crayfish in that it contains no lime. It consists entirely of a light, tough, horny substance called **chitin** which is usually protectively colored.

The mouth parts of the grasshopper. These are adapted for biting and chewing plant material, such as leaves and stems. Named in order from the anterior, they consist of (1) *labrum* (*lay*-brum); (2) *mandibles;* (3) *maxillae;* and (4) *labium* (*lay*-bee-um). Though the mouth parts of insects are greatly modified to suit different kinds of food, these four sets of organs are still usually present.

The **labrum** (see Fig. 2 5-2) is the two-lobed upper lip which fits over the strong, toothed, horizontal jaws, or **mandibles.** A pair of **maxillae,** or accessory jaws, are next behind the mandibles. They aid in cutting and holding food, and also have a sense organ, like a short antenna. This is called a **palpus** (*pal*-pus). Posterior to the maxillae comes the **labium,** or lower lip, a deeply two-lobed organ, also provided with palpi, which aid in holding food between the jaws.

In insects like the butterflies and moths, the maxillae join to make a hollow sucking tube. In the case of mosquitoes, the mouth parts are tiny lances placed around a sucking tube.

The thorax consists of three segments. These segments are: (1) the *prothorax;* (2) the *mesothorax;* and (3) the *metathorax.* The **prothorax** is a large saddle-shaped segment to which the head is attached and bears the first pair of legs. The middle segment, or **mesothorax** (mes-oh-*thoh*-raks), bears a

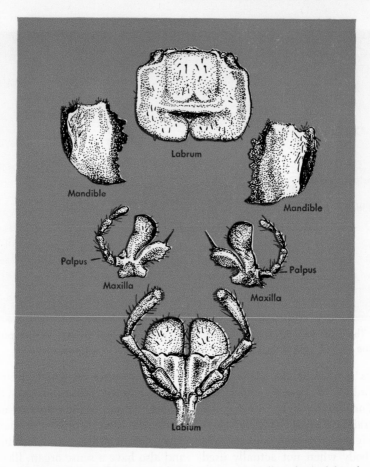

Fig. 25-2. The mouth parts of the grasshopper are especially adapted for chewing plant materials. The mandibles are notched and move from side to side.

pair of legs and the first pair of wings. The last segment, the **metathorax,** bears the leaping legs and the last pair of wings.

Legs of the grasshopper. The typical insect has six legs. Each of these consists of five parts or segments connected by strong joints and adapted for locomotion (see Fig. 25-1). In some insects, like the grasshopper, the posterior pair is enormously developed for leaping also. The foot, or **tarsus,** is provided with spines, hooks, or pads to give a firm grip when jumping or crawling. A joint near the body, almost like a ball and socket, permits freedom of motion.

The grasshopper's wings. The *anterior* wings are long, narrow, and rather stiff. They protect the more delicate underwings and act as planes in aiding flight and leaping. The *posterior* wings are thin and membranous. They are supported by many veins and, when not in use, are folded lengthwise like a fan under the narrower anterior wings.

The abdomen consists of ten segments. Each segment is composed of an upper and lower part, united by a membrane which allows the segment to expand and contract in the process of breathing. A pair of tiny openings called **spiracles** (*spy*-rah-kals) lead into

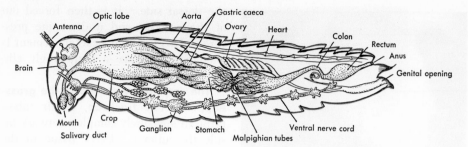

Fig. 25-3. The above diagram shows an internal view of the abdomen of the grass-hopper.

the abdomen through eight of the segments. These are the external openings of the respiratory system and connect with the trachea. The segment next to the thorax bears the ears, which are large, membrane-covered cavities.

The extreme posterior segments in the female grasshopper bear two pairs of hard and sharp-pointed organs called **ovipositors** (oh-vi-*poz*-ih-ters). The insect uses them to dig a hole in the ground in which the eggs are laid. Males lack such organs. The tip end of their abdomen is enlarged and rounded upward.

Some insects, like the sawfly and certain *ichneumon* (ik-*nu*-mon) flies, have long hairlike ovipositors with which they pierce wood and lay eggs deeply hidden. The sting of the bee and wasp is an example of an ovipositor modified for defensive purposes.

The skeletal and muscular systems. The skeletal system has been described before as an exoskeleton and its various parts mentioned. Inside the skeleton are arranged many sets of muscles, each attached to various parts of the skeleton. All are involved in producing the complex movements of the animal. In fact, there are more different separate muscles in the grasshopper than there are in the human.

The digestive system. The grasshopper bites off, by the horizontal action of

its mandibles, pieces of leaves or other materials which it uses for food. A blade of grass, for example, will be held edge-on to the mouth by the action of the labium and labrum, and then the mandibles will pinch off a piece. This is then sucked in and passes to the food tube, or **esophagus** (ee-*sof*-ah-gus). On either side of the esophagus is a salivary gland. The secretions from these glands sometimes leave the mouth of the grasshopper when it is disturbed or injured and forms a dark-colored material.

The food next enters the **crop** which is lined with thin plates of chitin-bearing teeth. Here the food is shredded. It then passes into the region known as the **gizzard.** At the end of the gizzard are thin plates through which the partly digested food is strained into a much larger region, the **stomach.** On the outside of the stomach are eight double elongate pouches called **gastric ceca,** which secrete digestive enzymes. The digested food is then absorbed by the walls of the stomach and goes into the circulatory system, which carries it to all the cells of the body.

The excretory system. Waste substances from the cells are picked up by the blood. Small **Malpighian tubes** collect these from the blood and pass them into the colon, from which they leave the body through the **anus.**

the dorsal side. It is then forced out of the anterior end under some pressure. This constant heart movement is enough to produce a surprisingly efficient circulation.

The respiratory system in the grasshopper. The *tracheae,* or air tubes, form an amazingly complex network inside the animal. Every tissue in the body is supplied with air which is used in respiration. Eight pairs of *spiracles* on the abdomen and two pairs on the thorax, each protected by hairlike structures, are the intake and outgo openings of the tracheae. The movement of the abdomen and wings is sufficient to pump air in and out of the tracheae. By diffusion, oxygen and carbon dioxide are exchanged in the tissues.

The grasshopper receives messages from the outside through its sense organs. The antennae, the most anterior appendages, are many-jointed and serve as the receptors of the senses of touch and smell. There are two kinds of eyes. Three *simple eyes* are located respectively at the base of each antenna and in the groove between them. The large *compound eyes* project from a part of the front and sides of the head and are composed of hundreds of six-sided lenses. The shape, location, and number of lenses in the eye seem to adapt the insect for sight in several directions at one time, but the image formed is probably not very sharp.

Most insects are considered to be nearsighted, yet they may be able to distinguish colors. We know that night-flying moths seek white flowers, while flies and some other insects are attracted by red and blue.

The stimuli received through the sense organs are then relayed by nerves to certain parts of the body, such as a muscle. The muscle will contract on thus being stimulated and action in the

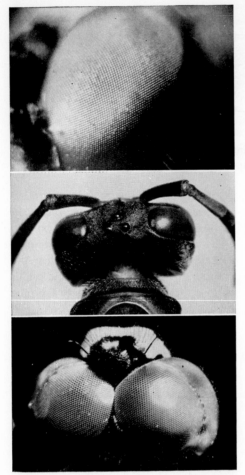

Fig. 25-4. The eyes of three insects are shown here. At the top is the eye of a housefly, below that is a wasp's eye, and at the bottom is the eye of a dragonfly. Note that these are compound eyes because they contain many separate and individual parts.

The circulatory system. Blood in the grasshopper is in what is called an *open system* as compared to the closed system found in man. This means that the blood flows throughout the body cavity of the insect instead of through tubes (arteries and veins). However, there is a definite circulation. Blood is sucked in at the posterior end of a long tubular, muscular heart on

Fig. 25-5. The life history of the grasshopper is an incomplete metamorphosis. Identify the different stages in the life history of this insect.

insects then occurs. Nerve centers, called **ganglia** (*gang*-lee-ah), act as switches for the message to go to the proper structures for coordinated action. The sight of your approaching hand is enough for the grasshopper to start moving away, and fast. This complicated activity is begun, controlled, and coordinated by the nervous system.

The reproductive system. In insects the sexes are separate. This means that male sperm cells are produced in organs called **testes** in some of the members of a species. Female egg cells are produced in organs called **ovaries,** found in female animals. Biologists use symbols to refer to the separate sexes. ♀ denotes a female organism or part, and ♂ refers to the male. The union of sperm and egg, called *fertilization,* occurs in the grasshopper in a special structure in the female. The male

deposits the sperm cells in a special storage place in the female.

The female grasshopper digs a hole in the ground with her *ovipositor.* Here she deposits her fertilized eggs which are protected by a gummy substance. About 100 or more eggs are laid in the fall and hatch in the next spring. When they hatch, the young grasshoppers are called **nymphs.** They are small and wingless, but they look like the adult in many ways. However, the head is large in proportion to the body.

Like all arthropods, the nymphs grow by molting, usually about five times. Molting takes 30 to 40 minutes and during it the insect is weak and sometimes dies. The old exoskeleton splits along the thorax and the nymph comes out head first. Then it grows rapidly and a new exoskeleton quickly forms.

A great many insects usually lay

		beetle		grub
THE LARVA OF THE	{	fly mosquito	IS CALLED {	maggot wiggler
		butterfly		caterpillar or "worm"
		moth		caterpillar or "worm"

their eggs in the ground. Some place them in water (dragonfly and mosquito), others protect them with a varnish (lac insect and tent caterpillar), or with a frothy mass (tussock moth), while other insects lay their eggs on leaves or stems of plants.

The larvae of many insects are so different from the adult that they have separate names, which confuse the relationship. Refer to the table on this page for the popular names of a few insects.

When we speak of silkworms, or apple worms, etc., we are really referring to larval forms of moths; cabbage worms are larvae of butterflies; the "carpet bug" is the larva of a beetle.

Metamorphosis in insects. In many animals, the development from egg to adult includes several more or less distinct stages instead of being a gradual increase in size. Such a series of stages in life history is a **metamorphosis** (met-ah-*mor*-foh-sis).

Among insects these stages may be several and the differences between them slight, as in the grasshopper. This type is an *incomplete metamorphosis* because the insect actually looks

Fig. 25-6. The praying mantis looks more ferocious than it really is. Actually, it is a useful relative of the grasshopper because it destroys other insects.

much like an adult in each stage. There are three stages here: (1) the **egg;** (2) the **nymph;** and (3) the **adult.** Or, there may be four distinct stages: (1) **the egg;** (2) the **larva;** (3) the **pupa** (*pew*-pa); and (4) the **adult.** This latter is *complete metamorphosis.* Here the insect does not resemble the adult at any of the various stages of its development. The fly, mosquito, and butterfly or moth are examples of this type.

Relatives of the grasshopper. It is easy to see that the meadow grasshopper and the katydid are related. The wings of the katydid look so much like leaves — even to the veining — that we cite this as a good case of *protective resemblance.* Other members of the

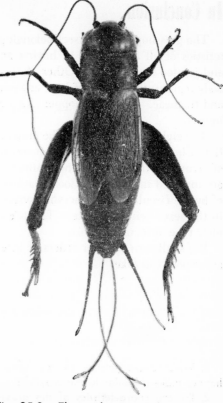

Fig. 25-8. The cricket is another member of the grasshopper family.

Orthoptera are: cricket, roach, walking stick, and praying mantis.

The grasshopper and its relatives are mostly harmful to man. Swarms of grasshoppers ("locusts") have plagued both the Old and New World throughout history. Every few years farmers in the Middle West have to fight these pests to save their crops.

The only useful relative of the grasshopper is the *praying mantis* which eats other insects, many of which are harmful. You can buy mantis egg cases at some seed stores. The eggs hatch in the spring and the adults remain in the garden where they eat other insects. Although the mantis looks ferocious, actually he is quite harmless to man and is one of the most helpful insects known.

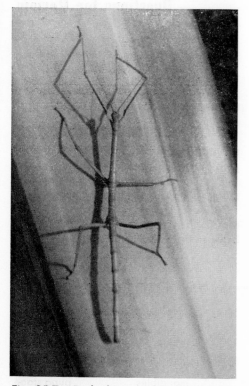

Fig. 25-7. By looking at this photograph, you can undoubtedly see why the walking stick is a good example of protective resemblance.

In Conclusion

The grasshopper, an insect belonging to the order Orthoptera shows the characteristics of all arthropods in having an exoskeleton of chitin, a segmented body, and jointed appendages. Other characteristics of its body structure include three body regions; three pairs of legs; one pair of antennae; and the presence of spiracles and tracheae. The grasshopper is a member of the largest class of arthropods, the insects.

The eight body systems of the grasshopper show what a high degree of specialization it has. The digestive, excretory, and respiratory systems are important groups of organs for the general functioning of the animal. Skeletal and muscular systems are involved in motion. Coordination and internal communication are taken care of by the circulatory and nervous systems. The type of reproductive system results in the sexes being separate. The life history of the grasshopper shows an incomplete type of metamorphosis.

We shall turn to other orders of insects to see what other variations this class of arthropods can take.

Questions for Review

1. What characteristics of the grasshopper make it similar to the crayfish?

2. List the characteristics of the grasshopper which relate it to other insects as a group.

3. Most animals have important organs located on the head. In what respects is the grasshopper an exception to this rule?

4. How do the grasshopper's legs illustrate adaptation?

5. What are the eight body systems of the grasshopper and the function of each?

6. What is the chief difference between the blood system of the grasshopper and that of man?

7. What is the chief difference between the respiratory system of the grasshopper and that of man?

8. (a) What kind of metamorphosis does the grasshopper undergo? (b) What happens during this metamorphosis?

9. What protection is given the eggs of the grasshopper during the winter?

10. After looking at the relatives of the grasshopper, what similarities can you see between them and the grasshopper?

Biologically Speaking

adult stage	labium	ovipositor
complete metamorphosis	labrum	palpus
compound eye	larva stage	prothorax
egg stage	mandibles	pupa stage
esophagus	maxillae	spiracles
ganglia	mesothorax	tarsus
gizzard	metathorax	thorax
incomplete metamorphosis	nymph	tracheae

Applying Facts and Principles

1. What is the difference between drowning in the higher animals and drowning in the grasshopper?

2. What reasons can you give for the insects' being able to withstand unusual temperatures, pressures, and other environmental conditions?

3. Give reasons to support the statement, "Insects are the most successful creatures in the world."

4. To illustrate circulation of blood in the insect, what type of apparatus can you propose by using a bathtub of water to represent the insect's blood supply.

5. What advantages are there to an insect in having a complete metamorphosis?

Fig. 25-9. The students in this high school biology class find this collection of mounted specimens of great value in helping them understand this branch of biology called entomology.

CHAPTER 26

Habits of Some Interesting Insects

Insects are all around us. They are so numerous and there are so many kinds that only very wintry weather could prevent an enthusiast from observing the ways of these six-footed creatures. One who studies insects is an **entomologist** (en-toh-*moll*-oh-jist) and the professional entomologist is always in demand. His services are needed by medicine, agriculture, and industry. Even the ordinary citizen occasionally seeks his advice.

But the amateur can also find entomology a useful hobby as well as an enjoyable pastime. The ants, bees, and wasps with their complex social orders are fascinating. Even the true bugs and the hard-shelled insects called beetles are worth a fleeting glimpse. The kinds of eggs, where laid, and how protected, the adaptations of larvae for food-getting and concealment, the methods of pupating and emergence of the adults make a round of absorbing events. When you actually see all the stages in the final three- or four-day transition from the green-jeweled pupa to the adult of the monarch butterfly, you will be amazed at the miracle.

Common orders of insects. We cannot study all the insects, but we can take a look at a few of them. There are 22 different orders of insects. The following table will show the names and representatives of the eight orders which are probably the most common in temperate regions.

Insects can be found in all probability in your home, your school, out-

EIGHT INSECT ORDERS	
ORDER	REPRESENTATIVE
1. Orthoptera (or-*thop*-ter-ah)	Grasshopper, cricket, mantis, roach
2. Lepidoptera (leh-pih-dop-ter-ah)	Moths, butterflies
3. Hymenoptera (hy-men-op-ter-ah)	Bees, ants, wasps
4. Odonata (o-don-*ah*-tah)	Dragonflies, damsel flies
5. Coleoptera (co-lee-op-ter-ah)	Beetles, ladybug beetle
6. Hemiptera (hem-*ip*-ter-ah)	Squash bugs, stink bugs, bedbugs, chinch bugs
7. Homoptera (hoh-mop-*ter*-ah)	Plant lice, scale insects, cicada, leaf hoppers
8. Diptera (*dip*-ter-ah)	Flies, mosquitoes, gnats

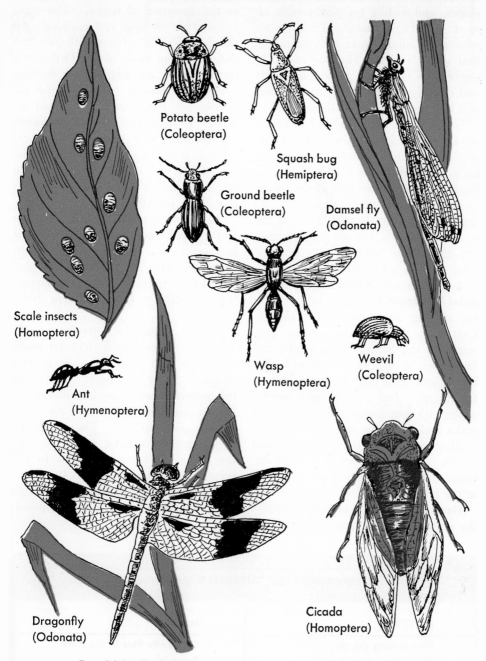

Potato beetle
(Coleoptera)

Squash bug
(Hemiptera)

Ground beetle
(Coleoptera)

Damsel fly
(Odonata)

Scale insects
(Homoptera)

Wasp
(Hymenoptera)

Weevil
(Coleoptera)

Ant
(Hymenoptera)

Dragonfly
(Odonata)

Cicada
(Homoptera)

Fig. 26-1.   These are representatives of several insect orders.

side in field and pond, on trees, under stones, and hiding on plants with almost perfect camouflage. The collector who only casually looks for insects will find quite a few. However, the observer who is willing to watch quietly and examine carefully his surroundings will find a great many of these animals.

Sometimes a net is helpful in catching them. In most cases though a covered jar in which you have put a poison, such as carbon tetrachloride (cleaning fluid), is a necessary part of the equipment. Pinning them after they are dead and putting them in a box is the next step. Then you are ready to classify them into orders. Let's examine some of these orders in more detail.

Butterflies and moths belong to the order Lepidoptera. Their brilliant colors are due to microscopic scales on their wings which make a mosaic pattern. If you handle living moths and butterflies, be sure to hold them by the thorax and with only light pressure of the fingers. Just a light touch on the wings with your hands will remove some scales and injure the insect for flight.

Most people confuse butterflies and moths. It is usually not difficult to distinguish between them if you will look at the table below.

Head of a butterfly or moth. Unlike the grasshopper, the head of a butterfly or moth is hairy, often even shaggy due to the presence of scales. The compound eyes are large and rounded, and the neck flexible. The mouth parts are different from those of the Orthoptera because they are adapted for sucking nectar from flowers. The maxillae are enormously lengthened and locked together to form the coiled **proboscis** (proh-*boss*-iss), or tongue. When extended, it may equal in length all the rest of the body. It is long enough to reach the nectar glands of the flowers that these insects visit.

The labium is reduced in size, two feathery palpi being all that is left of it in most cases. In this set of mouth parts, we have an example of organs *homologous* to those of the grasshopper, but adapted for quite different functions.

Thorax region of a butterfly or moth. The legs of the Lepidoptera are small and weak, but have the same general structure as in all insects. Obviously the butterfly spends much of its time in the air and uses its legs only for clinging to some surface. The wings are large, and the colored scales help the few veins in giving strength to the wing, and in some cases aid in protective coloration. The butterfly, though easily supported by its large wingspread, is not a swift flier.

COMPARISON OF BUTTERFLY AND MOTH

BUTTERFLY	MOTH
Flies during the day	Generally flies in the dark
Chrysalis, without cocoon	Pupa in cocoon
Wings vertical when at rest	Wings held horizontally
Antennae knobbed	Antennae feathery
Abdomen slender	Abdomen stout

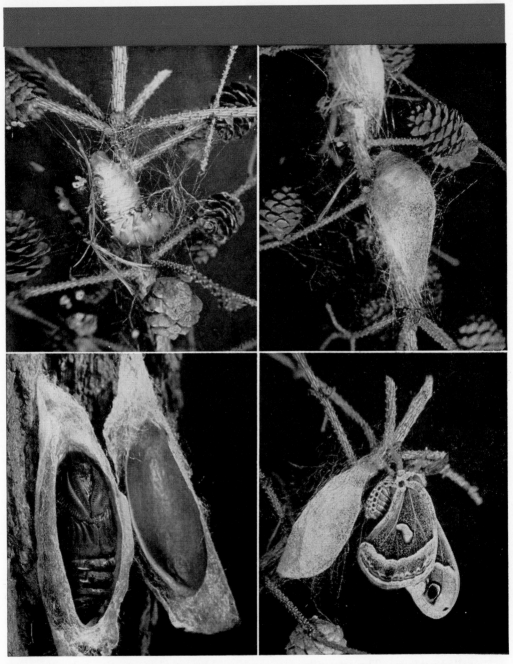

Fig. 26-2. In the upper left-hand photograph, a caterpillar is beginning to spin its cocoon which, when finished (upper right), makes a snug nest. The lower left-hand photograph shows a cocoon cut open to expose the pupa. Finally, the adult moth emerges
from the cocoon (lower right). What type of metamorphosis is represented in these
pictures?

Fig. 26-3. The monarch butterfly (top) resembles the viceroy butterfly (bottom). This similarity is called mimicry.

Abdomen of the Lepidoptera. The abdomen resembles that of the grasshopper, but has fewer visible segments and, as in all insects, is the least specialized body region.

Life history of a butterfly or moth. Most Lepidoptera deposit the eggs on or near the material which is to be the food of the young. Some pass the winter in this stage, but usually eggs are deposited in the spring and develop into caterpillars the following summer.

The egg does not hatch into a form anything like the adult. Instead, it produces a wormlike *caterpillar,* or **larva,** with biting mouth parts. But it has three pairs of legs and some extra pairs of legs at the end of the abdomen called **prolegs.** The caterpillar eats ravenously, grows big and fat, and molts several times. It needs terrific amounts of food to keep up this rapid growth, and during this stage the insect does extensive damage to various materials. Eventually it goes into a resting stage and becomes a **pupa.**

In butterflies the pupa rests in a **chrysalis** (krih-*sah*-lis), the outer covering of which becomes a hardened case, usually brown. This covering protects it during its long pause. The larva usually seeks a sheltered spot before this change occurs. The moth larva, on the other hand, usually spins a strong case of silk, the **cocoon** (kuh-*koon*). This pupa stage in which the Lepidoptera usually pass the winter is not a period of entire rest. A wormlike larva emerges as the *adult* butterfly or moth, totally changed, internally and externally.

While the function of the larva is simply to eat and grow, the adult eats only the nectar of flowers, and its life-work consists of producing or fertilizing the eggs for the next generation. Since the life development consists of distinct stages, it is an example of **complete metamorphosis.** Bees, beetles, and flies all pass through a similar series of changes which are given on page 329.

Protective coloration. Color protection is especially evident among insects and their larvae. Many are green like the grass and leaves among which they live and on which they feed. This is often due to chlorophyll in their food showing through their delicate tissues. Others are colored like dead leaves, flowers, or bark — whichever may be their usual background. The brown grasshopper resembles the ground on which it alights. The walking stick insect looks so much like the small twigs among which it lives that it can hardly be found.

Mimicry is protective coloration carried to such a degree that the animal resembles some particular object rather than just its background. Butterflies are some good examples. The leaf butterfly bears a startling resemblance to a dead leaf. The viceroy butterfly looks a great deal like the monarch butterfly.

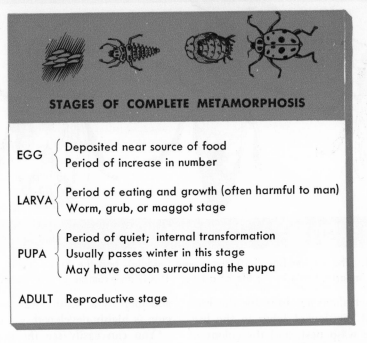

STAGES OF COMPLETE METAMORPHOSIS

EGG { Deposited near source of food
      Period of increase in number

LARVA { Period of eating and growth (often harmful to man)
        Worm, grub, or maggot stage

PUPA { Period of quiet; internal transformation
       Usually passes winter in this stage
       May have cocoon surrounding the pupa

ADULT   Reproductive stage

Some birds will not touch either kind because the monarch evidently has a bad flavor. Thus the viceroy as well as the monarch butterfly is protected.

Economic importance of Lepidoptera. Many butterflies and moths visit flowers to obtain nectar, which they drink through their long tubelike proboscis. In doing so, they aid in cross-pollination.

The greatest economic value of the Lepidoptera, however, is in the production of silk. The silkworm is the larva of a small moth which has been domesticated by man nearly 4,000 years.

Among the Lepidoptera are numerous forms which are notorious for the damage their larvae cause. The apple worm alone may destroy over $12,000,-000 worth of fruit annually. Millions of dollars are spent every year by the New England states in a losing fight against the gypsy and brown-tail moths. Cabbage worms, tomato worms, and corn ear worms, all of which are larvae of the Lepidoptera causing damage.

Social insects — Hymenoptera. It is fascinating to watch the activities around a beehive or an ant hill. We call these *social insects* because various members of the colony perform special tasks. One group gets food, another reproduces, and still another group protects the colony from enemies. The tasks differ of course depending on the kind of insect.

Fig. 26-4. The caterpillar, or larva, stage of the butterfly is a destructive one.

Fig. 26-5. The worker bee (left), the queen (middle), and the drone (right) each play an important role in the life of a hive. This is an example of communal life.

Instinct alone accounts for the high degree of division of labor in the beehive, the wasp nest, and the colony of ants. Contrary to common opinion, these insects probably are no more intelligent than any other insect forms. Yet the marvelous efficiency with which they carry on their routine tasks could well be imagined to illustrate high intelligence.

Ants, bees, wasps, and related insects are grouped together in the order **Hymenoptera.** The order includes not only those forms which live in colonies and show a high degree of division of labor, but numerous solitary forms as well. The members of the order indicate their close relationship by similarity in body structure and, in many cases, by the way in which they perform their life activities.

The structure of the body of the honeybee. A typical member of this order is the honeybee which we shall study in some detail as a remarkable example of adaptations of structure and function. The body regions are distinct, the head is attached to the thorax by a flexible neck, and the thorax to the abdomen by a slender waist. Each region is highly developed.

You can easily see the sensitive elbowed antennae, the enormous compound eyes, and three simple eyes. But the mouth parts are complicated and are a set of tools by themselves. The labrum is small, and the labium is developed into an efficient lapping tongue. They are used in making the cells of honeycomb from beeswax as well as collecting nectar from flowers.

The thorax is large, strong, and provided with powerful muscles which operate the legs and wings.

Bees are swift and enduring fliers. Their wings, small but well-proportioned, operate at high speed, producing the familiar hum. The *anterior* wings are much the larger, and the *posterior* wings may be attached to them by tiny hooks for aid in flying.

The abdomen consists of six segments, with ovipositor or sting at the posterior end. Only in the queen is the ovipositor developed as a true egg-laying organ. The worker bees, which are undeveloped females, produce no eggs and have the ovipositor modified into the well-known "sting." This is a complicated organ consisting of two barbed darts operated by strong muscles and enclosed in a sheath. The darts are connected with a gland which secretes the poison and makes a bee sting so painful. On the four last abdominal segments of the workers are glands which secrete the wax used in comb-making.

Life history of the honeybee. The life history of the honeybee is a fine example of communal life and mutual help. Each member of the colony works for the good of all. This habit has resulted in great success as a whole, as well as remarkable development for each individual. There are three forms of bees in any colony: (1) the *queen;* (2) the *drones;* and (3) the *workers.*

The queen. The **queen** is nearly twice as large as a worker, with a long pointed abdomen. Her particular function is the production of eggs to continue the colony. She may produce in one day as many as 3,000 eggs equivalent to twice her own weight. The queen develops from a fertile egg. The workers enlarge the wax cell in which the egg is to grow and feed the grublike larva with extra portions of special food, the "royal jelly." This causes the development of a queen, or fertile female, instead of a worker, which is a female without the ability to lay eggs. After being thus fed for five days, the larva spins a silken cocoon, changes to a pupa, and is sealed into her large waxen chamber by the workers. When the mature queen emerges from her cell, she seeks out other queen larvae in the colony and kills them, or if she finds another adult queen, they fight till one is killed. She never uses her sting except against another queen.

If the workers prevent her from destroying the other queens, she takes with her from two to 20,000 bees and "swarms" out to seek a home elsewhere. In this way new colonies are formed and overcrowding is prevented.

After a few days she takes a wedding flight up into the air where she mates with a drone, or male bee, receiving several million sperm cells. Then she returns to the hive and begins her lifework of laying eggs. This is no small task as one queen may produce as many as one million eggs per year and often lives from five to ten years. Although we call her a queen, she is in no sense the ruler of the hive but rather its common mother.

The drones. The **drones,** while larger than the workers, are smaller than the queen and have a thick broad body, enormous eyes, and very powerful wings. They develop from unfertilized eggs. They do not have pollen baskets, wax pockets, or stings. Their tongues are not long enough to get nectar, so that they have to be fed by the workers. During the summer a few hundred drones are tolerated in the colony because one of them must function as a mate for the new queen. The rest are of no use in the hive. This easy life has its troubles, however. With the coming of autumn, when honey runs low, the workers will no longer support the drones, but sting them to death. Their bodies may often be found around the hives in the early autumn.

The worker bees. The **workers** are by far the most numerous inhabitants of the hive. They are undeveloped females, smaller than drones, with the ovipositor modified into the sting, and with all the adaptations of legs, wings, and mouth parts. Workers may number from 10,000 to 100,000 in a hive. With the exception of reproduction, all the varied industries and products of the hive are their business. They perform, at different times, many different kinds of work as well as provide the three hive products — *wax, honey,* and *propolis* (*prop*-oh-lis), a type bee glue used to cover holes in the hive. In summer they literally work themselves to death in three or four weeks, but bees hatched in the fall may live five or six months.

One of the recent discoveries has been that bees communicate with each other by a complicated set of dances. By this novel method they inform the workers in the hive where a new supply of nectar may be found.

Products of the beehive. Wax is a secretion from the abdominal segments of workers. This comes after they have gorged themselves with honey, and have then suspended themselves by their feet in a sort of curtain. As the wax is produced, it is removed by other workers, chewed to make it soft, and then carried to still another group who build it into a comb.

The **comb** is a wonderful structure, composed of six-sided cells in two layers. It is arranged so as to leave no waste space, and to afford the greatest storage capacity with the use of the least material. Not only is it used for storage of honey and " beebread " (a food substance made from pollen and saliva), but also for the rearing of young bees. The eggs are put, one in a cell, by the queen and sealed up by the workers, making what is called a *brood comb.*

Honey is made from the nectar of flowers which is taken into the crop of the bee. They change the *cane sugar* to the more easily digested *fruit sugar* and then empty it into the comb cells. There it is left to ripen and thicken by evaporation before being sealed.

The removal of honey by man does not harm the bees if about 30 pounds are left for their winter use; that is,

enough to feed an average colony of 40,000 bees for an ordinary winter.

Propolis is another product of the hive. It is a brown substance gathered from the sticky leaf buds of some plants. Propolis is used to make the interior of the hive smooth, to help attach the comb, to close up holes and cracks, and even to varnish the comb if it is left unused for a time.

Industries of the colony. Not only do the workers prepare the wax, honey, and propolis as needed, but some attend and feed the queen or drones. Some act as nurses to the hungry larvae, which they feed with partly digested food from their own stomachs. Other bees clean the hive of dead bees or foreign matter, while still others fan with their wings to ventilate the hive. All the time thousands of workers are bringing in nectar, pollen, and propolis as needed for the use of the colony.

Such a *communal,* or colony life, illustrates the highest development of *division of labor* found among any animals lower than man. It occurs among some ants and wasps as well as bees, though nowhere is it carried to a higher point than in the honeybee.

Other Hymenoptera. Like the bees, ants are social insects and the colony requires a queen. Unlike the bees, most ants can't sting, but they bite with jaws more powerful in proportion to their size than those of any other insects. It is an interesting and generally unknown fact that during the early autumn the males and females acquire temporary wings and then start new colonies.

Wasps and ichneumon flies. Wasps, both solitary and social, and hornets are interesting, not only because of personal experiences we may have had with their stings, but because some of them are probably the original papermakers of the world. Their nests are made from a

Fig. 26-6. This exposed split log shows the interior of carpenter ants' nest. Note the runways cut by the workers and several cocoons containing young ants. This is another example of complete metamorphosis.

sort of pulp obtained from strips of wood chewed vigorously and mixed with secretions from the mouth.

It is quite probable that no members of the Hymenoptera are more valuable to us than the tiny ichneumon flies which manage to lay their eggs under the skin of living caterpillars and thus kill them.

The insect order Odonata. The word *Odonata* comes from the Greek word meaning *tooth*. The wings of the Odonata are membranous and do not overlap. The abdomen is long, but there is no stalk connecting it to the thorax. They do no harm; on the contrary, they are very beneficial. The nymphs which live in the water destroy the larvae of many insects, while the adults, as they fly over water, catch mosquitoes, gnats, and other small insects as well.

The order Coleoptera. About 250,-000 species of beetles have been recorded, and most of them can be recognized as beetles by anyone because of their hard shells. They all have strong jaws and complete metamorphosis.

Wood-boring beetles cause extensive losses; buffalo " bugs " are destructive to carpets and furs; potato beetles ravage gardens; weevils damage grain and cotton. Texas alone has paid over $150,000,000 in the attempt to control the cotton boll weevil. The Japanese beetle, first discovered in this country in New Jersey in 1916, has already become a great menace to fruit trees and other crops. On the other hand, carrion beetles are scavengers, ladybugs eat scale insects and thus aid the citrus fruit industry, and Calosoma beetles have been introduced into New England and elsewhere to help control gypsy moth.

Fig. 26-7. The potato beetle belongs to the order Coleoptera and is a menace to farmers.

Hemiptera include many pests. The half-winged insects have sucking mouth parts and incomplete metamorphosis. The edges of their wings overlap. One or two forms are wingless. The insects belonging to Hemiptera are the only insects constituting the *true bugs.* Among them are many of our worst pests, such as the chinch bug, bedbug, squash bug, and stinkbug. Others, less harmful to us, include aquatic insects like water striders, back swimmers, and water boatmen.

In the Homoptera we find sucking insects. The word *homoptera* means *similar wings,* though some of the members of this order are wingless. When wings are present, they are held over the body in an inverted V, like the roof of a house. All have sucking mouth parts and incomplete metamorphosis. Plant lice, scale insects, mealy bugs, leaf hoppers, and others take a huge toll of our wild and cultivated plants. We are indebted, however, to the lac insect,

which alone of the Homoptera is of economic benefit. We get *shellac* from it, which is used throughout the world as a base for lacquer, wood finishes, and in the manufacture of phonograph records.

The *cicada* (sih-*kay*-da) is a common representative which lives underground from two years in the case of one species to 17 years in the case of another species. They then tunnel to the surface and spend a week or two as adults. Their high-pitched and strident notes, coming from treetops, are familiar on hot summer days.

The Diptera are two-winged insects. They have mouth parts which are fitted for piercing, rasping, and sucking. Their metamorphosis is complete.

One of our most notorious enemies in the insect world is the housefly. Due to the fact that it breeds in filth, people are often infected with typhoid, dysentery, and other filth-borne diseases. Other Diptera include the mosquitoes

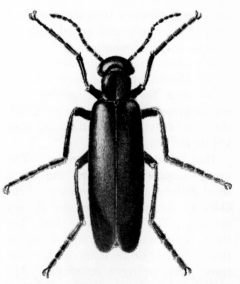

Fig. 26-8. Certain insects have peculiar ways of defending themselves against attack. The blister beetle, for example, is equipped with a very strong acid fluid that protects it from its enemies.

which are known for their annoying habits as well as their disease-carrying characteristics. The tsetse fly of Africa, responsible for the transmission of the protozoan-caused disease, sleeping sickness, also belongs in this order.

The housefly. The common housefly (*typhoid fly*) has large eyes, short, fleshy antennae, and a club-shaped sucking tube. It never bites, but the related stable fly or horsefly bites cattle and man. Its wings are well-developed and operate at high speed due to the powerful muscles of the thorax. The six legs are also well-developed and the feet have claws and sticky hairs which aid in locomotion. Unless these hair tips are free from dust, they will not stick well and the fly cannot walk easily on smooth surfaces. You have probably noticed the care with which it cleans its feet by constantly rubbing them against each other and its body.

Its *eggs* are deposited in horse ma-

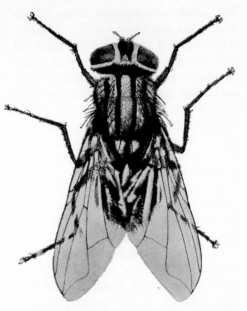

Fig. 26-10. The housefly carries bacteria among the hairs covering its body. Its six legs are well-developed.

nure or in similar matter, the female laying from one to two hundred eggs. They hatch in one day into the larval form called **maggots,** and in this stage do some good as scavengers. After eating and growing for five or six days, the larvae pass into the pupal condition, inside the last larval skin, which thus takes the place of a cocoon. From this stage, adults emerge in about a week.

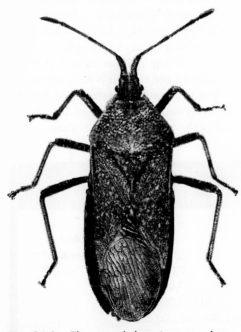

Fig. 26-9. The squash bug is a true bug. Notice how the edges of its wings overlap.

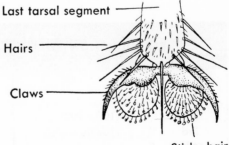

Last tarsal segment

Hairs

Claws

Sticky hairs

Fig. 26-11. This enlarged drawing of the foot of the housefly shows the claws and sticky hairs which help in carrying disease germs.

The whole development from egg to adult takes about two weeks. Breeding begins early in spring and continues till cold weather. Flies multiply at a tremendous rate. If reproduction were unchecked and all offspring survived (which fortunately is not the case), then flies in the different generations, each lasting about two weeks, would each produce offspring as shown in the table below.

The mosquito. In the mosquito, the mouth parts — labrum, tongue, mandibles, and maxillae — are reduced to sharp lancelike bristles. They are enclosed in the labium as a sheath, and are adapted for piercing and sucking. In order to dilute the blood so that they can withdraw it and prevent it from clotting in the proboscis, they inject a little saliva. This causes the usual irritation and swelling which we know as a *mosquito bite.*

The female usually lays her eggs in water. Ponds, rain barrels, and even tin cans furnish ideal breeding places. The eggs are deposited as single eggs or in tiny rafts, consisting of many eggs covered with a waterproof coating. When they hatch, the larvae emerge downwards into the water, and become the familiar *wigglers.* Though living in water, the mosquito larva breathes air which it obtains through a tube projecting from the posterior of its abdomen. You may often see it with this tube at the surface and the body hanging head downwards in the water.

The pupa stage is also passed in the water and differs from most insect pupae in being active like the larva. It differs from the larva in having a large head provided with two air tubes for breathing. The adult emerges from the pupa, whose shed skin acts as a raft. At this critical time the mosquito must not fall overboard or get its wings wet before they are expanded or it will die. There are exceptions to the above description but it pertains to most mosquitoes.

Our most common northern mosquito *Culex* (kew-lex) does not carry disease germs. It may be distinguished from *Anopheles* (an-*ah*-fell-eez), which carries malaria organisms, by the fact that the latter stands almost on its head when at rest, while *Culex* holds its body more nearly horizontal. Fortunately, *Aëdes* (ay-*ee*-deez), which is the mosquito which carries the germs of yellow fever, is a tropical species and does not usually invade our temperate regions.

The economic importance of insects. Probably only a minority of insects are distinctly detrimental to man. Yet

REPRODUCTION OF FLIES	
1st generation	200 (100 females)
2nd " (100 x 200)	20,000 (10,000 females)
3rd " (10,000 x 200)	2,000,000
4th "	200,000,000
5th "	20,000,000,000
6th "	2,000,000,000,000
	2,020,202,020,200 in 12 weeks

Fig. 26-12. Here are some larvae of the house mosquito, *Culex*. They get oxygen by means of a breathing tube which penetrates the surface film of the water.

these obnoxious forms are so prominent and well-known that popular opinion is apt to condemn all insects for this reason. To cope with animals so numerous and active as insects calls for accurate knowledge of the habits and life histories of these six-footed rivals of man.

Their harmful activities are to:

1. Destroy grain, vegetables, and fruit (numerous species).

2. Injure shade trees (tussock, gypsy, and leopard moths).

3. Carry many kinds of disease germs to animals and man (fleas, lice, flies, mosquitoes).

4. Act as agents in the spread of plant diseases by carrying spores and infected material (hoppers and aphids).

5. Destroy buildings and wood (beetles, ants, termites).

6. Annoy and injure many by bites and stings (wasps, mosquitoes, gnats).

7. Affect food (beetles, cockroaches).

8. Destroy clothing and fabrics (clothes moths, carpet beetles).

9. Act as parasites on domestic animals and man (botflies, fleas, lice).

On the other hand, we owe to insects many useful processes and products as:

1. Pollination of flowers (bees, butterflies, moths, certain types of flies).

2. Furnishing of silk (silk moth cocoon).

3. Furnishing of honey and wax (bees).

4. Furnishing of shellac (lac insect).

5. Source of dye (cochineal insect).

6. Furnishing of material for ink (gall insects).

7. Action as scavengers (maggots, beetles).

8. Killing of injurious insects (ladybugs, ichneumon flies).

In Conclusion

Eight orders include most of the insects you know best. Butterflies and moths compose the order Lepidoptera. This is readily distinguished from other orders by the brightly-colored scales of the wings of its members. In the adult stage, butterflies and moths are a decided contrast to the wormlike larvae (caterpillars) from which they develop through stages of a complete metamorphosis.

The order Hymenoptera includes bees, ants, and wasps, which are remarkable for the highly specialized societies in which they live. Three kinds of individuals: workers, queens, and drones divide the labors of the beehive. Most of the duties fall to the workers. The high degree of specialization of activities in the colony of social insects can be attributed to instinct rather than to intelligence.

Other orders include dragonflies, beetles, true bugs, cicadas, and scale insects, flies and mosquitoes, all curiously adapted for different kinds of life activities.

Questions for Review

1. What are some of the places in which insects can be found?

2. What are the chief characteristics of the eight common orders of insects?

3. Why are the mouth parts of the butterflies considered homologous to the mouth of the grasshopper?

4. Describe the four stages in the complete metamorphosis of the butterflies and moths.

5. How are mimicry and protective coloration useful among insects?

6. In what stage may the Lepidoptera be harmful?

7. Many of the Hymenoptera may be considered well-disciplined. In what ways may this be confused with intelligence?

8. (a) Do insects communicate with each other? (b) How?

9. (a) What are the different types of bees? (b) Describe the functions of each in the hive.

10. Name some products of the beehive and give some use for each one.

11. Give the life history of the housefly.

12. In what way is prevention better than cure in the case of eliminating flies and mosquitoes?

Biologically Speaking

chrysalis	maggots	pupa
cocoon	mimicry	queen
drone	proboscis	social insects
entomologist	prolegs	wigglers
larva	propolis	worker

Applying Facts and Principles

1. How would you suggest checking on bee habits in order to discover how they communicate with each other?

2. Biologists state that the army ant of the tropics is entirely blind. Name some other animals which lead successful lives in spite of the fact they are missing one or more of the senses of higher animals.

3. (a) Can a little fly grow to be a large fly? (b) Why?

4. What really is meant by an "order" of insects?

5. The bee's sting is a modified part of the reproductive system. To what part of the grasshopper would you say that it is homologous?

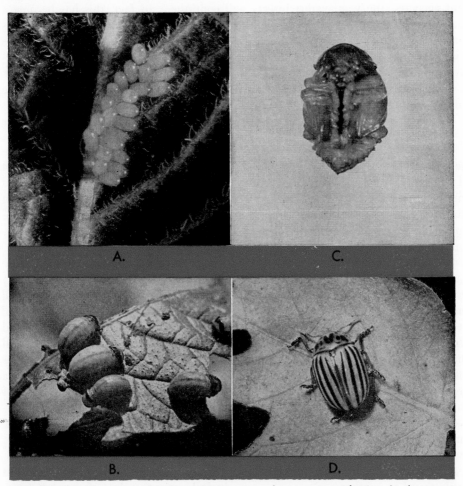

Fig. 26-13. The potato beetle undergoes complete metamorphosis. In A, you can see the tiny eggs on the underside of a potato leaf. B, shows the beetle larvae; C, shows a pupa. In D, you can see the adult beetle.

CHAPTER 27

The Control of Insect Pests

Biologists have established an international rogue's gallery of insects including the chief criminals. Methods of control have been discovered as a result of many hours of research in the laboratories of colleges and universities, the Department of Agriculture, and state agricultural institutes. Through these and other important agencies, the war against insects will continue. In fact, this has become a major activity, as it has been estimated that insects cause over 750 million dollars worth of damages to plants alone in the country each year. As pests new to this country make their appearance, measures must be developed to stop their destructive activities.

It remains for us as citizens to take full advantage of the weapons now available and to take an active part in the war against insect pests.

Why are insects apt to become dangerous pests? While most other forms of life have struggled to maintain their numbers with the spread of human civilization, insects have increased rapidly and have become a dominant form of animal life. There are three good reasons for this dominance.

1. *Small size* is a distinct advantage to the insect. Insects escape attention until the damage they have done has become noticeable. Shelter is no problem as hiding places need be no larger than a crack in the bark of a tree, the lower side of a leaf, or a tiny hole in the ground. Small size removes these organisms from the danger of starvation — a frequent problem faced by larger animals. Small amounts of food will maintain an insect and, if food becomes scarce in one locality, the insect can easily travel to another.

2. *Adaptability* gives the insect another advantage over most other forms of life. Many organisms are so definite as to their requirements that they cannot leave a specific environment. Not so with the insects. They range far and wide over the land and many seem equally at home in a great variety of conditions. Temperature changes, moisture variations, and other variable factors of environment seem to have little effect on most of them.

3. *Rapid rate of reproduction* is still another advantage. A single individual may lay from 100 to several thousand eggs, although not all of them will hatch. Thus the population increases into almost staggering figures during a single season as we saw in the case of the housefly on page 336.

Insects are often related to disease. World War II brought problems in the control of insect-borne diseases. Epidemics of deadly typhus fever broke out in Italy near the close of the war, causing high mortality among the troops and the civilian population. Medical science has proved definitely that this dis-

Fig. 27-1. The louse is a small, wingless insect that is parasitic on warm-blooded animals.

ease is carried by the human body louse. Therefore, the control of typhus depended on destruction of the carriers. Utilizing the powerful insecticide, DDT, the United States Army Medical Corps began the systematic " delousing " of all the communities in which typhus had appeared and the epidemic was stopped.

The rat flea is another dangerous carrier of disease. It is known to carry typhus, but is usually more closely associated with the carrying of *bubonic plague*, the " black death " of the Middle Ages. Ships from the Orient at one time carried many rats to American ports. Fleas present on the rats were a serious menace and introduced the disease to this country. Today rigid measures are used to prevent rats from gaining entrance to seaports.

Fig. 27-2. Inspectors at a plant quarantine inspection center are carefully examining all plants arriving from foreign countries for signs of insects and disease.

Although bedbugs are not directly associated with any particular disease, they may carry certain infections. These are infections which occur in the human blood stream. A few other diseases, especially one known as *relapsing fever,* have been traced to this insect pest. The best way to rid a house of bedbugs is to enforce cleanliness in all daily activities. But a spray containing DDT has been found to be sure death for them. Of course, the role of flies and the several species of mosquitoes in the spreading of disease remains the most pressing problem confronting us in insect control.

We have four good weapons against the insect world. The war against insects is fought with four principal methods as weapons used in the attack. The struggle against them is effective only when all four of these methods are employed: (1) *quarantine;* (2) *conservation of natural enemies of insects;* (3) *environmental control;* and (4) *chemical control.*

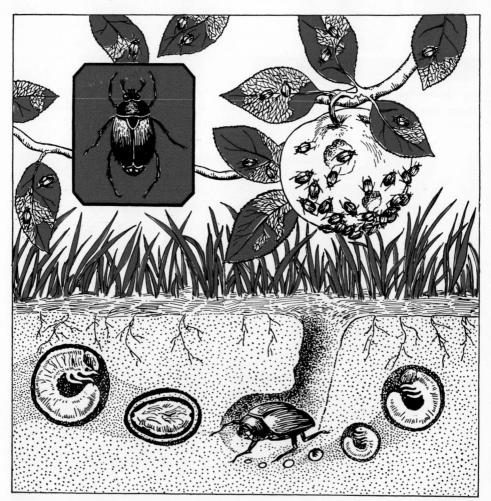

Fig. 27-3. The life cycle of the Japanese beetle. Below the ground (left to right): mature grub (late spring); pupa; adult beetle laying eggs (summer); developing grubs (late summer and fall).

Fig. 27-4. The boll weevil, about a quarter of an inch long, infests the cotton plant. It does serious damage throughout the cotton belt. Sprays are effective in dealing with these insects.

Quarantine as a control measure. Colonists and importers have brought unwittingly at least 75 species of our harmful insects into the country in the form of eggs or larvae concealed on plants or in fresh fruits. The Bureau of Entomology and Plant Quarantine operates under the U. S. Department of Agriculture. It has inspectors in every port of entry in the country. Their duty is to confiscate and destroy any plants or fruits coming into the country that are suspected of carrying harmful insects or fungus pests.

The Bureau is always alert to discover local areas in which insect pests exist inside our own country in order that unaffected areas may be kept free. Many state governments have special officials to help prevent widespread insect destruction. All roads and transportation lines leading out of an infected area are watched in the same way as ports of entry.

If quarantines had been in operation earlier in our history, we might not be struggling today with the European corn borer, the Mexican bean beetle, the Japanese beetle, the Oriental peach moth, the Mediterranean fruit fly, the gypsy moth, the cotton boll weevil, and many other foreign insect pests.

The conservation of natural enemies. Perhaps you have wondered how, if Japanese beetles are so terribly destructive, the Japanese are able to raise any plants at all. The answer concerns **natural**

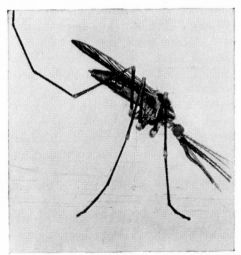

Fig. 27-5. The names, *Anopheles* and *malaria*, go together. The female mosquito carries the microorganism which causes the disease.

Fig. 27-6. The larvae of mosquitoes can be killed by spreading oil on the water where they live. Here a member of a sanitation squad is spraying oil on pools in a swampy region.

enemies of insects. Insects were present in America before our ancestors arrived from other lands. Yet, even without any control measures, these insects were held in check by natural enemies. The fact that our worst pests are imported species is explained also in terms of natural enemies. Introduced insects are free from those animals which held them in check in their native land. Consequently, they have multiplied here at a tremendous rate. Attempts have been made to import the natural enemies. Frequently, however, they also become pests, thus creating a still greater problem. This situation should impress on all of us how extremely important it is to preserve the balance of nature.

Birds are the most important natural enemies of insects. Much of our success in combating insects depends on conservation of our bird life. We still have not learned this lesson completely, for we needlessly destroy necessary nesting places and feeding grounds for our most important allies in the war on insects.

Snakes, frogs, spiders, and toads are other valuable natural enemies of the insect world. But our attitude toward these creatures is far from enlightened. How many of you have felt that you have rendered a valuable service in killing a harmless garter snake which lives largely on small rodents and insects?

Nature controls insect population by means of environment. Temperature changes and varying amounts of moisture are good examples. In some cases, man can control insects by changing their environment. For instance, we can control certain insects by rotating crops in one area. This method is good for such localized pests as beetle grubs and others, but it is ineffective against those insects which migrate.

Another way is to drain those places where they breed. Ditches, ponds, and various shallow bodies of water must be drained regularly so as to make it impossible for certain insects to complete their life cycle. This is especially true in the case of the mosquito.

Still another effective method of environmental control is to correct faulty methods of sewage disposal. Many insects breed in sewage. And if modern disposal is practiced, the breeding places are destroyed.

Equally important is proper garbage disposal. Again, some insects breed in this type of filth, and the best way to prevent such breeding is to burn or treat it to be sure that none of it is dumped in places where insects can get at it. We should not forget man's mechanical methods of insect control, however. The fly swatter, traps, fly paper, and electric screens are still common ways of insect destruction.

Where other methods fail, man resorts to chemistry to get rid of insect

Fig. 27-7. Elaborate spray rigs like this are used in orchards to distribute insecticides and fungicides to all trees.

pests. Although chemical control is expensive, it is most effective in the majority of cases.

There are five classes of poisons or **insecticides.** Each depends on the different ways in which insects feed. **Stomach poisons** are used against chewing insects such as beetles, grasshoppers, and various caterpillars. These insects eat the leaves of the plants they attack. If the leaves are coated with a poison, the insects usually die as a result. *Paris green, sodium fluoride,* and *arsenate of lead* are among the common stomach poisons.

The true bugs, aphids, lice, scale insects, and others get their food by sucking plant juices. Stomach poisons don't bother them because they never eat the surfaces of plants. Rather, they suck through these outer cells into the phloem and xylem cells. So we use **contact poisons** against them. Some of the effective ones include: various *oil emulsions, soap, nicotine, pyrethrum, rotenone,* and *lime-sulfur.* These insecticides kill as they come in contact with the insect's body. Your State Agricultural Experiment Station will gladly give you directions for making and using these.

A third type of chemical control em-

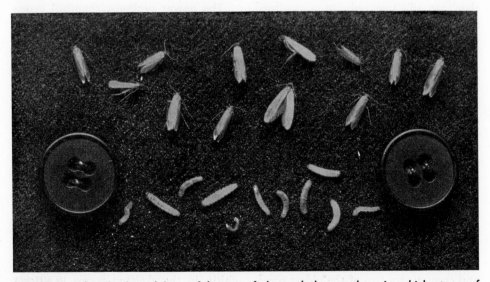

Fig. 27-8.   Identify the adults and larvae of these clothes moths.   In which stage of their life cycle do they damage woolens?

Fig. 27-9. The elm trees on the left were once beautiful. Their destruction was caused by beetles which carry the Dutch Elm disease fungus.

ploys *gases* like carbon disulfide or the very poisonous hydrocyanic acid. Peach borers, the pink bollworm, and the common clothes moth may be controlled by using such **fumigants.** But they are effective only in a confined area and should be used only by someone who is an expert at handling them.

Sprays, or respiratory poisons, depend for their success on clogging or poisoning the tracheae of insects. Pyrethrum (py-*ree*-thrum), or certain thin oils chemically treated and prepared, may be sprayed into the air and are effective in controlling such insects as the tussock moth, cabbage worm, cotton boll weevil, and codling moth.

Repellents actually do not kill adult insects although they may injure the larvae. They are either sprayed or dusted or merely allowed to evaporate in closed areas like closets. Camphor and creosote are two of the oldest repellents. The more modern types include *paradichlorobenzene* (par-ah-dy-klohrah-*ben*-zeen) and *naphthalene* (*naf*-thal-een). Certain insects, like the clothes moth, will not lay their eggs where these chemicals occur.

The newer synthetic chemical insecticides. This new field of chemical activity is best represented by DDT (which is short for *dichloro-diphenyl trichloroethane*). It is not a recent discovery, although we have only used it during the past ten or twelve years. It was first used effectively in World War II to control body lice and mosquitoes. Now we use it for fly and mosquito control as well as for general garden and farm insect control.

DDT is available in the form of powders, sprays, and convenient "bombs." It is extremely potent against many kinds of insects which it kills due to its effect on the nervous system. The chitin in the skeleton seems to attract and hold the DDT. Roaches, mosquitoes, and bedbugs succumb quickly in air containing DDT mist. It is effective in the dairy barn to control annoying flies. Important agricultural uses of DDT include spraying of orchards and garden crops. Unfortunately, DDT is as effective against bees as it is other insects. Hence, care must be used in its application to avoid the destruction of valuable insects and birds.

Convenient Aerosol bombs containing DDT are available for easy fumigation in a house. It is a good plan to close the windows every few weeks and open the valve on the bomb for about 30 seconds in each room in the house. The air will be filled with a fine mist which will soon settle to the floor and kill all hidden insects. All pets should be removed before fumigation.

DDT is a poisonous chemical. It is almost insoluble in water and so is usually available either in the form of a powder or as an oil-solvent spray. The powder can be absorbed through the skin as can the spray. Persons using it must use the greatest care and must see that none gets on any part of the body. Children and pets should never be allowed where it is being used. If people are careful, they can use it effectively in keeping certain insect pests under control.

Several new insecticides called *methoxychlor* (meth-*ox*-ih-clor) have recently appeared. But no one insecticide is perfect. Man still must know his old enemy, the insect, thoroughly before he can choose a successful weapon for its control.

In Conclusion

Insects, because of their small size, adaptability, and rapid rate of reproduction are among the worst pests to man. Certain forms may suddenly appear in epidemic proportions, causing serious damage to shade trees, fruit trees, and crops. Among the most annoying forms are those which invade our homes.

Several control measures are employed in the fight against insect pests. These measures include quarantines, the conservation of natural enemies of insects, environmental control, and chemical control. The most rapid results are obtained by using various types of chemical poisons.

Our next Unit will introduce us to the familiar animals with backbones, and perhaps some not quite so familiar. Compare them as you read about them with the invertebrates which you have just studied.

Questions for Review

1. Why is a knowledge of the life history of insects necessary in order to cope with them?

2. Why are insects likely to become dangerous pests?

3. In what ways can insects be related to the spread of disease?

4. List as many natural enemies of insects as you can.

5. How does nature control insects?

6. What specific measures can man take to control insect pests as far as their environment is concerned?

7. Make a chart in which you show the general types of chemicals used in insect control, the specific chemicals, and for what insects each is best suited.

8. Why is there no really perfect insecticide?

9. What are five most destructive insect pests in your neighborhood?

10. What effect may DDT have on man?

11. What action of DDT makes it an effective insecticide?

Biologically Speaking

chemical control	extermination	quarantine
contact poison	fumigant	repellent
DDT	insecticide	spray
environmental control	natural enemies	stomach poison

Applying Facts and Principles

1. In what ways are screens, netting, refrigeration, building codes, and flood control related to insect control?

2. Why is insect control considered an international problem?

3. What do you think are the chief reasons why malaria did not get a start in this country after World War II even though many men returned from service with the disease?

4. Make a chart in which you list as many insecticides as you can. Give the possible advantages and disadvantages of each.

5. Why is rat control bound up closely with insect control?

Research On Your Own

1. Collect samples of water from several sources, including a stagnant pool, back waters of a stream, or a fish pond. How many different kinds of protozoans can you find?

2. Make a chart of protozoan diseases, including the names of each disease, the organism afflicted, the nature of the disease, and the protozoan which causes it.

3. In a large gallon jar prepare a protozoan culture. Check the most common forms found each day. Keep records to show how the population of the culture changes daily. Describe the appearance of the water daily also.

4. The ability of Hydra to regenerate can be easily shown if a single specimen is isolated in a watch-glass and cut into three or more pieces with a finely drawn glass rod or very sharp razor.

5. Garden slugs and large snails are quite abundant in most areas. Kill them with chloroform and dissect them to show the intricate structure they have.

6. The culture of snails in an aquarium is also an interesting hobby. Notice their movement and reproductive cycle. Classify as many as you can.

7. Daphnia may be cultured in the laboratory by providing it with a culture which has an abundance of bacteria. Partially decayed material in the water will foster their growth. The Daphnia should be removed with a cloth net when their numbers seem to diminish and then be transferred to another aquarium.

8. Establish a demonstration ant colony in your classroom. The colony may be in a glass jar or in a special demonstration container. If a jar is used, wrap it in black paper until the ants have established runways along the glass. The ant colony may be obtained from nature or from a supply house.

9. Cut through a gall on a twig to expose the insects living inside. What stage are the insects in?

10. Count the number of chirps of a cricket per ten seconds. Find the exact temperature. Plot a curve to see if there is any relationship between the temperature and the number of chirps. Do other sound-making insects have any such relationship?

 **More About Biology**

Adrian, Mary. *FIDDLE CRAB.* Holiday House, Inc., New York. 1953

Bastin, Harold. *FREAKS AND MARVELS OF INSECT LIFE.* A. A. Wyn, Inc., New York. 1954

Berrill, N. J. *THE LIVING TIDE.* Dodd, Mead and Co., New York. 1951

Blackford, Charles M. *DEEP TREASURE.* John C. Winston Co., Philadelphia. 1954

Buchsbaum, Ralph. *ANIMALS WITHOUT BACKBONES.* The University of Chicago Press, Chicago. 1948

Clausen, Lucy. *INSECT FACT AND FOLK-LORE.* The Macmillan Co., New York. 1954

Cousteau, Jacques and Dumas, Frederic. *THE SILENT WORLD.* Harper and Brothers, New York. 1953

Curran, Charles Howard. *INSECTS IN YOUR LIFE.* Sheridan House, Inc., New York. 1951

Curtis, George. *BEES WAYS.* Houghton Mifflin Co., Boston. 1948

Diole, Phillipe. *THE UNDERSEA ADVENTURE.* Julian Messner, Inc., New York. 1953

Dudley, Ruth M. *SEA SHELLS.* The Thomas Y. Crowell Co., New York. 1953

Gaul, Albro. *THE WONDERFUL WORLD OF INSECTS.* Rinehart and Co., Inc., New York. 1952

Gertsch, Willis J. *AMERICAN SPIDERS.* D. Van Nostrand Co., Inc., New York. 1949

Hausman, Leon. *BEGINNER'S GUIDE TO FRESH-WATER LIFE.* G. P. Putnam's Sons, New York. 1950

Hegner, Robert. *PARADE OF THE ANIMAL KINGDOM.* The Macmillan Co., New York. 1935

Jahn, T. L. *HOW TO KNOW THE PROTOZOA.* William C. Brown Co., Dubuque, Iowa. 1949

Lane, Ferdinand C. *ALL ABOUT THE INSECT WORLD.* Random House, Inc., New York. 1953

Morgan, Ann Haven. *FIELDBOOK OF PONDS AND STREAMS.* G. P. Putnam's Sons, New York. 1930

Needham, James and Paul R. *A GUIDE TO THE STUDY OF FRESH-WATER BIOLOGY.* Comstock Co., Ithaca, New York. 1938

Neider, Charles (Ed.). *THE FABULOUS INSECTS.* Harper and Brothers, New York. 1954

Pinner, Erna. *CURIOUS CREATURES.* Philosophical Lib., Inc., New York. 1953

Robertson, Gladys Vondy and Graham, Vera. *STRANGE SEA LIFE.* Henry Holt and Co., Inc., New York. 1950

Sterling, Dorothy. *INSECTS AND THE HOMES THEY BUILD.* Doubleday Jr. Books, Garden City, New York. 1954

Swain, Ralph Brownlee. *THE INSECT GUIDE.* Doubleday and Co., Inc., Garden City, New York. 1948

Teale, Edwin Way. *THE JUNIOR BOOK OF INSECTS.* E. P. Dutton and Co., Inc., New York. 1953

Weyer, Edward J. (Ed.) *STRANGEST CREATURES ON EARTH.* Sheridan House, Inc., New York. 1953

Zim, Herbert Spencer. *INSECTS: A GUIDE TO FAMILIAR AMERICAN INSECTS.* Simon and Schuster, Inc., New York. 1951

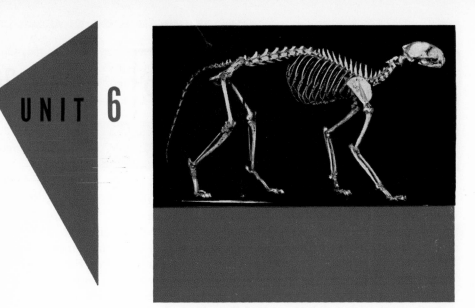

Animals with Backbones

This Unit introduces the most perfect group of animals in existence — a group which excels all others in body structure and efficiency in performing the life functions. Biologists call them vertebrates because of a spinal column composed of bones, called *vertebrae,* which runs down the back. But this spinal column, while responsible for the name, is not nature's greatest achievement in this group of super animals. More important is the nerve cord it encases and the highly developed brain it joins. The highly developed nervous system is the key to biological supremacy of the vertebrates.

On the land, in the air, and in the sea, vertebrates are the most important animals. In the study of various vertebrates, you are preparing for the study of your own body in the next Unit. And, in dealing with the sharks and rays, fish, amphibians, reptiles, birds, and mammals, you are becoming familiar with the animals which are most important to us as sources of food, beasts of burden, sources of pleasure, and as pets.

CHAPTER 28

Introduction to the Vertebrates

Today we live in an age of vertebrates. Across the wide stretches of ocean depths, sharks and rays, and salt-water fish reign supreme. They are the most important marine animals. Fresh-water fish dominate the inland lakes and ponds, rivers, and streams. Birds are nature's most perfect flying machines. And on land, mammals surpass all other organisms in importance. Man, the most perfect living thing, dominates the entire living world. Intelligence, ingenuity, and inventive genius have made him master of the land, the sea, and the air.

In the study of invertebrates, you followed a gradual development of body structure from a single cell to a complex organism, such as an arthropod or a mollusk. Among the vertebrates, you will find life in its most highly specialized form.

A quick review of invertebrate development. Nature seems to have tried several plans of body development in various invertebrate animals. Among the protozoans, the specialization of a single cell is carried to the limit. Consider *Paramecium* with its cilia and trichocysts, its gullet, and contractile vacuoles. The "slipper animal" is a truly marvelous cell, but it takes many cells to make a complex animal.

You were introduced to a large colony of cells in the sponges and coelenterates. You found the beginning of tissues in the ectoderm and endoderm of these animals. In the round and flat worms, you found organs which perform such functions as digestion, circulation, excretion, and irritability with much greater efficiency.

The clam and other mollusks have the greatest possible protection for a highly developed, soft-bodied animal. Their shells are both a fort and a prison. Mollusks have not advanced much in many millions of years.

The arthropods combine protection with freedom of movement. However, their suit of armor is heavy, so you can see how the size of an arthropod is limited by chitin. In most cases, arthropods have remained reasonably small. Numbers alone maintain their place of importance in the living world.

Why have the vertebrate animals become so important? They have neither shell nor hard exoskeleton (except certain reptiles and amphibia). A strong internal framework, or endoskeleton, supports a body which is able to move freely and gracefully. This prevents protection of the soft body parts, except in certain vertebrates, like the turtle and armadillo, which develop a hard outer covering. However, the highly developed vertebrate brain and nervous system more than make up for this lack of outer protection. In escaping from enemies, the vertebrate animals depend on their keen sense organs and efficient movement, as well as on their instinct and intelligence.

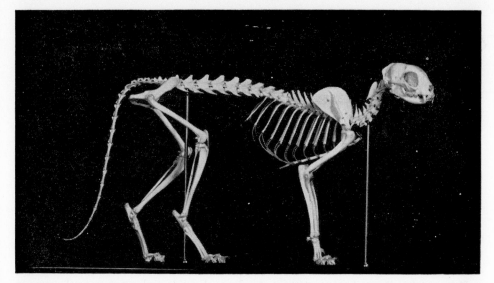

Fig. 28-1. The vertebrate skeleton shows one outstanding characteristic which is common to all members of this group. What is this characteristic?

What are vertebrates? The *Vertebrata* (ver-tuh-*bray*-tuh) is one of four subphyla of the phylum *Chordata* (kor-*day*-tuh). This phylum is the most advanced in the animal kingdom. Three subphyla of chordates are known by biologists but are unimportant to us. One includes two classes of wormlike animals which live in the sea. The strange sea squirt represents another subphylum. The fishlike lancelet, probably the best-known of the primitive chordates, represents a third subphylum. However, the vertebrates alone make the phylum Chordata important today.

How are chordates different from other animals? Early in their life all chordate animals have a gristlelike rod running lengthwise along the top side of the body. We call this a **notochord** (*no*-tuh-kord). The more primitive chordates keep their notochord throughout life. Some of the lower vertebrates, like the sea lamprey, retain the notochord but it becomes surrounded by cartilage structures of the spinal column. The notochord disappears early in the development of other vertebrates and is replaced by the vertebrae of the spine.

The phylum name, *Chordata,* refers to the notochord. *Vertebrata* refers to the vertebrae, or bones of the spinal column. Thus we usually speak of vertebrates as animals having a backbone.

Other characteristics of chordates include a nerve cord which runs down the dorsal, or top side of the body. In vertebrates, the bones of the spinal column enclose the dorsal nerve cord, or spinal cord. Among invertebrates, such as the earthworm, the main nerve trunk lies on the ventral or lower side of the body.

Paired gill slits form openings in the throat of chordates. However, like the notochord, these disappear early in the development of such higher vertebrates as the reptile, bird, and mammal.

Classes of vertebrates. The many kinds of living vertebrates are usually divided into seven classes as the table on page 354 shows.

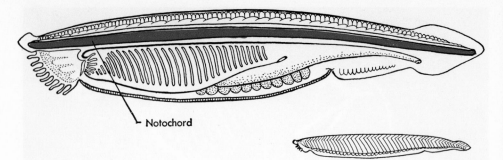

Notochord

Fig. 28-2. All chordates, like the *Amphioxus*, have a notochord in the early stages of their life. The lower right drawing shows the segmental arrangement of muscles.

The classes are listed in order of their complexity. In the chapters to follow, we shall consider each class as we make a brief survey of vertebrate animal life.

The outstanding characteristics of vertebrates. What do fish, frogs, reptiles, birds, and mammals have in common? Perhaps, they seem so different you wonder if they have anything in common. When you study the body structure of these animals, you will see that they are similar in many ways. These similarities make up the vertebrate characteristics. They include:

1. A body with a head and trunk and, in many cases, a neck and a tail.

2. Never more than two pairs of locomotive appendages present. These may be fins, flippers, wings, arms, or legs.

3. Eyes, ears, and nostrils in the head.

4. Eyelids and separate teeth present in most forms.

5. An internal skeleton (endoskeleton) of bone and/or cartilage (a gristlelike tissue).

6. A spinal column or backbone composed of vertebrae.

7. Two body cavities: (*a*) a dorsal cavity for the nervous system; and (*b*) a larger ventral cavity for the other internal organs.

8. A heart on the ventral side of the body; red blood corpuscles.

SEVEN CLASSES OF VERTEBRATES	
NAME OF CLASS	EXAMPLES
1. Agnatha (ag-*nay*-tha)	Sea lamprey, hagfish
2. Elasmobranchii (ee-las-moh-*brank*-ee-eye)	Shark and ray
3. Osteichthyes (os-tih-*ik*-thih-eez)	All bony fish
4. Amphibia (am-*fib*-ee-ah)	Frog, toad, salamander
5. Reptilia (rep-*till*-ee-ah)	Snake, lizard, turtle, crocodile
6. Aves (ay-veez)	All birds
7. Mammalia (mah-*may*-lee-ah)	Mouse, elephant, whale, cat, dog, hippopotamus

Mammalia (leopard)

Aves (gull)

Amphibia (salamander)

Reptilia (turtle)

Reptilia (snake)

Amphibia (frog)

Osteichthyes (fish)

Elasmobranchii (shark)

Elasmobranchii (skate)

Agnatha (lamprey)

Fig. 28-3.   There are seven classes of vertebrates.

Fig. 28-4. The skeleton of the whale shark, so-called because of its resemblance to a whale, is composed of cartilage rather than bone like the true fish.

The vertebrate body is composed of many specialized tissues. These tissues form highly developed organs which compose the body systems. These systems include:

1. *Integumentary system.* This is composed of the outer body covering and special outgrowths such as scales, feathers, or hair for protection.

2. *Muscular system.* Several different kinds of muscles make up this system. Some are attached to bones and produce body movement; others form the walls of the heart and of the digestive organs and blood vessels.

3. *Skeletal system.* This consists of the bones and cartilage structures which form the body framework.

4. *Digestive system.* Here are the many specialized organs concerned with the preparation of food for use by the body tissues.

5. *Respiratory system.* This is a highly specialized system. It includes gills or lungs which are used in the exchange of gases between the organism and its external environment.

6. *Circulatory system.* This system includes the heart and blood vessels which function as the transportation system of the body. Vertebrates have a " closed " circulatory system, as you have already learned.

7. *Excretory system.* The organs which make up this system remove wastes from the body.

8. *Endocrine system.* It is composed of glands which produce secretions necessary for the normal functioning of the other systems.

9. *Nervous system.* The nervous system is a very complex system composed of the brain, spinal cord, nerves, and special sense organs. It is the

most highly-developed system of a vertebrate.

10. *Reproductive system.* The male or female organs of reproduction are included in this system.

The classes of vertebrates show interesting lines of development. One of these is a change in the skeleton. The sea lamprey, sharks, and rays have a cartilage skeleton throughout life. Fish, amphibians, reptiles, birds, and mammals develop a bony skeleton. These animals start life with a cartilaginous (kar-tih-*laj*-ih-nus) framework. However, early in life, bone cells replace quite a bit of the cartilage. Minerals deposited in the bones make them hard and strong.

The classes of vertebrates show also an interesting change from water to a land existence. The lamprey eels, sharks, rays, and bony fish are adapted only for life in water. Their limbs are in the form of fins. Their gills absorb dissolved oxygen from the water during respiration. Water flows over the gills through gill slits in the throat. After you have studied the frog as a representative amphibian, you will find a transition from water to land. During the tadpole stage, a frog is a fishlike animal with gills and a fin for swimming.

The vertebrate heart and brain show great development over those of the invertebrates. The fish heart has only two chambers. One chamber receives blood from the body, while the other pumps blood to the gills. The frog has a three-chambered heart and a more complex circulation. Birds and mammals have a still more complex heart. Theirs consists of four chambers. One side of the heart receives blood from the body and pumps it to the lungs. The other side receives blood from the lungs and pumps it to the body. This heart is really a double pump. Man's

Fig. 28-5. Species preservation is one of the strongest instincts in animals. These opossum babies ride safely on their mother's back until they are old enough to take care of themselves.

heart, too, consists of four chambers.

You can see similar advances in the brain of the vertebrates. One brain region known as the **cerebrum** (*ser*-eh-brum) is the center of instinct, emotion, memory, and intelligence. This brain area increases in relative size through the classes of vertebrates. The brain of the mammal has the largest cerebrum in relation to the size of the body.

Vertebrate behavior is highly developed. In the discussion of field study of behavior in Chapter 8, we referred to instinct and intelligence as forms of animal behavior. The vertebrates are ideal subjects for the study of animal behavior because of the high development of their nervous systems.

There is a reason for every nervous response an animal makes. The reason is a stimulus. Often the response is purely automatic or **involuntary**. The animal responds to the stimulus without any control on its part. However, an animal can control many of its responses. We call such responses **voluntary**.

Much of the activity of a higher animal is controlled by instincts. These are forms of involuntary behavior. We don't know the actual cause of instincts. But we do know that they come from the brain and that they have a powerful influence on behavior.

Self-preservation is a basic instinct in all vertebrates as well as many invertebrates. In times of danger, an animal will respond to the " flight or fight " instinct of self-preservation. Have you ever cornered an animal which would normally flee from you? A seemingly harmless animal like a squirrel will bite and claw viciously if it cannot escape from an enemy.

Animals are born with instincts. The sucking instinct directs the nursing mammal early in life. Instinct causes the tiny bird to pick its way through the shell at the time of hatching.

A second and even stronger instinct directs animal reproduction and care of the young. This is **species preservation.** This is the instinct which drives the Pacific salmon up the streams of the Northwest to spawning beds. The adult salmon lose their lives so that a new generation may come downstream to the ocean. This powerful instinct causes the sunfish to defend its nest against an intruder from which it would flee at any other time.

Human behavior far surpasses that of the highest mammals. Yet the same basic instincts and emotions as well as still lower forms of behavior are present in us. We will consider the various levels of our own behavior patterns after discussing the human nervous system in Chapter 40.

In Conclusion

As you study the vertebrates, you will see some characteristics developed to the highest degree. The fish excels in swimming. Its streamlined body cuts through the water like a torpedo. The frog is at home both on land and in the water. The bird has long been the model for life in the air. We have even borrowed its wing design in the aircraft industry.

The antelope and gazelle hold speed records among land animals. The elephant is a symbol of strength. What about man? Man is no match for other vertebrates in physical abilities. But brain is superior to brawn. Man rules the living world.

In the next chapter, we shall begin our study of vertebrates of the ocean depths, lakes, rivers, and streams. Here we find the primitive fishlike vertebrates and the many bony fish, the most important of aquatic animals.

Questions for Review

1. What characteristics distinguish the vertebrate skeleton from that of lower animals?

2. How would you distinguish between the chordates and the vertebrates?

3. Describe and locate the notochord.

4. Name seven classes of vertebrates and give an example of each class.

5. What are eight vertebrate characteristics?

6. Name ten systems of a vertebrate body.

7. Which of the various brain regions is the center of instinct, emotions, and intelligence?

8. What is the relation between a stimulus and a response?

9. Which do you regard as more efficient, the endoskeleton or the exoskeleton?

Biologically Speaking

behavior	instinct	self-preservation
cartilage	intelligence	species preservation
cerebrum	involuntary response	stimulus
chordate	notochord	vertebrae
endoskeleton	response	vertebrate

Applying Facts and Principles

1. Why are instinct and intelligence more vital to survival of a vertebrate than to an invertebrate, such as a clam, a starfish, an insect, or a crayfish?

2. Discuss the improvement of vertebrates through the various classes, using the skeleton, organs of respiration, heart, and brain as illustrations.

3. Self-preservation and species preservation are instincts. Which is stronger? Give one or more illustrations to prove your answer.

4. How can you distinguish instinctive behavior from intelligent behavior in observing the activity of various vertebrate animals?

CHAPTER 29

Fish and Fishlike Vertebrates

It isn't hard to interest most people in a discussion of fish. From childhood on, fishing is a favorite sport for millions of Americans. The fly rod, spinning rod, casting rod, and tackle box may replace the more simple cane pole and a can of worms. But the thrill of the tug of a fish on a line remains the same.

The biologist classifies most of the fish you know as bony fish. In the oceans, these fish mingle with the more primitive sharks and rays. The shark and ray represent another class of vertebrates. The most primitive of the vertebrates are represented by several species of eel-like creatures which live in our fresh-water lakes and streams.

Fish are the most important animals of water environments. When you study the adaptations of the fish for life in water, you will discover why for millions of years they have controlled the oceans, lakes, and waterways as rulers of the deep.

Blood-sucking "vampires" of the Great Lakes. About 30 years ago, a deadly vertebrate menace made its way silently from the waters of Lake Ontario through the Welland Canal at Niagara Falls, and into Lake Erie. Sea lampreys, or just lampreys, as they are called locally, were invading new waters. During a much earlier migration sea lampreys had left their native waters of the Atlantic coastal region to move up the St. Lawrence River into Lake Ontario. Here their movement was stopped by Niagara Falls. But the Welland Canal, built to carry shipping around the Falls, gave them a free passage into Lake Erie. Ten years later, the lamprey hordes had spread through Lake Huron. They traveled through the Straits of Mackinac into Lake Michigan. Attached to the hulls of ships, they passed through the locks at Sault St. Marie into Lake Superior.

What sort of creature is this death-dealing lamprey? Biologists class it as a member of the vertebrate class, *Agnatha*. It is not a relative of the true eel which is one of the bony fish, although it does resemble an eel.

The head of the lamprey is curious and quite different from that of a fish. Instead of jaws the lamprey has a sucking disk lined with sharp, horny teeth. A rasping tongue, also bearing teeth, lies in the center of the mouth.

The sea lamprey attaches its sucking mouth to the side of a fish and chisels a hole through the scales with its rasping teeth. It feeds on the blood of its victim and may even suck out internal organs. Its favorite host is the lake trout, one of the finest game fish of the Great Lakes. When the lake trout is not available, the lamprey attacks whitefish, pike, and other species.

The sea lamprey has very nearly exterminated the lake trout in Lake Huron and is rapidly destroying other spe-

Fig. 29-1. This close-up shows the sucking mouth of the adult sea lamprey.

cies. At present the lake trout are disappearing quite fast in Lake Michigan and in Lake Superior.

What can biologists do to eliminate the sea lamprey menace? It would be impossible to destroy them in the vast waters of the Great Lakes. Biologists have found an answer, however. Lamprey spawn in fast-flowing streams which feed the Great Lakes.

This is the time when they are destroyed in great numbers. The weapon used is a trap. Electrodes charged with 100 volts of electricity are put in a row across the stream. This charges the water and stops the movement of all aquatic animals. The migrating lamprey and fish swim along the edge of the charge area into traps. Here, the lamprey are destroyed. The fish are caught and put back in the stream above the trap. This is our hope for restoring lake trout and other valuable fish to the Great Lakes.

Sharks and rays. To the class *Elasmobranchii* (ee-las-moh-*brank*-ee-eye) belong the few remaining fish which controlled the ancient seas. Sharks and rays make up this class of primitive fish. The shark resembles the true fish in

Fig. 29-2. The trout in this picture has been scarred by a sea lamprey, a menace to many game fish.

Fig. 29-3. Traps, charged with electricity, are effective in bringing about the destruction of the blood-sucking lampreys.

many ways. However, certain of its characteristics put it in a separate class of vertebrates.

The body of a shark is torpedo-shaped. Its fins resemble those of true fish. The upper portion of the tail fin is longer than the lower portion — a characteristic of ancient fish. The shark's mouth is a horizontal slitlike opening on the lower (ventral) side of the head. The jaws are lined with sharp razor-edged teeth. Water enters the mouth, passes over the gills on each side of the head, and is forced out through pairs of gill slits. **Gills,** as you probably know, are the special respiratory organs of fish and their relatives. The skeleton of sharks and rays is composed of cartilage rather than bone.

Sharks include the largest living fish. The whale shark, the giant of sharks, reaches a length of 50 feet or more. The great white shark, or man-eating shark, may exceed 40 feet in length.

The rays are often called devilfish,

blanket fish, or sting rays. They swim gracefully through ocean waters, moving their great flat bodies like wings. Often they lie half-buried in the sand of the ocean bottom. The whiplike tail of a ray has a sharp barbed stinger on the tip. It causes a painful wound when driven into a victim. Sting rays often come close to shore.

The true fish. Biologists put all true fish in the class *Osteichthyes* (os-tee-*ik*-thih-eez). These have a bony skeleton with **gills** as respiratory organs. Limbs are in the form of **fins.** Most fish have an outer covering of overlapping **scales,** or plates. Fish are ideally suited to aquatic life. In a wide variety of forms, they live in practically every water environment of the earth.

The body of a fish is divided into three regions: (1) head; (2) trunk; and (3) tail. In most cases, the body is perfectly streamlined — tapered at both ends, or spindle-shaped. The lack of a neck is no disadvantage to a fish.

Fig. 29-4. The white shark, a man-eating species, is found in the warm waters of tropical regions.

It can turn its body as easily as other animals can move their heads.

Many people confuse the tail of a fish with the tail fin. However, the tail is the solid muscular region beyond the trunk.

Scales cover the body of most fish. The exceptions, however, are the head and fins which lack scales. In some cases, the scales are large and loose. Trout have extremely small scales. Catfish have no scales at all.

Scales grow from pockets in the skin. They overlap like shingles on a roof. A slimy secretion from the skin covers the scales and lubricates the body. This aids in locomotion and escape from enemies. The body slime is important, too, in protecting the fish from attack by parasitic molds and other organisms. If you handle a fish with dry hands, you remove some of the slimy secretion and expose the body to infection. You can avoid this by wetting your hands before you pick up a fish.

The coloring of a fish lies in the skin whose scales are transparent. These animals are perfect examples of **countershading** because the upper part of the body is usually colored to blend with the bottom of a lake or stream. The lower part is light in color and blends with the sky overhead.

Structure of the head of a fish. The head is usually pointed and is covered with *plates* instead of individual scales. The mouth is usually at the extreme anterior end. Many fish have numerous sharp teeth arranged in three sets of *jaw bones*. The teeth slant inward making it easy for the fish to swallow its prey, but hard for the prey to escape.

The fish has two *nasal cavities,* each

Fig. 29-5. The tail of the sting ray has a sharp barbed stinger which is capable of inflicting a severe wound.

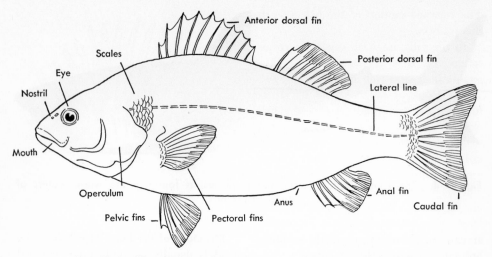

Fig. 29-6. This drawing shows the external structure of the fish.

with two nostrils. The nostrils serve for smelling only. They do not connect with the throat and cannot be used in breathing.

The eyes are large and somewhat movable. Eyelids are lacking because the eyes do not need to be kept moist. The pupils are large compared with other vertebrate eyes and thus admit the maximum amount of light. For any animal to see under water, the eye must be adapted to receive as much light as possible.

The *ears* are embedded in the skull and have no external openings. They probably function as balancing organs and are used to detect vibrations carried by the bones of the skull. Fish probably do not hear sounds in the sense that we do, but they feel the vibrations when you hit stones on the bottom, walk along the bank, or move your feet in a boat.

The gills are the organs of respiration. At each side of the head is a crescent-shaped slit which marks the rear border of the gill cover (operculum). These slits almost meet on the ventral side, leaving only a narrow space

at the throat region. They expose the gills to water which the fish takes in through its mouth. If you look inside the mouth, you can see that the throat has five slits on each side, leaving four gill arches between them. If you lift the gill cover, you can see the outer sides of those gills. (See Fig. 29-7.)

Each gill consists of an arch of bone between the slits in the throat wall to which are attached two rows of thin-walled threadlike appendages called the **gill filaments.** These filaments are richly provided with capillaries, so the blood is brought into close contact with the water over a large surface. This permits the exchange of oxygen (dissolved in water) and carbon dioxide. The gill arches have fingerlike projections called **gill rakers** on the side toward the throat. These prevent food or dirt from getting into the filaments and keep the arches separate to allow free circulation of water. They also keep small bits of food from escaping.

The water enters at the mouth, which is then closed for a moment, forcing the water through the gill slits over the filaments and out beneath the gill cover.

The forward motion of the fish aids in this process.

In the gills, as in all organs of respiration, we find a large surface, thin membranes, and rich blood supply.

The trunk of the fish and its structure. If you examine the sides of a fish closely, you will notice a row of pitted scales extending from the head to the tail fin. This is the *lateral line.* Nerve endings lie under the pitted scales. The nerves of the lateral line probably aid the ears in feeling vibrations. The lateral line functions also as a pressure organ, indicating the depth at which a fish may be swimming.

Various kinds of fins develop from the trunk. Each fin consists of a double membrane, supported by cartilaginous or spiny rays.

The number and form of fins vary in different kinds of fish. However, all fish have two kinds of paired fins. The *pectoral fins* are nearest the head. They correspond to the front legs or arms of other animals. The pair of *pelvic fins* corresponds to hind legs. The paired fins serve as oars when the fish is swimming slowly. In addition, they aid in steering and in maintaining balance when the fish is resting in the water. The *caudal fin,* growing from the tail, is the principal propeller. The fish swims by lashing the tail back and forth. *Dorsal fins* are attached along the top middle line of the trunk. The perch shown in Fig. 29-6 has two dorsal fins.

The anterior or spiny dorsal fin contains sharp projections which aid in defense. The posterior or soft dorsal fin lacks these spines. Both dorsal fins serve as a keel and keep the fish on its course while swimming. Many fish have a single dorsal fin, while others, like the cod, have three. Another single fin grows along the middle line on the

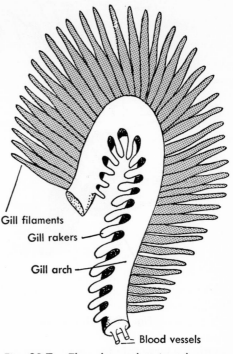

Gill filaments

Gill rakers

Gill arch

Blood vessels

Fig. 29-7. The above drawing shows an entire gill, much enlarged, as seen from the side.

lower side, just behind the anal opening. The *anal fin,* like the dorsal fin, serves as a keel in maintaining balance.

Powerful muscles, arranged in plates, occupy the region of the trunk above the spinal column. The tail is solid bone and muscle. The weight of these muscles makes the body topheavy and causes a dead fish to float upside down. Slow movement of the fins while a fish is at rest prevents it from turning over in the water.

The digestive system in the fish. Many fish are vegetarians and feed on algae and other water plants. Carnivorous (kar-*niv*-oh-rus) species eat other animals such as crayfish, frogs, other fish, and a wide variety of invertebrates. Some fish, like the bass and pike, swallow fish almost as large as themselves. Especially in carnivorous fish, the

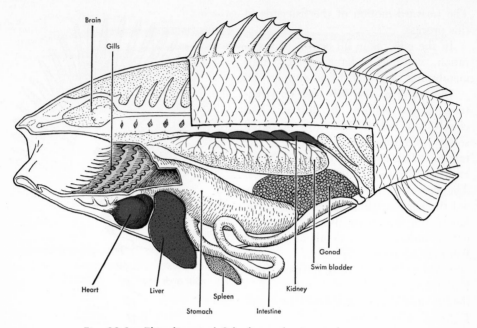

Fig. 29-8. This dissected fish shows the internal structure.

mouth is a large trap for capturing prey. The conical teeth hold the prey while it is being swallowed. The tongue is fastened to the floor of the mouth and is not movable. It functions more as an organ of touch than as one of taste.

Food is swallowed whole through a short **esophagus** (ee-*sof*-uh-gus) into the *stomach.* Here, powerful fluids partially digest the food. Digestion is completed in the rather short **intestine.** Fingerlike projections grow from the stomach at the point where it joins the intestine. A well-developed liver lies close to the stomach. The **gall bladder,** attached to the liver, passes bile into the intestine. Indigestible food moves out from the intestine through the anal opening on the lower side.

The blood of the fish is like that of other vertebrates. It contains both red and white corpuscles. The heart lies in a cavity on the lower side, just behind the gills. This heart consists of two chambers, a receiving chamber, or **auri-** cle (*aw*-rih-kil), and a pumping chamber, or **ventricle** (*ven*-trih-kil). (See Fig. 29-9.) The auricle receives blood from a large vein which ends in a saclike enlargement (*sinus venosus*). Blood passes from the auricle into the ventricle where it is pumped out with great force through an artery leading to the gills. This artery begins with a muscular bulb-like structure (the *conus arteriosus*) which is attached to the ventricle. This structure is very noticeable in the fish heart. The artery to the gills (*ventral aorta*) branches to the two sides of the head and then rebranches to each of the four gills. All the blood pumped by the heart lacks oxygen. It circulates through the gill filaments, and discharges carbon dioxide and receives dissolved oxygen from the water.

Another large artery (*dorsal aorta*) carries oxygenated blood to the head, trunk, and tail. Various branches of the large veins carry blood from the

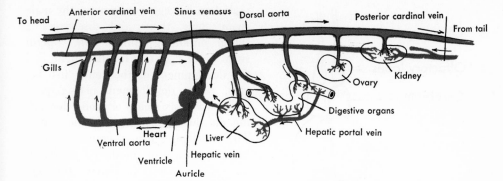

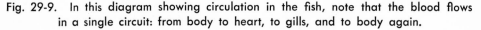

Fig. 29-9. In this diagram showing circulation in the fish, note that the blood flows in a single circuit: from body to heart, to gills, and to body again.

liver and digestive organs, trunk and tail, and head. The large veins return blood to the heart to complete the circulation. During each complete passage of the blood around the body, it goes through the kidneys where various cell wastes are removed.

An essential internal organ of the fish is the swim bladder. This thin-walled sac lies in the upper part of the body cavity. In the majority of fish it connects with the pharynx by a tube. The swim bladder is inflated with gases (oxygen, nitrogen, and carbon dioxide) which pass into it from the blood. The bladder acts as a float and adjusts the weight of the fish so that it equals the weight of the water it displaces. This balance allows the fish to float in the water without rising or sinking.

Fish live at various water levels at different seasons of the year. The swim bladder adjusts to these variations by losing air to the blood or receiving additional air. When a fish is adjusted to deep water and is caught and brought to the surface suddenly, the swim bladder expands and may push the esophagus into the mouth. One group of fish known as darters have no swim bladder. They sink to the bottom after each of their jerky swimming motions.

The nervous system is quite complex. It includes the brain, spinal cord, and the many nerves which lead to all parts of the body.

The brain lies in a small bony cavity, the **cranial cavity.** It consists of five distinct parts. At the anterior end are the **olfactory lobes** from which the nerves, sensitive to odors, extend to the nostrils. Behind these lobes are the two lobes of the **cerebrum** (ser-ee-brum) which control the voluntary muscles. It is in these lobes that instincts are centered. Back of the cerebrum are the **optic lobes,** the largest of the fish's brain. Optic nerves lead from these lobes to the eyes. Behind them lies the **cerebellum** (ser-uh-bell-um) which coordinates muscular activity, and finally the **medulla** (meh-dul-ah) **oblongata** which controls the activities of the internal organs. The **spinal cord** passes down the back from the medulla and is encased in the vertebral column. Nerves connect the spinal cord with all parts of the body.

The fish's brain is not highly developed when you compare it with those of higher vertebrates. It shows, however, a great advance over the so-called brains of invertebrates. As you study the brains of other vertebrates, compare

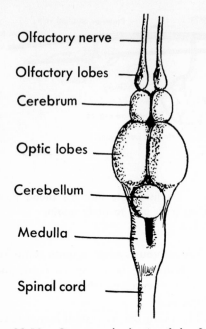

Olfactory nerve

Olfactory lobes

Cerebrum

Optic lobes

Cerebellum

Medulla

Spinal cord

Fig. 29-10. Compare the brain of the fish with that of invertebrates as to development.

them with the fish brain. The same regions are present.

There is, however, a gradual increase in the size of the cerebrum in proportion to the other brain regions in the other groups of vertebrates. As the cerebrum increases in size, you will find a corresponding improvement in nervous activity on the higher levels. It is the region which determines the emotional and intelligent levels among the highest forms of life, including ourselves.

How do fish reproduce? The reproductive organs (*gonads*) lie in the posterior region of the body cavity. Tubes from them lead to an opening just behind the anal opening. Eggs develop in the *ovary* of the female fish over a period of several months. As the eggs enlarge, the ovary swells and may bulge the sides of the fish. Sperm develops in the *testes* of male fish. Soon after the fe-

male lays her eggs, or *spawns,* the male swims over them and discharges a sperm-containing fluid, or **milt.** Sperm swim to the eggs and fertilize them, and the development of the young fish begins. This development may require from two to six weeks or more, depending on the temperature of the water. The developing fish is nourished by a large quantity of nonliving material, the yolk, which is present in the egg. Part of the yolk remains attached to the young fish a short while after hatching and is known as the *yolk sac.*

Many fish, like the sunfish, deposit their eggs in a depression made in the bottom of a stream. After spawning, the male guards the nest, fighting off any intruder. Another fish, the stickleback, makes a curious nest of algae. The male builds the nest and drives the female into it for spawning. Then he chases her away and takes entire charge of the nest and eggs. Channel catfish spawn in holes in a bank or in a discarded can or other receptacle which they find on the bottom.

Guppies, mollies, moons, and swordtails are fresh-water tropical species commonly reared in home aquaria. These curious fish bear their young alive. The female retains the eggs within her body and receives sperm from the male during mating. The young fish develop internally and are brought forth alive.

Many eggs never receive sperm. Large numbers are eaten by fish and other aquatic animals before they have had a chance to hatch. After hatching, the young fish are in constant danger of being eaten by cannibalistic fish and other animals. Regardless of the high mortality rate, the species survives because of the tremendous number of eggs laid. This number varies from about 500 in the case of the trout to several

Fig. 29-11. Some fish build nests. The stickleback nest (left) consists of strands of algae. Compare this with the nest of the sunfish (right).

million in the case of the codfish, sturgeon, or flounder.

Spawning habits of various fish. The spawning habits and life history of fish vary with different species. As a rule, fresh-water fish spawn in the waters where they normally live, although they often travel to shallower water for this purpose.

Among the most interesting fish migrations is that of the eel. These long, slender fish live in the rivers and streams of the coastal regions and may be found much farther inland. As the spawning time approaches, the eels, living in streams flowing into the Atlantic Ocean, begin a long journey to the sea. They swim to spawning grounds in the deep water off the coast of Bermuda and after spawning, the adults die. The young eels make their way to the mouths of rivers and begin the journey upstream. There they will live until

maturity and until they make the long migration back to the waters from which they came.

Many fish migrate upstream from salt to fresh-water to spawning areas. Among these are the shad, sturgeon, herring, and salmon. The migration of the Pacific salmon from the ocean to small, fast-flowing streams is one of the remarkable events in the world of fish.

Life history of salmon. The adult Pacific salmon lives in the ocean all along the northern coast. In spring or early summer, both sexes migrate in enormous numbers up the Columbia and other rivers, often for hundreds of miles. It is during these " runs " that the canners make their annual catches by means of barriers or machines which scoop up the passing fish.

This migration may be for the purpose of finding greater safety, cooler water, or better food. In any case, the

Fig. 29-12. Events in the life of a perch. Top: caught by a common enemy, the pickerel. Left: enticed by a baited hook. Right: eating larvae of dragonfly. Lower left corner: eggs (laid in April or May) on the bottom in a gelatinous mass which resembles accordion-pleated lace.

adults begin to make their last journey during the month of March. Slowly at first, and later at the rate of many miles per day, they work their way against the current of the river to the spawning beds where they first swam far from their adult home. Here, in water not warmer than 54 degrees, each female deposits about 3,500 eggs. The male spreads milt over them, but many eggs are not fertilized, and hence, do not develop.

The eggs are deposited on fine gravel, the process extending over several days, after which the strength of the parent fish seems to be exhausted and both frequently die. After 30 to 40 days, the eggs hatch. However, as usual with fish, the yolk remains attached until it is absorbed and the **fry,** as young fish are frequently called, can shift for themselves.

The economic importance of fish. Of the 13,000 known species of fish, at least 5,000 have food value. Among the most important salt-water food fish are the cod, haddock, mackerel, herring, and halibut, sole, tuna, and sea perch. Fresh-water species, taken from the Great Lakes and other lakes and the larger rivers, include the yellow perch, whitefish, lake trout, wall-eyed pike, northern pike, buffalo, carp, catfish, and others. It is hard to estimate the annual revenue from *commercial fishing* and the number of people who depend on the fishing industries. The value of the Pacific salmon catch each year amounts to about $15,000,000, while the Atlantic cod returns about $20,-000,000. The value of *sport fishing* cannot be measured in financial terms.

Fish supply many products in addition to food. *Cod liver oil* is one of the

Fig. 29-13. Salmon travel upstream against the current to the spawning beds.

best sources of vitamins D and A. Similar oils are extracted from the livers of halibut and sharks. *Fish oil* is used in the manufacture of certain paints. Many dog, cat, poultry, and other livestock feeds contain *fish meal,* made from fish not generally used as human food. *Glue* is made from the waste parts and bones of fish. The scales of certain fish are used in making artificial pearls.

Commercial fishing. Ocean fishing usually involves a fleet of small boats which tow nets between them or set nets in the form of a large trap. The ocean, or marine, fisherman generally concentrates on a few varieties of edible fish which are abundant in the waters of his region. In the case of the tuna, the fish are caught individually with hook and line from the sides of special boats.

Fresh-water commercial fishing is most frequent in the Great Lakes and in the larger rivers. Gill nets, which catch the fish just below the gill covers, are widely used in the Great Lakes for catching whitefish, lake trout, wall-eyed pike, and yellow perch. Catfish, buffalo fish, carp, sheepshead, and suckers are caught abundantly in the larger rivers.

Sport fishing. *Game fish* are the delight of the angler because of the sport in catching them. To save the fresh-water game fish for anglers, most states have imposed rigid regulations on the methods used in catching them.

The yellow perch is called the fish for the beginner because so little skill is required in catching it. It is found in the Great Lakes and in many of the smaller inland lakes and ponds. The bass family is well represented in inland lakes and streams in the form of the large-mouthed black bass, the small-mouthed black bass, the silver bass, the rock bass, the crappie, and others.

The members of the pike family are fighters. Among them are the great northern pike which weighs 25 pounds or more, the pickerel which is smaller, and the giant of them all, the muskellunge. This is found in the larger lakes of northern United States, and Canada.

Trout are the prize of the more advanced angler who has mastered the use of the fly rod. This fresh-water member of the salmon family is found in cold mountain streams, and in the case of certain species, in lakes.

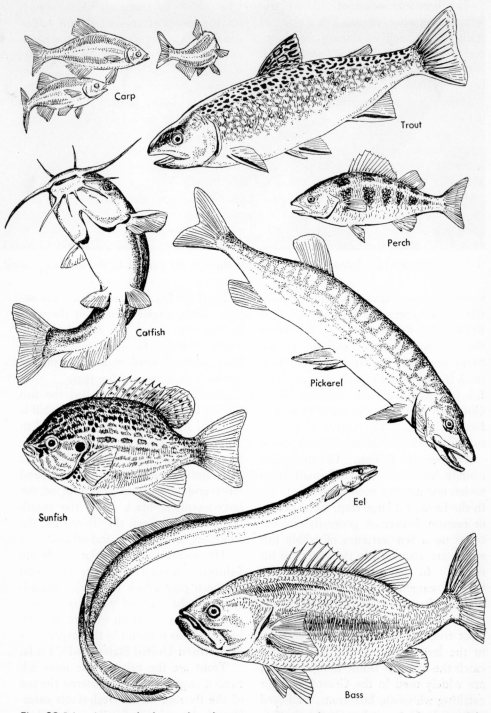

Fig. 29-14. As you look at this drawing, compare these common fresh-water fish. The trout, pickerel, and bass are considered " game fish." They put up a considerable fight when caught on a hook.

The amateur aquarist. Many collectors specialize in small varieties of native fish, such as darters and minnows. The collection of native fish may be housed in any standard aquarium, although an air pump is usually necessary to maintain a sufficient supply of oxygen in the water. In collecting native fish, one should be careful not to include small specimens of game fish which are under the legal size limit. The number of small varieties upon which there is no restriction is great enough to provide the collector with abundant collecting possibilities.

Goldfish are a specialty among many collectors. As a result of years of specialized breeding, a large selection of beautiful forms is available. Comets, fantails, veil-tails, telescopes, moors, and shubunkins are among the many forms available.

Brightly-colored tropical fish in a wide variety of forms are ideal subjects for the more advanced collector. The supply of these varieties has become an important industry in America and many other countries. Species from southern United States, Central America, South America, Africa, China, and far-off Borneo are available in tropical fish stores. They must be maintained in water ranging from 70°–80° F., thus necessitating heaters in most sections of the country. Along with the brightly-colored fish, the tropical aquarium provides opportunity to grow numerous aquatic plants.

Fish conservation is a complex problem. It involves reconditioning the lakes and streams, a hatchery program, law enforcement, and public cooperation. Fish conservation is tied in closely with water, soil, forest, and wildlife conservation. We will discuss all of these topics more fully in Chapter 54.

In Conclusion

No vertebrate has challenged the fish for control of the oceans and bodies of fresh water. The streamlined body with scales and fins, gills, and a two-chambered heart seems to be perfectly adapted to an aquatic environment. Alligators and water-dwelling snakes, swimming and diving birds, whales and seals share the water with fish. But none of these higher vertebrates compare with fish in importance.

In your study of the next group of vertebrates, the amphibians, you will find many fishlike animals. Others, like the toad, are land dwellers. In the study of these animals you will find the basic structures of fish carried to a higher degree of perfection in the development of a land animal.

 **Questions for Review**

1. Why were sea lampreys not present in the Great Lakes, other than Lake Ontario, until recent years?

2. Describe the mouth of a lamprey.

3. Of the various fish of the Great Lakes, which species has been most attacked by the sea lamprey?

4. How are the sea lampreys eliminated?

5. What characteristics of a shark distinguish it from a bony fish?

6. Why is the slime on a fish's body important?

7. (a) What are the parts of a gill? (b) What is the function of each of its various parts?

8. (a) Locate and describe the various fins of a fish. (b) What uses are made of each?

9. (a) Describe the structure of a fish heart. (b) How does blood move through the heart?

10. (a) Discuss the swim bladder, its location and structure. (b) What is its function?

11. Name the various regions of a fish brain and the kind of nervous activity centered in each part.

12. Describe the migration of the salmon and the eel.

13. What products are made from fish?

Biologically Speaking

anal fin	fry	olfactory lobe
auricle	gill	optic lobe
bony skeleton	gill arch	pectoral fin
caudal fin	gill filament	pelvic fin
cerebellum	gill raker	scales
cerebrum	lateral line	spawn
cranial cavity	medulla	swim bladder
dorsal fin	milt	ventricle

Applying Facts and Principles

1. Explain how the body covering, limbs, and sense organs of a fish are ideally suited to life in the water.

2. Give possible reasons why a fish dies in the air even though the air contains more oxygen than the water in which it lives.

3. Tropical aquarium fishes sometimes develop a strange disorder as a result of chilling. The fish float to the surface or sink to the bottom when they are not actively swimming. They may even turn over while swimming. What internal organ would you believe to be affected by this disorder?

4. Fish lay enormous numbers of eggs, yet seldom overpopulate the waters in which they live. Give several reasons to account for this.

5. What conclusions might you draw regarding the ancestry of the salmon and eel on a basis of the spawning habits of these fish?

CHAPTER 30

Amphibia-Vertebrates with Double Lives

Nature has revealed a very important secret in the class including salamanders, frogs, and toads which are grouped together under the name of *Amphibia* (am-*fib*-ee-ah). They show how vertebrates left the water to live on land. The term " double life " refers to the two distinct phases of the life of most of these curious animals. Certain kinds remain aquatic throughout life. Others live in marshes and alternate between sun baths and dips in the pool. Still others leave the water entirely early in life and never return except to establish new generations of their kind in the water where they began their lives.

Characteristics of the Amphibia. The name Amphibia means literally " having two lives." It refers to the fact that the frog and its relatives are, for the most part, aquatic, fishlike animals when young, but when they become adults they abandon that way of life for land. This series of changes is a *metamorphosis* just as is the life history of certain insects. In this transition from water to land forms, many strange combinations of gills and lungs, fins and legs occur. Gills are found on animals with legs, and fins occur, too, sometimes accompanied by lungs.

In general, the amphibia are distinct from other vertebrate animals in the following ways: (1) body covered by a thin, flexible, and usually moist skin, without scales, fur, or feathers; (2) feet, if present, often webbed; (3) toes soft and lacking claws; (4) immature or larval forms, vegetarian; adults usually carnivorous; (5) heart two-chambered in larvae, but three-chambered in adults; circulation well developed; (6) eggs fertilized externally as soon as laid; and (7) pass through a metamorphosis.

Some examples of amphibia. Amphibians flourished in an era of the geological past called the *Carboniferous period*. It was during this same period that many of the plants which formed our coal deposits were living, but since that time, at least ten orders of amphibians have become extinct. Today the class Amphibia is represented by just three orders. One of these (*Apoda*) includes strange, wormlike amphibians of the tropics, commonly called "glass snakes." The remaining two orders are well represented in the United States by the *salamanders* and *newts* (*Caudata*), or those having tails, and the *frogs, tree frogs,* and *toads* (*Salientia*), which lack tails as adults. Both of these groups show a transition from water, as larvae, to land in the adult stages.

Salamanders and newts have elongated bodies. You're probably familiar with some of these amphibians. You call them " lizards " because they resemble true lizards in the general form of their bodies. However, true lizards are not amphibians but are reptiles. The reptile body is elon-

Fig. 30-1. The mud puppy is an aquatic salamander familiar to many fishermen.

gated, ending in a long tail, and supported on four short legs. If you examine the salamander more closely, however, you will find that it differs considerably from the lizard. It has smooth, moist skin like a frog rather than the scaly covering of a lizard, and soft toes lacking the characteristic claws. As a matter of fact, some salamanders have no legs at all and you might easily mistake them for eels.

The terms *salamander* and *newt* are confusing and are used interchangeably in referring to many forms.

Some salamanders are aquatic throughout life and are therefore considered to be the most primitive amphibians. One of the most familiar of the large aquatic salamanders of the Middle West is the *mud puppy* or *water dog (Necturus)*. It has startled many an unsuspecting fisherman when he pulled this slimy creature from the muddy bottom of a stream. It may reach a length of two feet, has a flattened head, small eyes, a long body, a flattened tail, and two pairs of short legs. The most striking feature of the body is the pair of dark red, bushy gills

which are attached at the base of the head just above the front legs. When the animal is in water, these gills wave slowly back and forth.

The mud puppy spends the day hiding under rocks or buried in the mud of a stream bottom, but comes out at night in search of crayfish, insect larvae, and worms. When caught, it usually bites vigorously, although the bite is not dangerous and definitely not poisonous. The animal does secrete a poison from glands in its skin, but this poison is not harmful to man.

Numerous species of smaller salamanders emerge on land during adult life and live in moist ravines and lowland areas. While they do not live in water as adults, they are not able to survive in places far distant from water. One of the most common of these forms is the *spotted salamander* which has a typical elongated body, a rounded tail, and four well developed legs. The terrestrial habits of this salamander are shown by the absence of webbing between the toes. The blue-black body, six inches long, covered with round, yellow spots, makes it easy to identify.

You can find salamanders if you look carefully under flat rocks in moist stream beds, under leaves, and other wet places along the edges of pools, or in abandoned wells. They live nicely in moist terrariums and, with a little coaxing, can be induced to take worms and small insects from the hand.

Toads are the most valuable members of the Amphibia. They are, at least, from the standpoint of insect destruction. While some people are careful to avoid toads in the woods or destroy them, better informed gardeners protect them for the service they render in destroying insects.

The toad is the most terrestrial of all amphibians, and after leaving the water

Fig. 30-2. The salamander is somewhat terrestrial in the adult stage, living in moist, dark places. It is harmless and feeds on aquatic worms, insects, and other small animals.

early in life, never returns except to lay eggs. The toad starts life as a tiny black tadpole which soon grows legs, absorbs its tail, and hops onto land as a small, black froglike creature. It soon develops the warty skin characteristic of its kind. Adults of the common toad, *Bufo,* are usually greenish- or reddish-brown above and grayish-yellow beneath.

Toads sleep most of the day under rocks or boards, but are active at night, snatching insects with their quick, sticky tongue. When disturbed, they have no choice but to lie close to the ground. The toad has lost the swimming ability of other amphibians and on land moves with clumsy motion. In its " in between " existence, this unfortunate creature lacks efficient locomotion in any environment and is able to survive only because of its protective coloration.

Tree frogs are not often seen. Another member of the Amphibia is the tree frog, *Hyla,* which, though common, is seldom seen because of its almost perfect protective coloration. Its song is familiar enough when the " peep-

Fig. 30-3. The diet of the common toad is almost entirely insectivorous. As you can imagine, it is a good friend to have around gardens and should never be killed.

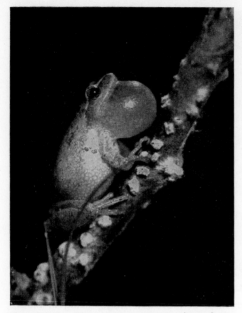

Fig. 30-4. The spring peeper breeds in ponds and swamps. Its shrill piping notes are among the earliest signs of spring.

ers " cheerful chorus ushers in the early spring. It seems hardly possible that so loud a song can come from so tiny a frog, little more than an inch long. But if we are patient and successful enough to hunt one out with a flashlight at night, the reason for their loud voice is clear. The little *Hyla* can expand its throat into a vocal sac twice the size of its head, and with this enormous drum can produce its remarkable music.

On each toe these true tree climbers have a sticky disk by which they can climb safely on the bark of trees and even cling to grass. Their color, stripes, and shape protect them perfectly from observation.

The eggs are laid in early spring and the tiny reddish *tadpoles* feed on mosquitoes. The adults eat ants and gnats which ought to give these frogs a place in our affection. A curious fact about their tadpole stage is that they often leave the water before the tail is entirely

absorbed. Apparently, they are able to breathe air earlier in their metamorphosis than the majority of other frogs.

Frogs are the best known of the Amphibia. The most common frog in the United States is the *leopard frog* which inhabits nearly every pond, marsh, and roadside ditch. It frequently travels considerable distances from the water and may be seen hopping through the grass in meadows. The name comes from the large black spots, or blotches, surrounded by yellow or white rings which cover the grayish-green background color of the skin. The under surface of the leopard frog is creamy white, thus blending with the light sky when viewed from below while resting on the surface of the pond.

The *bullfrog,* so named because its sound resembles the distant bellowing of a bull, is the most aquatic of all frogs. It never leaves the water except to sit on the bank of a lake or pond at night. The color of the bullfrog varies from green to nearly yellow, although the majority of them are greenish-brown. The under surface of the body is grayish-white mingled with numerous dark splotches.

The large fully-webbed hind feet of

Fig. 30-5. The leopard frog is a common American grayish-green frog with large black spots on its back.

Fig. 30-6. The bullfrog is thus named because of its loud bellowing notes and heavy build. It is the most aquatic of all frogs.

the bullfrog make it an excellent swimmer. These legs are well developed and ten inches long in large specimens. The diet of the bullfrog is quite varied and includes insects, worms, crayfish, and small fish.

The economic importance of frogs. Much of the diet of frogs consists of insects. If they had no other value at all, this service alone would justify their protection. Many states have recognized their value and have passed laws regulating the hunting of frogs and prohibiting their capture during the breeding season.

The large hindlegs of the bullfrog are a table delicacy. Frog farms, occupying large marshy areas, supply much of this demand. The smaller species of frogs are widely used by fishermen for bait. As a biological specimen for dis-

section in the laboratory, the frog has long been a favorite. Since its internal organs are arranged similarly to those of the human body, the frog dissection is an excellent introduction to human anatomy.

In recent years, male frogs have been used for pregnancy tests. Hospitals and clinics have become one of the best customers of frog collectors. With all of these uses, you can see that we must guard our frog population and conserve the lakes and marshes where they thrive.

Anatomy of the frog. Facing page 390 you will find a leopard frog as seen by the " Trans-Vision " process. The first page (Plate I) shows the lower side of the frog. The upper side is shown on the last page (Plate VIII). As you turn the pages between these, you will see the internal organs at various depths of the body. Pages on the right show the front (ventral) side of the organs. The left transparencies show the organs on the back (dorsal) side.

As we discuss the structure of the frog — its form and body covering, legs, head structure, and internal organs — find the various organs in the Plates of the " Trans-Vision."

External structure of the frog. The frog's body is short, broad, and angular. It lacks the perfect streamlined form we found in the fish. For this reason, the frog is not the graceful swimmer the fish is, nor does its awkward hopping on land compare with the graceful move-

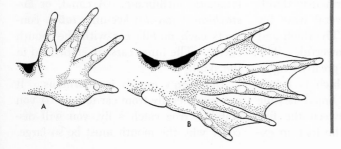

Fig. 30-7. This drawing shows the front and hind foot of a frog. The fully-webbed hind foot enables the animal to become an excellent swimmer.

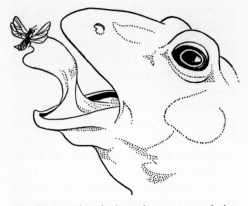

Fig. 30-8. The thick sticky tongue of the frog makes it a good trap for catching flies and other insects.

ment of most other land animals. This is the price the frog must pay for living in two environments.

The skin is thin, moist, and loose. It is richly supplied with blood vessels. Glands in the skin secrete **mucus** which reaches the surface through tiny tubes. This slimy substance makes the frog difficult to hold. The skin lacks any protective outgrowths such as the scales and plates of fish and reptiles.

Adaptations of the frog's legs. The front legs are short and weak. Each has four inturned toes with soft rounded tips. (See Fig. 30-7.) The front feet lack a web and are not used for swimming. The inner toe of a male frog is enlarged, especially during the breeding season. The front legs are used to prop up the body on land and to break the fall after a leap.

The hindlegs are enormously developed and adapted in several ways for swimming and leaping. The thigh and calf muscles are very powerful. The ankle region and toes are greatly lengthened, forming a foot which is longer than the lower leg. A broad flexible **web membrane** lies between the five long toes. This makes the foot an ex-

tremely efficient swimming organ. The hindlegs fold together along the body when the frog is resting on land. In this position, they are ready for a sudden leap.

The head and its structures. Probably the most noticeable structures of the head are the eyes. The eyes of frogs and toads are among the most beautiful of the animal kingdom. The bronze-colored iris surrounds the large black pupil opening. Muscles attached to the eyeball rotate the eye in its socket. The frog's eyes bulge above the head, but can be pulled into their sockets and pressed against the roof of the mouth. In this position, they help to hold food in the mouth.

When the eyes are pulled down, the upper and lower eyelids fold over them. The bulging eyes serve as periscopes when the frog is under water. It can float just below the surface with its eyes above water. A third eyelid, the **nictitating** (*nick*-tih-tay-ting) **membrane,** joins the lower lid. This thin covering keeps the eyeball moist on land and serves as a protective covering when the frog is under water.

The nostrils are located far forward on top of the head. This allows the frog to breathe air with all but the top of the head submerged.

The frog has no external ears. The eardrum, or **tympanic** (tim-*pan*-ick) **membrane,** lies on the surface of the body just behind the eyes. The cavity of the middle ear lies just below the tympanic membrane. A canal, or **Eustachian** (you-*stay*-kee-un) **tube,** connects each middle ear with the mouth cavity. The inner ears are embedded in the skull.

The frog's mouth is enormous. It extends literally from ear to ear. If you watch a frog catch a fly, you will discover why the mouth must be so large.

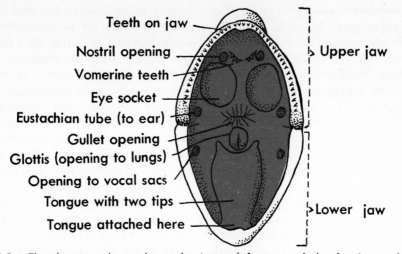

Teeth on jaw

Nostril opening

Vomerine teeth

Eye socket

Eustachian tube (to ear)

Gullet opening

Glottis (opening to lungs)

Opening to vocal sacs

Tongue with two tips

Tongue attached here

Upper jaw

Lower jaw

Fig. 30-9.   The drawing above shows the internal features of the frog's mouth.   Its enormous size is a necessary adaptation for food-getting.

It serves as an insect trap.   Its thick sticky tongue is a food-getting device. This curious tongue is attached at the *front* in the floor of the mouth.   It has two fingerlike projections on the free end.

When a frog catches an insect, the mouth opens wide and the tongue flips over and out.   The insect is caught on the sticky tongue surface and is thrown against the roof of the mouth.   The mouth snaps shut and the insect is swallowed.   This happens so quickly you can hardly see it.   Two **vomerine teeth,** projecting from bones of the roof of the mouth, aid in holding the prey.   The frog has no teeth on the lower jaw. Those on the upper jaw are small.   In toads, both sets are lacking.

Inside the frog's mouth, as shown in Fig. 30-9, you can see various openings. The internal nostril openings lie in the roof near the front, on either side of the vomerine teeth.   Far back on the sides of the roof of the mouth are the openings of the Eustachian tubes.   In a corresponding position in the floor of the mouth of a male frog are openings

to the **vocal sacs.**   When a frog croaks, air is forced through these openings into bladderlike sacs which expand between the ears and the shoulders.   This adds resonance and volume to the sound. When the frog croaks under water, air is forced from the lungs, over the vocal cords, into the mouth and back to the lungs.   The throat contains two single openings.   A large **gullet opening** leads to the stomach.   Below the gullet opening is the slitlike **glottis opening** to the lungs.

Digestive system of the frog.   While the diet of the adult leopard frog consists largely of insects and worms, it can swallow even larger prey because of its large, elastic *gullet.*   The short gullet leads to the *stomach,* an oval enlargement of the food tube.   The stomach is large at the gullet and tapers at the lower end.   Here the stomach joins the small intestine at a point referred to as the **pylorus** (py-*lor*-us).   The stomach content passes into the small intestine through a muscular **pyloric valve.**

The small intestine lies in several loops supported by a fanlike membrane, the **mesentery** (*mes*-en-ter-ee). The small intestine of the frog is proportionally longer than that of the fish. At its lower end, the small intestine leads to a short, broad *large intestine,* or *rectum.* The lower end of the large intestine, leading to the anal opening, is termed the **cloaca** (*kloh*-ay-kah). The walls of the cloaca contain openings of the tubes, the ureters, from the kidneys, the urinary bladder, and the egg tubes, or oviducts, in the female.

The large three-lobed **liver** partially covers the stomach. This is a large storehouse for digested food and a digestive gland which secretes *bile.* The bile collects in the **gall bladder** on the lower side of the liver and passes into the upper small intestine through the **bile duct.** The **pancreas,** a second digestive gland, lies inside of the curve of the stomach. Pancreatic fluid passes into the small intestine with bile through the bile duct. Both of these fluids are necessary for intestinal digestion. *Mucous glands* in the walls of the stomach and intestine secrete mucus, a lubricating fluid. Tiny *gastric glands* in the walls of the stomach secrete gastric fluid, another vital digestive fluid.

We find in the frog a digestive system like that of other vertebrates. A long food tube, or *alimentary canal,* is composed of specialized regions where digestion and absorption of digested food take place. The length of the alimentary canal increases the efficiency of both these processes.

The respiratory system of the frog. Have you ever wondered how the frog, an air breather, can stay under water for long periods and lie buried in the mud at the bottom of a pond through a winter hibernation? The answer lies in *skin respiration.* The skin of the frog and other amphibians is thin and richly supplied with blood vessels. While the frog is in the water, dissolved oxygen passes through the skin to the blood. Carbon dioxide is given off. Respiration through the skin supplies the frog's needs as long as it is quiet. During hibernation, the body processes continue at a very slow rate. The oxygen need is very low. However, body activity, such as swimming, greatly increases the need for oxygen and the skin cannot supply enough. The frog therefore comes to the surface and breathes air.

We inhale and exhale air by increasing and decreasing the size of our chest cavities. This is accomplished by movement of the **ribs** and **diaphragm** (*dy*-uh-fram), a muscular partition at the bottom of the chest cavity. The frog has no diaphragm and therefore has no chest cavity; nor does the frog have ribs. This explains why it must force air into and out of the mouth by up-and-down movement of the floor of the mouth. When the frog lowers the floor of its mouth with the mouth closed, air rushes into the mouth through the open nostrils. When the floor of the mouth springs up, air passes out through the nostrils.

The lining of the mouth is well-adapted for respiration because it is thin, moist, and richly supplied with blood vessels. At this point we need to distinguish mouth breathing from lung breathing. The frog may pump air in and out of its mouth for some time without using its lungs at all. When the lungs are used, the nostrils are closed by flaps of skin as the floor of the mouth rises. The glottis opens and admits air to the trachea and lungs. Then, with the nostrils still closed, muscles along the sides contract with a twitching action and the floor of the mouth is thrust down. This creates a partial vacuum in the mouth. Thus air is partially forced and partially drawn

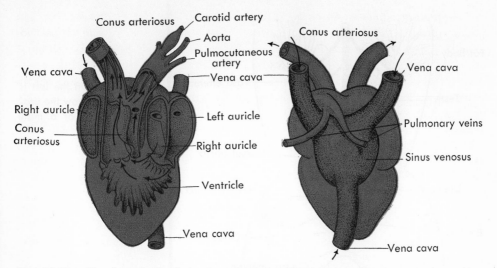

Fig. 30-10. The front half of the frog heart on the left has been removed to show the chambers and valves. Three branches of the vena cava lead to the right auricle. Pulmonary veins lead from the lungs to the left auricle. Blood from both of these chambers passes through valves to the ventricle, then out of the heart through the conus arteriosus. This large vessel divides above the heart and gives rise to the right and left carotid, aorta, and pulmocutaneous arteries. Complicated valves channel blood into these vessels.

The right figure shows the heart viewed from the back side, where the vena cavae enter the sinus venosus and the pulmonary veins enter the left auricle.

out of the lungs. The upthrust of the mouth immediately following this seems to be higher than usual. This forces air back into the lungs. After exchanging air once or twice from mouth to lungs and lungs to mouth, the frog resumes mouth breathing through the open nostrils.

Thus, the frog depends on its lungs only to supplement mouth breathing of air. As you might expect, their lungs are small when compared with higher animals which depend entirely on lung breathing. The lungs are thin-walled sacks that lack the spongy tissue ours have.

The circulatory system. The circulatory system of the frog shows an advance over that of the fish and a step toward the complex system of the higher vertebrates. One of these advances is a three-chambered heart, consisting of *two auricles* and a *muscular ventricle.* (See Fig. 30-10.) *Deoxygenated* blood which has supplied its oxygen to the tissues enters the right auricle from various parts of the body. Blood from the lungs, which is oxygenated when the lungs are in use, enters the left auricle. The auricles contract simultaneously and fill the ventricle. Contraction of the ventricle forces blood out a large vessel (*conus arteriosus*) which lies against the front side of the heart. This large vessel divides at once into two branches like a letter Y. Each of these branches divides again into three arteries. The anterior pair of branches are the **carotids** (kah-*rot*-ids). They carry blood to the head. The middle pair, or **aortic arches,** bend to the right and left around the heart and join just

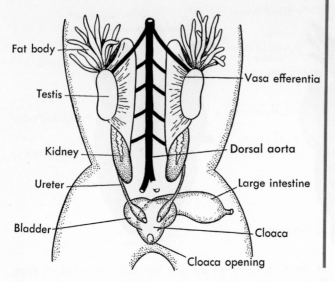

Fat body

Testis

Kidney

Ureter

Bladder

Vasa efferentia

Dorsal aorta

Large intestine

Cloaca

Cloaca opening

Fig. 30-11. On the left is a drawing to show the urogenital organs of a male frog.

below the liver to form the **dorsal aorta.** This great artery supplies the muscles, digestive organs, and other body tissues. The posterior, or **pulmocutaneous** (pull-moh-kew-*tain*-ee-us) arteries, form branches which supply the lungs, mouth, and skin.

Blood returning from the body is laden with carbon dioxide and other cell wastes and has been relieved of much of its oxygen. Three large veins (*vena cavae*) join a triangular, thin-walled sac (*sinus venosus*) on the back side of the heart which in turn empties into the right auricle. Part of the blood returning to the heart from the lower parts of the body flows through vessels of the digestive organs and absorbs digested food. This branch of the circulatory system, the **portal vein,** passes through the liver on its way to the right auricle. During each complete circulation of the blood, some of the blood passes through the kidneys where nitrogen-containing wastes from cell activity and water are removed.

The frog's circulatory system shows several advances over that of the fish. Blood passes through the two-chambered

heart of the fish only once in making a round trip through the body. The three-chambered frog heart receives blood both from the body and from the lungs and pumps blood to the head and body as well as to the various centers where respiration takes place.

The excretory system of the frog. The frog's skin is a vital organ of excretion since it is here rather than in the mouth or lungs that most of the carbon dioxide is discharged from the blood. The liver removes certain wastes and eliminates them with bile or converts them into urea for removal by the kidneys. The large intestine eliminates undigested food and other wastes. However, the kidneys are the principal organs of excretion. They receive wastes from the blood which flows into them through the renal arteries and out through the renal veins. The kidneys are large, dark red organs lying on either side of the spine against the back body wall. *Urine* collects in the kidneys and flows to the cloaca through tiny tubes, the **ureters,** as you can see in Fig. 30-11. The urine may be excreted immediately. Or it may be forced into the bladder through an opening in the cloaca for storage.

The frog's nervous system. The frog's brain shows a considerable advance over that of the fish. *Olfactory lobes* lie at the anterior end of the brain. The elongated lobes of the **cerebrum** are proportionally larger than those of the fish. Posterior to these are the prominent **optic lobes.** The **cerebellum** is just behind the optic lobes. It is small in the frog and is a band of tissue lying at right angles to the long axis of the brain. The spinal cord enlarges at its anterior end to form the **medulla.** The spinal cord is shorter and thicker than that of the fish. Pairs of *spinal nerves* branch from the cord and pass to various parts of the body through openings between the vertebrae. The brain also has nerves leaving it. There are ten pairs of these cranial nerves.

Reproductive system. Since the reproductive organs of the frog are internal, it is difficult to distinguish the sexes except during the breeding season when the thumb of the male is enlarged. The male reproductive organs are two oval, creamy white or yellowish *testes.* They lie in the back, one on each side of the spine, above the anterior region of the kidneys. Sperm develop in the testes and pass through tiny tubes (*vasa efferentia*) into the kidneys. When the sperm are discharged, they follow the ureters to their openings in the cloaca. Some species of frogs have an enlargement (*seminal vesicle*) at the base of each ureter.

Eggs develop in a pair of large, lobed *ovaries* in the female. These attach along the back above the kidneys. During the breeding season, the eggs enlarge and burst the thin ovary walls. This frees them into the body cavity. Movement of the abdominal muscles

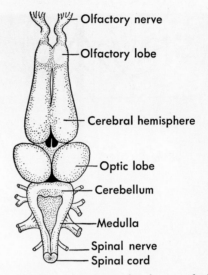

Olfactory nerve

Olfactory lobe

Cerebral hemisphere

Optic lobe

Cerebellum

Medulla

Spinal nerve
Spinal cord

Fig. 30-12. Compare the brain of the frog with that of the fish in Fig. 29-10.

works the eggs toward the anterior end of the body cavity. Here are funnel-like openings of the long coiled oviducts. The eggs are fanned into the oviduct openings by cilia. Near their opening into the cloaca, the walls of the oviducts secrete a gelatinous substance which surround each egg. At the base of each oviduct is a saclike *uterus* in which the eggs are stored until they are laid through openings into the cloaca.

Most frogs have a mass of yellow *bodies of fat* attached above the kidneys. These contain much of the food used during hibernation.

Fertilization and development of the eggs. The female leopard frog usually lays her eggs sometime between the first of April and the middle of May. The male is present with the female at the time the eggs are laid. As the eggs pass from the cloaca of the female, the male spreads sperm over them. As a result of this *direct fertilization* most of the eggs receive sperm.

The jellylike coat which surrounds each egg swells in the water. This joins

Fig. 30-13. The lower mass of frog's eggs has only been laid a few hours. Those above have been in the water longer, though the jelly spheres are still relatively small.

the eggs in a rounded, gelatinous mass. In this clump, the eggs look like small beads, each surrounded by a transparent covering. Not only does the jelly protect the eggs from injury, but it makes them more difficult for a hungry fish to eat. Also it serves as the first food of the young tadpole.

The frog egg is partly black and partly white. The white portion is the yolk or stored food material which will nourish the tadpole during development. The dark portion contains the living protoplasm of the egg and a dark pigment. The yolk is heavier than the rest of the egg, causing the eggs to float in the water dark side up. The black pigment on the upper side absorbs heat from the sun while the lighter lower half blends in with the light from the sky and makes them hard to see from below. The gelatinous covering holds

much of this heat in the mass. After eight to twenty days, depending on the weather conditions and water temperature, the tadpole hatches and wiggles away from the egg mass.

From tadpole to adult — the metamorphosis of the frog. Just after hatching, the tadpole is a tiny, short-bodied creature with a disk-like mouth. It clings to the egg mass or to a plant. Yolk stored in the body nourishes the young tadpole until it starts to feed. Soon after hatching, the body lengthens and two pairs of external gills appear at the sides of the head. The tail lengthens and develops a caudal fin. The mouth opens and the tadpole begins scraping the leaves of water plants with horny lips.

Soon after the tadpoles become free swimmers, the horny lip disappears. A long, coiled digestive tract develops and the tadpole starts living on vegetable scums. Gradually a fold of skin grows backward over the gills like a flap. This leaves a small opening on the left side through which water passes out of the gill chambers. At this stage the tadpole is a fishlike animal with a lateral line, fin, two-chambered heart, and a one-circuit circulation. It also has a relatively long, spirally-coiled intestine.

The change to an adult frog is remarkable. The hind legs appear first. The front legs begin to form at about the same time but do not appear for some time. They remain hidden under the operculum. Soon after the appearance of the front legs, the tadpole starts resorbing (i.e., not shedding or eating) its tail. Late in the metamorphosis, the tadpole's mouth broadens and teeth develop. While these external changes have been taking place, equally important internal changes have been occurring. A saclike chamber, resembling the swim bladder of the fish,

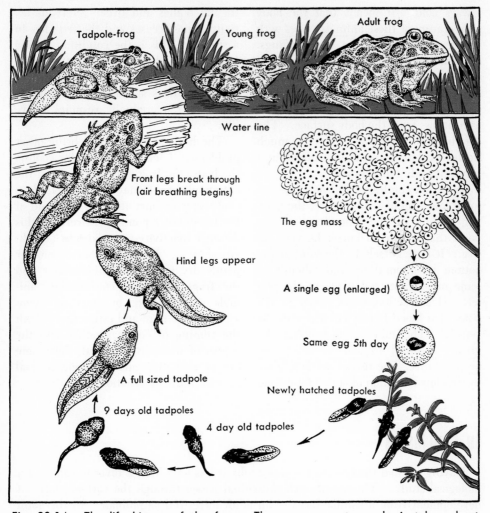

Fig. 30-14. The life history of the frog. The average metamorphosis takes about three months.

forms back of the throat. This divides into two sacs which become the lungs. The heart becomes three-chambered and the gill arteries change to the carotids, aortic arches, and the pulmocutaneous arteries. The gills stop functioning and the tadpole comes to the surface frequently to gulp air. The thin skin and the broad, flat tail still play an important role in respiration during this critical time.

Even before the tail is entirely resorbed, the tadpole leaves the water and

comes to land as a young frog. From this stage to the full-grown adult frog requires usually about a month. The metamorphosis of the leopard frog varies from 60 to 90 days. Full-grown adults usually appear about the first of July. The bullfrog usually spends two winters as a tadpole and its entire metamorphosis may last as long as three years.

Hibernation and estivation in the frog. The frog, as well as the fish and reptile, are cold-blooded vertebrates. This does not mean that their blood is always cold. It means that the body temperature of these animals varies with the temperature of the surroundings. Man maintains a constant average body temperature of about 98.6° F. by regulating the rate of food oxidation and resulting heat release in the tissues as well as heat loss from the body surface. The cold-blooded vertebrates carry on much slower oxidation and do not maintain a constant body temperature.

With the coming of fall and the seasonal lowering of temperature, the body temperature of the frog drops to the point that it can no longer be very active. It buries itself in the mud at the bottom of a pond or finds shelter in some other protected place in the water. Heart action slows down to the point that blood hardly circulates in the vessels. The moist skin supplies the greatly reduced oxygen necessary for keeping alive. The tissues are kept alive by the slow oxidation of stored food from the fat bodies and liver. Nervous activity almost ceases and the frog lies in a stupor. This is the condition during **hibernation** (hy-ber-*nay*-shun) or winter rest. With the coming of spring, the warm days speed up body activity and the frog gradually resumes active life.

The hot summer months bring other problems. Lacking a device for cooling the body, the frog must escape from the extreme heat. It may lie quietly in deep cool water or bury itself in the mud at the bottom of a pond. We refer to this summer inactivity as **estivation** (es-tih-*vay*-shun). In many cases, smaller ponds dry up during midsummer and the frogs and other cold-blooded animals survive only by burying themselves in the mud and estivating. With the coming of cooler weather and the return of water to the pond, they come out of estivation and continue normal activity until hibernation.

In Conclusion

Having studied the frog, you can see why it has long been a favorite subject for biological study. The life of each individual passes through the various stages of development from a fishlike larva to an adult terrestrial amphibian. In the adult stage, its organs and systems are complex and efficient. Biologists still marvel at its three-chambered heart with the complicated valves and arteries. The respiratory system is fascinating, too. Lungs alone cannot supply the frog's breathing needs. But lungs, mouth, and skin compose an efficient respiratory team. Of course, if the skin is to be used in respiration, it must be thin and moist. This limits the possibility of leaving the water or a moist environment entirely.

In the next class of vertebrates, you will find animals which, while similar to the frog in many ways, are much better suited to life on land. Scales furnish a more efficient protective covering for the reptile. Claws on its toes, if it has toes, make climbing and running possible. Lungs have taken over the role of respiration. You will find many well-known and interesting vertebrates in this next class.

Questions for Review

1. What several characteristics of amphibians distinguish them from other vertebrates?

2. How many orders of amphibians are represented by living members today?

3. (a) In what ways do salamanders resemble lizards? (b) Name several characteristics which make them different from lizards.

4. Of what economic value are toads?

5. What are several economic uses of frogs?

6. How does a frog go about catching a flying insect?

7. How can a frog croak under water?

8. Name the organs forming the alimentary canal of a frog in the order in which they receive food.

9. What three arterial branches carry blood from the great artery leading from the frog's heart?

10. What are the chambers of a frog's heart?

11. How is urine conducted from the frog's kidneys to the cloaca and bladder?

12. What various changes occur during the development of a tadpole? Name them in the order in which they occur.

Biologically Speaking

amphibian	fat body	pulmocutaneous artery
aortic arch	hibernation	sinus venosus
carotid artery	lung	tadpole
cloaca	mucus	trachea
conus arteriosus	nictitating membrane	tympanic membrane
deoxygenated blood	ovary	uterus
estivation	oviduct	vomerine teeth
Eustachian tube	oxygenated blood	web membrane

Applying Facts and Principles

1. Discuss problems in the life of a toad resulting from its " in between " existence.

2. Frogs breathe air, yet they lie buried in the mud at the bottom of a pond during the winter months. Explain how this is possible.

3. In what respect is the direct fertilization of the frog's eggs more efficient than spawning in fish?

4. Explain how the frog illustrates relationship to the fish in its early development.

5. In what ways are the heart and circulatory system more highly developed in the frog than in the fish?

KEY TO THE
ORGANS OF THE FROG

1. Transverse abdominal muscles
2. Vertical abdominal muscles
3. Muscles to floor of mouth
4. Sockets for attachment of arms
5. Shoulder muscles
6. Right auricle of heart
7. Left auricle of heart
8. Ventricle of heart
9. Great veins to right auricle
10. Great artery from heart (conus arteriosus)
11. Liver
12. Stomach
13. Pancreas
14. Small intestine
15. Large intestine (rectum)
16. Spleen
17. Mesentery
18. Abdominal vein
19. Leg muscles
20. Tongue
21. Glottis opening
22. Trachea
23. Lungs
24. Sinus venosus
25. Pulmonary veins
26. Gall bladder
27. Bile duct
28. Hepatic-portal vein
29. Sockets for attachment of legs
30. Gullet
31. Vein from kidneys (posterior vena cava)
32. Kidneys
33. Dorsal aorta
34. Fat bodies
35. Ovaries
36. Oviducts
37. Openings of oviducts
38. Egg sac (uterus)
39. Urinary bladder
40. Cloaca
41. Lining of mouth
42. Veins from legs to kidneys (renal portal vein)
43. Ureters
44. Internal nostril openings
45. Vomerine teeth
46. Teeth of the upper jaw
47. Openings of Eustachian tubes
48. Eye sockets
49. Brain
50. Spinal cord
51. Spinal nerves

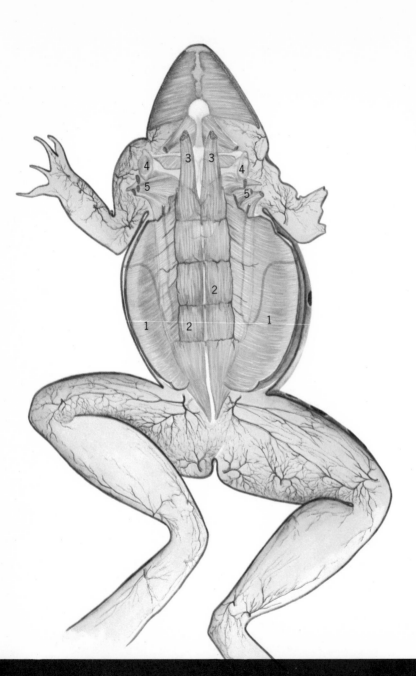

II **LAYER OF SKIN AND MUSCLES REMOVED FROM VENTRAL SIDE OF THE FROG.**
Looking at this layer from the inside, you see the many blood vessels of the skin.
Notice the transverse abdominal muscles (1), and the vertical abdominal muscles (2).
The large muscles (3) which aid in mouth breathing have been cut. The ends which
attach to the floor of the mouth show in the next drawing. In the shoulder are the bones
which form the socket (4) for the attachment of the arms and the cut ends of some of

III CUTAWAY VIEW SHOWING THE FROG LYING ON ITS BACK WITH FRONT BODY WALL REMOVED. The heart is composed of a right auricle (6), a left auricle (7), and a ventricle (8). Great veins (9) carry blood into the heart and a great artery (10) carries blood away from the heart. The liver (11) covers most of the stomach (12) and pancreas (13). The small intestine (14) leads from the lower end of the stomach to the large intestine (15). The spleen (16) lies in the thin layers of mesentery (17) which fasten the abdominal organs to the body wall. The large abdominal vein (18) carries blood from the legs to the liver. Powerful leg muscles (19) enable the animal to swim and jump.

VI CUTAWAY VIEW SHOWING DEEPER ORGANS AS SEEN FROM THE BACK. The lining of the mouth (41) shows its rich blood supply. You see the gullet (30) and stomach (12) from the dorsal side. Veins (42) carry blood from the legs to the kidneys (32). Near these are the ureters (43) which carry urine to the cloaca (40) which is cut open in the drawing. Urine passes from the cloaca into the urinary bladder (39), where it is stored.

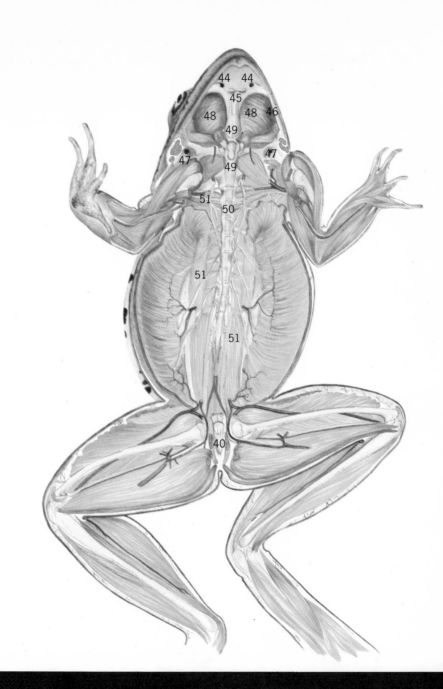

VII CUTAWAY VIEW SHOWING BACK BODY WALL AS SEEN FROM THE FRONT WITH ORGANS AND SOME OF THE LARGE LEG MUSCLES REMOVED. Internal nostril openings (**44**), vomerine teeth (**45**), teeth of the upper jaw (**46**), Eustachian tube opening (**47**) and eye sockets (**48**) can be seen in this view of the head. The cranium and spine are shown as though they were transparent to show the brain (**49**) and spinal cord (**50**). Spinal nerves (**51**) emerge from each side of the spinal cord. Dissection of the lower leg muscles exposes bones and joints, blood vessels, and the dorsal wall of

CHAPTER 31

The Reptiles

No other group of animals is so surrounded by prejudice, superstitions, and foolish ideas as the reptiles. True, the reptiles include in their numbers many poisonous species. However, condemning an entire animal group because of the behavior of a few members is as logical as saying that all humans are dangerous because some commit crime.

The biologist learns to recognize the relatively small number of dangerous reptiles and gives them free range. But his knowledge of the group prevents him from mistreating the large number of harmless and beneficial reptiles he meets. In your study of biology, you should adopt the same attitude. You will learn to recognize four kinds of poisonous snakes, one poisonous lizard, one dangerous turtle, and one group, the crocodiles and alligators, which you should avoid. Aside from these specific reptiles, you need fear none.

The Age of Reptiles. Unfortunately, the human reptile enthusiast arrived on the earth about 200 million years too late. While about 300 species of reptiles still inhabit North America, this number is only a sampling of the widely varied forms which roamed our land and seas during the Age of Reptiles. Today, the biologist must resort to fossil bones, eggs, footprints, and considerable imagination to picture what the world must have been like when the reptiles held full sway.

Most famous of these ancient reptiles were the *dinosaurs* (*dy*-no-sors), which ranged in size from creatures no larger than a modern lizard to monsters larger than an elephant. The largest dinosaurs were the thunder lizards, or *Brontosaurus* (bron-toh-*sor*-us). This giant measured 75 feet long and 15 feet high and reached a weight of 30 tons or more. The king of dinosaurs was the ferocious tyrant reptile, called *Tyran-*

nosaurus (ty-ran-oh-*sor*-us), which is probably the most terrible creature ever to roam the earth. It walked erect on its hind legs and balanced its heavy body with its long tail, much like a kangaroo. Its front legs were short but powerful and its long claws could tear most prey into shreds. Its large mouth was rimmed with double-edged teeth three to six inches long and could rip the hide of even an armored victim.

You may wonder how creatures such as these ever became extinct. Had they possessed a brain in proportion to their brawn, they might exist today. But many fell victims to more intelligent animals which invaded their haunts, while others wandered into asphalt pits or bogs and sank to their doom. Other forms could not survive the gradually changing earth. Large numbers must have starved to death when their own numbers created serious food problems they were not able to meet.

Fig. 31-1. The king of dinosaurs was the *Tyrannosaurus*.

How do we classify reptiles today?
Some 4,000 species of reptiles exist in the world today as remnants of this once flourishing age. Certain of these forms are much like their ancestors. Others have become greatly modified since the Age of Reptiles.

Biologists group the more common North American reptiles into three orders as the table below shows.

The characteristics of reptiles. Reptiles resemble the amphibians in many respects, although they are higher in the scale of animal development. Like amphibians, all reptiles are cold-blooded. However, many of the body characteristics of reptiles distinguish them readily from the frog and its relatives.

These differences include: (1) the body is usually covered with scales; (2) the skin is dry, not moist and slimy; (3) the feet, if any, have claws; (4) eggs are internally fertilized and, if laid, have a protective shell. Certain species retain the eggs within the body and bring forth the young alive; (5) they have no metamorphosis; and (6) gills are not present as in the fish and amphibian, both young and adult reptiles breathing by means of lungs.

Snakes are the most widespread reptile forms. Snakes constitute not only the most numerous reptilian form, but the most widely distributed as well. They are abundant in the tropical regions, but range over the majority of the

ORDERS OF NORTH AMERICAN REPTILES	
NAME OF ORDER	REPRESENTATIVES
Squamata (squah-*may*-tah)	Snakes and lizards
Testudinata (tes-too-dih-*nay*-tah)	Turtles and tortoises
Crocodilia (kroh-koh-*dil*-ih-ah)	Alligators and crocodiles

earth. Of the more than 2,000 species, only a relatively small number are poisonous. The harm done by a few snakes is far overbalanced by the valuable service rendered by others in destroying large numbers of insects and destructive rodents.

The body of the snake is highly specialized and quite different from other animals. It is legless. Most snakes have lost even the internal bones and muscles concerned with legs, although the remains of hind legs are found on certain species including the *boa constrictor* and *python*. The entire body is covered with scales. The upper surface of this body has small, oval scales and the lower side has broad plates which are used in locomotion.

Snakes shed the outer layer of their scales several times each season during a process called **molting**. Just before shedding, the scales covering the eyes become milky and the snake is partially blind.

The mouth is large and equipped with two rows of sharp teeth on the upper jaw and one row on the lower. These point backward toward the throat. Near the front of the mouth in the floor of the lower jaw is a long forked tongue which may be thrust through a small pore between the jaws when the mouth is closed. Snakes thrust out their tongues when alarmed, possibly as a frightening device, but more to sense what is going on. The tongue is sensitive to smell and functions as an organ of smell. It is not a fang and is quite harmless. Snakes have no eyelids and hence cannot close their eyes.

The internal organs of the snake are much like those of other vertebrates, although the long, slender body results in their being somewhat differently arranged. Ribs are attached to each of the nearly 300 vertebrae of the spine.

Fig. 31-2. Pythons obtain their food by crushing their prey in powerful coils.

False ideas about snakes. In reading the following common superstitions which concern snakes, you will probably find several which you have heard and perhaps have believed. Reptile authorities who have devoted their lives to the study of reptiles say they are not true.

To begin with, snakes are not slimy and nasty. Their skin is usually clean and dry and feels cold only because they do not maintain a body temperature higher than their surroundings. They cannot jump from the ground when they strike, nor do they spring from a perfect coil. They cannot inflict a wound with the tongue. Though reflex motion continues in a snake long after death, the setting of the sun has nothing to do with its death. However, the cool temperature of evening may slow muscular reflex action. Snakes do not swallow their young to protect them. Certain kinds of snakes devour other snakes and digest them in their stomachs. The young would suffer a similar fate if swallowed for protection.

No snake was ever known to take the tip of its tail in its mouth and roll down

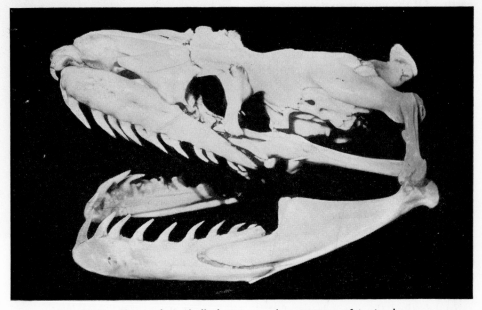

Fig. 31-3. This snake's skull shows you the structure of its jawbones.

a hill like a hoop. While several species live around barns, they do not milk cows. Horsehairs do not turn into snakes. Rattlesnakes do not add one rattle per year, but usually two or three, depending on the number of times they shed their skin. Removal of fangs does not render a poisonous snake permanently harmless as other fangs take their place very soon. Snakes do not possess hypnotic powers and cannot cause birds to fall from branches by swaying beneath them.

How snakes get food. Snakes eat other animals. They catch their food in three ways. The first way involves merely swallowing the food alive. Garter snakes, and many others, catch the prey in their mouths and swallow the whole animal. The second way involves squeezing the food animal in powerful coils and then swallowing it. Snakes which do this are called **constrictors.** The boas, pythons, and common black snake use this method. The third way involves the injection of a poison into the victim. This is done through sharp fangs which act like a hypodermic needle. The animal is thus killed and is swallowed. Rattlesnakes, cobras, and copperheads catch their food by this means.

Adaptions for swallowing food. The whole snake, but particularly its head, is adapted for this peculiar habit of swallowing prey. Some of the animals thus eaten are larger in diameter than the snake's body. For this purpose, there are numerous sharp incurved teeth on three sets of jawbones. Any of these teeth may grow again if broken off. The lower jaw is not fixed directly to the upper jaw, but is attached to a separate bone, the **quadrate,** which, in turn, is attached to the skull. This attachment lets the jaw drop downward and forward and open as wide at the back as at the front. The two halves of the lower jaw are fastened at the front by an elastic ligament, allowing each half to operate independently of the other.

During swallowing, one-half of the jaw may be thrust forward for a new grip on the prey and, while that half is pulling the victim into the mouth, the other half is pushed forward for another grip. The jaws operate much in the manner in which you pull in a rope by pulling with each hand alternately. Thus, the snake literally crawls around its prey. However, the teeth are not adapted to tearing or cutting nor to chewing as we think of it.

The process of swallowing is so long that special adaptations are necessary to permit breathing to go on. The *trachea* extends along the floor of the mouth to a *glottis* opening near the front rim of the jaw.

The *gullet* and *stomach* are highly elastic and the digestive fluids are very powerful to accommodate food in such large doses. The flexible *ribs* and lack of breastbone or limb girdles allow for the passage of these enormous mouthfuls.

The delicate and slender *forked tongue* is protected during swallowing by being drawn back into a sheath.

Snakes can endure long periods of time without eating. The longest recorded instance is perhaps the case of a regal python which, when brought to the New York Zoological Park, went on a hunger strike for almost two years.

How snakes move. Snakes have no legs; yet they move from place to place or climb trees with ease and rapidity. They accomplish these feats by means of the broad *plates* on their ventral surface. These plates have their free edge toward the rear, so that they will catch against the slightest roughness. To each plate is attached a pair of *ribs* which act somewhat like legs with each plate as a foot. To allow free motion of the ribs, the vertebrae have a flexible ball and socket joint, and the whole

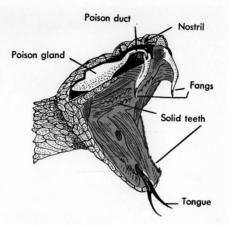

Fig. 31-4. Study this snake's head and note how well-adapted it is for swallowing food. Note, too, the poison gland and the needlelike fangs.

body is provided with very strong muscles, so that a snake really travels on hundreds of muscular legs (ribs).

Reproduction in snakes. The majority of snakes lay eggs which resemble those of the other reptiles. Each egg contains stored food to nourish the young snake during its development, and is enclosed in a tough white shell. The eggs receive no care from the female after being laid and no incubation except the warmth of the sun. Egg-laying snakes are called **oviparous** (oh-*vip*-ar-us), and include the black snake and blue racer.

A smaller group of snakes, including the garter snake and the copperhead, bring forth their young alive, usually in the late summer. The eggs are retained in the reproductive organs, where they develop into young snakes. During development, there is no nourishment provided from the mother's body as in the highest group of animals, the *mammals*. Snakes which bring forth the young are classed as **ovoviviparous** (oh-voh-vy-*vip*-ar-us). This distinguishes them from the higher animals which are called **viviparous** (vy-*vip*-ar-us) and

Fig. 31-5. The garter snake is ovoviviparous, bringing forth its young alive.

which nourish their young during development.

Some nonpoisonous snakes of North America. *Garter snakes* are the most common snakes in North America, about 20 species being included in its wide range. They live in fields and along stream banks where they feed on insects, worms, frogs, and toads. Garter snakes are harmless and do considerable good in holding smaller animals in check.

Probably the most terrifying snake to approach is the *hog-nosed* snake, also called the *spreading viper* or *puff adder*. When surprised along the path, this plump-bodied little snake puts on an act which terrifies all but the most informed student of snakes. Amid loud hisses it suddenly raises its head and spreads its neck widely in true cobra fashion. If this act fails, it twists its head, opens its mouth and falls limp on its back as though dead. However, one familiar with the ways of this little creature knows that the hog-nosed snake is one of few species which will not bite even when picked up.

The *black snake* and its western variety, the *blue racer,* inhabit the central eastern United States. They are large snakes, usually four to six feet long and are covered with smooth satiny scales. When disturbed, they may fight viciously, though their bite is not poisonous. They are exceedingly valuable since their diet includes large numbers of small rodents. The intelligent farmer never destroys a black snake near his barn, because one snake destroys more small rats and mice than several cats.

The *bull snake* of the Middle West is one of the largest snakes in the United States, and may reach nearly seven feet in length. It is a powerful constrictor and crushes rats, mice, gophers, squirrels, and rabbits in its coils. It is exceedingly valuable in the wheat fields where it lives, and certainly warrants protection.

Anyone who does not appreciate snakes should be especially interested in conserving the *king snake,* for this individual is among the worst enemies of other snakes. It attacks them viciously and does not hesitate to seize the deadly copperhead or rattlesnake in its strong coils. Strangely, it is immune to the venom of poisonous snakes. King snakes vary in color from nearly black with narrow white lines to the brilliantly colored *milk snake* falsely accused of milking cows.

Poisonous snakes of North America. About 20 kinds of poisonous snakes live in the various parts of the United States. We can group them as follows: (1) rattlesnakes (about 15 kinds); (2) copperhead and water moccasin; (3) coral snakes (2 kinds); and (4) yellow-bellied sea snake.

The rattlesnakes are the most widely distributed poisonous snakes. They belong to the family of **pit vipers,** so named because of a deep pit between the eye and the nostril. Of the 15 or more kinds of rattlesnakes found in the United States, at least 12 species occur in the southwest. These include the prairie rattlesnake, western diamond rattlesnake, and horned rattlesnake, or " side-winder " of the desert regions. The range of the timber rattlesnake includes most of eastern United States. The largest of North American rattlesnakes, the diamond-back, lives in marshy areas of the southeast. Six to eight-foot specimens have been taken in the swamps of South Carolina, Florida, and the Gulf States.

Rattlesnakes have a series of dry segments, or **rattles,** on the end of the tail. When the snake is disturbed, it vibrates these rapidly, causing a whirring sound. This explains why, even though rattlesnakes are widely distributed, few people are bitten by them. The snake does not strike without warning. Usually you can step away from danger when you hear and recognize a rattlesnake's warning. Contrary to popular belief, a rattlesnake does not add a rattle each year. Usually two or three are added.

The head of a rattlesnake is large and triangular. The jaws are puffy, due to the presence of poison glands which are modified salivary glands. (See Fig. 31-4.) Near the front of the upper jaw is a pair of large, hollow teeth, or **fangs.** Ducts lead from the poison glands to the base of the fangs. The fangs are fastened to a bone which is hinged on the upper jaw so that when the snake's mouth is closed, the fangs fold upward against the roof of the mouth. They are pulled down by muscles when the snake opens its mouth to strike. The rattlesnake can strike fiercely a distance of one-third the length of its body or more. The fangs are driven deep into the flesh of its victim and poison flows from the glands, through the fangs, and into the wound. Both the length of the fangs and the large amount of poison injected make the rattlesnake bite especially dangerous, especially when the fangs happen to go into a vein. The poison, or **venom,** destroys red corpuscles and tissues around the bite.

Rattlesnakes, especially the diamondback, have several economic uses. The skin is used for purses, belts, and other articles. The flesh is eaten in many regions. The venom is "milked " from captive specimens and is used for making **antivenin,** a biological product used in treating bites of all the pit vipers.

The *copperhead,* another of the pit vipers, is more dangerous than the rat-

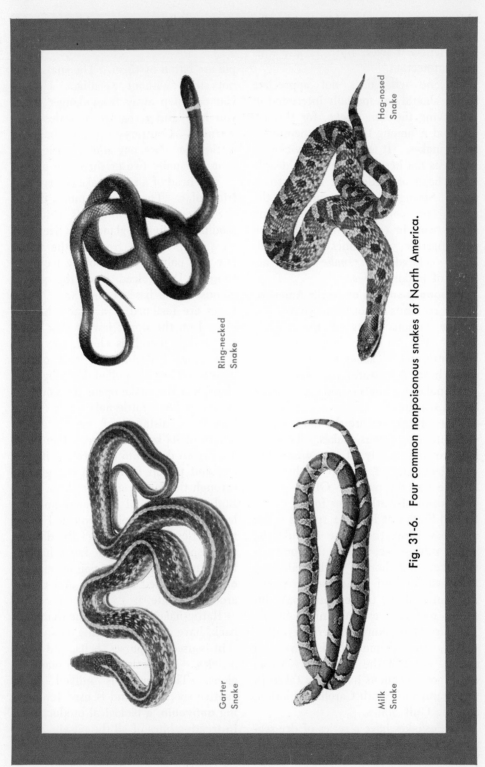

Ring-necked Snake

Hog-nosed Snake

Garter Snake

Milk Snake

Fig. 31-6. Four common nonpoisonous snakes of North America.

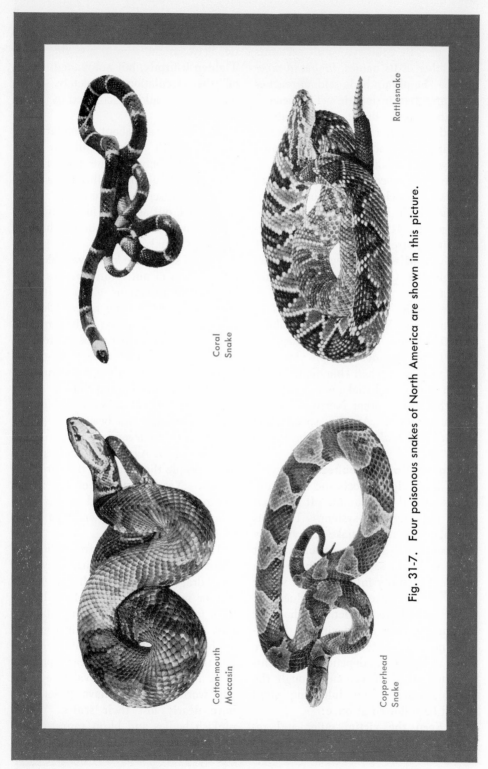

Coral
Snake

Rattlesnake

Cotton-mouth
Moccasin

Copperhead
Snake

Fig. 31-7. Four poisonous snakes of North America are shown in this picture.

tlesnake since it strikes without warning. Copperheads usually live in dry woods of hilly country. This accounts for another of its names, *highland moccasin.* The plump body seldom reaches over three feet in length. The head is a bright copper shade. The body is marked with alternate irregular bands of light brown and dark reddish-brown arranged in an hourglass pattern.

The *water moccasin,* or *cotton-mouth moccasin,* is a close relative of the copperhead, both being members of the same genus. It lives in the warm, sluggish rivers, streams, and backwaters of the lower Mississippi region and east through the Carolinas, Georgia, and Florida.

One species of *coral snake* lives in eastern United States and is most abundant in Florida. This snake does not strike in the manner of a pit viper but bites viciously when handled. The venom of the coral snake is more deadly than that of any other North American poisonous snake. Another species, the *Sonora coral snake,* inhabits the southwest.

Treatment of snakebites. The venom of a pit viper affects the blood and tissues around the wound. It does not affect the digestive system. For this reason, a venomous snake can swallow prey containing its own poison without effect, while the same poison injected in sufficient quantity into the blood would kill even the snake which produced it.

We now have efficient methods of treating the bites of pit vipers. Treatment must be started immediately since much of its success depends on preventing the spread of venom through the blood stream. The following steps should be followed at once:

1. Keep the victim quiet and reassured. This is to prevent speeding up of heart action.

2. Put a constricting band, made from a piece of cloth, a cord, or a necktie, between the wound and the heart. Tighten it firmly, but not enough to cut off the circulation completely. The tourniquet should be loosened by a doctor.

3. Cut a gash about one-quarter of an inch, with a clean knife or razor blade, deep between the fang marks. The blade should be sterilized in a flame or in an antiseptic before use.

4. Suck out as much blood and venom as possible with a suction bulb if you have a snake-bite kit.

5. If a snake-bite kit is available, give an injection of antivenin serum according to the directions given. If not, rush the victim to the nearest doctor's office or hospital, where antivenin shots and other treatments can be started.

Lizards. Of the more than 2,500 species of lizards, only a small number are native to the United States. They are chiefly tropical animals. Many lizards are strange and beautiful. Their resemblance to legendary dragons and monsters of the Age of Reptiles has given many people the idea that they are dangerous. Yet, among all of the fierce-looking creatures included in this large suborder of reptiles, only one type is poisonous.

Lizards vary in size from the tiny *swifts* or *skinks* and tropical *geckos* to the " dragon " lizard which may be 15 feet or more in length. Many lizards have four legs and climb and run rapidly. Others have lost their legs and might be mistaken for snakes, except for their jaw structure, ear openings (but no ears), and movable eyelids. The wormlike lizards have no legs and have nearly lost their scales. Their pinkish bodies and blunt rounded tails resemble worms. These curious lizards live in rich soil, especially in the tropics.

Fig. 31-8. The Komodo dragon lizard, found in the Dutch East Indies, is the largest of all known species. This 15-foot reptile may weigh as much as 250 pounds.

The American *chameleon* (kuh-*meel*-yun) is probably the best-known of lizards. This graceful lizard with two inches of body and three inches of tail has the ability to change its color to match its surroundings. This protective adaptation results from change in size of pigment glands in the skin. Its colors range from bright green to grayish and brown, depending on the color of the surroundings.

The *horned toad,* which has plenty of horns, but isn't a toad, lives in the dry plains of western United States. It is a relative of the dragonlike iguana (ih-*gwah*-nah) of the tropics. Its spiny skin not only protects it from enemies but prevents evaporation of water. Horned toads often spend many hours basking in the sun without moving. They appear dead except for occasional blinking of the eyes. This small lizard survives because its color blends closely with the sand, rocks, and spiny cacti of its environment.

The common *swift,* or fence lizard, may be seen darting swiftly along wooden fences and fallen tree trunks. The *skinks* include several kinds of lizards, some with and some without legs. They have large rounded, shiny scales which give them a glassy appearance. The *collared lizard* is one of the most beautiful animals of the Southwestern desert region. These lizards, especially the males, have a bright green body covered with yellow spots. The collar is sooty black and the throat a deep orange.

The *Gila* (*hee*-lah) *monster* of the Southwest is the *only poisonous lizard.* Its skin is covered with rounded, raised scales arranged in beautiful designs of orange or pink, and black or brown. Their bodies resemble Indian beadwork. The name " monster " is misleading, for a large Gila monster is less than two feet long. Poison glands and grooved teeth are situated in the rear of the lower jaw. When the Gila monster bites, it closes its jaws with great force and turns the head from side to side, thus digging the teeth into the victim. The poison affects the heart and can be fatal

Fig. 31-9. The horned toad is actually a true lizard. It has several hornlike spines on the head and its broad, flat body is covered with spiny scales.

to man. While not as dangerous as poisonous snakes, this lizard should be avoided.

Crocodilians. To the order *Crocodilians* belong the 25 species of alligators, caymans, crocodiles, and gavials. These great reptiles live in tropical and subtropical waters. Stories about crocodilians hunting and devouring human beings have been exaggerated. However, one species, the man-eating crocodile of the Nile River, will attack a man if molested or if hungry enough. One species of alligator is found throughout the coastal area of South Carolina, Florida, and the Gulf States as far west as the Rio Grande. Alligators spend much of their time lying half-submerged in the water or basking in the sun on the edge of a stream or on an island. Projecting eyes and snouts permit them to float almost completely under water and still breathe freely and look about. Their scaly backs look like a rough log

as they wait for the approach of a fish or some other aquatic animal.

Alligator hide is in great demand for the manufacture of fine shoes, purses, and luggage. Newly hatched alligators are shipped to pet stores all over the nation. If they are kept in an aquarium or tank of warm water and fed regularly, they may live in captivity for many years. Many of the alligators used or sold commercially come from alligator farms in the southern states.

Crocodiles are the most widely distributed of the crocodilians, especially in the Old World. The largest of the crocodiles is the salt-water crocodile which lives in the ocean and comes up the rivers of the Far East. The Nile crocodile is most famous. These large reptiles, from 15 to 20 feet long, can dash out of the water, seize a victim, including a man, knock it down with a blow of the powerful tail, and then drag it under water to drown. The *Ameri-*

Fig. 31-10. The Gila monster, the only poisonous lizard, has a sluggish but ugly disposition. It may reach a length of two feet.

can crocodile is found in southern Florida, the West Indies, Mexico, and Central America. The crocodile is more aquatic than the alligator. Its body is slenderer and its head much more pointed. The greenish-gray color of the crocodile distinguishes it easily from the dark brownish-black of the alligator.

Turtles are familiar reptiles. Thousands of small turtles pass through pet stores on their way to fish bowls. And it is not uncommon to find a pet box turtle or painted turtle thriving in a backyard enclosure or pond.

Many people are confused about such names as tortoise, terrapin, and turtle.

Fig. 31-11. The American alligator, found in the warmer parts of the United States, is usually about ten feet long when it has reached adult size.

Fig. 31-12. Here are four different species of turtles. Top left: box turtle; top right: painted turtle; bottom left: snapping turtle; bottom right: soft-shelled turtle.

Biologists speak of land-living turtles as *tortoises*. Their feet have strong claws for digging and walking on land, but lack a web for swimming. They refer to fresh-water turtles, especially the hard-shelled edible varieties, as *terrapins*. These turtles have claws and webs, especially in the hind feet. The large ocean-dwelling forms with limbs in the form of flippers are *true turtles*. However, for convenience, we will refer to all of them as turtles.

What the turtle lacks in speed and agility on land, it makes up for in protection. The ribs are enormously widened and joined edge to edge. They are covered, in most species, with the horny plates of an upper shell. The under side is protected by a lower shell. The

two shells join in a bridge along the sides. The amount of protection given by the shell varies in different species. The *soft-shelled turtle* has a leathery upper shell and an extremely small lower shell.

The *snapping turtle* has a hard upper shell and a small lower shell. It cannot pull its limbs and tail into the shell entirely, but it has a large head, long neck, and powerful jaws which can bite off a finger. The *painted turtle* and many other species have large upper and lower shells into which the head, limbs, and tail can be completely drawn. The greatest shell protection is found in the *box turtle* which can close its whole shell by bending a hinge in the lower part.

Fig. 31-13. The largest living land turtle is the giant Galapagos tortoise. It weighs about 300 pounds and can easily carry a man on its back.

Turtles have no teeth. The food is cut on a sharp beak and swallowed in chunks. Because of its shell, a turtle cannot expand its ribs. Air is drawn into the mouth by lowering the throat as in the case of the frog.

More than 50 species of turtles are found in the United States and in the waters off our coasts. We will discuss only a few of the better-known species. Various species of the *box turtle* range over much of the United States. The eastern form is most widely distributed. This turtle lives in the woods and fields and may enter ponds. Food consists of earthworms, grubs, and other small animals as well as berries, tender shoots, and other plant parts. The shells of box turtles vary widely in markings. The eastern form often has yellow lines and E-like markings on an olive or brownish background.

In Conclusion

The vast expanses of the tropics have been a refuge for many rare reptile species. But in most regions of the earth, reptiles are secondary to birds and mammals.

Long ago when reptiles ruled the earth, a strange creature about the size of a crow glided from the trees. What sort of creature was it? Biologists found its fossil remains and named it Archaeopteryx (ark-ee-*op*-tear-iks), a name meaning "ancient bird." It had a long beak with teeth set in sockets. Feathers grew from the forelimbs forming wings, but each wing had three claws. Its long lizardlike tail had two rows of feathers. Was it reptile or bird? Biologists class it with the birds, but it couldn't compare with a modern bird in efficiency. In the next chapter, we will discover how nature modified certain vertebrates for life in the air and produced her most perfect flying machines, the birds.

Questions for Review

1. What are three groups of living reptiles native to North America?

2. What four characteristics of reptiles distinguish them from other vertebrates you have studied?

3. What use does the snake make of its tongue?

4. Describe three methods by which various snakes capture their prey.

5. How is the snake's mouth adapted for swallowing large prey?

6. By what means do snakes move around?

7. Name three nonpoisonous snakes of your region.

8. What four groups of poisonous snakes are found in North America?

9. List the steps in treating a victim of the bite of a poisonous snake in the order in which you would carry them out.

10. Name three lizards of North America.

11. In what respect is the Gila monster an unusual lizard?

12. What characteristics of a crocodile distinguish it from an alligator?

Biologically Speaking

antivenin	ovoviviparous	tortoise
constrictor	pit viper	turtle
fang	quadrate bone	venom
oviparous	terrapin	viviparous

Applying Facts and Principles

1. In what respects are reptiles better suited to life on land than are amphibians?

2. Make a list of possible reasons for the disappearance of the dinosaurs.

3. Why do you think the eggs of reptiles require a shell while those of fish and frogs do not?

4. Account for the fact that many unusual and rare animals are found today only on islands.

5. What arguments can you give for conservation of snakes, especially the nonpoisonous species?

6. Why do turtles whose normal habitat is water come on land in order to lay their eggs?

CHAPTER 32

Nature's Flying Machines—the Birds

For centuries, man watched the birds soaring easily through the sky and wished that he, too, could fly. Several early inventors even made large wings which they strapped to their arms in the hope that they could soar in the air. But such experiments only ended in exhaustion and disappointment. With all our adaptations and abilities, we lack the power in our shoulders and arms to fly, even with perfectly designed wings. Look at a bird and you will see what it takes to fly.

Blue-winged teal ducks cut through the air with outstretched necks at 90 miles an hour. The ruddy turnstone flies each autumn from Alaska to Hawaii in a single flight. And the golden plover flies from northern Canada to southern South America, a distance of 8,000 miles and later makes a return trip. These records compare favorably with those of transcontinental planes, even in this age of jet propulsion.

No forms of life have challenged the birds in the air. They have an advantage over all other living things in being able to change environments as conditions may require. Birds have spread their numbers from the jungles of the tropics to the wastelands of the polar regions, and from mountain top to valley. They vary in size from the tiny humming bird to the ostrich.

The food of various birds includes the nectar of flowers, seeds, insects, worms, fish, and even other birds and smaller animals. The variation in the form and use of the beaks and feet, protective coloration, nesting habits, care of the young, migration, and many other phases of the lives of birds are interesting studies in adaptation. Nature has given the birds many advantages in the struggle for survival in the living world.

Characteristics of birds. While birds vary greatly in form, size, diet, and life habits, they have certain characteristics in common. The following distinguish them easily from the other vertebrates: (1) body covering of feathers; (2) bones light, porous, and air-filled; (3) forelimbs (arms) developed as wings for locomotion (in most birds) and never for grasping; (4) body supported on two limbs; (5) mouth provided with a horny, toothless beak; (6) eggs with a protective shell and, in most cases, incubated in a nest; (7) warm-blooded; and (8) heart divided into four chambers.

Adaptations for flight. Did you ever compare a bird with an airplane? We probably got our first ideas for airplane design from the birds.

The body is streamlined and cuts through the air with a minimum of resistance. The beak and head are pointed and serve to reduce air resistance. Then the air sweeps along the body, made smooth by feathers. The body tapers at the tail where large feathers

Fig. 32-1. The ability of birds to fly enables them to migrate easier and further than most animals. Here you see wild geese in flight. Notice how they fly in wedge-shaped formation.

act as a steering device. The wings are attached high on the body at the center of gravity. " Fore and aft " balance are provided by the head and neck and the posterior part of the body, legs, and tail.

The wings are rounded and thicker on the front edge and taper on the rear edge. Look at the wing of a bird and see how we have duplicated this principle in the airplane. The wings of a bird can be tilted to give upsweep or downsweep or act as a break. The wings of an airplane have ailerons. The airplane tail has a rudder and elevators. The porous bones of the bird give maximum support with minimum weight. We have learned to use aluminum and magnesium, both strong, light metals, in airplane construction. Most birds pull their feet against the body in flight. Did you ever watch an airplane fold its landing gear? Compare a bird and an airplane. You may find still other similarities in these two flying machines.

Structure and functions of feathers. Strange as it may seem, feathers are modified scales. Some unchanged scales remain on the feet and legs of birds to remind us of the relationship of birds to reptiles. Feathers develop from pits in the skin. They grow in lines which lie in only certain regions of skin. However, the feathers spread out to cover featherless regions. There are four kinds of feathers.

Soft *down feathers* form the plumage of newly hatched birds. In older birds, especially waterfowl, they form an insulation close to the skin. Down reduces heat loss so efficiently that a bird can fly through cold winter air and still maintain a body temperature of over 100° F. The slender hairlike feathers

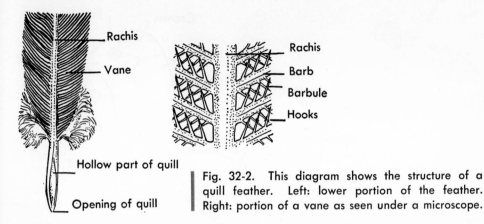

Rachis

Vane

Hollow part of quill

Opening of quill

Rachis

Barb

Barbule

Hooks

Fig. 32-2. This diagram shows the structure of a quill feather. Left: lower portion of the feather. Right: portion of a vane as seen under a microscope.

with a tuft on the end are known as **pin-feathers.**

Contour feathers cover the body and round out the angles, giving the bird a smooth outline. They also form an effective shield against injury and provide the coloration so important in the life of a bird. Often the female blends more closely with the surroundings than her brightly-colored mate. **Quill feathers** grow in the wing and tail. These large feathers provide the surface the bird needs in flying and steering in flight.

Fig. 32-2 shows the structure of a quill feather. A broad **vane** spreads from a central axis, the **rachis** (*ray*-kis). The rachis ends in a hollow **quill.** If you magnify the vane, you can see the many rays or **barbs.** Each barb is like a tiny feather with many projections, the **barbules** (little barbs). These are held together with tiny interlocking hooks. This complicated arrangement makes the vane strong, light, and elastic. If a vane is " split," the bird shakes its feathers and locks the barbules together again. Or it may preen the feather by drawing it through its beak, making it whole again. The rachis is grooved and the quill hollow, a condition which gives a feather the greatest strength with the least weight. At the

base of the quill is an opening through which nourishment is supplied while the feather is growing.

The vane of the wing feather is wider on one side than the other. When the wing strikes the air in a power stroke, the vane turns up and rests against its neighbor. On the return stroke it is free to turn. The air passes through the wing as each feather turns slightly on its axis (feathering) and the wing meets less air resistance.

You have probably noticed birds oiling their feathers after a bath or a swim. They transfer oil from a gland at the base of the tail and spread it over the surface of the feathers. This makes them waterproof. Oil on the feathers is vital to swimming and diving birds such as ducks, geese, swans, loons, and grebes. Not only does water not penetrate the feathers to the skin, but also this oil makes the birds buoyant and prevents chilling of the body.

Molting in birds. The bird sheds its feathers at least once a year. Feathers, especially those of the wings and tail, may be lost or broken, and since molting usually occurs in the late summer, the bird is provided with new quills before the fall migrations. A second partial molt often occurs in the spring before the breeding season. This molt

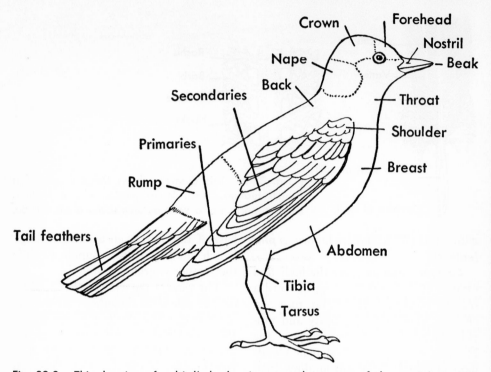

Fig. 32-3. This drawing of a bird's body gives you the names of the most important feathers and the various other external parts.

provides the bright breeding plumage of many birds. In some species, including the ptarmigan (*tar*-mih-gan), two complete seasonal molts occur. The early summer molt provides a plumage which blends with rocks and soil. The fall molt arrays the bird in a snow white winter plumage.

The new feathers grow from the same pits from which the old ones are shed. In most species, the wing feathers are shed gradually and in pairs. This allows the bird to fly during the molt.

A bird's wing is a modified forelimb adapted entirely for flight. You can see the resemblance to your own arm if you examine a chicken wing closely. The upper arm is a large single bone which is attached to the shoulder at a ball and socket joint. The part corre-

sponding to the lower arm has two bones like your own. The end section includes the wrist and the hand. This is covered with skin and contains the partial bone structure of a thumb and two fingers.

The shoulder is braced by three bones in a tripod arrangement: (1) the *shoulder blades* are embedded in the muscles of the back; (2) the *collarbone* (wishbone) extends from each shoulder to the breastbone; and (3) the *coracoid* (kor-ah-koid) *bones* also brace the shoulder against the breastbone. Thus the wing is firmly braced to withstand the tremendous force required in flying.

The muscles necessary to power the wings are enormous. Let's compare the human body with a one-pound pigeon and see how much power it would take to fly. A pigeon of this size has a

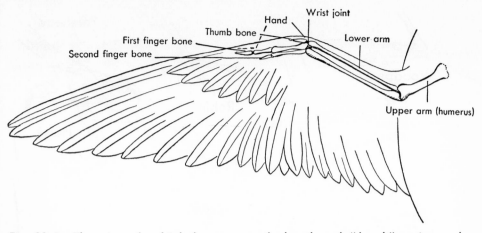

First finger bone
Second finger bone
Thumb bone
Hand
Wrist joint
Lower arm
Upper arm (humerus)

Fig. 32-4. The wing of a bird shows a greatly lengthened "hand" region and a reduced number of "fingers."

wing spread of about two feet. This would mean that a person of about 110 pounds weight would have to swing through the air a pair of wings each from 50 to 70 feet long. And they would have to swing these wings at a rate of 100 to as many as 500 strokes per minute! Try to swing your arm at this rate for a minute!

The muscles of the lower arm bend the hand at the wrist. Those of the upper arm move the lower arm. These muscles are involved in folding the wings. But the movement of the wings in flight is largely a movement at the shoulder. These muscles are enormous and in many birds make up one-third or more of the whole body weight. The breast muscles are attached to the greatly enlarged breastbone and form the white meat. These muscles of a chicken or turkey are tender and light in color because the birds do not fly. Tendons from these muscles pass over the shoulder like ropes over pulleys. This gives tremendous leverage in the operation of the wings.

The longest quill feathers, the **primaries,** grow from the end section of the wing, where leverage is the great-

est. The quills of these feathers are covered by small **secondaries.** These, in turn, are covered by other rows both above and below. The outline of the wing as a whole is concave on the lower side, thick on the forward edge, and thin and flexible on the rear edge and tip — a perfect design for flight.

Motion of the wings in flight. You might compare the motion of a bird's wings in flight to a horizontal figure eight — down and back, up and forward. The down stroke is the power stroke. The upward movement returns the wing to position for another power stroke. These two actions of the wing require two sets of muscles, arranged in layers on the breast. You may have noticed that these layers separate on the breast of a chicken. The tougher muscles of the outer layer pull the wing down in a power stroke. Those of the more tender inner layer raise the wing for the next stroke.

Structure of the legs and feet. The hip joint of a bird is high on the back. The body hangs suspended between the legs. This gives ideal balance and lets the bird bend easily to pick up food.

Though you may not realize it, man

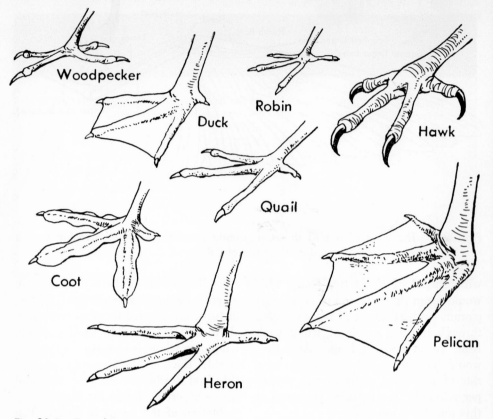

Fig. 32-5. For what type of activity is each of these types of bird's feet best adapted?

has a much greater balance problem in walking. The baby has to learn to walk and falls many times in the process, but walking or hopping is natural with the young bird because it has no balance problem.

The thigh extends from the hip to the knee joint. The lower leg is the familiar drumstick. The second bone of the lower leg is the small, long " sliver " you find along the drumstick. The heel joint is just below the feather line. What appears to be the leg is really a greatly lengthened foot, covered with scales in most birds but bearing feathers in many species.

The feet of various birds differ widely in structure, depending on the particular purpose required. Some are adapted for perching or climbing. Others are adapted for swimming or for scratching or, like the hawk, for catching food. See the table on page 413 for examples of these foot adaptations and note how widely they differ.

How a bird perches. When at rest or asleep, the bird usually perches on a support. The tendon that closes the claws passes over the leg joints; hence the more the leg is bent, the tighter the claws close up. Thus, when the bird settles down on a branch to sleep, the more it relaxes and the more its legs bend, the closer the claws grasp the perch. This and the balancing adaptations enable birds to cling to a swinging twig when awake, or to a perch when asleep.

TYPES OF FEET		
STRUCTURE OF TOES	EXAMPLES	ADAPTED FOR
3 front; 1 rear	Songbirds	Perching
2 front; 2 rear	Woodpecker	Climbing
All webbed, separate	Coot	Swimming
All webbed, united	Pelican	Swimming
3 webbed, united	Duck, goose	Swimming
3 front; 1 rear (heavy claws)	Hawk, owl, eagle	Catching prey
Small, weak	Hummingbird, swift	Little used
Long legs	Crane, heron, snipe	Wading
Legs short, far back	Loon, duck	Diving

The structure of the bird's head and neck. With the forelimbs developed as wings, the head and neck must assume most of the functions performed by the hands or forefeet of other animals. The bird's neck is long and flexible. This aids in balance and permits free movement of the head.

Sense organs are located on the head. The eyes are large and the sense of sight is very keen. It is said that some birds, especially hawks and owls, have vision eight times as keen as that of man. Owls and certain other birds have excellent vision in the dark due to the peculiar structure of their eyes. Birds have a remarkable ability to judge distance both at close range and at great height. They can drop out of the sky and light on a rock in a stream, fly through a deep woods, or swoop down onto a slender perch. The eyes are protected by an upper and a lower eyelid as well as a thin transparent third eyelid, or *nictitating membrane.*

Ear canals are covered by a tuft of feathers. Eustachian tubes lead from the ears to a single opening in the upper wall of the throat. The sense of hearing is very keen and the ears are especially sensitive to high notes.

The sense of smell is very poor. The sense of taste also is poorly developed. This is due in part to the horny nature of the mouth.

The *beak* is light, strong, and horny. The tongue of most birds is small and serves as an organ of touch. The beaks of various birds vary greatly with the nature of the food and the manner in which the bird catches it. Like the feet, the beak has special adaptations, as you can see by referring to the table on page 415.

Birds eat various kinds of food. Certain birds eat animal food exclusively, others are strict vegetarians, while many use a mixed diet. Their intense activity requires large amounts of food.

Since birds require so much food, they seem to be eating nearly all the time. Watch any common bird, such as a robin, for a few minutes to observe the way it eats. Robins are ground-feeders and you can see them searching the lawn for insects and earthworms. Both sight and hearing seem to be used to locate their quarry. A swift motion

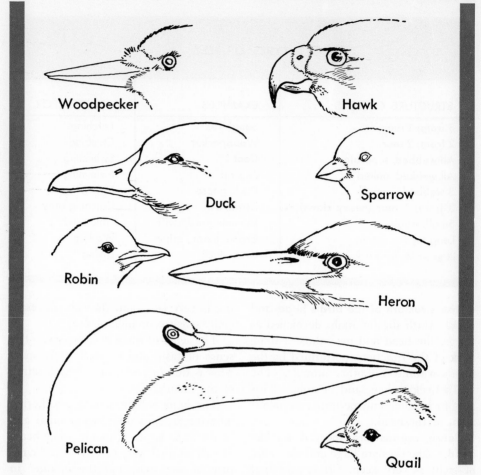

Fig. 32-6. The beaks of these birds vary greatly with the food they eat. Name the food that makes up the diet of each of these.

of the beak usually secures it, though an earthworm, with its tail securely anchored in its burrow, sometimes requires a considerable amount of pulling.

Most birds drink by taking a beakful of water and tilting back the head so that it will run down their throat. They drink large quantities of water, especially in hot weather, and they also frequently enjoy bathing their feathers. One of the easiest ways to attract birds is to provide them with a shallow dish of water for a bird bath. The edges and bottom should be rough enough to afford safe footing and the bath should

be put where cats or birds of prey cannot attack its visitors.

Among birds using animals for food are large birds of prey, such as hawks and owls, which feed on rats, rabbits, field mice, and other small animals, as well as on some other birds. There are many whose diet is largely or entirely fish which they catch by diving. Such birds as the loon, grebe, pelican, and kingfisher do this. Some, like the vulture or buzzard, are scavengers and eat any dead animal they can find; such birds have a very keenly developed sense of sight. Probably the largest number

TYPES OF BEAKS

KINDS	EXAMPLES	ADAPTED FOR
Hooked	Hawk, owl	Catching prey
Chisel-shaped	Woodpecker	Drilling in trees
Wide but weak	Nighthawk, swift	Catching insects on wing
Broad and notched	Duck	Scooping and straining
Slender and sensitive	Snipe	Probing in mud
Short and straight	Sparrow, finches	Crushing seeds
Notched and hooked	Parrot	Climbing
Crossed mandibles	Crossbill	Opening pine cones
Slender tube	Hummingbird	Sucking nectar

of birds which enjoy an animal diet live chiefly on insects which they may catch in the air (swifts), in wood (woodpecker), on the ground (robins), or on trees (warblers).

Many birds live almost exclusively on seeds, doing much good by the destruction of weed seeds, while others, such as blackbirds and bobolinks, do considerable damage by their preference for grain, peas, and rice. Various kinds of both wild and cultivated fruits, especially berries, are preferred by certain birds.

Sometimes birds enjoy the same seeds or fruits that man raises, or they may at times rob his yard of a stray chicken. But very careful study has proved that there are only three or four birds which do more harm than good. The rest many times repay for their fruit by destruction of insects and vermin. Birds in whose favor little can be said are the Cooper's and sharp-shinned hawks, great horned owl, starling, and English sparrow. The first three destroy poultry and useful birds, while the sparrow drives away many valuable and attractive native songbirds.

The digestive system of the bird. The bird is the first warm-blooded animal we have studied. A constant body temperature as high as 112° F. is maintained in some species. The maintenance of this high temperature, together with the tremendous muscular exertion during flight, requires that the bird's body be a highly efficient, living power plant. The systems which supply this great energy need are highly developed.

As with an engine running at full throttle, much of the time the fuel need of a bird is proportionally greater than that of other animals. Birds spend much of their time eating. To say that someone has an "appetite like a bird" is actually no compliment.

Food is swallowed whole down a long esophagus into a large **crop,** located just below the base of the neck. Here the food is stored and moistened. The crop permits a bird to eat a large amount of food and digest it later on. From the crop, food passes into the first division of the *stomach* where glands in the thick walls add *gastric fluid,* a digestive secretion. The stomach content then

FOOD USED BY SOME OF OUR COMMON BIRDS

NAME OF BIRD	INSECT FOOD	VEGETABLE FOOD	RODENTS, ETC.	POSSIBLE HARM
Quail	Potato bugs, etc., 14%	Weed seed, 63%		
Woodpecker	Wood borers, ants			
Nighthawk	Grasshoppers, flying ants, fleas			
Kingbird	Flies, bees, beetles	Wild fruit		
Phoebe	Beetles, spiders, 93%	Wild fruit		
Bluejay	Harmful insects, 19%	Nuts, acorns	Mice, fish, salamanders	Eats some corn, eggs, young birds
Crow	Grasshoppers, beetles	Corn, wild fruit	Mice	Pulls corn, eats eggs, chicks, frogs
Red-winged blackbird	Grasshoppers, weevils	Weed seed, 57%		Grain, fruit, peas, corn
Meadow lark	Grasshoppers, etc., 73%	Weed seed, 12%		
Grackle	Insects, 35%	Grain, fruit	Mice and snails	Some fruit, grain
Junco	Beetles, caterpillars	Weed seed		
Field sparrow		Weed seed, mainly		
Swallow	Flies, ants, wasps, in enormous numbers			
Cedar waxwing	Insects, caterpillars	Wild fruit, seeds, 74%		Cherries, 5% Cultivated fruit, 13%
Wren	Insects, 98%			Some cultivated fruit
Robin	Grasshoppers, 43%, caterpillars	Wild fruit, 47%		
Bluebird	Insects, 76%	Wild berry seed		
Great-horned owl			Rabbits, rats, mice	Some native birds
Cooper's hawk			Rabbits, birds	Chickens, grouse
Sharp-shinned hawk			Mice, birds	Chickens, other birds

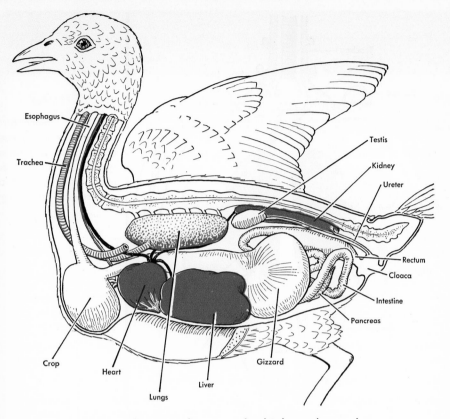

Esophagus

Trachea

Testis

Kidney

Ureter

Rectum

Cloaca

Intestine

Pancreas

Crop

Heart

Liver

Lungs

Gizzard

Fig. 32-7. The internal organs of a bird are shown above.

passes into the second stomach region, the **gizzard.** Here the thick muscular walls, aided by pebbles, churn and grind the food. A U-shaped loop of intestine joins a short **rectum,** or large intestine, which leads to a **cloaca** somewhat like that of the frog.

The two-lobed liver is large and may or may not have a gall bladder on the lower side, depending on the species of bird. Bile is poured into the small intestine through two ducts. The **pancreas** lies along the U-shaped portion of the small intestine and pours its secretion into the intestine through three ducts.

Respiration, circulation, and excretion in the bird. The lungs of a bird lie in the back against the ribs in the anterior region of the body cavity. The capacity of the lungs is greatly increased by a system of **air sacs** which extend from the lungs into the chest area and the abdomen and connect with cavities in the larger bones.

Air is drawn through the nostrils in the beak and down the **trachea** (*tray*-kee-ah) and its lower divisions, or **bronchi** (*bron*-kye) [sing. *bronchus*], to the lungs and air sacs by expansion of the chest and abdomen. Relaxation of the muscles in these areas forces air out. Though the lungs are small, a rapid rate of respiration fills them often. This supplies the blood with the great amount of oxygen necessary to carry on the high rate of oxidation in the body tissues.

The respiratory system of the bird is also its principal excretory system. It has no sweat glands and cannot elimi-

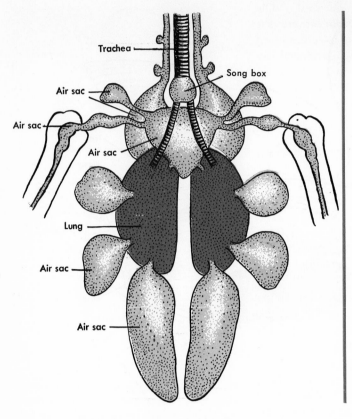

Trachea

Song box

Air sac

Air sac

Air sac

Lung

Air sac

Air sac

Fig. 32-8. Since birds are so active, they need a complete respiratory system to provide for rapid oxidation of food and release of energy.

nate heat through its skin. Most excess heat is discharged from the body through the lungs. The air sacs are believed to assist in heat elimination. You may have noticed that birds often pant with their mouths open on a hot day. At times like these, the insulation provided by feathers is more of a liability than an asset.

The lungs also supply air for singing. The bird's song is not produced in the throat, but at the base of the trachea, where it divides into the bronchi. Here is located the *song box,* a delicate and highly adjustable structure.

The *kidneys* are dark brown, three-lobed organs lying along the back. They excrete *uric acid,* a waste product of cell activity. This uric acid is discharged with very little water through the ureters into the cloaca. Waste from

the kidneys is excreted along with intestinal waste.

The *heart* of a bird is large and powerful. It consists of two thin-walled *auricles* and two muscular *ventricles.* The right side of this four-chambered heart receives blood from the body and pumps it to the lungs. Blood returns from the lungs to the left side and is pumped to the body. The heart of the bird beats at an amazing rate. With the bird at rest, the beat is several hundred times per minute. Under exertion, the heart may beat as many as a thousand times a minute.

The nervous system of a bird. In birds, the brain is large and broad, completely filling the cranial cavity. The *olfactory lobes* are small, indicating a poorly developed sense of smell. The *optic lobes* are large, thus accounting for the keen vision of the bird. The hemispheres of the **cerebrum** are the largest of any animal we have discussed thus far. The highly developed instincts of birds center in the brain region. The large **cerebellum** accounts for the excellent muscular coordination of the bird, especially in flight. The **medulla** joins the spinal cord, which extends down the back, encased in vertebrae.

The reproductive system. The oval **testes** of the male bird lie in the back in about the same position we found them in the male frog. Tiny tubes carry sperms to openings in the cloaca. During mating, sperm are deposited in the cloaca of the female.

The female reproductive organs include an **ovary** in which eggs develop and a long, coiled **oviduct** which leads to the cloaca. In most birds, the right ovary disappears early in life.

If you examine a hen you are preparing for dinner, you will find a mass of orange spheres in the region of the back. These are developing yolks. On the surface of each yolk is a tiny egg cell,

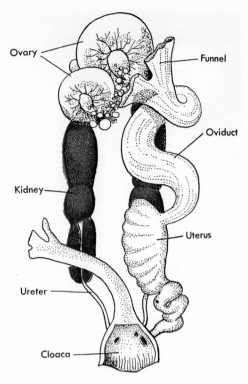

Fig. 32-10. The ovaries with immature eggs and oviduct are shown in this drawing of the reproductive system of a hen.

surrounded by protoplasm. When a yolk has grown to full size, it is drawn into the upper end of the oviduct by lashing cilia. As the yolk travels down the oviduct, it is surrounded with layers of **albumen** or " white of egg." Two enclosing membranes form around the albumen. Sometimes an egg is laid in this condition. We refer to it as a soft-shelled egg. Normally, a shell is secreted around the membranes by *lime-producing glands* in the lower part of the oviduct before it is laid.

Thus, we must distinguish between an *egg* and an *egg cell*. The tiny spot surrounded by protoplasm on the side of the yolk will develop into a new organism. It is the only living part of an egg. The protein of the albumen and oils of the yolk are stored nourishment

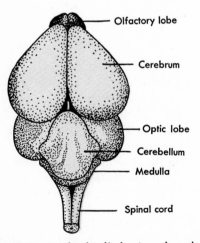

Fig. 32-9. In the bird's brain, what does the size of the olfactory lobe and optic lobe reveal about development of its senses?

Fig. 32-11. Ducklings hatch fully feathered and are able to feed themselves.

for the developing embryo. The shell prevents drying out, but must be porous enough to admit air. The pores are also large enough to admit bacteria, which accounts for the spoilage of eggs, especially in warm weather.

Incubation and development of a bird. An embryo can develop in an egg only if a sperm has fertilized the egg cell before the shell is formed. Development begins as soon as the egg is *incubated* or kept continuously warm. The mother provides this warmth by sitting on the egg. The incubation temperature of most birds is slightly above 100° F.

The time of incubation varies from 13 to 15 days in smaller birds to as many as 40 to 50 days in a large bird like the swan. The hen's egg is incubated 21 days, while that of a duck requires 28 days. It is usually the female which sits on the eggs. However, the male bird takes his turn in some species, including the ostrich. Just before hatching, the baby bird absorbs the remainder of the yolk. The shell is " pipped " in a line after which the baby bird pushes the shell halves apart and works itself out. Some birds have hardly any body covering when they are hatched. Others are covered with a dense coat of down.

Egg number and parental care. Birds like the robin, bluebird, sparrow, and warbler usually lay less than six eggs. Incubation starts when the last egg is laid. Thus the baby birds hatch at about the same time, but they are helpless and must be fed almost continuously by their parents. They remain in the nest until they are able to fly.

Hawks and owls usually lay only one to four eggs and incubate them as soon as each is laid. This results in a " stair step " family. The young of these birds, too, are fed in the nest until they are feathered and able to fly.

Ducks (except the wood duck), geese, quail, grouse, turkeys, chickens, and other fowl-like birds lay a much larger number of eggs in a nest on or close to the ground. The eggs are not incubated until the last one is laid. As many as 12 to 15 birds may hatch at the same time.

Getting acquainted with birds. In 1810, John James Audubon, an American naturalist who was also an artist, began his famous study of birds. He roamed the fields and forests for several years, making life-size drawings of each species he met. Then he took his work to England where he supervised the coloring of each drawing to be sure it was accurate. These were published a few years later as *The Birds of America,* in two large volumes.

From the time of Audubon, scores of other great **ornithologists,** who are students of birds, have added contributions to the study of bird life. Today, bird study is a highly organized science. National, state, and local bird societies list thousands of members in their roles.

Bird study is a delightful challenge. Distinctive marks like wing bars, white

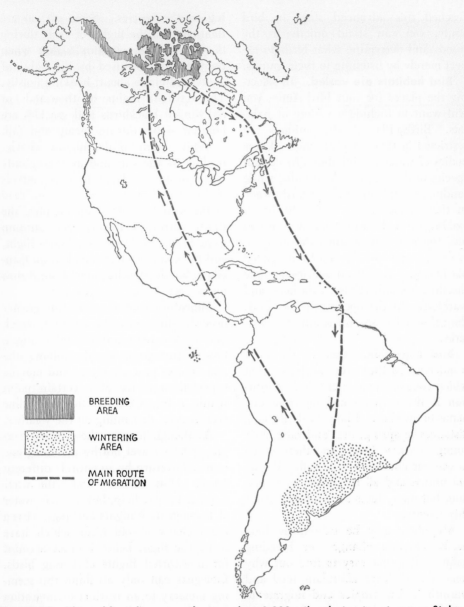

BREEDING
AREA

WINTERING
AREA

MAIN ROUTE
OF MIGRATION

Fig. 32-12. The golden plover travels more than 8,000 miles during its migratory flights.

outer tail feathers, a black band under the throat, or white lines on the crown may be a means of identifying a bird with only a brief glimpse. A good pair of field glasses will greatly help you in bird identification since even the trained ornithologist often has difficulty approaching them closely.

In addition to size, shape, and color, you can recognize birds by the way in which they fly, walk, hop about, and seek their food. Songs, too, are very characteristic. At first, most bird notes may sound alike, but you will soon learn to associate certain calls with the birds which make them. When you have reached this advanced stage in bird study, you can stand quietly in the woods and determine what birds to expect merely by listening to their sounds.

Bird habitats are varied. In selecting the places for your bird study, you will want to include a variety of habitats. Birds, like all other animals, are restricted in their surroundings. Large bodies of water are inhabited by certain species of ducks, loons, and gulls, while sandpipers and other shore birds wade in the shallow water along the beach looking for food. In the marsh, you will find the rails and herons, the bitterns, coots, swamp ducks, and red-winged blackbirds. Woodland species include the thrushes and orioles, thrashers, and warblers. In the open field, one finds the goldfinches, sparrows, and meadowlarks.

Bird migration. One of the most wonderful instincts of birds is that which controls their migration. *Migration* is the periodic moving from one home to another. Many birds fly long distances in spring, nest and raise their young in a new home, and then return to warmer climates in the fall. We do not understand all the causes of migration, but many facts are available about this activity.

Migration may be caused by food needs, climatic changes, or breeding habits. It is not easy to find out why some species leave abundant food and warmth in the tropics and migrate to breeding grounds in the far north. Much more explainable is the southward migration of insect-eaters when cold weather kills their prey, and the southward flight of water birds before the ponds and lakes freeze over. It is logical, too, that fruit and seed-eaters would tend to follow the crops.

Some make their migratory flights at night and some during the day, depending on the species. Some of you are familiar with the flights of geese during the spring and autumn nights when they become confused by the lights of a city and circle about, honking noisily. The daylight flights of thousands of red-winged blackbirds and grackles are familiar sights during spring and fall.

While many birds migrate slowly, feeding by the way and averaging only 20 to 30 miles a day, others are marvels of speed and endurance. As you read in the introduction to this chapter, the ruddy turnstone travels each autumn from Alaska to Hawaii in a single flight, and the golden plover travels from Canada to South America, more than 8,000 miles (see Fig. 32-12).

Migratory routes. An even greater mystery surrounds the instinct which governs the time and routes of migration. Any given species follows the same routes year after year and may be expected to arrive at a certain point within a few weeks of the same time each season, depending on the weather.

As though to vary the scenery, certain species travel northward along one route and return by an entirely different route. How do they know the way? Keen sight may help, but not over water or through dark nights and fogs. Even the memory of old birds which have made the flight before cannot account for unescorted flights of young birds. Biologists can only attribute the seeming memory to an instinct of migration and a " sense of direction " developed to a high degree.

Bird banding. This interesting phase of bird study is carried on by ornithologists all over the country. Individuals of certain species are caught in special cage traps, removed carefully, and marked with a light aluminum band. Each band contains the date of banding, the place, and the name of the in-

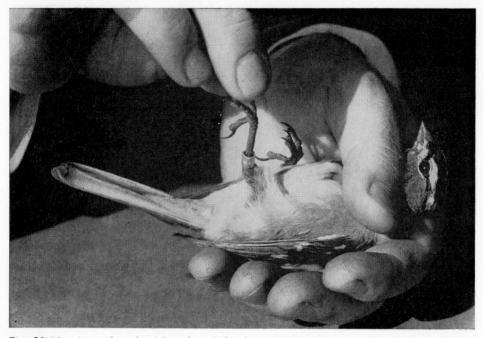

Fig. 32-13. How does bird banding help the ornithologist trace the migratory routes of birds?

dividual who caught the bird. It is then released to go its way. Later, it may be caught by another bird-bander who examines the band and reports its new location. Through the *Bird Banding Association* and other bird societies, records of banding and observations of banded birds are assembled. Bird banding is also valuable to determine the age to which a certain species may live.

Seasonal bird study. Migration adds much to the study of birds, for new species are arriving during many seasons of the year. Each locality has *permanent residents* which remain the year round. In addition, certain species may be present in the winter only, moving farther north with the coming of spring. These species are called *winter residents*. *Summer residents* spend the summers in a given locality and migrate southward with the approach of fall. Many species are found only at certain

times in the spring and fall. These are the *migratory birds* which are passing through a given locality on their journey between wintering areas farther south and breeding areas farther north.

Nest building. During the breeding season, the ornithologist watches carefully for nests in the variety of places birds choose to rear their young. The skilled observer may study nests and young birds with no annoyance to the parent birds. The place selected, form, and size of the nest, color and number of the eggs, and the way in which the parents rear the young are as characteristic as the birds themselves.

Next to migration, the highest development of bird instinct is shown in nest construction. Nests differ widely both as to materials and construction. Earth, clay, sticks, grass, hair, feathers, moss, and even string are used. The structure itself may vary from a mere hole

Fig. 32-14. The robin's nest (left) is rather bulky and clumsy, while that of the yellow-throated vireo (right) is dainty and cleverly woven from various plant fibers.

in the sand (ostrich) to the dainty nest of a vireo.

Kinds of nests. Water birds usually lay their eggs on rocks with only sticks enough to keep the eggs from rolling. The kingfisher and bank swallow dig holes in clay banks. Owls and woodpeckers live in excavated homes in dead trees.

Ducks and wading birds make simple grass nests. Orioles and vireos build long nests which hang securely from limbs. They weave these cleverly from horsehair and various plant fibers.

Each species builds its own nest in its own way, in the same general type of location, and of the same type of materials. See the table on page 425 for details.

Birds destroy many insects. Birds are the chief enemies of insects. There are about 13,000 species of birds in the world, of which about 850 live in North America and about 200 kinds may be found in one region. On the other hand, there are 15,000 species of insects within 50 miles of New York City, many of which are harmful to man. The fact that such hordes of insects are even partially held in check by

birds shows the services birds give.

Nature tends to establish a balance. Unfortunately, man often disturbs it. Native birds could completely regulate native insects, but man has introduced many insects from other countries, such as the gypsy moth and corn borer. These, not having their natural enemies to check them, multiply almost beyond the power of bird or man to control, and constitute one of our hardest problems. Without our bird allies, it would be insolvable.

Destruction of weed seeds. Look at the food table on page 416 and note that weed seeds constitute a large portion of the food of many birds.

Weeds cost the farmer many dollars to keep down. But sparrows, juncos, quail, and finches destroy thousands of tons of weed seeds each year.

Ornithologists have estimated that the tiny tree sparrow eats nearly one ounce of weed seeds every day. It is hard to say how much money this bird alone saves farmers of our country. But when we consider all the birds that eat these seeds, the figure is staggering. Without birds, weed control would probably be a losing battle.

NESTS OF SOME COMMON BIRDS

NAME	LOCATION OF NEST	MATERIAL AND DESCRIPTION
Kingfisher	Hole in bank	6 to 8 ft. deep; eggs on ground or on feathers
Woodpecker	Holes in trees	Usually cut into hollow or dead tree through side
Crested flycatcher	Holes in trees	Bulky, of grass, etc.; may use a snakeskin
Robin	On branch or crotch	Bulky, case of mud, grass-lined, heavy
Bluejay	On branches	Bulky, ragged, of twigs, leaves, rags, string, etc.
Crow	In trees	Very bulky, of sticks, cedar bark, sod, hair, etc.
Grebe	In bogs	Decayed damp plants
Red-winged blackbird	In bushes and reeds	Deep, mouth contracted, of grass and rushes
Phoebe	Under bridges, on houses or rocks	Moss, cemented with mud and lined with hair
Barn swallow	Hollow trees or eaves	Mud and straw, lined with hay or feathers
Chimney swift	Hollow trees, chimneys	Sticks glued with "saliva," cup-shaped
Whippoorwill	Dead leaves	No real nest, slight depression
Quail	Underbrush	Arch of vegetation over nest made of grass
Meadow lark	Underbrush	Similar to above, but smaller
Marsh wren	On reeds in swamps	Made of reeds and grass, down-lined; many dummy nests
Hummingbird	On high branches	Tiny, shallow nest, saddled onto branch, lichen-covered
Oriole	Overhanging branch of elm tree	Pendant, woven of hair, string, and grass
Oven bird	On ground	Under arch of grass, entrance at side

Fig. 32-15. The English sparrow drives away many native birds and is therefore not protected by bird laws.

Destruction of harmful mammals. Hawks, owls, and other birds of prey were formerly regarded as harmful, but recent studies have proved this to be false. Only five species are harmful, six are wholly beneficial and thirty chiefly so, and seven others do about equal amounts of good and harm.

Their eating of mice, rats, squirrels, rabbits, and other harmful animals more than pays for any poultry these birds may take. Of the diet of the *red-tailed hawk,* commonly called a " hen hawk," harmful mammals comprise 66 per cent, while poultry forms only 7 per cent. *Cooper's hawk* really should be called a " hen hawk " since poultry and wild birds constitute much of its fare. This hawk and the *sharp-shinned hawk, goshawk, great horned owl,* and *snowy owl* do more harm than good.

Harm done by birds. Three hawks and two owls have been mentioned as killers of wild and domestic birds. To this list should be added the English sparrow which drives away native birds, kills the young, and breaks up nests, especially of bluebirds and swallows. The starling is a similar pest in some regions. Both are immigrants and, lacking their natural enemies, have multiplied fast in their adopted country. Crows do considerable harm to corn and, together with their cousins the bluejays, destroy eggs and young of other birds. To balance this, both birds destroy many insects and it is doubtful if they ought to be killed except in regions where the harm they do is really serious.

Birds could hold their own against natural enemies if man would not interfere. It is important to remember that exterminating birds is likely to produce disastrous results in the upsetting of a normal biological balance. Destructive animals should be killed only to the extent demanded by control. This policy is undoubtedly a wiser one.

In Conclusion

A flock of wild geese winging their way southward in perfect V-formation, like a squadron of fighter planes, is a thrill to see. Who hasn't watched eagerly for the first robin or bluebird to announce the coming of spring in the northern states? Haven't you wondered what keeps the buzzard aloft as it glides lazily in the summer sky? Have you watched a tiny hummingbird pause briefly at a flower to drink a drop of nectar, then dart away with wings fluttering almost invisibly in a blur?

Birds are a subject of never-ending interest. Their bright colors and songs add beauty to the landscape. Their instincts have long been a subject of scientific study. Their bodies are models of flight engineering and aerodynamics. They contribute so much to the balance of nature we cannot be without them.

Protection of our birds is a major phase of conservation. We will discuss what you can do to help them in Chapter 54.

Our study of vertebrates now shifts to the highest class, the mammals.

Questions for Review

1. What are some characteristics of birds which make them ideally suited for life in the air?

2. Discuss the functions of four kinds of feathers forming the plumage of birds.

3. How do birds oil their feathers?

4. Where are the bird's powerful shoulder muscles used in flight located?

5. How does the attachment of the bird's legs provide excellent balance?

6. How can a bird sleep on a perch without losing its grip and falling off?

7. Where is the bird's song box located?

8. In what ways are air sacs important in the bird?

9. What advance in structure is shown in the bird heart?

10. How are the albumen and shell added to the yolk of a bird egg?

11. At approximately what temperature are the eggs of most birds incubated?

12. Describe several field identification marks which are used in distinguishing various birds.

13. For what purpose are birds banded by ornithologists?

14. What are some materials used by birds in making nests?

15. In what ways do birds render a valuable service to man?

Biologically Speaking

air sac	crop feathers	quill
albumen	game bird	quill feathers
barbs	gizzard	rachis
barbules	incubation	secondaries
bird banding	molting	song box
contour feathers	ornithologist	vane
coracoid bones	primaries	yolk

Applying Facts and Principles

1. Compare the amount of food consumed, rate of respiration, and oxidation in the bird with other vertebrates that you have studied.

2. Explain the meaning of the term, "warm-blooded," as it applies to birds.

3. Discuss the development of the special senses of birds.

4. Discuss the relation between parental care and the number of eggs laid.

5. Discuss several possible explanations for bird migration.

Fig. 32-16. Not all birds fly. Above are shown photographs of some that stay on the ground: an ostrich, a flock of penguins, and an Australian kiwi. Can you think of some others?

CHAPTER 33

Mammals—Highest Forms of Animal Life

Near the close of the Age of Reptiles, some 60 million years ago, a dramatic change was taking place in the animal population of the land masses. Giant reptiles which had ruled the earth unchallenged for many ages were disappearing. Mammals were replacing them. It was as though nature were encouraging the mammals in their struggle for supremacy.

To some extent, the mammals are a " super " group of more than 4,000 species. What the mammal may lack in special adaptations and in number of individuals is more than compensated for in superior development of the nervous system. This quality has placed the mammals above all other animal groups. But it remained for man, the most developed of all mammals, to gain domination of the earth. In structure, man resembles other mammals. In intelligence, however, he is far superior to even the most highly developed of them.

What are the characteristics of mammals? Mammals vary in size from the tiny *shrew,* less than two inches long, to the enormous *blue whale,* over 100 feet long. In their widely varied forms, mammals are found in all parts of the world except a few Pacific islands. They are for the most part land animals, although certain forms including the whale, sea cow, and porpoise have become adapted to life in the seas. Others, like the bat, have taken to the air. While a shrew and a whale or a mouse and an elephant may seem entirely different, size alone is the greatest difference. All mammals are fundamentally alike in body structure, and possess the following characteristics of the class *Mammalia:*

1. Young born alive and nourished during development in the body of the mother; hence, *viviparous,* except in the duckbill and the spiny anteater.

2. Young nourished after birth by milk secreted by the *mammary* (milk) *glands* of the female, a characteristic for which this class is named.

3. Body mostly covered with hair.

4. Cerebrum highly developed.

5. *Diaphragm* (breathing muscle) dividing the thoracic (chest) and abdominal cavities.

6. Two sets of teeth and fleshy lips usually present.

7. High circulatory development; left aortic arch only.

8. Seven cervical (neck) vertebrae.

The body covering of mammals usually consists of hair. Hairs grow from follicles deep in the skin. The roots are nourished by a blood supply. Oil glands lubricate the hair shaft. Tiny muscle fibers attach to the hair follicles and may change their angle in the skin in times of anger or fear or when the body surface is chilled. This causes

429

Fig. 33-1. The porcupine, a rodent, has stiff, sharp spines mingled with its hair.

the hair to " stand on end." You have seen the hair on the back of a dog or cat bristle when the animal was annoyed. The same mechanism causes " goose pimples " on your skin in areas where hairs are small or lacking.

The quills of a porcupine are interesting variations in the body covering of mammals. These are groups of modified hairs. They bristle from the back and tail. Contrary to common opinion, the porcupine cannot throw its quills. However, a quick whip of its tail can

Fig. 33-2. The special body covering of the armadillo acts much like a coat of armor. Modified hairs makes up the shell.

sink a mass of quills deep into the skin of an annoying animal.

Many horny structures grow from the skin of mammals. Fingernails and toenails are examples of these. They grow from roots and lie over nailbeds of the fingers and toes. In many mammals, such as the dog, cat, and squirrel, they develop as claws.

The limbs of mammals are as varied as their environments. These modifications, especially of the forelimbs, have contributed much to the success of mammals in the world of life.

Have you ever considered how much you owe to the marvels of the human hand? Teamed with the brain, it can repair a watch, paint a portrait, play a musical instrument, rivet the girders in a skyscraper, or perform a delicate surgical operation. Much of the progress of the human race has involved the hand. The limbs of the other mammals are just as vital to their lives.

Most mammals have two pairs of limbs, but there are exceptions even to this. Whales and sea cows have lost all external evidence of hind limbs. The forelimbs are modified into finlike organs for swimming. Unlike the fins of a fish, however, these fins contain the bone structure of a hand.

Seals and walruses have limbs in the form of flippers. They make these mammals powerful and graceful swimmers. But on land they serve as little more than props and levers to propel the animals with a clumsy, bouncing motion.

In the bat, long bony fingers support a thin membrane which forms a winglike organ for flight. The hind limbs are small and of little use, except to grasp a perch when the bat folds its wings, hangs upside down, and sleeps through the day.

The horse, cow, bison, antelope, and

deer have limbs modified for running on hard ground. The toes form a hard hoof capable of supporting great weight. Smaller animals, like the dog, fox, and wolf, have separate toes adapted for running on land. The lynx, lion, tiger, and other members of the cat family use their limbs for running, climbing, defense, and food-getting. Strong toes equipped with sharp claws rip the flesh of an enemy or prey. The squirrel, raccoon, and opossum have flexible claws adapted for climbing. Squirrels, especially, are masters in climbing, running through tree tops, and leaping from tree to tree.

Fig. 33-3. The limbs of the tiger, like those of all cats, are especially adapted for running, defense, and food-getting.

The teeth of mammals are of four kinds. We classify them as: (1) *incisors;* (2) *canines;* (3) *premolars;* and (4) *molars.* These four kinds of teeth are developed about equally in the human mouth. Your front teeth are incisors. The canines, sometimes called " eye teeth," are near the corners of the mouth. Next in order come the premolars, and finally the jaw teeth or molars.

Gnawing mammals like the beaver, porcupine, and rat have enormously developed incisors. These chisel-shaped teeth in the front of each jaw grow rapidly and replace the cutting edges as they wear down. Greatly enlarged canine teeth form the " fangs " of the dog, cat, bear, and weasel. These powerful teeth are used for ripping flesh. Large premolars and molars of the vegetarian mammals, like the horse and cow, serve for grinding hard plant substances.

The brain of a mammal is proportionally larger than that of any other animal. The *olfactory lobes* are well developed and provide a keen sense of smell in many mammals, including the dog, cat, skunk, and deer. The *cerebrum* (*ser*-eh-brum) is by far the largest

brain region in the mammal. The surface is greatly increased by numerous rounded ridges known as **convolutions** (con-voh-*lu*-shuns). Optic lobes are not present as separate brain regions as they were in lower vertebrates. The optic nerves lead to regions in the lower posterior area of the cerebrum where sight occurs. The *cerebellum* (ser-eh-*bel*-um) is large, thus accounting for the excellent muscular coordination of mammals. The short medulla lies below the cerebrum.

Many mammals respond to training. Mammals learn to associate a particular kind of behavior with certain conditions. For example, certain dogs can be trained to retrieve a pheasant or quail shot down by a hunter. A bear can be trained to ride a bicycle. And a sea lion can balance a ball on its nose.

Biologists classify many of these activities as *conditioned reflexes.* They are activities which become automatic after a period of training. You can compare them with such activities as riding a bicycle or driving an automobile. While conditioned reflexes in mammals involve the brain, they are not on the level of intelligence. The animal trainer does not teach his lions to jump through

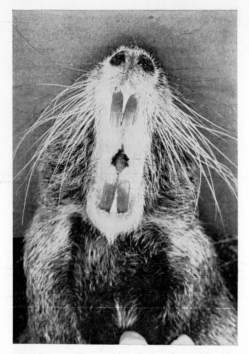

Fig. 33-4. The teeth of a rodent, like the nutria shown here, are used especially for gnawing. Note the four prominent incisors.

hoops in the way your teacher taught you to read. During a long training period, they associate the leap with a command or a crack of a whip.

Many mammals make long journeys from one place to another. In some cases, this migratory journey is necessary because of seasonal changes in the food supply. Other mammals migrate to a more favorable climate regardless of food supply. Still others make seasonal journeys to regions where they can produce their young under the most favorable conditions.

Among the most remarkable migrations is that of the fur seal. During the winter, females, young males, and pups roam the waters of the Pacific Ocean as far south as California. The older males winter in the cold waters near

Alaska and the Aleutian Islands. With the approach of the breeding season in spring, the males migrate to the Pribilof Islands, a group of small rocky islands in the Bering Sea, north of the Aleutians. The males arrive several weeks before the females and battle for a " territory " on one of the islands. The females and young seals start their long journey of 3,000 miles or more to the Pribilofs in spring and arrive in June. A herd of 50 or more females gathers around each male. Pups from the past year's breeding are born almost immediately and within a week, breeding occurs again. After this, the seals migrate southward.

The seasonal migration of the elk is easily observed in the Yellowstone Park region. During the summer, elk live on the higher mountains at altitudes above 8,000 feet. Early in September small herds move down the mountains to winter quarters in protected valleys. As spring approaches, the herds move back up the slopes in long, single file processions.

Some mammals hibernate. Various mammals differ in degrees of inactivity and hibernation during the winter months. The woodchuck (groundhog) and ground squirrels enter a period of true *hibernation* during which the body processes slow down to a point approaching death. The heartbeat may slow down to four or five beats per minute. The body temperature may drop to as low as 45° F. Breathing may occur at a rate as low as once in five minutes. The animal lies in a stupor and cannot be awakened.

The bear enters a period of winter sleep, but does not hibernate in the true sense. Heartbeat and respiration slow down and the animal lives on stored food in its body. However, a high body temperature is maintained. The bear may wake up on a mild day and even walk about before continuing its winter nap. The skunk, raccoon, and opossum undergo a partial winter hibernation similar to that of the bear.

Mammals have a highly efficient method of reproduction. Development of the embryo takes place within the mother's body (except in one Order) and may require from a few weeks to nearly two years. The mother's blood supplies nourishment to the developing young until they are born.

Eggs develop in female organs called **ovaries.** The two ovaries are located in the lower abdominal cavity. Several eggs may mature at the same time, coming from both ovaries. This results in multiple births as in the case of dogs, cats, rabbits, swine, and other mammals. Or a single egg may develop in most cases, as in the case of horses, cows, and elephants.

When an egg matures, it leaves the ovary by passing through a tube called the oviduct. Many tiny cilia fan the egg into the funnel-like opening of the **oviduct** (*oh*-vih-duct) which connects the ovary with the **uterus** (*yew*-teh-russ). The uterus is the organ in which the young organisms are nourished until the time when they are born. In some mammals the uterus is divided into a left and right portion which join at the lower ends. In others, both oviducts lead to a single uterus.

If the animal has mated, sperms from the male have migrated through the uterus and up the oviducts. The mature egg meanwhile passes down an oviduct. Thus the union of egg and sperm, known as **fertilization,** takes place somewhere in the oviduct.

Division of the fertilized egg begins immediately. The first division results in a two-celled condition. These cells divide to form four, and so on until a

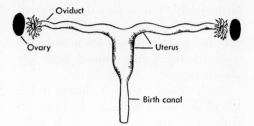

Fig. 33-5. The reproductive organs of a female mammal are shown in this drawing.

many-celled, ball-shaped structure is produced. As growth of the mass continues, it moves down the oviduct and enters the uterus, where it becomes attached to the wall of the uterus. As the embryo continues to develop, an absorbing structure, known as the **placenta** (pla-*sen*-ta) spreads over the inner membrane of the uterus. A cord called the **umbilical** (um-*bil*-ih-kal) **cord** leads from the placenta to the embryo. Blood flows from the embryo in arteries which lead through the umbilical cord to the placenta. The arteries branch into numerous thin-walled capillaries in the placenta. Here the blood of the embryo comes into close contact, but *does not mingle,* with the blood of the mother. Blood returns from the placenta to the embryo through a vein in the umbilical cord.

As blood from the embryo circulates through the placenta, it receives oxygen and dissolved food materials from the mother's blood. Carbon dioxide and cell wastes are poured into the mother's blood stream.

Later in the development, the embryo is called a **foetus** (*fee*-tus). At the end of its term of development in the uterus, or **gestation** (jes-*tay*-shun) **period,** the foetus is forced through the birth canal leading from the uterus. Soon after the young mammal is born, the placenta is loosened from the wall of the uterus and passes through the birth canal. This is sometimes referred to as the " after-birth." The mother cuts the cord with her teeth and thus separates the young animal from the placenta.

Birth brings a sudden change in the life of the young animal. Its lungs fill with air for the first time. Body nourishment must now come from its own digestive system. However, the mother will supply this nourishment for some time in the form of milk secreted by the mammary glands in her breasts.

There are variations in periods of gestation. Among the shortest is that of the opossum, which lasts about 13 days. The young are born prematurely and are so small that several can rest in the bowl of a teaspoon. They continue to develop in a brood pouch of the mother containing the mammary glands.

The table on this page shows the approximate gestation periods of several well-known mammals.

Young mammals must have parental care. Mice and rats are born hairless and blind. A baby bear, born during the winter hibernation, weighs less than a pound and does not open its eyes for six weeks.

On the other hand, a cow or a horse is born in a much more advanced condition and can stand and nurse and walk with the mother a few hours after birth.

The young whale, born in the water after a long gestation period, is large and well developed. The new-born porpoise is half as long as its mother.

Mice, rabbits, and other small animals are prey for many carnivorous animals. They bear several litters, often numbering ten or more each season. Larger mammals produce a smaller number of young and provide parental care which results in a larger percentage of them maturing.

Homes of mammals. Many mammals range over a wide area and have no permanent shelter. However, certain kinds of mammals build more or less permanent homes.

One of the most familiar to visitors of the marsh is the muskrat house. These dome-shaped mounds of willow branches, sedge, cattail stems and leaves, grasses and mud, vary from the size of a bushel basket to eight or ten feet in diameter. The hollow interior may accommodate six or more muskrats. A hole near the water line serves as a door.

The circular lodge of the beaver has a floor just above the water level. The walls are made of sticks, plastered with mud and grass. Ten or more beavers may live in a single lodge. The woodchuck constructs a series of underground tunnels leading to grass-filled chambers.

GESTATION PERIODS

MAMMAL	PERIOD	MAMMAL	PERIOD
Opossum	13 days	Human	36 weeks
Mouse	21 days	Cow	41 weeks
Rabbit	30 days	Horse	48 weeks
Cat	63 days	Whale	20 months
Dog	63 days	Elephant	20 to 22 months
Pig	120 days		

Fig. 33-6. The beaver shows great ingenuity in constructing its lodges, or " houses," and dams across streams.

The nest usually has more than one exit.

The fox squirrels and gray squirrels of eastern United States build bulky nests of branches and leaves in tree tops. The cottontail rabbit makes a fur-lined nest in a shallow depression, but conceals it so perfectly you could almost step on it without noticing it.

Orders of mammals. Examples of twelve orders of mammals are shown in Fig. 33-7. We will discuss each of these orders and some of their better-known families briefly in a survey of the class, *Mammalia.*

Egg-laying mammals belong to the Monotremata (mon-oh-*tree*-mah-ta). This order of primitive mammals is represented by the duckbill and the spiny anteater. These mammals are of great interest to the biologist because they are so different from other members of the class. The duckbill is a small brown

animal, about 12 to 18 inches in length. It has waterproof fur like a beaver, webbed feet like a muskrat, and a horny bill like a duck. It lives in the streams of Australia and New Guinea where it probes in the mud with its curious bill in search of insects. Its home is a burrow dug several feet into a bank which ends in a grass-filled nest. The duckbill usually lays two or three eggs which resemble those of reptiles. After hatching, the young are nourished on milk. This milk which is secreted by the mammary glands is licked from the mother's fur.

The spiny anteater has a tubular bill and a long tongue, used in catching ants. Its body is covered with long spines resembling those of a porcupine. It lays two eggs which are placed in a brood pouch on its lower side. The young remain in the brood pouch several weeks before hatching.

Fig. 33-7. The principal orders of mammals are shown in this drawing.

Fig. 33-8. What adaptations of a mammal does the duckbill show?

Pouched mammals are classified as Marsupialia (mar-soo-pih-ay-lih-ah). What do the opossum and the kangaroo have in common? They certainly do not look alike. Nor are their diets similar. One lives in North America and the other in Australia and islands close by. But they do have one thing in common. Both have a brood pouch in which the young develop after premature birth. This characteristic sets the marsupials in a class by themselves. An opossum is born as a tiny, hairless creature less than an inch long. It could not possibly live outside its mother's brood pouch. Here it is nourished on milk from mammary glands for about two months before it is large enough to leave the pouch. From six to fifteen young are produced in one litter and a female usually bears two or three litters each year. The opossum usually sleeps curled up in a tree through the day. At night it roams the countryside in search of small birds and mammals, eggs, insects, and fruit.

The kangaroo is a helpless, naked creature about an inch in length at birth. It spends four months in the mother's brood pouch before venturing out. Even then, it scampers back to the protection of the pouch when frightened.

Toothless mammals are grouped together as the Edentata (ee-den-tay-tah). In this order we include the armadillo, sloth, and anteater. Actually, they are not entirely toothless, but teeth are absent in front. If we were to rate the mammals on the basis of brain development, this group would be far down the scale. Various species of armadillos live in our southwestern states, Mexico, Central and South America. Our North American species is known as the nine-banded armadillo. It hides in a burrow during the day and spends its nights digging in the ground for insects. The young of the armadillo are identical quadruplets. They start life as a single egg. Separation of cells early in development results in four individuals which ordinarily would have been one.

The sloth is a bearlike creature of the jungles of Central and South America.

Fig. 33-9. Marsupials, like the kangaroo, have a brood pouch in which the young develop after birth.

It hangs upside down on tree limbs with long claws and moves in slow motion in search of leaves, its chief diet. In some species, the hair is green due to the presence of minute algae which grow in the hair.

Marine mammals — Cetacea (see-tay-she-ah) and Sirenia (sy-ree-nee-ah). It is highly probable that the members of these two orders have developed from mammals which originally lived on land and then took up life in the sea at some early period.

Whales, dolphins, and porpoises belong to the order *Cetacea*. The *blue whale* is the largest living animal and probably the largest which ever lived. Specimens may reach a length of 100 feet or more and weigh as much as 150 tons.

The head of the sperm whale con-

tains an enormous reservoir of oil which is used commercially as a lubricant and as a base for cosmetic creams. The most valuable product of this whale is *ambergris* (*am*-ber-greese), a secretion of the intestine. For centuries sailors have watched for ambergris floating on the ocean. Its principal use is in the manufacture of perfumes.

Dolphins are smaller relatives of the whale, usually under ten feet in length. They travel in herds in the ocean bays and mouths of rivers. Porpoises also travel in herds, often close to moving ships and delight the passengers with their graceful leaps. They feed on fish which they catch in their narrow tooth-lined jaws.

Sea cows belong to the order *Sirenia*. These large-bodied mammals reach a weight of one ton. The large rounded head resembles that of a walrus. The tail is fishlike. Sea cows live in shallow stretches of warm oceans close to the coast. They feed on algae and other marine plants.

Insect-eating mammals are known as the Insectivora (in-sek-*tiv*-oh-rah). Moles and shrews are the best-known mammals of this order. The *mole* spends its life underground, digging long burrows just below the surface. Its long nose is adapted for rooting out grubs and worms in the soil. Its small sightless eyes are covered with skin. Its soft fine fur is valuable for making coats and capes. While the mole is valuable in destroying many harmful beetle grubs, it is a pest in lawns and golf courses because it digs up the turf.

The *shrew* is a tiny mammal resembling both a mole and a mouse. It is a bloodthirsty killer, feeding on insects, mice, and even other shrews. We seldom see the shrew because it runs along tunnels in the grass and hides easily under a leaf.

Fig. 33-10.   The sloth hangs from the branches back downward.   It feeds entirely on leaves, shoots, and fruits.

Flying mammals belong to the order Chiroptera (ky-rop-ter-ah). The name of this order means literally *bone-winged*. It includes more than 600 species of bats and vampires. True flight is accomplished by membranous wings formed by the greatly lengthened finger bones. Bats are insect feeders and fly mostly at night when insects are abundant in the air. They spend the days hanging upside down in a cave or hollow tree. A bat can fly through the dark passages of a cave. It does this by the principal we use in radar. While flying, it makes sounds which we cannot hear and guides itself by bouncing these sounds off objects. Thus the ears and not the eyes direct the bat in its flight. Vampires are large bats which live in tropical America. They pierce the skin of cattle and other warm-blooded animals including humans, and draw blood flowing from the wound.

Gnawing mammals are grouped in the order Rodentia (ro-den-she-ah). The gnawing mammals include some of our most valuable as well as some of our most destructive mammals. All have very strong chisel-shaped incisor teeth. These teeth have sharp edges which become even sharper with use because the front edge is harder than the back edge, causing the biting surface to wear on an angle.

Rats and mice are among the most common rodents. Others include the squirrel, woodchuck, prairie dog, chipmunk, and gopher. The beaver is the largest North American rodent. The great value of beaver pelts brought the early trappers to the Northwest Territory. Another rodent, the muskrat, is an important fur-bearing mammal of North America.

Fig. 33-11. The mole lives almost entirely underground and feeds on small animal and plant life, especially earthworms. Its front feet are adapted for digging.

The Lagomorpha (lag-oh-mor-fa) include the rodent-like mammals. Rabbits, hares, and picas resemble rodents in many ways, but differ from them in tooth structure. These mammals have four enlarged incisor teeth in each jaw, rather than two as in the rodents. They grind plant foods with a characteristic sideways motion of the lower jaw.

The *cottontail rabbit* is the most widely hunted mammal of the United States, and supplies more flesh than any other wild mammal. But even though preyed upon by man as well as by predatory birds and other animals, these rabbits have been able to hold their own in most localities. The *jack rabbit* is common in the broad expanses of the western prairies and plains. It reaches a length of nearly 30 inches and has characteristic long ears and large powerful hind legs. Both sight and hearing are especially keen. These keen senses enable them to escape from their enemy.

The Ungulata (ung-gu-lay-tah) include the hoofed mammals. Man has lived in close association with the *ungulates* since prehistoric times. The goat was probably the first to be domesticated. For ages man has depended on the horse, camel, ox, llama, and other hoofed mammals as beasts of burden. The cow, pig, and sheep are our principal food animals. Deer, elk, caribou, moose, and antelopes are our most important big game ungulates.

Biologists classify the ungulates as follows: (1) *odd-toed,* including the horse, tapir, and rhinoceros; (2) *even-toed,* non-ruminants, or non-cud-chewers, including the pig and hippopotamus; and (3) *even-toed ruminants,* or cud-chewers, including the cow, bison, sheep, goat, antelope, camel, llama, giraffe, deer, elk, caribou, and moose.

The ruminants (*room*-in-ants) have a four-chambered stomach. While grazing, they eat large quantities of food

Fig. 33-12. The beaver, a rodent, has webbed hind feet and a broad, flat tail. It is valued for its fur.

which pass into a large paunch, or **rumen,** the first of the stomach divisions. Here food is stored for later chewing. Later, the food is forced back into the mouth for leisurely chewing as **cud.** After thorough chewing, the cud is swallowed into the second stomach where digestion begins. From there it passes through the other stomach regions to the intestine.

Trunk-nosed mammals, the Proboscidea (pro-boh-*sid*-ee-ah) are scarce. Only two species of elephants remain as representatives of this order. The Asiatic elephant is the familiar performing elephant of the circus. In many parts of the world, it is used as beast of burden. The African elephant is a taller, slenderer animal with a sloping forehead and enormous ears. African elephants travel in herds in the deepest

Fig. 33-13. The cottontail rabbit is a common North American wood rabbit. Its name comes from the white-tufted underside of the tail, which can be seen as it scampers away. It is usually found in heavy thickets or dense grass.

Fig. 33-14. Hoofed animals, like these deer, belong to the order Ungulata.

parts of Africa and are not as easily domesticated as their Indian cousins. Elephants are among the largest of all land animals and reach a weight of seven tons or more.

During the glacial and pre-glacial eras, more than 30 species of mastadons, mammoths, and other elephant-like mammals lived in Asia, Europe, Africa, and North America.

Flesh-eating mammals comprise a large order, the Carnivora (kar-*niv*-or-ah). All of the members of this order have enlarged canine teeth for tearing flesh, and their other teeth are pointed for cutting it. Most of them are predatory animals, feeding on birds, insects, and other small animals. Some, like the bear, feed on vegetable matter as well. Variations in foot structure are used in dividing the order into families, many of which are familiar to everyone.

These families are listed in the table on page 443.

In addition to these families of *terrestrial* carnivores, several forms, including the seal, sea lion, and walrus, are *aquatic*.

A glance at a few typical carnivores. The black bear lives in the northern and western forest states and at one time was common throughout eastern North America. In regions where it lives you may see one perched high in a tree. The grizzly is larger and more dangerous than the black bear. It lives in the Northwest, and is especially abundant in Yellowstone Park. It frequently wades the shallow water of streams in search of salmon and other fish. The brown bears, especially the Kodiak bear of Alaska, are the largest of all bears. The polar bear of the Arctic region is an expert swimmer. Its snow white coat, slender head, and long neck are different from those of other bears.

The raccoon, with its black mask and long-ringed tail, is a favorite of many people because if captured young it makes a nice pet. The raccoon prefers fish and clams as its food but will eat other things as well if these are unavailable. It has a habit of washing its food before eating. This is probably to moisten the food rather than to clean it.

The weasel family includes some of

SOME FAMILIES OF CARNIVORES

FAMILY NAME	REPRESENTATIVE ANIMALS	FOOT STRUCTURE
Bear	Black bear Grizzly bear Brown bear Polar bear	Walks on entire foot, five toes on both front and back feet
Raccoon	Raccoon Coati	Walks on entire foot, five toes on both front and back feet
Ringtail cat	Ringtail cat	Feet resemble those of the cat, thick fur between pads of feet, semi-retractile claws
Weasel	Weasel Ferret Mink Skunk Otter Badger Wolverine	Walks partially on toes
Cat	Jaguar Mountain lion Bobcat Lynx Lion Tiger Domestic cat	Walks on toes, five toes on front feet and four on back feet, retractile claws
Dog	Wolf Coyote Fox Domestic dog	Walks on toes, five toes on front feet and four on back feet, feet are adapted for running on land

the most bloodthirsty carnivores and some of the most valuable fur-bearing mammals. The mink especially is prized for its fur. These long-bodied, short-legged animals live along streams. The ermine is an Arctic weasel which grows a coat of white fur except for a black-tipped tail in winter, but is brown in summer. The largest and most destructive member of the family is the wolverine of the northern forest. Its body, including its bushy tail is about 36 inches long and weighs between 30 and 35 pounds.

The dog and cat families are not as well represented in America as in other lands. The mountain lion (puma or panther) was found over the majority of North America at one time, but civilization has driven it to the remote regions of the southwest. It is not as dangerous as supposed and often seeks the friendship of man. Its chief importance lies in its destruction of livestock, especially young horses. Both

Fig. 33-15. The polar bear is a large bear that inhabits the Arctic regions. It feeds largely on aquatic animals.

Fig. 33-16. The red fox of North America is noted for its craftiness and raids on poultry.

Fig. 33-17. The gorilla, an erect primate, is one of the most powerful of animals.

the bay lynx, or bobcat, and the Canada lynx live in deep forests and are seldom seen.

The gray wolf, or timber wolf, is most frequently found in the northern forests and may be dangerous during the winter when it runs in packs. The coyote, or prairie wolf, has been more successful than its larger cousin in surviving the effects of civilization. It is still abundant on the western plains. However, in some regions, too many coyotes have been destroyed and their natural prey, including rodents and jack rabbits, have become pests. It has therefore been necessary to import coyotes into these regions.

The red fox ranges over much of the United States. It is sly and a very fast runner for short distances. Color phases of the red fox include the black fox, cross fox, and silver fox. The Arctic fox grows a white coat in winter. The gray fox resembles the red fox but lives in the warmer regions of the southern states.

Erect mammals belong to the Primates (pry-*may*-teez). None of the wild forms of this order lives in the United States. Biologists usually include man in the *primates,* but place him in a family by himself, Hominidae (home-*in*-id-ee). This sets him completely apart from the monkeys and apes. He belongs to the genus *Homo,* the species *sapiens,* which makes his biological name, *Homo sapiens.*

Superior brain development places

the primates at the top of all groups of living things. Primates have well-developed arms and hands. Their fingers are used for grasping and one or more fingers or toes are equipped with nails. Primates walk erect. Most of them live in South America, Africa, or the warm regions of Asia.

The *anthropoid apes* are most like man in body structure. They have no tails. The arms are longer than the legs. When walking, the feet tend to turn in. These primates, especially the chimpanzee, respond to a very high degree of training. They include:

1. The *gorilla,* the largest of the apes, lives in Africa. It walks on two feet and certainly is one of the most powerful animals.

2. The *chimpanzee* also lives in Af-rica. It is smaller than the gorilla and when trained reveals much intelligence.

3. The *orangutan* is a native of the East Indies. It is a droll animal with reddish hair.

4. The *gibbon* is a long-armed type found in Asia.

The Old World monkeys have long tails, but do not use them in climbing. They sit erect. Food is stored in cheek pouches. The baboon, an Old World monkey, has a long, doglike nose.

New World monkeys have flat, long tails which are used for grasping. The septum between the nostrils is wide and they lack cheek pouches.

Marmosets are small primates ranging from Central America to South America. They resemble squirrels in appearance and activity. Lemurs are primates found in Madagascar.

In Conclusion

Mammals are our closest animal companions. From the earliest times, they have supplied us both food and clothing. As beasts of burden, they have relieved man of back-breaking labor. In a more direct way, the carnivorous mammals have prevented destructive rodents from overrunning the earth. Thus our lives are bound closely to the mammals. In various services, they are partially responsible for the highly advanced standard of living we are able to enjoy.

But with much of our land given over to domestic mammals, many of the wild species have retreated farther and farther into the remaining wilderness. Many face possible extinction. Thus conservation of the mammals is a major problem facing our generation. We will discuss the preservation of mammals and other forms of wildlife in Chapter 54.

Questions for Review

1. What characteristic of mammals is referred to in the class name, Mammalia?

2. List several structures, other than hair, which develop as a body covering in certain mammals.

3. Most mammals have two pairs of limbs. Name two exceptions.

4. What four kinds of teeth are present in mammals?

5. Which of the brain regions is more

highly developed in a mammal than in any other vertebrate?

6. Name several problems of existence which are solved by the migration of various mammals.

7. What is the difference between true hibernation in the ground squirrel and the winter sleep of the bear?

8. (a) What do we mean by the term gestation period? (b) Give examples of gestation periods of several mammals.

9. In what respect are the duckbill and spiny anteater exceptions to the rule among mammals?

10. Why can kangaroos and opossums be born prematurely and yet survive?

11. (a) Describe the specialized tooth development of the rodent. (b) What uses are made of these teeth?

12. Make a list of six or more ungulates which are raised by man as domestic animals.

Biologically Speaking

canine	gestation	premolar
conditioned reflexes	incisor	rumen
convolution	mammal	ruminant
cud	mammary gland	umbilical cord
diaphragm	molar	uterus
foetus	placenta	viviparous

Applying Facts and Principles

1. Discuss adaptations in the limbs of five or more mammals and show how such adaptations have helped to make mammals the rulers of the earth.

2. Distinguish between instinct, conditioned behavior, and intelligence in mammals and give an illustration of each kind of behavior.

3. What is the relation between parental care and mortality and the number of young produced by various mammals?

4. The mammals exceed all other vertebrates in efficiency of the reproductive process. Compare mammalian reproduction with that of the lower vertebrates and list its points of greater efficiency.

5. The rodents, carnivores, ungulates, and primates are the most abundant orders. Give reasons why each of these orders has reached such supremacy.

6. Account for the fact that carnivores are often hard to domesticate.

Research On Your Own

1. Place a living fish (a goldfish can be used) in a large jar or an aquarium and watch its movements carefully. Notice the action of the operculum in pumping water into the mouth and through the gill chambers. Watch the fish rise and sink in the water, swim forward and backward, and rest quietly. List the various fins and the use the fish makes of each. You may wish to make a drawing, showing the general form of the fish, its head structures, fins, and some of the scales. Label all of the parts you show.

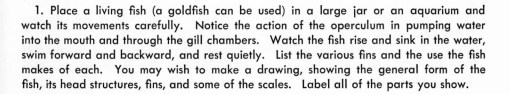

2. Make a community aquarium of small native fish in your classroom. Include such species as sunfish, bullheads, and minnows (not small game fish). An aquarium of this type should have an air pump or an abundant supply of oxygenating plants.

3. Put a living frog in a large jar or an aquarium containing enough water to submerge the frog and a rock or other object for the frog to rest on. Study the movement of the throat and the sides of the body and movement of the nostril flaps when the frog is out of the water. Watch it closely while under water. Notice the structure and use of the front and hind legs. Touch the eyes and see what happens. Open the mouth carefully. Examine the tongue and the lining of the mouth. Notice the rich blood supply to the mouth lining. You should be able to locate the internal nostril openings, and the openings of the Eustachian tubes, gullet, and glottis as well as the vomerine teeth.

4. Make a study of a living turtle. Include a sketch of the arrangement of plates forming the upper and lower shells. You can find the names of the various plates (shields) in a reptile or turtle book. Study the head and limbs of a turtle and compare them with other reptiles.

5. Prepare a table of data for twelve common birds of your region. Include the name of each bird, a small drawing of the bird (taken from a bird book), its resident classification, diet, nesting habits, number and description of eggs, and general economic importance.

6. Dissect the joint end of a chicken foot to expose the tendons. See if you can find the tendon which bends each toe and the one which closes the entire foot.

7. Make a table of the common native mammals of your region. Include the name of each, the order to which it belongs, habitat, diet, whether it migrates, hibernates or remains active through the winter in your locality, economic importance, and any other data you might be able to include.

8. Using books on mammals or first hand observations, make a chart showing the footprints or tracks of various mammals.

 **More About Biology**

Andrews, Roy Chapman. *ALL ABOUT WHALES*. Random House, Inc., New York. 1954

Bourlière, François. *THE NATURAL HISTORY OF MAMMALS*. Alfred A. Knopf, Inc., New York. 1954

Bridges, William. *ZOO EXPEDITIONS*. William Morrow and Co., New York. 1954

Cahalane, Victor H. *MAMMALS OF NORTH AMERICA*. The Macmillan Co., New York. 1947

Caine, Lou S. *NORTH AMERICAN FRESHWATER SPORT FISH*. A. S. Barnes and Co., Inc., New York. 1949

Ditmars, Raymond L. *THE REPTILES OF NORTH AMERICA*. Doubleday and Co., Inc., New York. 1936

Ditmars, Raymond L. *REPTILES OF THE WORLD*. Rev. Ed. The Macmillan Co., New York. 1933

Ditmars, Raymond L. *SNAKES OF THE WORLD*. The Macmillan Co., New York. 1931

Earle, Olive Lydia. *BIRDS AND THEIR NESTS*. William Morrow and Co., New York. 1952

Hegner, Robert. *PARADE OF THE ANIMAL KINGDOM*. The Macmillan Co., New York. 1935

Innes, William T. *EXOTIC AQUARIUM FISHES.* 17th Ed. Innes Publishing Co., Philadelphia. 1953

Kieran, John. *INTRODUCTION TO BIRDS.* Garden City Publishing Co., Garden City, New York. 1950

Lane, Frank. *ANIMAL WONDER WORLD.* Sheridan House, Inc., New York. 1951

Morgan, Alfred. *AN AQUARIUM BOOK FOR BOYS AND GIRLS.* Charles Scribner's Sons, New York. 1936

Morris, Percy A. *BOY'S BOOK OF SNAKES.* The Ronald Press Co., New York. 1953

National Geographic Society. *THE BOOK OF FISHES.* The Society, Washington, D.C. 1952

Peterson, Roger Tory. *A FIELD GUIDE TO THE BIRDS.* Houghton Mifflin Co., Boston. 1939

Pope, Clifford H. *TURTLES OF THE UNITED STATES AND CANADA.* Alfred A. Knopf, New York. 1939

Sanderson, Ivan Terrance. *HOW TO KNOW THE MAMMALS.* Little, Brown and Co., Inc., Boston. 1951

Stebbins, Robert. *AMPHIBIANS AND REPTILES OF WESTERN NORTH AMERICA.* McGraw-Hill Book Co., Inc., New York. 1954

Trefflich, Henry. *THEY NEVER TALK BACK.* Appleton-Century-Crofts, Inc., New York. 1954

Verrill, A. Hyatt. *STRANGE ANIMALS AND THEIR STORIES.* L. C. Page and Co., Boston. 1939

Writers' Program. *REPTILES AND AMPHIBIANS.* Albert Whitman and Co., Chicago. 1939

Zim, Herbert S. *ALLIGATORS AND CROCODILES.* William Morrow and Co., New York. 1952

Zim, Herbert and Smith, Hobart M. *REPTILES AND AMPHIBIANS: A GUIDE TO FAMILIAR AMERICAN SPECIES.* Simon and Schuster, Inc., New York. 1953

UNIT 7

How Biology Applies to Ourselves

Good health is a priceless possession. It reflects in our personalities, our success, and in the enjoyment we get out of living. Still, we often take good health for granted and assume that we will always have it. It is normal to be healthy, but we have sufficient intelligence and choice in the things we do to abuse our health — or to safeguard it.

Science has given us a wonderful opportunity to be healthy. We can expect to live longer than has any generation before us. And, we expect to live this long life without worry about many of the health problems which plagued our ancestors. What better reason could there be for finding out more about the marvels of your own body?

Our study of plant and animal life has led to the climax of biological study — a more perfect machine than man will ever assemble — your own body.

CHAPTER 34

Structure of the Human Body

Because man has a highly developed brain, he is more advanced than any other living organism. The human brain is larger in proportion to body size than the brain of any other mammal, and is much more highly specialized. This brain has enabled men to form habits easier, to think out problems and to reach satisfactory solutions, to acquire skills by constant practice, and to achieve the highest possible type of living.

One of the several subdivisions in the study of biology is **anatomy** (a-*nat*-oh-mee) which takes up the internal structure of an organism. Another is **physiology** (fizz-ee-*ol*-oh-jee) which probes the workings and functions of the body parts and shows how they operate. In the following chapters we will discuss fully the discoveries of these sciences and their relation to man.

Man and the vertebrates. Man is not structurally adapted, as are many vertebrate animals, for skill in climbing, running, flight, and swimming. Although he can do these skills, he is unable to do them as well as certain animals. In fact, there is nothing that man can do unaided by his intelligence which many animals cannot do much better. But with his intelligence to direct him there is no animal that can compete with him. Man has learned the use of tools, devised a spoken and written language, found a means of controlling fire, and developed mental faculties and social habits that put him in a position far above that of any of the animals.

The cellular structure of the human body. The body of a human being, like that of any other organism, is composed of cells which are essentially like those of any other organism.

The study of the human body is a study of specialized *cells*. It is also a study of great numbers of similar cells functioning together to constitute a *tissue*. Various kinds of tissues are grouped together in *organs*. Various kinds of organs are grouped together in *systems*. Each system is specialized to perform certain processes with the highest degree of efficiency. The systems taken together constitute the *organism*.

Tissues of the human body. All the cells which compose the human body are grouped into eleven principal kinds of tissues, classified into four groups as follows:

1. Connective tissues
   (a) Bone
   (b) Cartilage
   (c) White fibrous tissue
   (d) Yellow elastic tissue
   (e) Adipose tissue (fat)
   (f) Liquid tissue — blood and lymph
   (g) Reticular tissue
   (h) Areolar tissue
2. Muscle tissues
3. Nerve tissues
4. Epithelial tissues

451

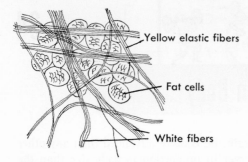

Yellow elastic fibers

Fat cells

White fibers

Fig. 34-1. This drawing shows the way some of the connective tissues in the human body look under the microscope.

The organization of tissues into organs and systems. Familiar examples of organs in the human body include the arms, legs, ears, eyes, heart, liver, and lungs. Each of these organs is specialized to perform a definite function or a group of related functions involving several different tissues. The arms, for example, are composed of epithelial tissue, bone tissue, cartilage, muscle tissue, blood tissue, nerve tissue, and other tissues. All these function together to perform such acts as grasping, writing, and sewing.

Fig. 34-2. When you look at epithelial cells under the microscope, this is what you see.

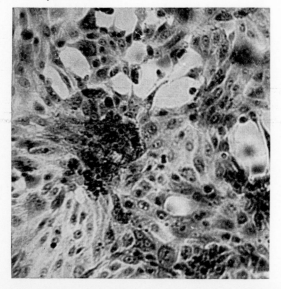

Organs are grouped together into ten *systems* as follows:

1. Skeletal (bones)
2. Muscular (muscles)
3. Digestive (teeth, mouth, esophagus, stomach, intestines, liver, pancreas)
4. Respiratory (lungs, trachea, nose, pharynx)
5. Circulatory (heart, arteries, veins, capillaries)
6. Endocrine (glands)
7. Excretory (kidneys and bladder)
8. Integumentary (skin and hair)
9. Nervous (brain, spinal cord, nerves, eyes, ears)
10. Reproductive (testes, ovaries, uterus, oviducts)

The body regions in man. The general form of the human body is similar to the other vertebrate animals. It includes the head, neck, trunk, and limbs in the form of arms and legs. The head includes the *cranial* (*kray*-nee-al) *cavity,* formed by the bones of the skull. The brain lies safely enclosed by the bones of the skull. The head also contains the sense organs which are located close to the brain, to which they transmit impulses.

The *thoracic* (thor-*ass*-ick) *cavity* is formed by ribs, breastbone, and spine. It encloses the lungs, trachea, heart, gullet, and other organs. A muscular partition, the *diaphragm* (*dy*-ah-fram), separates the thoracic cavity from the abdominal cavity which is included in the lower part of the trunk. Inside the abdominal cavity are: the *stomach, liver, pancreas* (*pan*-kree-as), *intestines, spleen, kidneys,* and in the case of the female, the *ovaries.* While the abdominal organs lack the bony protection of the cranial and thoracic cavities, they are protected by the vertebral column along the back and by layers of skin and muscle on the front.

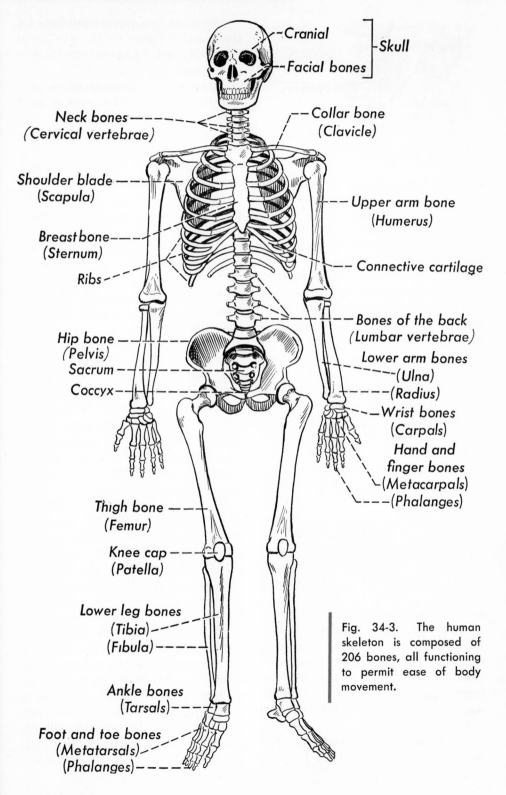

Cranial

Facial bones

} Skull

Neck bones
(Cervical vertebrae)

Collar bone
(Clavicle)

Shoulder blade
(Scapula)

Upper arm bone
(Humerus)

Breastbone
(Sternum)

Connective cartilage

Ribs

Bones of the back
(Lumbar vertebrae)

Hip bone
(Pelvis)

Lower arm bones

Sacrum

(Ulna)

Coccyx

(Radius)

Wrist bones
(Carpals)

Hand and
finger bones
(Metacarpals)
(Phalanges)

Thigh bone
(Femur)

Knee cap
(Patella)

Lower leg bones
(Tibia)
(Fibula)

Fig. 34-3. The human
skeleton is composed of
206 bones, all functioning
to permit ease of body
movement.

Ankle bones
(Tarsals)

Foot and toe bones
(Metatarsals)
(Phalanges)

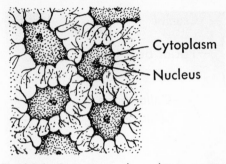

Fig. 34-4. Bone tissue, shown here, consists of living cells and deposits of minerals.

The body framework. When a contractor builds a house, he starts with the framework. First he puts up the main beams and joists, then the studding and rafters. Next come the walls and the roof, and finally the outer sheeting and the plaster. The strength of the entire structure depends on the framework to which all the other parts are fastened.

By far the most efficient system of support is illustrated in the internal, or **endoskeleton,** of man and the other vertebrates. You will recall that the arthropods have an exoskeleton. Many of the other invertebrates have other methods for the support of their bodies. Man's bony framework gives him the greatest support with the least amount of weight. It permits movement far superior to any other type of framework. The animal with an internal skeleton is, however, at one great disadvantage. Much of the protection against injury from the outside that is given by an external skeleton is lost. Many soft parts of the body are thus exposed. Consequently, the organism must rely on its nervous system and sense organs to make up for the protection which the skeleton does not provide.

The functions of the skeleton. The functions of the bones of the body are classified as: (1) support and form for the body; (2) place for the attachment of muscles; and (3) protection for delicate organs.

Many of the 206 bones which compose the human skeleton work in more than one way. For example, the vertebral column, the shoulder girdle, the hip girdle, the bones of the legs, and those of the arms support the body and give it definite form. The bones also serve as places where muscles are attached and permit the many types of body movement.

Certain delicate organs lie under special protective bones. Examples are: the brain which is encased in the cranial bones, the heart which lies under the breastbone, and the lungs which are protected by the ribs.

Bone is a living tissue. We commonly use the expression, *dry as a bone,* and assume that living bone is like a dried-out bone. Actually, bone is far from dry. It is moist and active and requires nourishment the same as any other living tissue. True, part of what we call bone is nonliving, for bone tissue is a peculiar combination of living cells and mineral deposits.

Of what is bone tissue composed? The formation of bone involves not only bone substances but cartilage as well. Among some of the primitive vertebrates the skeleton is composed entirely of cartilage, which lasts throughout their entire lives. This results in a tough but flexible skeleton.

In the early stages of the development of the human embryo, the skeleton is composed almost entirely of cartilage, a few membranes taking the place of bone in some regions. After about the second month of development, however, certain of the cartilage cells disappear and are replaced by other cells. (See Fig. 34-4.) These deposit minerals in the form of *calcium phosphate* and *calcium carbonate* in the spaces between them. The process is called **ossification** (oss-ih-fih-*kay*-shun) and occurs throughout childhood. In fact, this continues at a reduced rate throughout a person's entire life.

Certain factors control mineral deposit in bone. *Ossification* involves the deposit of calcium compounds between the bone cells which results in an increase in the strength of the bone. Naturally, this deposition cannot occur unless the proper minerals are present. Calcium compounds enter the body with food and are carried to the bone tissues by the blood. The diet therefore governs mineral deposition in bone. Especially in childhood, the diet must be controlled carefully to be sure that the developing bone tissues receive proper supply of minerals. Milk, the natural food of all young animals, is the ideal source of these calcium compounds.

Bones grow along lines of stress. In other words, they become heaviest and strongest where the strain is greatest. This is important in dealing with bone fractures. (See Fig. 34-5.) If a broken bone is protected by a cast and is unused during the period of repair, the fact it is under no stress delays healing.

For example, if a leg bone is broken, the patient is provided with a walking cast which puts a broken bone under limited stress during the healing period. This speeds up the repair process. It also explains why mineral deposition in the leg bones is much greater than in that of the arms. If, on the other hand, a limb is paralyzed or made useless, the minerals are reabsorbed by the blood and deposited elsewhere.

Certain vitamins, especially vitamin D, are necessary for good bone growth. We shall study these in Chapter 35 under vitamins.

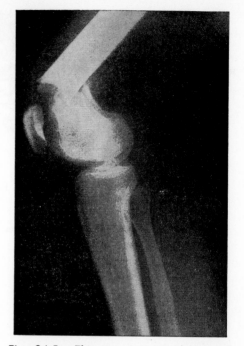

Fig. 34-5. This is an X-ray photograph of a complete fracture and separation of the lower end of the femur (thigh) bone just above the knee joint. This unusual fracture resulted from the impact of an automobile bumper.

The structure of a bone. If a long bone, such as a bone from the leg or arm, is cut lengthwise, several distinct regions can be seen. (See Fig. 34-6.) The outer covering is a tough membrane called the **periosteum** (per-ee-*os*-tee-um). This membrane aids in nourishing the bone due to its rich blood supply, in repairing injuries, and also provides a surface to which muscles are attached. Within the periosteum is a *bony layer* containing the deposits of mineral matter. This may vary in hardness from an extremely hard to a spongy material, depending on its location in the bone. The bony layer is very hard through the mid-region of the bone, but becomes porous and spongy at the ends. The bony layer is penetrated by nu-

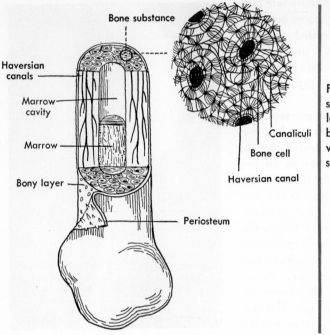

Fig. 34-6. The internal structure of a bone. Left: longitudinal section of a bone. Right: microscopic view of a bone in cross section.

merous channels, the **Haversian** (ha-*ver*-shan) **canals,** which form a network extending throughout the region. These canals carry nourishment to the living cells of the bony layer. The blood vessels of the Haversian canals connect with those of the outer membrane from which nourishment is received.

The larger bones have a hollow interior and contain a soft tissue called **marrow.** The marrow is richly supplied with nerves and blood vessels. There are two distinct types of marrow, *red* and *yellow.* The **red marrow** is active and forms the red corpuscles and one kind of white corpuscle of the blood. The **yellow marrow** fills the central cavity of the bone and extends into the Haversian canals of the bony layer. It is normally inactive, but may produce corpuscles in time of great blood loss and in certain blood disease.

The smaller bones are solid rather than hollow and vary considerably in the amount of spongy bone tissue present. Though they are solid, they are completely penetrated with blood vessels.

Parts of the body are supported by cartilage rather than bone. This **permanent cartilage** remains as such and is not replaced by bone as in the case of **temporary cartilage.** Permanent cartilage forms such structures as the end of the nose, the external ear, and the walls of the larynx and trachea. The inner surfaces of the joints, too, are covered with layers of cartilage. A secretion of the cartilage called **synovial** (sin-*oh*-vee-al) **fluid** serves to lubricate the joints. In some joints such as the knee or shoulder, a sac, called the **bursa** (*bur*-sah), serves as a cushion between the bones.

The joints of the body. The point at which two separate bones meet is called a **joint.** The various bones of the human body are connected by several different kinds of joints. (See Fig. 34-7.)

The elbow is an example of a *hinge joint.* Such a joint moves as a hinge in one plane only, but has the advantage of giving great power because there is little danger of twisting. When certain muscles of the upper arm contract, the lower arm is pulled upward only. The knee is another example of a hinge joint. The hip and shoulder joints are examples of *ball and socket joints.* Here the bone of the upper arm ends in a ball which fits into a socket of the shoulder girdle. Such a joint has the advantage of universal movement, or movement in any direction within the limits imposed by the muscles. The hip joint is similar, with a ball on the end of the *femur* (*fee*-mur), or thigh bone, fitting into a socket of the hip bone, the *pelvis.*

Ball and socket and hinge joints are held in place by tough strands of connective tissue called *ligaments.* Ligaments may be stretched with exercise, thus " loosening " joints and permitting freer movement.

The ribs are attached to the **vertebrae** (*ver*-teh-bree) by joints which are only *partially movable.* Long strands of cartilage attach the ribs to the breastbone in front so as to allow for chest expansion during breathing. The junction between the spine and pelvis, the sacroiliac joint, is a well-known example of this. It is a frequent place for injuries from sudden falls. All joints are held securely by layers of cartilage which stretch to allow movement. Some joints, such as those of the adult skull bones, are **immovable.**

Other joints include the **angular joints** of the wrists and ankles, the **gliding joints** of the vertebrae, and the **pivot joint** of the head on the spine.

How do muscles produce movement? Bones, even in a living body, have no power to move by themselves because

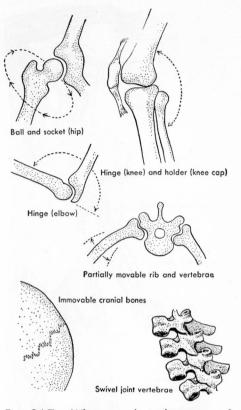

Ball and socket (hip)

Hinge (knee) and holder (knee cap)

Hinge (elbow)

Partially movable rib and vertebrae

Immovable cranial bones

Swivel joint vertebrae

Fig. 34-7. What are the advantages of each type of joint shown here?

their hard layers of calcium prevent contraction. Muscles accomplish this movement admirably. There are about 400 different muscles, comprising approximately one-half of the body by weight.

We can move our arms whenever we desire. This fact shows that certain muscles are under the control of our will. Such muscles are called **voluntary** muscles. There are many others which help in the operation of our digestive, respiratory, circulatory, and excretory systems which are never controlled by our will. They are the *involuntary* muscles. Some muscles are both voluntary and involuntary, as, for instance, those that operate the eyelids and the diaphragm.

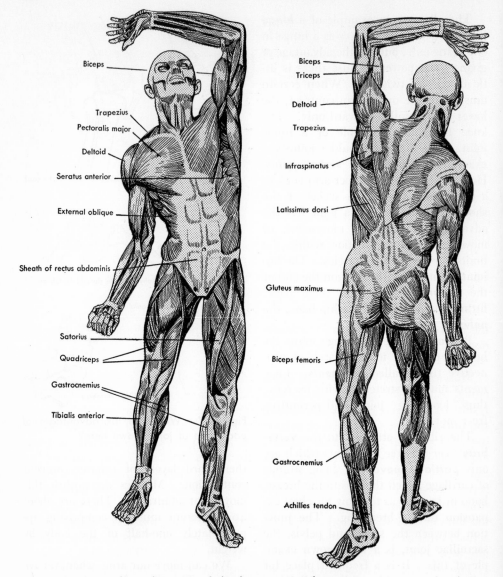

Biceps
Trapezius
Pectoralis major
Deltoid
Seratus anterior
External oblique
Sheath of rectus abdominis
Satorius
Quadriceps
Gastrocnemius
Tibialis anterior

Biceps
Triceps
Deltoid
Trapezius
Infraspinatus
Latissimus dorsi
Gluteus maximus
Biceps femoris
Gastrocnemius
Achilles tendon

Fig. 34-8. From these drawings of the human muscular system, you can see what a perfect machine the human body is.

The microscope reveals three kinds of muscle cells. These are: (1) *striated* or *skeletal:* cells with bands (striations) and many nuclei (voluntary); (2) *unstriated* or *smooth:* spindle-shaped cells with one nucleus (involuntary); and (3) *cardiac:* branched, striated fibers (heart muscles).

A **striated,** or **skeletal, muscle** is usu-

ally spindle-shaped, as shown in Fig. 34-9. The body of the muscle is called the **belly.** Inelastic **tendons** extend from each end of the muscle and attach directly, or indirectly, to bones. These are dense bands of white fibrous tissue. The tendon at one end of a muscle, called the **origin,** remains stationary when the muscle moves, while

Smooth muscle   Striated muscle   Cardiac muscle

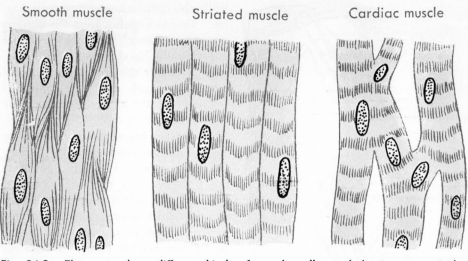

Fig. 34-9. There are three different kinds of muscle cells, each having a particular function.

the tendon at the other end, the *insertion,* is attached to the movable part and is shortened.

Muscles have only the power of shortening, or contracting. The contraction results from a nerve impulse stimulating the muscle fibers. A period of relaxation, during which the muscle relaxes, must follow before another contraction can occur. Since muscle tissue is very active, it requires a rich blood supply. Abundant food and oxygen must reach the muscle, and waste products of cell activity must be removed from them rapidly or otherwise fatigue will occur.

The skeletal muscles which move joints of the trunk and limbs are always arranged in pairs. One contraction is necessary to bend a joint, another to straighten it. Muscles which bend joints are *flexors,* while those that straighten them are *extensors.* When you bend your elbow joint, the tendon of the *biceps* muscle pulls against the radius bone of the lower arm and raises it, the other end of this muscle being securely anchored at the shoulder. During this contraction, you can feel the belly of the biceps muscle swell on the front side of your upper arm. The extensor muscle involved in this movement is called the *triceps.* It lies on the back side of the upper arm. When you lower the arm, the muscle contracts and the biceps muscle relaxes. If you straighten the arm completely, you can feel the belly of this muscle contract.

Even when a joint is not being moved, flexor and extensor muscles oppose each other in a state of slight contraction, called **tone.** Increased use of muscles results in enlargement and increased tone. When totally unused, muscles become weak and flabby, may decrease in size, and may lose tone.

Muscular coordination. The skeletal muscles, like all other muscles, contract as a result of nerve impulses. Any body activity involves many impulses and many muscles. The combined action of muscles to produce a movement results in *muscular coordination.* The skill with which movement is produced depends on the coordination of nerve impulses and muscular contractions. To a great extent, muscles may be

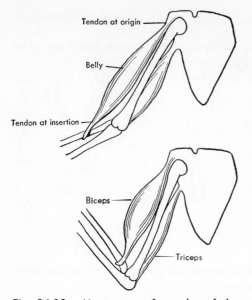

Fig. 34-10. Movements of muscles of the upper arm. Top: the arm is straightened by the contraction of triceps muscle on the under side. In this movement, the biceps muscle, on the upper side of the arm, is relaxed. Bottom: the arm is flexed by the contraction of the biceps muscle, a flexor for the arm. The triceps muscle is now relaxed.

trained to produce a particular kind of movement by means of practice. One must learn to play tennis, drive a golf ball, dribble a basketball, or play a piano. As one's nervous system and muscles become accustomed to the activity, a skill is developed.

Unstriated and cardiac muscles. The **unstriated** or **smooth muscles** differ in their arrangement from striated or skeletal muscles. Their cells are arranged usually in two layers. When the muscle contracts, the entire layer draws up. Layers of smooth muscle form the walls of many internal organs. The stomach and intestine walls contain such layers and may contract in waves to churn food or pass it along through the digestive tract. Artery walls also contain layers of smooth muscle. Due to impulses from the nervous system, the artery walls may constrict and raise the blood pressure during periods of danger or emotional upset. All action of smooth muscle is controlled by parts of the nervous system over which we have no conscious control.

Cardiac, or **heart, muscle** is similar to striated muscle when one views it under the microscope. The cells, however, are branched and contain specialized disks or bands of materials at varying intervals. Like striated muscle, cardiac muscle is capable of rapid movement, but it does not tire easily. In this respect it is like smooth muscle.

The action of heart muscle is unlike that of any other muscle. It has an *automatic beat* and conducts this beat from cell to cell throughout the muscle. A beat originates in a small mass of tissue on the top of the heart, called the **sino-auricular node.** From this point, the beat is carried through the muscle of the upper chambers to another node, the **auricular-ventricular node,** where it is relayed through the muscles of the lower chambers. Conduction of the beat through the cells of heart muscle results in a rhythmic wave of contraction characteristic of the heart.

Muscular exercise. Normal body activity is a balance between physical and mental exertion. However, the average person today, surrounded by labor-saving devices, uses less than one-tenth of his muscles in the course of a day's activity.

Relief of tension fatigue is probably the greatest benefit to be obtained from physical exercise. This emphasizes the importance of your participation in physical activities at school and after school.

America has a well-deserved reputation as a nation of sportsmen. It is well to support your school athletic program, but your interest in sports should not be confined to a seat on the sidelines. An exciting contest may even increase tension fatigue, except in the players themselves.

Extreme exertion in an individual who has been inactive for some time is unwise and may be dangerous. Heart action, respiration, and other vital activities have been geared to a sluggish existence and may have difficulty adjusting to a sudden great increase in muscular activity. For this reason, muscular exercise should be increased gradually and maintained at a fairly constant level.

Competitive athletics is a valuable experience for at least two reasons. In the first place, it requires gradual but regular attainment of a physical peak under a trained coach. In addition, it trains participants in the cooperation of team play and provides situations in which one must be a good loser and a graceful winner. Interest in athletics should also include training in individual sports such as tennis, golf, bowling,

archery, and swimming, which can be carried on later in life.

Good posture is important for good appearance. What is your impression of a person who stands with his back bent, his shoulders drooping, and his head hanging forward? If you were an employer, would you hire him to fill a job requiring initiative and leadership?

Posture which demands that the spine be held straight is equally undesirable. The spine normally has a distinct curve which is often more visible in thin people than those with more fat or muscle. Such stiff posture may lead in later life to inflexibility of the back. Good posture is hard to define, but in brief, it is the maintenance of good muscular tone giving the most flexibility to the internal organs and the whole body.

The emotional state of an individual exerts a powerful influence on posture. A dejected unhappy person usually maintains a slumped posture and the poor posture adds to the dejection.

In Conclusion

The human body is organized into tissues, organs, and systems. The body framework consists of an internal skeleton composed of bones which give the body form, act as levers for muscles, and protect the more delicate organs.

Muscles produce movement. Those which are attached to bones by means of tendons are skeletal, or striated, muscles. Smooth, or unstriated, muscles form layers in the walls of such internal organs as the stomach, intestines, and the arteries. Their control is involuntary.

Our attention next is focused on the nature of foods which have several functions in a living organism. If we know what foods are and what they do, we can study the digestive system with better understanding.

Questions for Review

1. What reasons can you give for starting with the cell in describing the human body?

2. How do the tissues, organs, and systems of the human body illustrate division of labor?

3. (a) What are the three body cavities? (b) Name some of the organs found in each.

4. Why does an internal skeleton necessitate a highly developed brain and nervous system?

5. (a) What are the principal functions of bones? (b) Give an example of a bone serving each purpose.

6. In what ways does the diet affect bone development?

7. What are some important functions of the Haversian canals?

8. Describe some of the tissues surrounding a joint.

9. Describe four kinds of joints found in the body.

10. (a) How do we classify muscle cells as to appearance? (b) As to control? (c) As to location?

11. Why are muscles so often found in opposing pairs in the body?

12. Describe the process when an individual muscle contracts.

Biologically Speaking

auricular-ventricular node	flexor	red marrow
belly	Haversian canals	sino-auricular node
biceps	insertion	striated muscle
bursa	involuntary	synovial fluid
cardiac muscle	joint	tendon
cartilage	ligament	tone
connective tissue	origin	triceps
contraction	ossification	unstriated muscle
endoskeleton	periosteum	voluntary muscle
extensor	permanent cartilage	yellow marrow

Applying Facts and Principles

1. Explain the importance of intelligence and reasoning in the rise of modern man.

2. Why is modern man more likely to suffer from a breakdown of the nervous system than any other system?

3. What relations do you see between the way man lives in his societies and his physical and biological make-up?

4. What are some flaws in the habit of scientists describing the human body in systems?

5. How do you explain the fact that whales which are stranded on beaches usually die within a short time even though they breathe by lungs?

6. Why does a single stimulus often cause the entire heart to contract?

CHAPTER 35

Foods and Digestion

There is no more dramatic chapter in biology than the story of foods and the complex food changes that take place in living things. Let's start with a wheat plant and a stalk of corn growing in the fields. Each day, these plants draw water and dissolved minerals from the soil and, with additional substance from the atmosphere, form foods. All this takes place in the plant's remarkable cell factories. Now, if we add a cow, a packing plant, and a bakery, we might end up with a roast beef sandwich and bring you, the reader, into the food cycle.

You eat the sandwich and, some time later, send much of its substance to your tissues. But in what form — as sandwich bun and roast beef? No, as glucose, amino acids, and fatty acids. What happened to the sandwich? As it passed through a 30-foot tube, your **alimentary canal,** several organs broke it down chemically in a series of changes included in the process of digestion. Your digestive system is like an assembly line in reverse. It starts with the many complex foods you eat and simplifies them to a few basic tissue foods. You owe much to this remarkable system. It allows you to enjoy the wide variety of foods in your daily diet and, still, to send your tissues the basic, simple foods you would find no real pleasure in eating.

What is food? **Food** is any substance which, when absorbed into the body tissues, yields materials valuable for the production of energy, the growth and repair of tissue, and the regulation of life processes without harming the organism. This is another way of saying that you eat to be active and to grow and maintain your bodies. Six classes of substances meet the requirements of this definition: (1) water; (2) minerals; (3) carbohydrates; (4) fats; (5) proteins; and (6) vitamins.

Water has many uses. It is inorganic, and does not yield energy to the tissues. However, it is so vital in the maintenance of life that a person deprived of it dies sooner than he would if deprived of other types of food.

If you weigh 100 pounds, your body contains between 60 and 70 pounds of water. Much of this water is organized into your body protoplasm and into the spaces between the cells. As water is lost, first from the intercellular spaces and then from the cells themselves, the protoplasm becomes more and more solid and finally dies. This water loss is part of a process we call **dehydration.**

The fluid part of blood, called **plasma,** is 91 to 92 per cent water. Here, water is essential as a solvent in the transportation of food and waste products to and from the body tissues. Water serves further as a solvent in the movement of dissolved foods from the digestive tract to the blood and in the removal of tissue wastes from the skin and

Fig. 35-1. Many vegetables and fruits are good sources of mineral salts in the diet.

kidneys. The kidneys alone pass two to five pints of excess water daily, and this contains many cellular wastes which the body must eliminate.

The flow of sweat is essential, too, in the regulation of heat loss from the body. **Evaporation,** or the change of a substance from a fluid to a gas, requires heat. When perspiration evaporates from the body surface, heat resulting from internal oxidation is lost.

Water requirements of the body are met in three ways: (1) some water is present in the food you eat; (2) some is a by-product of oxidation in cells; and (3) some is consumed as drinking water. The amount required varies with the temperature and humidity of the air and the amount of body activity.

Mineral salts are important for body functions. Table salt, or *sodium chloride,* is consumed directly and in considerable quantities in the diet. Other salts, chemical compounds composed of a mineral and one or more other elements, are also present in food. Since salts are lost in perspiration, persons exposed to excessive heat over long intervals must either increase the salt in the diet or supplement the normal diet with salt tablets.

Besides sodium chloride, other mineral elements are removed from the soil by plants and stored in the plant tissues. *Calcium* and *phosphorus* are required in greater abundance by animals than other mineral elements because of the importance of calcium phosphate in the formation of bones and teeth. In addition, these elements form about five per cent of animal tissue when combined with other elements as proteins. Milk is an ideal source of these two elements. Other sources include whole grain cereals, meat, and fish.

Iron compounds are essential for the formation of red blood corpuscles. Meats, green vegetables, and certain fruits such as plums (prunes) and raisins are important sources of iron in the diet. Iodine salts are essential in the formation of the secretion of the thyroid gland. Iodine may be obtained from drinking water or eating sea foods.

Minerals are vital to the body in many ways. Each of the minerals, however, must be in a compound form before it can be used by the body. Thus eating chemically pure elements, such as sodium or chlorine, would result in death. When, however, these elements are in a compound form, such as sodium chloride, they are harmless and necessary for the body. Calcium is necessary to insure the proper clotting of blood and, together with magnesium, to nerve and muscle action. Potassium compounds are essential to growth.

What are organic nutrients? We call carbohydrates, fats, and proteins *organic nutrients* because they are originally formed by living cells and contain the element, carbon. Carbohydrates and fats supply energy. The tissue-building value of foods cannot be measured except by observing growth in animals when they are fed. But the energy value can be measured in heat units, called *Calories*. A *Calorie* (large Calorie) is the amount of heat required to raise the temperature of 1,000 cubic centimeters (about one quart) of water one degree Centigrade. This is 1,000 times as great as the small calorie used in physical measurements of heat.

The number of Calories required in an average day's activity varies with the kind of activity and with the age and body build of the person concerned. A daily requirement of 2,500 to 3,500 Calories is probably about average. The Calorie needs for persons of different ages, performing different activities are shown in Table I on this page. The heat output of the body in Calories per hour in various kinds of activities is shown in Table II on page 466. If you list all your activities in the course of 24 hours, you can determine your approximate daily Calorie requirement.

More than half of your total diet is carbohydrate food. Regardless of this high percentage, the accumulated carbohydrate reserve in your body is less than one per cent of your total weight. This is evidence that carbohydrates are primarily fuel foods, and that they are oxidized rapidly to supply the energy required for body activity.

Simple sugars are obtained from fruits in the form of grape sugar (glucose) or fruit sugar (fructose). These sugars require no further simplification, since they are already in the chem-

TABLE I

DAILY CALORIE NEEDS (APPROXIMATELY)

1. For child under 2 years	1,000 Calories
2. For child from 2 to 5 years	1,300 "
3. For child from 6 to 9 years	1,700 "
4. For child from 10 to 12 years, woman (not working)	2,000 "
5. For girl from 12 to 14 years, woman (light work)	2,200 "
6. For boy (12–14), girl (15–16), man (sedentary)	2,600 "
7. For boy (15–20), man (light work)	3,000 "
8. For man (moderately active)	3,200 "
9. For farmer (busy season)	3,500 to 4,500 "
10. For excavator, hard laborer, etc.	4,500 to 5,000 "
11. For lumberman (winter)	5,000 to 8,000 "

TABLE II

AVERAGE NORMAL OUTPUT OF HEAT FROM THE BODY

CONDITIONS OF MUSCULAR ACTIVITY	AVERAGE CALORIES PER HOUR
Man at rest, sleeping	65 Calories
Man at rest, awake, sitting up	100 "
Man at light muscular exercise	170 "
Man at moderately active muscular exercise	290 "
Man at severe muscular exercise	450 "
Man at very severe muscular exercise	600 "

ical form in which carbohydrates are absorbed into the blood from the organs of the digestive system. More **complex sugars** come from cane, beets, maple trees (sucrose), and from milk (maltose). This latter sugar is used in malted milk. These more complex sugars require conversion to simple sugars before absorption. We will discuss them later in the chapter.

Starches are abundant in cereal grains. We use wheat, corn, rye, barley, oats, and rice. Breakfast foods, bread, pastry goods, macaroni, and many other food items are made from these. Potatoes and tapioca are other sources of starch.

One class of carbohydrates, the **celluloses,** come from the cell walls of plants. Celluloses are indigestible in man and many animals and are, therefore, non-energy foods. However, they provide bulk or roughage in the digestive system. They expand the intestine and stimulate the movement of food by muscular contractions of the intestine wall. Without this stimulation, there would not be normal movement of food.

Carbohydrates are stored in the liver and muscles of man as **glycogen** (gly-ko-jen), or animal starch. This activity is essential in maintaining the proper sugar content of the blood. If it were not for the liver, we would probably have to eat a small quantity of food continuously. However, sugar (dextrose or glucose) is absorbed from the digestive system and is carried by the blood directly to the liver. Here excess sugar is converted to glycogen and stored until needed. As the level of blood-sugar decreases, glycogen is converted back to sugar and the supply in the blood is replenished.

Fats are highly concentrated energy foods. The fats yield more than twice as much energy by weight as carbohydrates. They may be formed in the body by conversion of excess carbohydrates or may be used directly as fat from plant or animal origin. The chief storehouses of fat are the tissue spaces just beneath the skin, the region of the kidneys, and the liver.

Fat in the diet is obtained largely from butter, cream, cheese, oleomargarine, lard, and other shortenings, oils, nuts, and meats. They undergo digestion slowly and delay the hunger sensation between meals. However, excess fats should be avoided, especially by individuals with limited physical activity,

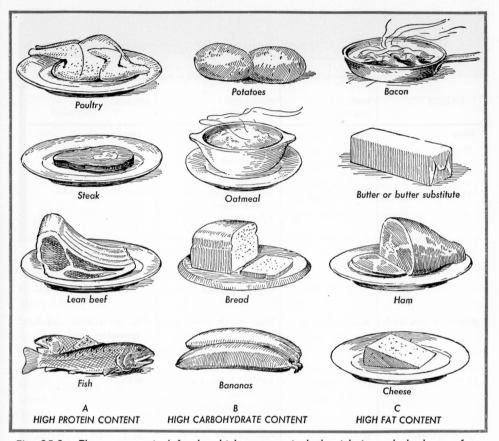

Poultry

Potatoes

Bacon

Steak

Oatmeal

Butter or butter substitute

Lean beef

Bread

Ham

Fish

Bananas

Cheese

A
HIGH PROTEIN CONTENT

B
HIGH CARBOHYDRATE CONTENT

C
HIGH FAT CONTENT

Fig. 35-2. These are typical foods which are particularly rich in carbohydrates, fats, and proteins.

and during warm weather. Also, fats should be avoided if a person has a tendency to " put on weight."

What are proteins? The *proteins* (*pro*-tee-ins) are extremely complex chemical compounds which might be compared to buildings. The " blocks " which form the building are called **amino** (ah-*mee*-no) **acids.** During digestion, the " buildings " which a person eats are completely wrecked and the individual " blocks," or amino acids of several kinds, enter the blood stream.

Cells absorb these " blocks " and then build new " buildings," or proteins. These proteins then become part of the person's protoplasm and growth or repair of tissue is accomplished. During childhood growth is important, but the adult uses protein principally for the replacement of protoplasm which has worn out and " crumbled." Protoplasm can be constructed *only* from protein.

Amino acid " blocks " not required in the growth and maintenance of protoplasm may be oxidized to supply energy. These excess amino acids are carried to the liver where separation of their parts takes place. The carbon-containing part is sent to the tissues, and it is oxidized there. The nitrogen-containing part is changed to *urea,* delivered by the blood to the kidneys and excreted in the urine. This urea is in addition to that which is formed during the breakdown of tissue protein.

FOOD SUBSTANCES

SUBSTANCE	KIND OF SUBSTANCE	FUNCTION	SOURCE
Water	Inorganic compound	Basic part of protoplasm and blood Vital solvent	Present in all foods Released during oxidation
Sodium compounds	Mineral salts	Essential in blood and other tissues Appetizer	Table salt, vegetables
Calcium compounds	Mineral salts	Deposition in bones and teeth Heart and nerve action Clotting of blood	Milk, whole-grain cereals, vegetables, meats
Phosphorus compounds	Mineral salts	Deposition in bones and teeth Formation of protoplasm	Milk, whole-grain cereals, vegetables, meats
Potassium compounds	Mineral salts	Essential in blood and cell activities Essential for growth	Vegetables
Iron compounds	Mineral salts	Formation of red blood corpuscles	Lettuce, leafy vegetables, liver, meats, raisins, prunes
Iodine	Mineral salts	Secretion by thyroid gland	Sea foods, water, iodized salt
Carbohydrates	Organic nutrients	Energy Stored as fat or glycogen Bulk in diet	Cereals, bread, pastries, tapioca, fruits, vegetables
Fats	Organic nutrients	Energy Stored as fat or glycogen	Butter, cream, cheese, oleo-margarine, lard, oils, nuts, meats
Proteins	Organic nutrients	Growth, maintenance, and repair of protoplasm	Lean meats, eggs, milk, wheat beans, peas
Vitamins	Complex organic substances	Regulation of body processes Prevention of deficiency diseases	Various foods, especially milk, butter, lean meats, fruits, leafy vegetables; can also be made synthetically

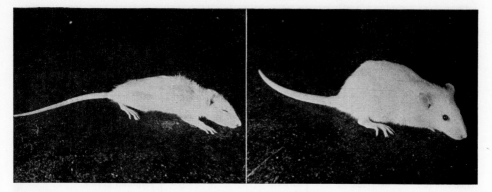

Fig. 35-3. The rat on the left is suffering from a deficiency of vitamin B_1. The same rat is shown on the right after being given sufficient vitamin B_1 to restore it to normal health.

In a normal diet, carbohydrates and fats supply the body's energy needs, although a little protein is usually oxidized. However, when carbohydrates and fats are lacking in the diet, the body draws on its reserve of glycogen and fat or increases protein oxidation. At this point a person begins to lose weight.

The most valuable protein sources include: lean meat, eggs (albumen), milk (casein), and cheese, whole wheat (gluten), beans, and corn.

Vitamins should not be neglected in the diet. Many years ago, when sailing vessels rode the high seas for many months between ports, sailors often developed a disease called *scurvy*. British sailors carried limes and found that by eating them in the course of long voyages, scurvy was avoided. Today we know these fruits contain vitamin C and that scurvy results from lack of it.

In 1911, Dr. Casimir Funk found that certain substances, apart from ordinary nutrients, are present in foods. They seemed to be necessary for normal growth and body activity and in the prevention of certain diseases called **deficiency diseases**. He called these substances, **vitamins**.

Vitamins were first designated by letters — A, B, C, etc. Later it was discovered that certain vitamins thought to be single were made up of many different vitamins as, for example, the vitamin B-complex. Then such names as B_1, B_2, and so forth were adopted. Today, most of the vitamins have names, although letters are still used as a means of easy and simple reference.

Some vitamins are **oil-soluble**. Others are **water-soluble** and occur in fruits and vegetables. Some may be stored in the body, while others must be supplied constantly because they are excreted in the urine when present in excess quantities in the diet. Only one vitamin, vitamin D, can be produced in body tissues. Others must be supplied by the diet or taken in the form of extracts, if the normal diet lacks them. In a final analysis, the best source of vitamins is a properly balanced diet.

Vitamins seem to act in a similar way to the digestive enzymes. Chemically, they can be called **catalysts** (*cat*-ah-lists). This means that they assist or speed up chemical reactions but are largely unchanged themselves in the process.

The best sources, functions, and defi-

FUNCTIONS AND IMPORTANT SOURCES OF VITAMINS

VITAMINS	BEST SOURCES	ESSENTIAL FOR	DEFICIENCY SYMPTOMS
Vitamin A (oil soluble)	fish liver oils liver and kidney green and yellow vegetables yellow fruit tomatoes butter egg yolk	Growth Health of the eyes Structure and functions of the cells of the skin and mucous membranes	Retarded growth Night blindness Susceptibility to infections Changes in skin and membranes Defective tooth formation
Thiamine (B$_1$) (water soluble)	sea food meat soybeans milk whole grain green vegetables fowl	Growth Carbohydrate metabolism Functioning of the heart, nerves, and muscles	Retarded growth Loss of appetite and weight Nerve disorders Less resistance to fatigue Faulty digestion (beriberi)
Riboflavin (B$_2$) (water soluble)	meat soybeans milk green vegetables eggs fowl yeast	Growth Health of the skin and mouth Carbohydrate metabolism Functioning of the eyes	Retarded growth Dimness of vision Inflammation of the tongue Premature aging Intolerance to light
Niacin (P–P) (water soluble)	meat fowl fish peanut butter potatoes whole grain tomatoes leafy vegetables	Growth Carbohydrate metabolism Functioning of the stomach and intestines Functioning of the nervous system	Smoothness of the tongue Skin eruptions Digestive disturbances Mental disorders (pellagra)
Folic acid (B$_{12}$) (water soluble)	green vegetables liver	Prevents pernicious anemia	A reduction in number of red blood cells
Ascorbic acid C (water soluble)	citrus fruit other fruit tomatoes leafy vegetables	Growth Maintaining strength of the blood vessels Teeth development Gum health	Sore gums Hemorrhages around the bones Tendency to bruise easily (scurvy)
Vitamin D (oil soluble)	fish liver oil liver fortified milk eggs irradiated foods sunshine	Growth Regulating calcium and phosphorus metabolism Building and maintaining bones, teeth	Soft bones Poor teeth development Dental decay (rickets)
Tocopherol (E) (oil soluble)	wheat germ oil leafy vegetables milk butter	Normal reproduction	Undetermined
Vitamin K (water soluble)	green vegetables soybean oil tomatoes	Normal clotting of the blood Normal liver functions	Hemorrhages

Fig. 35-4. These are the Seven Basic Food Groups which make up a scientifically balanced diet. Suggested numbers of daily servings are given to insure getting the proper amounts.

ciency symptoms of the better-known vitamins are summarized in the table on page 470.

Synthetic vitamins. Most of the vitamins discussed are available in highly concentrated synthetic form. These preparations are very important in supplementing the natural vitamins of the diet where deficiency occurs. However, even with all the publicity given commercial vitamin preparations, you should keep in mind the fact that a normal, balanced diet is much more valuable than supplementary doses. Your doctor can diagnose vitamin deficiency and prescribe concentrated vitamins if he thinks you need them. If a proper diet is followed, taking additional vitamins is a waste of money and unnecessary for the average person.

What is a balanced diet? We need carbohydrates, fats, and proteins in about the proportions of 4:1:1. In addition, the diet must contain adequate

Carbohydrates

Starch

Double sugars
(Maltose, lactose, sucrose)

Simple sugar
(Glucose)

Fats

Fats

Emulsified fats

Fatty acids and glycerin

Proteins

Protein   Proteose and peptone   Peptid   Amino acid

Fig. 35-5. These diagrams show phases in the digestion of carbohydrates, fats, and proteins. Why can they not be used by tissues in the form in which you eat them?

mineral salts and vitamin sources. One food cannot supply all these. Thus a mixed diet is necessary. When foods in proper proportion conform to all the body needs, we have a balanced diet.

People who are trying to lose or gain weight by " dieting " should still aim for a balanced diet. Otherwise severe nutritional diseases can result.

The Basic Seven foods. Probably the simplest guide to proper eating is the *Basic Seven,* determined as a result of research of the United States Govern-

ment in cooperation with many noted food authorities. These seven groups of foods were found to contain all the essentials for a well-balanced diet. The chart in Fig. 35-4 gives you these.

If you eat one food in each group daily, your diet will automatically include a minimum of all the essential vitamins and minerals, and the proper proportions of protein, fat, and carbohydrate foods. Of course, it is better to eat several foods in each group daily.

The phases of digestion. There are two reasons why tissues cannot use most

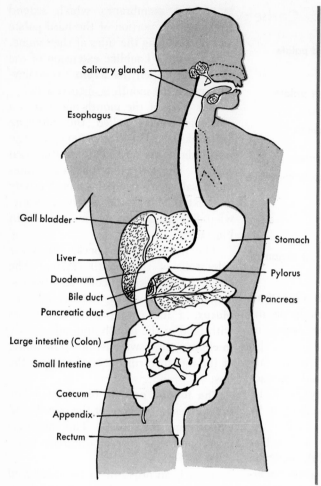

Salivary glands

Esophagus

Gall bladder

Liver

Duodenum

Bile duct

Pancreatic duct

Large intestine (Colon)

Small Intestine

Caecum

Appendix

Rectum

Stomach

Pylorus

Pancreas

Fig. 35-6. The organs of digestion in the human body are shown in this drawing.

foods in the form in which you eat them. First, many substances are insoluble in water and could not enter the cells if they reached them. Second, they are too complex chemically for tissues to use, either in oxidation or for growth and repair. Digestion brings about changes in both of these conditions with the result that cells can absorb and use the products. All carbohydrates eventually become *simple sugars;* all fats become *fatty acids* and *glycerin,* and all proteins become *amino acids.* These foods are both *simple* and *water-soluble.* But changing all the complex foods we eat into these simple

forms is a long and complicated process. (See Fig. 35-5.)

The first part of the change occurring during digestion is *mechanical.* This phase involves the chewing of food in the mouth, and the constant churning and mixing action. This mixing action is caused by the muscular movement of the walls of the digestive organs. The breaking of food into small particles and thorough mixing during digestion aid the *second phase* of digestion which is *chemical.* This phase is accomplished by *digestive enzymes.* These substances are present in various secretions produced by the digestive *glands.*

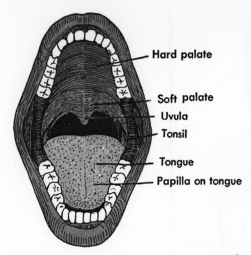

Hard palate

Soft palate

Uvula

Tonsil

Tongue

Papilla on tongue

Fig. 35-7. The mouth is the first organ of the alimentary canal.

The special organs of digestion. The digestive system includes the organs which form the **alimentary canal,** or *food tube.* (See Fig. 35-6.) It also includes those organs which do not actually receive undigested food, but act on foods in the alimentary canal by means of secretions delivered to it by tubes, or **ducts.**

Food enters the alimentary canal at the *mouth.* It is swallowed through the **esophagus** (ee-*sof*-ah-gus) to the *stomach.* From the stomach, the food goes through the long, coiled *small intestine* to the *large intestine,* or *colon.* The *liver* and *pancreas* form secretions which act on food in the small intestine. Secretions from these digestive glands enter the small intestine near its upper end.

The mouth first receives food. Its chief function is to prepare the food for digestion. The mouth also is an organ of sensation and an organ of speech.

The **hard palate** forms the roof of the mouth in the chewing area. It consists of bony structure, covered with several membranes. The **soft palate** lies just back of the hard palate. It is formed

by folded membranes which extend from the rear portion of the hard palate and fasten along the sides of the tongue. You can see a knoblike extension of the soft palate called the **uvula** (*you*-view-lah) when the mouth is opened wide.

The back of the mouth opens into a muscular cavity called the **pharynx** (*fair*-inks). This cavity extends upward, above the soft palate, to the nasal cavity. The soft palate partly separates the nasal cavity from the mouth cavity and extends into the pharynx, somewhat like a curtain, as you can see in Fig. 35-7.

The inside of the cheeks forms the side walls of the mouth cavity. The cheek linings are mucous membranes, containing numerous mucous glands. **Mucus,** a lubricating secretion, mixes with food in the mouth and aids greatly in chewing and swallowing. The lining of the mouth turns outward to form the lips.

The tongue and its functions. The *tongue* lies in the floor of the mouth and extends into the throat. This muscular organ performs several different functions, as follows:

1. It is an organ of taste. Scattered over the surface of the tongue are numerous tiny projections called **papillae** (pah-*pill*-ee). These papillae contain *taste buds.* Nerve endings lie at the base of the taste buds. When food is mixed with mucus and saliva, it contacts the taste buds, and the nerve endings are stimulated. The result of this stimulation is that we taste. The taste buds are sensitive to only four flavors: salt, sour, bitter, and sweet.

2. The tongue aids in chewing by keeping the food between the teeth.

3. During swallowing, food is worked to the back of the tongue. When the tongue is jerked downward, food lodges in the pharynx and passes

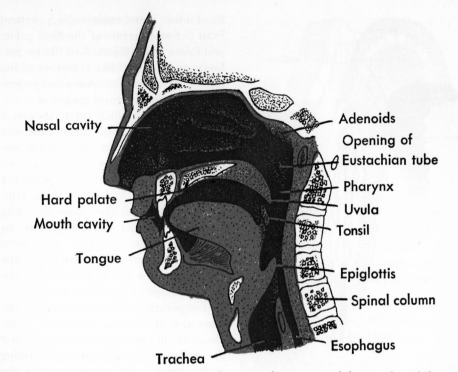

Nasal cavity

Adenoids

Opening of Eustachian tube

Pharynx

Hard palate

Uvula

Mouth cavity

Tonsil

Tongue

Epiglottis

Spinal column

Esophagus

Trachea

Fig. 35-8. In this diagram, you can see the internal structures of the mouth and throat.

into the esophagus opening. During swallowing, the opening of the trachea, or windpipe, is closed by the pressure of the tongue and breathing ceases for a moment.

4. The tongue, rolling in the mouth keeps the inner surface of the teeth clean.

5. It is essential in *speech*. In forming certain word sounds, the tongue acts together with the lips, teeth, and hard palate. Without such action these sounds could not be formed into words.

The structure of the teeth. A tooth is composed of three general regions. The exposed portion above the gum line is called the **crown.** A narrow portion at the gum line is called the **neck,** while the **root** is encased in a socket in the jawbone, and holds the tooth securely in place. Roots vary in form in the different kinds of teeth. They may be long

and single, or may consist of two, three, or four projections. The crown is covered with a hard white substance, the **enamel.** The covering of the root is called **cement** and holds the tooth firmly together.

If you cut a tooth lengthwise, you can see the *dentine* beneath the protective layers of enamel and cement. (See Fig. 35-9). **Dentine** is a relatively softer substance than enamel and forms the bulk of the tooth. The **pulp cavity** lies within the dentine area. It contains small nerves and blood vessels, which join larger nerves and blood vessels in the jawbone through the *nerve canal.*

The number and kinds of teeth. The first set of teeth, sometimes called *milk teeth,* are temporary and are replaced by the *permanent teeth.* The first temporary tooth usually appears between the sixth and ninth month

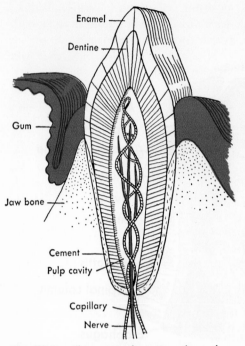

Fig. 35-9. This vertical section through a cuspid tooth shows its various parts.

after birth. "Cutting" teeth continues for about two years, when the last of the *twenty* temporary teeth appear. The first permanent teeth usually appear during the sixth year. They are the first molars, and erupt behind the temporary molars. The last permanent teeth, or "wisdom" teeth, usually appear between the ages of 17 and 25. The full adult or permanent set of teeth consists of *thirty-two* teeth, or four kinds.

If you start between the two front teeth and count back, the permanent teeth are arranged in the following order. The first two are the flat **incisors** with sharp edges for cutting food. Next, near the corner of your lips, is a large conical **canine**, or *cuspid*, tooth. These teeth are often called "eye" teeth, although they have no connection with the eyes. Behind the canine teeth are two **premolars**, or *bicuspids*.

Next come three **molars** (if you have "cut" your "wisdom" teeth). The premolars and molars have large surfaces and are grinding and crushing teeth. Many jaws are too small to provide space for the third molars or "wisdom" teeth. In such cases, they may grow in crooked, lodge against the second molars, or remain embedded or impacted in the jawbone.

The permanent teeth form below the temporary teeth and push these temporary teeth out as they come up. The temporary incisors and canines are replaced by corresponding permanent teeth. The permanent molars occupy a portion of the jaw which did not produce temporary teeth.

Temporary teeth should be given the same dental care as permanent teeth. Decay of the temporary teeth may cause damage to the permanent teeth forming under them. Of course, care of the permanent teeth is a basic rule of good health. Loss of teeth interferes with normal chewing and puts an extra burden on the digestive organs.

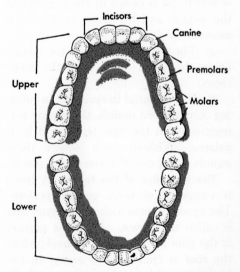

Fig. 35-10. Permanent teeth, which consist of thirty-two teeth, form under the primary teeth.

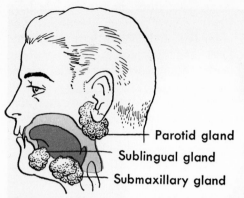

Parotid gland
Sublingual gland
Submaxillary gland

Fig. 35-11. Three pairs of salivary glands aid in producing saliva.

Hygiene of the teeth. The mouth provides ideal conditions for the growth of bacteria. It is warm and moist, and particles of food between the teeth supply the necessary organic food for the growth and development of bacteria. Decay of food in the mouth releases acids which dissolve the enamel of the teeth and permits the formation of a cavity. Such a cavity, unchecked, will deepen and may result in loss of a tooth.

Many dentists have wondered why certain people experience no tooth decay for long periods and then suddenly develop many cavities. Careful checks have revealed no diet deficiency or neglect of oral hygiene in most of these patients. In studies being conducted on this problem, dentists have found that many patients have undergone a period of great emotional tension coinciding with the period of greatest decay.

Dentists speak of a period of " galloping caries," or increased tooth decay, occurring in adolescence. It is probably no mere coincidence that this period is one of increased emotional stress. Many of us have noted a dry mouth during emotional stress. The salivary glands are underactive at such times. The flow of saliva has a considerable cleansing effect and, being alkaline, neutralizes corroding acids in the mouth which damage tooth enamel.

Mouth hygiene demands that you include abundant minerals in your diet, brush your teeth regularly, and visit your dentist twice a year for a checkup.

Fluorine may help fight the battle of tooth decay. In certain areas of our country where the fluorine content of the soil and water is high, natives of the region experience little, if any, tooth decay. This has led public health officials to recommend that dentists apply fluorine compounds to the teeth of many children. They have also suggested that these compounds be added to the water supply. However, research on the effectiveness of fluorine is still going on and it is too early to determine the possible results.

The salivary glands secrete saliva. The chemical phases of digestion are carried on in the mouth by the action of *saliva,* produced by three pairs of *salivary* (*sa*-lih-very) *glands.* (1) The *parotid* (pah-*rot*-id) *glands* are the largest of these glands. One lies on each side of the face below and in front of the ears. Ducts from these glands empty saliva into the mouth opposite the second upper molars. An infection of the parotid glands, causing swelling and irritation, is the disease called *mumps.* (2) The *submaxillary glands* lie within the angles of the lower jaws. (3) The *sublingual* (sub-*ling*-gwal) *glands* are embedded in the mucous membranes in the floor of the mouth, under the tongue. Ducts from both of these glands open into the floor of the mouth under the tongue. The smell of food as well as the sight of it, the presence of it in the mouth, and the taste of it stimulate the secretion of saliva. In other words, your mouth " waters."

Saliva is a thin, alkaline substance.

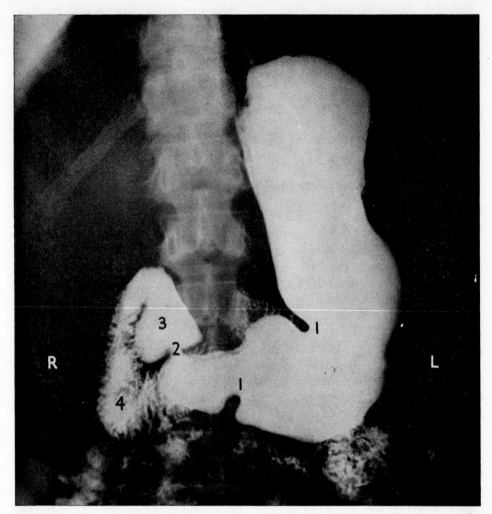

Fig. 35-12. This X-ray photograph of the normal stomach is filled with barium to make the parts visible on a film. Note the (1) contractions; (2) pyloric valve; (3) beginning of the small intestine; and (4) region of villi in the small intestine. R indicates right side; L indicates left.

It is more than 95 per cent water, and contains dissolved mineral salts and the enzyme, **ptyalin** (*ty*-ah-lin). Ptyalin converts starch, especially cooked starch, to grain sugar, or *maltose*. Cooking starchy foods, such as potatoes, is necessary to burst the cellulose cell walls which enclose the starch grains. Otherwise, the ptyalin does not come in contact with the starch. Saliva also contains mucus which lubricates the food.

Since saliva acts on starches in the mouth, it is important that we chew these foods thoroughly to allow plenty of digestive action. Unlike starches, neither fats nor proteins are altered during mouth digestion.

The esophagus connects the mouth with the stomach. When food leaves the mouth, it enters the esophagus and passes for a distance of about one foot to the stomach. Swallowing is accomplished by layers of smooth muscle in the wall of the esophagus. One layer is *circular,* and squeezes inward. The other layer is *longitudinal* and contracts in a wave which travels downward, pushing the food ahead of it.

The stomach is somewhat J-shaped. The stomach lies in the upper left region of the abdominal cavity just below the diaphragm (See Fig. 35-12).

The stomach walls contain three layers of smooth muscle, each arranged differently. One layer is *longitudinal,* one is *circular,* and one is angled, or *oblique.* Contraction of the smooth muscle fibers of the various layers in different directions causes the twisting, squeezing, and churning movement of the stomach.

The lining of the stomach is a thick wrinkled membrane. Numerous **gastric glands** are embedded in the stomach lining. Each gland is a tiny tube with an opening into the stomach. The walls of each gland are lined with cells, some of which secrete **gastric juice** while others produce **hydrochloric acid.** Both secretions pass directly into the stomach.

Gastric juice contains two enzymes: (1) *pepsin;* and (2) *rennin.* **Pepsin** acts on protein and splits the complex molecule into simpler groups of amino acids called **peptones** and **proteoses.** This chemical change is the first in a series involved in protein digestion. Pepsin acts only in the presence of hydrochloric acid. Contrary to common opinion, the stomach must be sour, or acid, to function properly.

Rennin acts on milk, changing the *casein (case-*een), or milk protein, to a *curd.* It has little digestive action, but prepares the milk for action by other enzymes by making it more solid.

Hydrochloric acid, in addition to providing the proper medium for the action of pepsin, dissolves insoluble minerals and kills large numbers of bacteria

which enter the stomach with food. It also causes the valve to open, allowing food to enter the small intestine.

Food usually remains in the stomach two to three hours. During this period, rhythmic contractions of the stomach muscles churn the food back and forth in a circular path. This action separates the food particles and mixes them thoroughly with the stomach secretions. At the completion of stomach digestion, the valve at the intestinal end opens and closes several times. With each opening of the valve, food squirts into the small intestine. Finally, the stomach is relieved of its content and enters a period of rest. After several hours without food, stomach contractions start again and cause the sensation of hunger.

The food which passes from the stomach to the small intestine contains: (1) fats, unchanged; (2) sugars, unchanged; (3) starches which were not acted upon by the ptyalin of saliva; (4) coagulated milk casein; (5) some proteins unchanged by the pepsin of the gastric fluid; and (6) peptones and proteoses formed from the action of pepsin on protein.

The small intestine. In addition to digestion, the small intestine is the seat of absorption of digested food by the blood and lymph for delivery to the tissues.

The chemical phases of digestion in the small intestine involve three secretions from different glands. The small intestine receives: (1) bile from the liver; (2) pancreatic fluid from the pancreas; and (3) intestinal fluid from the intestinal glands.

The liver and bile. The **liver** is the largest gland in the body, weighing between three and four pounds. It lies in the upper right region of the abdominal cavity. This organ performs several vi-

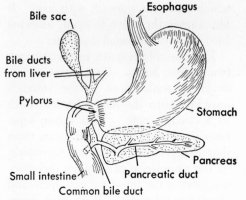

Fig. 35-13. The pancreas and its digestive fluid, pancreatic fluid, play an important role in digestion.

tal functions. In receiving glucose from the blood and changing it to glycogen, it serves as a *chemical factory* and a *storehouse* by holding this in reserve. It serves as a *storehouse* in holding reserve carbohydrates as glycogen. In acting on amino acids and forming urea, it is an *organ of excretion.* All these changes involve food *after* digestion. As a *digestive gland,* the liver secretes bile which acts on food in the small intestine. Even in the formation of bile, the liver plays a part in using what might otherwise be discarded as waste. Part of the bile is formed from worn-out hemoglobin that the blood system can no longer use.

Bile is a brownish-green fluid. It passes from the liver in a series of bile ducts which form a Y. As bile is secreted in the liver, it passes down one branch of the Y, then travels up the other branch to the *gall bladder.* Here the bile is stored and concentrated as a part of the water is removed. The base of the Y is the *common bile duct.* This tube carries bile from the gall bladder to the upper end of the small intestine, the *duodenum.* If the common bile duct becomes clogged by a gallstone, or a plug of mucus, bile enters the blood

stream and causes a yellowing of the eyes and skin, known as *jaundice.*

Bile has several important functions:

1. It is partially a waste substance containing material from dead red blood corpuscles filtered from the blood stream by the liver.

2. It changes fats to emulsions.

3. It increases the digestive action of **steapsin** (stee-*ap*-sin), an enzyme produced in the pancreas, by breaking globules of fat into small droplets.

4. It helps to neutralize the hydrochloric acid from the stomach so that digestion can take place in the intestine.

Actually, bile is not a digestive secretion. In emulsifying fats, it splits large fat particles into smaller ones, producing a milky liquid called an **emulsion.** In this form, pancreatic fluid can act on fats more readily.

The pancreas and pancreatic fluid. The *pancreas* is a many-lobed, elongated, whitish gland, similar in general appearance to a salivary gland. It lies behind the stomach and the upper end of the small intestine, against the back wall of the abdominal cavity. It performs two entirely different functions. The production of insulin by the pancreas will be discussed in Chapter 38. The digestive secretion, *pancreatic fluid,* passes into the small intestine through a long tube, the *pancreatic duct.*

Pancreatic fluid acts upon all three classes of organic nutrients. It contains the following four enzymes: (1) *trypsin;* (2) *amylopsin;* (3) *steapsin;* and (4) *rennin.*

Trypsin (*trip*-sin) continues the breakdown of proteins which began in the stomach by changing peptones and proteoses to still simpler amino acid groups called **peptids.** In addition, it may act upon proteins which were not simplified during stomach digestion. Peptids are not the final product of protein digestion. Only one additional step is necessary to form the amino acids which are used by the body tissues.

Amylopsin (am-ee-*lop*-sin) duplicates the action of the ptyalin in saliva in changing starch into maltose. This is the point where the potatoes you did not chew enough are changed to sugar.

Steapsin splits fats into *fatty acids* and *glycerin*. This is the only digestive action on fats which reduces them to the form in which they are absorbed.

Rennin duplicates the curdling of milk which was started by the gastric fluid.

The intestinal glands secrete intestinal fluid. The mucous lining of the small intestine contains numerous tiny embedded glands called **intestinal glands.** They secrete *intestinal fluid,* a highly alkaline substance containing four principal enzymes: (1) *erepsin;* (2) *maltase;* (3) *lactase;* and (4) *sucrase.*

Erepsin (ee-*rep*-sin) completes protein digestion by changing peptids, formed by the pancreatic fluid, to *amino acids.* **Maltase** splits the double sugar, maltose, into the simple sugar, *glucose,* the final product of carbohydrate digestion. **Lactase** has a similar action on lactose, or milk sugar, in changing it to glucose. **Sucrase** acts on sucrose, or cane sugar, and changes it to simple sugars, chiefly glucose.

Thus, with the combined action of bile, pancreatic fluid, and intestinal fluid in the small intestine, all three classes of foods are completely digested. As simple sugars, fatty acids and glycerin, and amino acids, they leave the digestive system and enter the blood and lymph (*limf*).

Absorption takes place in the small intestine. A magnified part of the small

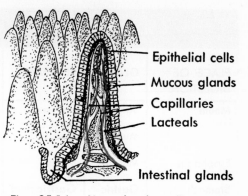

Epithelial cells

Mucous glands

Capillaries

Lacteals

Intestinal glands

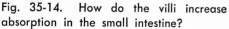

Fig. 35-14. How do the villi increase absorption in the small intestine?

intestine shows that its irregular lining gives rise to great numbers of fingerlike projections called **villi** (sing. *villus*). These projections are so numerous that they give a velvety appearance to the intestinal lining. Within the villi are branching lymph vessels, called **lacteals** (*lak*-tee-als), and blood vessels. The villi bring blood and lymph close to the digested food and increase the absorbing area of the intestine enormously. Absorption is increased further by a constant swaying motion of the villi through the intestinal content.

Fats and fatty acids enter the villi and are carried away by the lymph. They eventually reach the general circulation and travel to the tissues. Glucose and amino acids enter the blood vessels of the villi. Here they are carried directly to the liver through the portal vein.

The large intestine, or colon. The small intestine ends at a junction with the large intestine in the lower right region of the abdominal cavity. Below the point of junction is a blind end of the large intestine called the **caecum** (*see*-kum). The *vermiform appendix* is a fingerlike outgrowth of the caecum. (Appendicitis results when the appendix becomes inflamed.)

SUMMARY OF DIGESTION

PLACE OF DIGESTION	GLANDS	SECRETION	ENZYMES	ACTIVITY OF DIGESTION
Mouth	Salivary	Saliva	Ptyalin	Starch to maltose
	Mucous	Mucus		Lubricant
Esophagus	Mucous	Mucus		Lubricant
Stomach	Gastric	Gastric fluid	Pepsin	Proteins to peptones and proteoses
			Rennin	Coagulates casein
		Hydrochloric Acid		Activates pepsin
				Dissolves minerals
				Kills bacteria
	Mucous	Mucus		Lubricant
Small intestine	Liver	Bile		Emulsifies fats
				Activates steapsin
	Pancreas	Pancreatic fluid	Trypsin	Proteins, peptones, and proteoses to peptids
			Amylopsin	Starch to maltose
			Steapsin	Fats to fatty acids and glycerin
			Rennin	Coagulates casein
	Intestinal glands	Intestinal fluid	Erepsin	Peptids to amino acids
			Maltase	Maltose to glucose
			Lactase	Lactose to glucose
			Sucrase	Sucrose to glucose
	Mucous	Mucus		Lubricant
Large intestine (colon)	Mucous	Mucus		Lubricant

The colon is usually five to six feet long and about three inches in diameter. It forms an inverted U in the abdominal cavity. The **ascending colon** runs upward along the right side, where it curves abruptly to the left to form the **transverse colon**. This portion extends across the upper region of the abdominal cavity. Another curve leads to the **descending colon** on the left side. At its lower end, the descending colon forms an S, called the **sigmoid colon**. The *rectum* is a muscular cavity at the end of the large intestine. The lower end of the rectum forms the *anal opening*. A **sphincter muscle** in the lower end of the rectum controls elimination of intestinal waste.

The large intestine receives a watery mass of undigestible food bulk from the small intestine. As this mass progresses through the colon, water is absorbed from it and returned to the tissues. The intestinal content, or *feces* (*feeseez*), becomes more solid.

A comparison of plant and animal nutrition. The food that animals consume is either plants themselves or animal tissue made directly from plants. Plants, on the other hand, manufacture their own food from raw materials.

Plants do not have digestive organs. But they secrete enzymes like those in animals. In plants, *diastase* digests starch. *Protease* digests protein and *lipase* digests fat. The digestion of food is followed by the oxidation of some food. The rest is assimilated in the formation of protoplasm. In both plants and animals, new protoplasm can only be produced by protoplasm already formed; but the proper types and proportion of food are necessary for normal growth and replacement of tissues.

In Conclusion

When you consider the different uses the body makes of food, in growth and repair of its tissues, as an energy source for maintaining life, in the regulation of life activities, and in the maintenance of a normal, healthy condition in the body tissues, you can see why a balanced diet is essential. No single class of foods can do all of these things. And, when you realize that all of the varied foods you eat in your daily meals reach the tissues in a few basic, simplified forms, you can see why your life depends, not just on your next meals, but on the physical and chemical digestive processes which must follow them.

 ——————————————— **Questions for Review**

1. List six classes of foods and the general use of each by the body.

2. Explain several ways in which your body depends on water.

3. Explain the double role of proteins in the diet.

4. Distinguish between water-soluble and oil-soluble vitamins and the kinds of foods which supply each group.

5. Vitamins act as catalysts in various activities of the body. What does this mean?

6. In what two general ways must foods be changed during digestion?

7. List in order the divisions of the alimentary canal, or food tube.

8. Discuss five or more uses of the tongue.

9. Name the regions you can distinguish in a tooth cut lengthwise.

10. Where are the three pairs of salivary glands located?

11. Why is it especially important that you chew your bread and potatoes thoroughly, even though the potatoes may be mashed?

12. List the sources of the various digestive fluids which act on foods in the small intestine.

13. List four functions of bile.

14. Name two important functions of the large intestine.

Biologically Speaking

alimentary canal	gall bladder	proteose
amino acid	gastric gland	ptyalin
amylopsin	glycogen	pulp cavity
ascorbic acid	hard palate	riboflavin
balanced diet	incisor	saliva
bicuspid	intestinal gland	soft palate
bile	lacteal	sphincter muscle
Calorie	molar	steapsin
catalyst	niacin	sublingual gland
cement	pantothenic acid	thiamin
cuspid	parotid gland	tocopherol
dentine	pepsin	trypsin
enamel	peptone	villi
erepsin	pharynx	vitamin

Applying Facts and Principles

1. Why is it advisable that most people reduce the fat content of their diets during warm weather?

2. Discuss the role of the liver in maintaining a constant level of blood sugar.

3. Why must age and occupation be considered in determining daily Calorie needs?

4. Discuss the value of the Basic Seven foods as a guide to eating.

5. Explain how interference with the rhythmic waves of the walls of the large intestine may cause either constipation or diarrhea.

6. Why is it easier to digest sour milk than fresh milk?

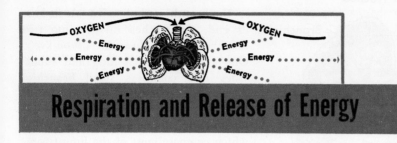

CHAPTER 36

Respiration and Release of Energy

When a new-born child first fills his lungs with air, it is a dramatic event. From the moment when his breathing movements first begin, the process continues 16 to 24 times per minute throughout life. When the person is under exertion the movements are much faster than they are when he is at complete rest or asleep.

Each living cell takes in oxygen, uses it in the oxidation of foods, and gives off carbon dioxide and water. Without oxygen cells are unable to carry on their life processes.

Respiration is a life process common to all living things. The process involves the exchange of gases between cells and their external environments. If cells are in direct contact with the atmosphere, or are in a water environment, an exchange of gases between the cells and their surroundings occurs directly. Each cells receives its own oxygen. Each cell also releases its carbon dioxide and water vapor. Such activity occurs in protozoan cells, in sponges, in jellyfish, and in other animals of simple structure. Plant cells, too, respire in this way. In an insect air is delivered directly to the tissues through the trachea. However, as animals become more complicated in their structure, cells are deprived of this direct contact with the external environment. Some means of receiving oxygen at one place and carrying it to the body tissues becomes necessary.

Respiration in man involves two direct phases. One is *external* and concerns the exchange of gases between the atmosphere and the blood. This phase involves lungs. The second phase is *internal* and concerns an exchange between the blood and the body tissues. It occurs in every living cell. *Breathing* is merely a mechanical process involved in getting air containing oxygen *into* the body and air containing waste gases from respiration *out* of the body.

The respiratory system in man. We can divide the organs concerned with breathing and external respiration into two groups. The first group includes the passages through which air travels in reaching the blood stream: the nostrils, nasal passages, pharynx, trachea, bronchi, and bronchial tubes.

The second group is concerned with the mechanics of breathing by changing the size of the chest cavity. This group includes: (1) the ribs and rib muscles; (2) the diaphragm; and (3) the abdominal muscles.

The nose and nasal passages. Air enters the nose through two streams because the nostrils are divided by the *septum*. From the nostrils, air enters the nasal passages which lie above the mouth cavity. The nostrils contain hairs which aid in filtering dirt out of the air. Other foreign particles may lodge on the moist mucous membranes

485

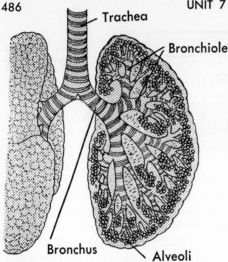

Trachea

Bronchioles

Bronchus

Alveoli

Fig. 36-1. This is a cutaway view of one lung, showing the trachea, bronchus, and alveoli.

in the nasal passages. The length of the nasal passages allows warming of the air and adds moisture to the air before it enters the trachea. All of these advantages of nasal breathing are lost in mouth breathing.

The trachea. From the nasal cavity, the air passes through the *pharynx* and enters the *trachea*. The upper end of the trachea is protected by a muscular flap, or lid, the **epiglottis** (ep-ee-*glot*-tiss). During swallowing, the end of the trachea is closed by the epiglottis. At other times, the trachea remains open to permit breathing. The *larynx* (*lar*-inks), or "Adam's Apple," is the enlarged upper end of the trachea. Inside it are the *vocal cords*. The walls of the trachea are supported by horseshoe-shaped rings of cartilage which hold it open for the free passage of air.

The trachea and its branches are lined with **cilia.** These are in constant motion, and carry dust or dirt taken in with air upwards towards the mouth. This dust, mixed with mucus, is removed when you cough or clear your throat.

The bronchi and air cells. At its lower end, the trachea divides into two branches called **bronchi** (*bron*-kye). One extends to each lung and subdivides into countless small **bronchial** (*bron*-kee-al) **tubes.** These end in air sacs, the walls of which contain the elastic **alveoli** (al-*vee*-oh-lye), or air cells, which compose most of the lung tissue. Thus the lungs provide enough surface to supply air by way of the blood for the needs of millions of body cells having no direct access to air. The total area of the alveoli in the lungs is about 2,000 square feet, or more than 100 times the surface area of the body.

The lungs. These organs fill the body cavity from the shoulders to the diaphragm, except for the space occupied by the heart, trachea, esophagus, and blood vessels. The lungs are spongy and consist mainly of the air tubes and cells and an extensive network of blood vessels and capillaries, held together by connective tissue.

The lungs are covered by a double **pleural membrane.** Below them is the **diaphragm** (*dye*-ah-fram). This is a muscular partition curving upward so that the lower lung surface is sharply concave. The pleural membrane that covers the lungs and lines the chest cavity is constantly moist and allows free motion of the lungs in the chest for breathing.

The blood supply. The **pulmonary artery** brings dark (deoxygenated) blood to the lungs. There it divides into an extensive network of capillaries, completely surrounding each air cell (Figs. 36-2 and 36-3). The thin moist walls of both cell and capillary aid the gaseous exchange of oxygen from air to blood and of carbon dioxide and water from blood to air. The **pulmonary veins** return the blood to the heart laden with oxygen for the tissues. Carbon

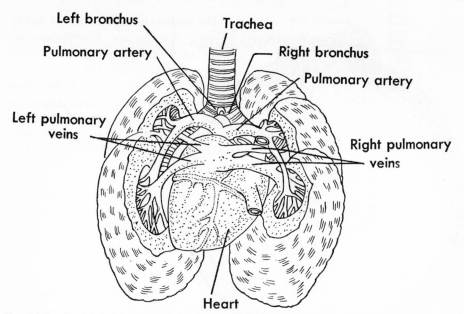

Fig. 36-2. In this back view of the lungs and heart, you can see the branches of the pulmonary artery, and the pulmonary veins.

dioxide in the lung capillaries has a higher concentration than that in the connecting air cells. Hence, carbon dioxide diffuses outward into the area of lower concentration in the air cells. Water passes out of the blood for the same reason.

The air capacity of the lungs. When the lungs are completely filled, they hold about 300 cubic inches of air. However, only about 30 cubic inches are involved each time we inhale and exhale. The air involved in normal, relaxed breathing is called *tidal air*. However, air movement is increased with forced breathing.

To illustrate forced breathing, inhale normally without any forcing. Your lungs now contain about 200 cubic inches of air. Now exhale normally. You have moved about 30 cubic inches of tidal air from the lungs. Now, without inhaling again, force out all the air you can. You have now exhaled an additional 100 cubic inches of

supplemental air. The lungs now contain about 70 cubic inches of *residual air* which you cannot force out.

When you inhale normally again, you replace the supplemental and the tidal air, or about 130 cubic inches. However, if you inhale with force, you can add 100 cubic inches of *complemental air,* raising the total capacity of the lungs to about 300 cubic inches. In other words, the total, or *vital capacity,* of the lungs consists of:

Tidal air	=	30 cu. in.
Supplemental air	=	100 cu. in.
Complemental air	=	100 cu. in.
Residual air	=	70 cu. in.
Vital capacity	=	300 cu. in.

The mechanics of breathing. Many people think that the lungs draw in air, expand, and bulge the chest. Actually, this is the opposite of what happens.

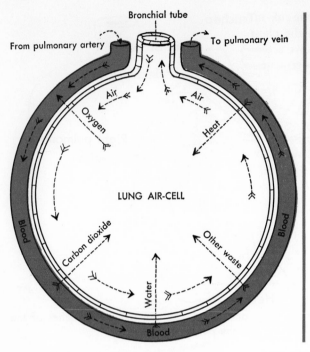

Fig. 36-3. The diagramatic drawing on the left shows how gases are exchanged between the air in the alveoli and the lung capillaries.

The lungs contain no muscle, and cannot expand or contract of their own accord. They are spongy, air-filled sacs, anchored in the chest cavity. Breathing is accomplished by changes in size and air pressure of the chest cavity. This can be shown by substituting apparatus for the body parts (Fig. 36-4).

A Y-tube (*trachea* and *bronchi*) is inserted in a stopper and set in a bell jar (*chest*). Balloons (*lungs*) are fastened to the Y-tube. A piece of rubber sheet (*diaphragm*) is fastened securely to the open base of the bell jar. When you pull the rubber sheet downward, you increase the volume of the bell jar and decrease the pressure within it. Air moves through the Y-tube and inflates the balloons. When you release the rubber sheet, the volume of the bell jar is decreased and the pressure within it is increased. Again air moves to equalize the pressure. But this time it leaves the balloons and passes through the Y-tube to the atmosphere.

Breathing movements. *Inspiration,* or the intake of air, occurs when the chest cavity is increased in size and therefore decreased in pressure. Enlargement of the chest cavity involves the following movements:

1. The rib muscles contract and pull the ribs upward and outward. If you force an inhalation, you carry this action further with the aid of the shoulder muscles.

2. The muscles of the resting, dome-shaped diaphragm contract. This action straightens and lowers the diaphragm and increases the size of the chest cavity from below.

3. The abdominal muscles relax and allow compression of the abdominal organs by the diaphragm.

The enlargement of the chest cavity results in decrease of the air pressure within. In an equalizing movement, air passes through the trachea and inflates the lungs.

Expiration, or the expelling of air from the lungs, results when the chest cavity is reduced in size. This action involves the following four movements:

1. The rib muscles relax and allow the ribs to spring back.

2. The diaphragm relaxes and rises to assume its dome-shaped position.

3. The compressed abdominal organs push up against the diaphragm. This action is increased during a forced exhalation by contraction of the abdominal muscles.

4. The elastic lung tissues, stretched while the lungs are full, shrink and force air out. This is a very important part of air movement.

Artificial respiration. This can be described more accurately as artificial breathing. Any stopping of the breathing motions can be serious because the blood will then lack oxygen and the cells will suffer. Artificial respiration is simply a method of artificially forcing the lungs to inspire and expire air rhythmically. The back-pressure arm-lift method, shown in Fig. 36-7, is the one approved by the American Red Cross. It involves pressure on the region of the shoulder blades and chest and then the release of pressure and the stretching of the body to make the chest cavity larger. The purpose is to reproduce artificially the breathing motions by alternately decreasing and increasing the size of the chest cavity. This forces air in and out of the lungs until normal muscular breathing motions are restored.

The control of breathing. Inspiration and expiration occur from 16 to 24 times per minute, depending on the body activity, position, and age. The greater the oxygen need in the tissues, the more rapidly the lungs must function to supply the necessary oxygen. This is automatically regulated by the

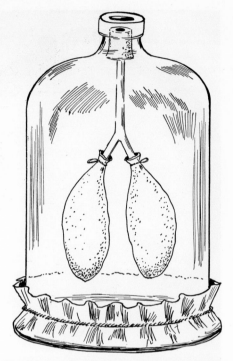

Fig. 36-4. Identify the different apparatus used here for the parts of the body used in breathing. How does this demonstration show the processes involved in breathing?

amount of oxygen or carbon dioxide present in the blood. Abundance of carbon dioxide stimulates breathing. Oxygen surplus in the blood has the opposite effect.

Air changes in breathing. Oxygen is absorbed from the air cells of the lungs by blood in the lung capillaries. It combines with the *hemoglobin* (*hee-moh-glo-bin*) of the red blood corpuscles. *Hemoglobin* is an iron-containing compound giving red corpuscles their color. The amount of oxygen which is absorbed from the blood by the body tissues is smaller than you might think. In the first place, the air we breathe is only one-fifth oxygen. Of this amount, only about one-fourth is absorbed by the blood in the lungs. Furthermore, the hemoglobin gives up only about one-

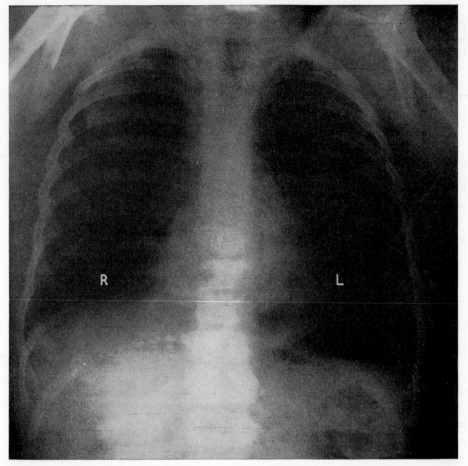

Fig. 36-5. This is an X-ray photograph of the chest during exaggerated inspiration. Notice the lowering of the diaphragm and the stretched and spread ribs. Compare the shape of the chest, especially in the shoulder region, with the same chest during expiration in Fig. 36-6.

third of the oxygen it is carrying in the tissues.

In the tissues, oxygen is used in the oxidation of food to release energy. This process is especially rapid in active muscle tissue. In oxidation of glucose, *lactic acid* is produced. Part of the lactic acid is oxidized further to form carbon dioxide and water. The remaining lactic acid seems to be changed back to glycogen for re-use in the muscle tissues.

If oxygen is lacking, lactic acid accu-

mulates and produces fatigue. This stops muscular action unless it is removed by oxidation. It is thus apparent that oxidation is essential to muscle action, but in a different way from what we supposed formerly.

What is an oxygen debt? During times of muscular exertion, the need for oxygen in the tissues is greater than the body can possibly supply. The lungs cannot take in oxygen nor can the blood deliver it rapidly enough. Consequently, the body builds up an oxygen

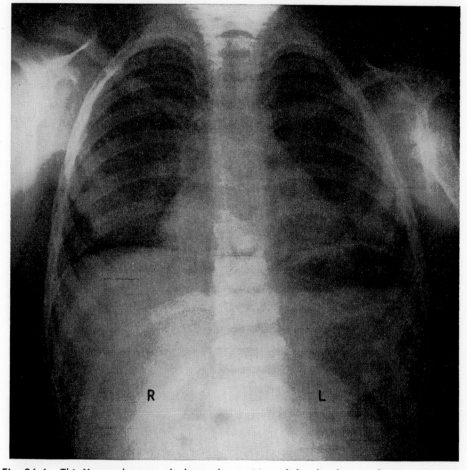

Fig. 36-6. This X-ray photograph shows the position of the diaphragm during expiration. Notice that the diaphragm is raised well into the chest cavity.

debt. All the available supply is used in oxidizing glucose to release energy. Lactic acid accumulates and muscle fatigue increases. Breathing becomes harder and continues at a rapid rate until the oxygen is restored to the normal level; that is, until the full debt is paid.

If you continue to work your muscles to exhaustion without resting to repay the oxygen debt, the nerves to the muscles finally block and paralyze the muscle temporarily.

Metabolism concerns all the vital body processes. Respiration and oxidation are part of a complex series of body processes which are included in **metabolism** (meh-*tab*-oh-lism). All processes, both physical and chemical, which are concerned with the activity, maintenance, and growth of an organism, make up metabolism.

Growth and maintenance are concerned with the assimilation of food. During assimilation, food substances are reorganized in the tissues to form new protoplasm. In some way, the new protoplasm is given the power of life from the protoplasm which organized it. These build-up activities of metabolism are called **anabolism.**

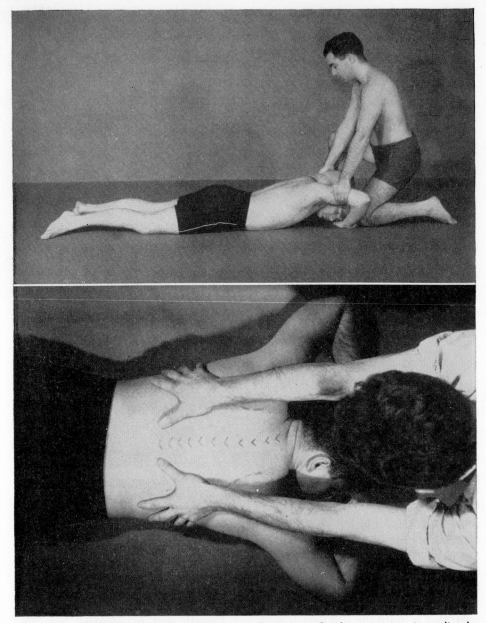

Fig. 36-7. Whenever breathing has stopped, give artificial respiration immediately. The back-pressure arm-lift method is recommended by the American Red Cross.

These processes, like all other types of protoplasmic activity, require energy. This must come from food and must be released through the process of oxidation. Thus the energy exchange between food and living matter constitutes another important phase of metabolism. The tearing-down activities, for example in energy production, are called **catabolism.**

The rate of respiration affects the rate of oxidation, while the amount of energy released is governed directly by the rate of oxidation. All three are regulated by the activity of the body.

Body oxidation and its measurement. The rate of oxygen intake, respiration, and energy released is increased in proportion to the activity of the body. This activity may be muscular, as in the case of walking, running, or some other form of exertion, or it may be mental. Other factors governing the rate of oxidation include exposure to cold and activity of the digestive organs during digestion of food. The rate of oxidation in the body may be measured directly by determining the amount of heat which is given off from its surface. This may be measured by means of a device called a **calorimeter** (kal-oh-*rim*-ih-ter).

The person to be tested enters a closed compartment which is equipped to measure accurately all the heat which is given off by his body. He may lie quietly in bed during the process, or he may sit in a chair, or exercise vigorously, depending on the nature of the activity to be tested. The amount of heat energy given off during each type of activity is a direct indication of the rate of oxidation in the body tissues. Calorimeter tests are important in determining the energy needs of various individuals in order to adjust a diet to their specific requirements.

Basal metabolism and its measurement. Even when the body seems completely inactive as in sleep, respiration, oxidation, and energy release are continuing. With the cessation of muscular and, to a great extent, nervous activity, the rate of oxidation is greatly reduced. The activities required to maintain the body and to supply energy necessary to support the basic life processes are included in the term **basal metabolism.** But it must be remembered that

Fig. 36-8. During great muscular exertion, this track man has built up an oxygen debt. When the oxygen is restored to its normal level, the full debt will be paid.

the term metabolism refers to the total activity of the individual cell. When the amount of oxygen intake is measured for the whole body, this is termed the **basal metabolism rate.**

The rate of basal metabolism may be determined by means of the calorimeter test.

Another method, widely used in hospitals, measures the amount of oxygen consumed in a definite period (Fig. 36-9). The patient rests for at least an hour before the test. The test is usually run in the morning and the patient is instructed to eat no food until after the test is completed. After a rest period, during which the body is completely relaxed, the nose is plugged to avoid breathing from the atmosphere. A mouthpiece, connected to a tank of oxygen, is fitted into the mouth.

Thus all oxygen inhaled during the test period is from the measured tank.

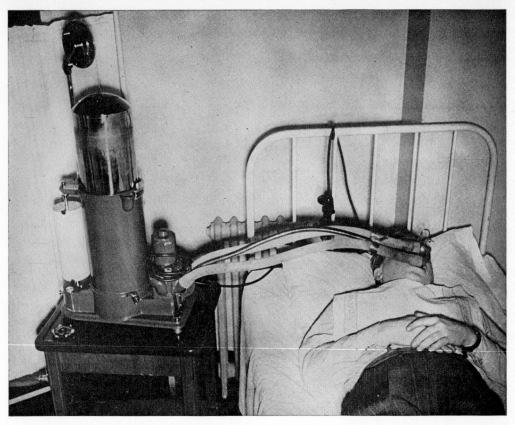

Fig. 36-9. The basal metabolism test determines the amount of fuel food you are burning when at complete rest.

The amount of oxygen used from the tank is recorded on a graph. From these data, the rate of oxidation is determined. The rate of basal metabolism is calculated from the rate of oxidation in the tissues during complete rest.

External influences upon breathing and respiration. External factors, such as temperature, moisture in the air, and the oxygen and carbon dioxide content of air, are very important influences on the rate of breathing and respiration. Certain of these factors are involved in *ventilation.*

Stuffiness in a room is due mainly to increase in the temperature and moisture content of the air, rather than to accumulation of carbon dioxide and decrease of the oxygen content. Movement of air in a ventilating system in-creases its flow over the body surfaces and speeds up the evaporation of perspiration. Modern air-conditioning systems not only circulate air, but remove moisture and heat as well.

The air in most homes, especially those equipped with a central heating system, becomes too dry during the cold months. This dries out mucous membranes and lowers their resistance to infection. The moisture content of the air, therefore, should be kept as high as possible by means of humidifiers or other devices.

Many people carry the ventilation of bedrooms at night to extremes. Your body requires less oxygen while you are asleep than at any other time. If the windows are open too much during cold weather, your body may chill during the night. There is little logic in piling covers on a bed to keep part of the body warm and chilling the exposed parts with cold air from an open window.

Carbon monoxide poisoning. Far too often, we read of people who have died in a closed garage where an automobile engine was running or in a house filled with gas from an open stove burner or a defective furnace. The cause of death is given as *carbon monoxide poisoning*. Actually, the death is not due to poisoning, but to *tissue suffocation*.

Carbon monoxide will not support life. Yet it combines with the hemoglobin of the blood 250 times as readily as oxygen. Thus a small concentration of carbon monoxide in the air will be absorbed in preference to a much larger concentration of oxygen. Furthermore, when carbon monoxide combines with hemoglobin, it is very difficult to separate the two. This results in loading the blood with carbon monoxide and the decrease in its oxygen-combining power. As tissues suffer from oxygen starvation, the victim becomes lightheaded and ceases to care about his condition. Soon paralysis sets in and he could not move if he wanted to. Death follows from tissue suffocation.

Respiration problems at high altitudes. The oxygen content of the air remains at approximately 21% of the total volume of the air at sea levels in our atmosphere. In a sense, we are living at the bottom of a large sea of air. However, as we increase our altitude the amount of air on top of us is decreased and thus the pressure is reduced. The pressure of the air is an important factor in how we breathe and how oxygen combines with the hemoglobin of the blood. Thus, mountain climbers and airplane pilots experience increasing difficulty in breathing and progressive weakness as they increase their altitude. At elevations near 12,000 feet they almost approach exhaustion.

These problems are even more acute in air travel. You can fly much higher than you can climb because the plane motor is doing the work and your oxidation requirements are much reduced. However, when a pilot nears 20,000 feet, the oxygen becomes so reduced that he experiences difficulty in seeing and hearing. This condition, called **anoxia** (an-*ok*-see-ah), is the result of oxygen starvation in the tissues. It is a dangerous condition and will cause death if not corrected within a short time. Anoxia may be avoided by equipping the pilot with an oxygen tank and a mask.

Passengers in modern airliners can fly at high altitudes in the safety and comfort of pressurized cabins. These cabins maintain an internal pressure

Fig. 36-10. This new high altitude flying suit provides airmen with protection in the event cabin pressurization is lost when flying at high altitudes. Tubes along pilot's arms and legs are used to pressurize suit.

and oxygen content equivalent to an altitude of approximately 5,000 feet.

However, man traveling at supersonic speeds in the new aircraft and rockets finds that the problems involved are similar to those experienced by divers under high pressure. Force produces profound changes in the circulatory system, too, and aviation research scientists are working hard to find effective methods of coping with them. See Fig. 36-10 on page 495.

In Conclusion

Respiration is the exchange of gases between living matter and its surroundings. It is closely related to the chemical process, oxidation, in which energy is released during the breakdown of foods. In lower forms of life, individual cells are in direct contact with their surroundings. In higher animals, blood is necessary as a conducting medium between the body tissues and a respiratory center which is in contact with the outer environment. The movement of air in and out of lungs is accomplished by the mechanical process, breathing.

During external respiration, gases are exchanged between the air in the alveoli and the lung capillaries. Air enters the chest cavity because of lowered pressure during expansion. Reduction of the size of the chest cavity causes expiration.

Metabolism includes respiration, oxidation, and the growth processes. The rate at which these processes occur during rest is expressed as the rate of basal metabolism.

 ———————————— Questions for Review

1. What are the differences between respiration and breathing?
2. (a) What happens to the air taken in through the nose? (b) What advantage is this over mouth breathing?
3. How can the capacity of the lungs be determined?
4. How do pressure changes within the chest cavity cause inspiration and expiration of air?
5. What is the purpose of artificial respiration?
6. What factors influence the rate of breathing?

7. (a) How can you build up an oxygen debt? (b) How can the oxygen debt be repaid?
8. What is the difference between cell metabolism and basal metabolism?
9. Outline one method by which the rate of basal metabolism may be determined.
10. What are the chief factors involved in ventilation?
11. Explain the physiology of carbon monoxide poisoning.
12. How does pressure influence breathing and the intake of oxygen?

Biologically Speaking

alveoli	catabolism	pleural membrane
anabolism	complemental air	residual air
anoxia	diaphragm	respiration
artificial respiration	epiglottis	septum
basal metabolism	expiration	supplemental air
breathing	inspiration	tidal air
bronchi	larynx	ventilation
bronchial tubes	metabolism	vital capacity
calorimeter	oxygen debt	vocal cords

Applying Facts and Principles

1. One type of artificial respiration is to breathe directly into the victim's mouth through a handkerchief. Explain why this method may be effective.

2. What happens to the respiratory system of a pilot who is in a power dive or in a supersonic speed plane?

3. After several very deep breaths, breathing stops for a time. Explain.

4. People who live in dry climates, such as the southwestern parts of our country, report that high temperatures are easier to take there than the same temperatures in the more humid parts of the United States. Why?

5. If plants produce oxygen in photosynthesis, how do you explain the fact that they also respire?

CHAPTER 37

The Blood and Circulation

Circulation is no problem to a sponge or to a jellyfish. The type of circulation these lowly creatures use literally pumps the ocean into their bodies! The sea water supplies each cell with its individual oxygen and food needs and washes its wastes away. Actually, the cells in man's body are bathed in a fluid which has a salt content very much like sea water. We call this fluid *blood plasma*. However, man's circulatory system is far more complex than that of the invertebrates.

Man produces his own " sea water," and adds other vital substances to it. Then it is piped through his body, and circulated with a pump — the heart. If the pump stops working, man's cells are in the same predicament as a sponge would be in when thrown up on the beach.

What is blood? **Blood** is a *fluid tissue*. The fluid portion is the **plasma**. The blood cells, or solid elements, are the **corpuscles** (*kor*-pus-uls). The average person has about ten pints of blood. These compose about nine per cent of the body weight.

Blood plasma. If you remove the cells from whole blood, the straw-colored, sticky plasma remains. Nine-tenths of plasma is water.

The proteins in plasma give it the sticky quality. One of them, **fibrinogen** (fy-*brin*-oh-jen), is essential in the clotting of blood. When fibrinogen is removed from plasma, two other proteins remain. One is **serum albumin** (al-*bew*-min) which is necessary to normal blood and tissue relationship during absorption. The other is **serum globulin** (*glob*-you-lin) which gives rise to antibodies causing immunity to various diseases.

Prothrombin (pro-*throm*-bin) is an enzyme produced in the liver when vitamin K is present in the body. It is inactive normally, but changes during clotting.

Inorganic minerals, dissolved in water, give plasma the approximate salt composition of sea water. These compounds include carbonates, chlorides, and phosphates of the elements calcium, sodium, magnesium, and potassium. These minerals are absolutely essential to the blood and to the normal functioning of the body tissues. Without calcium compounds, blood will not clot in a wound.

Digested foods are present in plasma in the form of glucose (*blood sugar*), fats, and amino acids. They are received in the digestive organs, liver, and other places of storage, and travel to the tissues.

Nitrogen-containing wastes, from protein metabolism in tissues, and *urea,* produced largely in the liver during the breakdown of amino acids, travel in the plasma to the organs of excretion. We call these nitrogen-containing wastes **non-protein nitrogens.**

Red blood cells. The *blood cells,* or solid elements, include the red corpuscles, white corpuscles, and platelets. (See Fig. 37-1.) Blood is a peculiar tissue in that the cells are scattered among the nonliving substances composing the plasma.

The red color of blood is due to *hemoglobin* present in the *red cells,* or *corpuscles.* Red corpuscles are so small that ten million of them can be spread in one square inch. They are so numerous that, placed side by side, they would cover an area of 3,500 square yards. It is estimated that the blood of a normal person contains 25 trillion (25,000,000,000,000) red blood cells, or sufficient to go around the earth four times at the equator, if laid side by side.

A red cell is shaped like a disk with both sides concave. Red corpuscles travel in the blood in rows which resemble stacks of coins, although they may separate and float individually. They are produced in the red marrow of bones. The life of the average red corpuscle is about 30 days. The remains of worn-out red cells are filtered out of the blood in the spleen and liver.

Hemoglobin combines readily with oxygen to form a bright red compound called **oxyhemoglobin** (ox-ee-*hee*-moh-glow-bin). In this form, oxygen is carried from the lungs to the tissues. When part of the oxygen is left in the tissues, hemoglobin changes from bright red to dark red, forming reduced hemoglobin. This accounts for the dark color of blood in the veins, traveling from the body tissues to the heart.

Carbon dioxide enters the red blood cells from the tissues and forms carbonic acid (the acid in soda water). This combines with potassium in the red cells to form *potassium bicarbonate.* In the lungs, the process reverses and carbon dioxide is released.

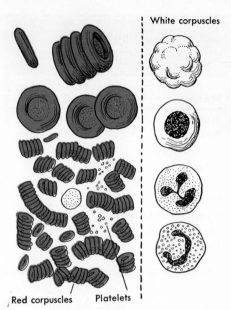

Fig. 37-1. Blood cells include red corpuscles, platelets, and white corpuscles.

White blood cells. The large, nearly colorless blood cells are the **white corpuscles.** They are less numerous than red cells, the ratio being about one white cell to 600 red cells. White cells are formed in the blood marrow and lymph glands. Normally there are about 8,000 in one cubic millimeter of blood as against 5 to 5½ million red cells.

White blood cells, or **leucocytes** (*lu*-koh-sytes), are of several types and sizes. These cells move about in the blood and ooze through capillary walls into the tissue spaces. Here, they engulf solid materials, including bacteria. They are an important defense of the body against infection. When an infection develops in the tissues, the white cells increase rapidly. The white cell count may go from 8,000 to more than 25,000 per cubic millimeter. White corpuscles collect in the area of an infection and destroy bacteria in enormous numbers.

SUMMARY OF COMPOSITION OF BLOOD

PLASMA	BLOOD CELL
Water	Red corpuscles
Proteins	White corpuscles
Fibrinogen	Platelets
Serum albumin	
Serum globulin	
Prothrombin	
Inorganic substances	
Digested foods	
Tissue wastes	

The remains of dead bacteria, white corpuscles, and tissue fluid is *pus.*

Blood platelets are the third type of solid material in blood. They are only half the size of red corpuscles. They are probably formed in the red bone marrow and aid in the formation of a clot.

The functions of blood. Blood is the transporting medium for all substances in the body. Its functions are best shown in the table below.

How blood clots. When you cut small blood vessels in a minor wound, blood oozes out. Such an injury is not alarming. Within a few minutes, a clot will form and the blood flow will stop. You probably take this for granted, without considering what would happen if the flow did not stop.

Clotting results from chemical and physical changes in blood. When blood leaves a vessel, the platelets disintegrate and form **thromboplastin** (*throm*-boh-plass-tin). This substance combines with the enzyme *prothrombin* and *calci-*

BLOOD AS A TRANSPORTING MEDIUM

TRANSPORTATION OF	FROM	TO	FOR THE PURPOSE OF
Digested food	Digestive organs and liver	Tissues	Energy, growth, and repair of cells
Cell wastes	Active tissues	Lungs, kidneys, and skin	Excretion
Water	Digestive organs and tissues	Kidneys, skin, lungs	Excretion and equalization of body fluids
Oxygen	Lungs	Tissues	Oxidation
Heat	Tissues	Skin	Equalizing the body temperature
Secretions	Ductless glands	Various organs, glands	Regulation of body activities

um to form **thrombin.** The thrombin unites with *fibrinogen,* a blood protein, to form **fibrin** (*fy*-brin). Clotting changes may be summarized as in the table below. If *any* of these substances is not present, clotting will not occur.

After fibrin is produced, clotting is largely a physical process. Fibrin is a white insoluble protein which forms a network in the blood flow. This entangles blood corpuscles, much as you might collect leaves and sticks in a stream by stretching a net across it (Fig. 37-2). The trapped corpuscles dry out and form a scab. As the scab hardens, the edges of the wound grow toward the center, thus aiding healing.

If blood vessels are broken under the skin in a bruise, a " black and blue " spot may appear. Clotting occurs under the skin. Gradually, the clotted blood is absorbed and the color of the bruise changes to greenish and yellow, and finally disappears.

What is anemia? This condition results from a reduction in either the number of red corpuscles or the quantity of hemoglobin, depending on the type of the disease. The many types of anemia may be due to the following causes: (1) loss of blood; (2) deficiency of iron in the diet; (3) failure of the blood-forming organs to produce red blood cells (pernicious anemia); (4) destruction of red blood cells by chemical poisons; and (5) loss of red blood cells during infection.

A diet rich in iron is valuable in correcting forms of anemia in which the

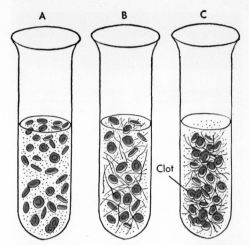

Fig. 37-2. This diagram shows the microscopic changes which occur during the clotting of blood. A. Before clotting has started. B. Formation of threads of fibrin. C. Shortening of the fibrin threads and trapping of the blood cells in the mesh.

hemoglobin content of the red blood cells is low. *Pernicious anemia,* in which the number of red blood cells is low due to a defect in the red bone marrow, is a much more serious condition.

Leukemia is a disease of the blood. When the white cell-forming elements of the bone marrow " go wild " and produce white cells in enormous numbers, **leukemia** (lu-*kee*-mee-ah) results. It is a malignant condition in the bone marrow. Bone marrow, which normally produces both red and white blood cells, becomes so crowded with white cells that the red corpuscle-forming elements are literally crowded out. The white corpuscle-count rises rapidly as the red cell-

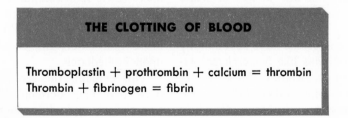

THE CLOTTING OF BLOOD

Thromboplastin + prothrombin + calcium = thrombin
Thrombin + fibrinogen = fibrin

Fig. 37-3. This laboratory technician is engaged in special blood typing work on an unknown sample.

count decreases. The liver and spleen enlarge in an effort to correct the condition. Leukemia is of several types: it may be chronic, with alternate periods of illness and relief; or it may be acute, resulting in death in a fairly short time.

Effects of radioactivity. In these days of threats of radioactivity, we should be aware that primary damage in the body is to the blood. When the body has been exposed to radioactivity, the white blood cells are damaged and then the white blood-cell forming marrow of the bone is destroyed. There is also a great destruction of blood platelets. Treatment consists of the prevention of infection due to loss of white blood cells, and the prevention of blood loss.

Blood transfusions have saved many lives. Conditions like *hemorrhage* (severe bleeding), wound shock, severe burns, and various other illnesses may require *blood transfusions*. If whole blood is used, the patient receives both the necessary plasma and blood cells. However, the blood of the one who gives it must be typed and matched with that of the patient. Blood types are designated as A, B, AB, and O. There is also an *Rh* type. Using the wrong type may result in serious blood reactions and clotting and death of the patient.

Often the patient needs an immediate increase in the volume of liquid in the blood stream and does not require additional blood cells. This condition is called **shock**. The red corpuscles form rapidly if the blood volume is maintained. In such cases, plasma may be transferred in preference to whole blood. Typing is not necessary in the use of plasma because of the absence of the cells.

The Rh factor in blood. The **Rh factor** may be any one of six or more protein substances, or **antigens**, present on the red corpuscles of 87 per cent of all people. If you have one of these antigens, you are *Rh positive*. If you are one of the 13 per cent lacking any of them, you are *Rh negative*.

If you are *Rh* negative and receive *Rh* positive blood in a transfusion, you produce an antibody against the factor. This antibody causes the corpuscles of *Rh* positive blood to clump together (agglutinate) and to dissolve. There is little danger during the first transfusion since the antibody is not present when the *Rh* positive blood is added. However, a second transfusion with *Rh* positive blood may result in serious, or, in many cases, fatal complications. Since the patient's blood now contains antibodies against the factor, the transfused blood that enters his vessels is acted upon immediately.

This explains the serious complications that may develop during some transfusions, and why some mothers occasionally lose all but their first-born children as a result of a strange blood destruction.

Two scientists, Landsteiner and Wiener, discovered the *Rh* factor in the blood of a Rhesus monkey. They named the factor *Rh,* as an abbreviation for Rhesus. When they added a portion of blood taken from a Rhesus monkey to a rabbit, they discovered that the rabbit's blood affected the corpuscles of human blood. Further studies showed that this effect on human corpuscles occurred in 87 per cent of the persons tested in New York City. The reaction had no relation to the common blood groups designated as A, B, AB, and O. They discovered that the blood of the Rhesus monkey contained the *Rh factor,* and that the rabbit's blood formed an antibody against it. All the people whose blood was affected by the antibody had *Rh* positive blood.

How the *Rh* factor may affect childbirth. Similar reactions occur with childbearing in about one case in three or four hundred mothers. In such cases, the mother is *Rh* negative and the father is *Rh* positive. The child has inherited *Rh* positive blood from the father. During development, blood from the child, containing the factor, may seep into the mother's circulation through tiny ruptures in the membranes which normally separate the two circulations. Blood from the mother seeps into the child through the same channels.

Such seepage is uncommon, and explains why many *Rh* negative mothers bear normal *Rh* positive children. However, if seepage occurs with a second *Rh* positive child, the antibody in the mother's blood enters the child's circulation and causes serious anemia, hemorrhage, and liver and bone damage. Occasionally, the child dies before birth. But if the damage to the child is not too extensive, an immediate transfusion after birth may save its life. In some cases, the child's blood is almost entirely removed and replaced by transfused blood. Blood used in such a complete transfusion is *Rh* negative but does not contain the antibody. In other words, the donor has never received positive blood.

Now you can see why a mother whose blood contains the antibody because of an *Rh* positive transfusion may sometimes lose even her first child. For this reason, blood used in a transfusion for a woman under 40 is checked carefully for presence of the *Rh* factor.

The recent discovery of **hapten** may be of great significance in controlling complications resulting from the *Rh* factor. This substance is obtained from washed red blood cells in blood banks. It seems to prevent destruction of red blood cells by the antibody. Hapten may be extremely effective in preventing damage to a child during development, or in preventing damage to the blood after birth without resorting to transfusions.

Blood banks store blood. In recent years, great advances have been made in the preservation of whole blood and plasma for use in transfusions. Whole blood can be safely kept in vacuum bottles under refrigeration (40° F.) for as long as a month. Each bottle contains 500 cubic centimeters, or about one pint of blood, mixed with sodium citrate, citric acid, and dextrose. When a transfusion is needed in a hospital, blood of the correct type is immediately available in the blood bank. Or a friend or relative of the patient may supply the kind of blood he needs, if a direct transfusion appears advisable.

Plasma may be prepared in powdered form. When used in a transfusion, it

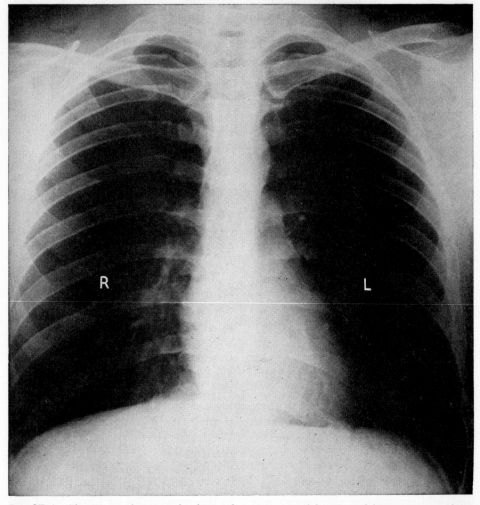

Fig. 37-4. The X-ray photograph above shows a normal heart and lungs as seen from the front. Notice that the heart points toward the patient's left side. The curved, white area below the heart is the diaphragm.

is dissolved in sterile distilled water. Since the dried plasma and water can be easily carried without the necessity of refrigeration, it can be administered at once. This was practiced during World War II and saved the lives of many wounded men.

The heart. The heart is a cone-shaped muscular organ situated under the breastbone and between the lungs. It is enclosed in a sac called the **peri-**

cardium (per-ih-*kar*-dih-um). It usually lies a little left of the mid-line of the chest cavity with its point extending downward and to the left between the fifth and sixth ribs. Since the beat is strongest near the tip, many people have the mistaken idea that the entire heart is on the left side.

The heart is composed of two sides, right and left. The two halves are entirely separated by a wall called the

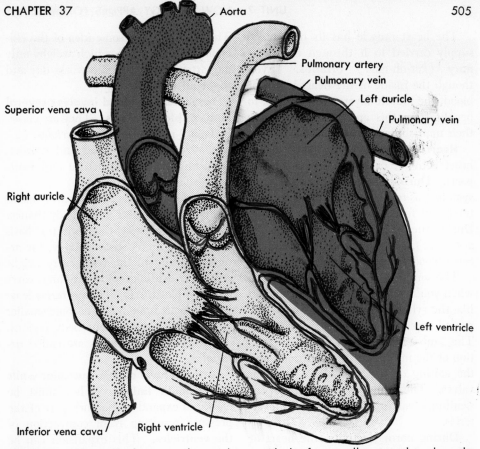

Fig. 37-5. You are looking at a human heart with the front wall removed to show the chambers and valves. Blood passes from auricle to ventricle on the right side through the tri-cuspid *a-v* valve. The corresponding valve on the left side is the bi-cuspid *a-v* valve. Find the *s-l* valves at the base of the pulmonary artery and aorta. These valves prevent backflow of blood into the heart when the ventricles relax between beats.

septum. Each half is composed of two chambers, a relatively thin-walled **au-ricle,** and a thick, muscular **ventricle.** The auricles act as reservoirs for the blood entering the heart from the great veins. When the auricles contract, they fill the ventricles rapidly. The thick muscular walls of the ventricles are composed of twisted bands of heart muscle. Contraction of the ventricles forces blood out through the great arteries.

Flow of blood from the ventricles under pressure and maintenance of pressure in the arteries between beats require two sets of one-way heart valves. The valves between the auricles and ventricles (*a-v* or *auricular-ventricular* valves) are flaplike structures which are anchored to the floor of the ventricles by slender tendons. When the auricles contract, blood passes through these valves freely into the ventricles. However, the valves cannot be opened from the lower side because of the strands which anchor them. Thus blood is unable to flow backward into the auricles during contraction of the ventricles. Other valves (*s-l* or *semilunar* valves) are located at the openings of the arteries. These cuplike valves are opened by the force of blood passing from the ventricles into the arteries.

The heart muscle has its own blood supply carried to it through the **coronary** (*kor*-oh-nary) **arteries.** Even though the inside of the heart is full of blood, the muscle layers are too thick to benefit from this and the cells receive their nourishment through these vessels.

Heart action. A complete cycle of heart activity, or beat, consists of two parts. During one part of the cycle, or **systole** (*sis*-toh-lee), the ventricles contract and force blood into the arteries. During the other part, or **diastole** (*dy-as*-toh-lee), the ventricles relax and receive blood from the auricles.

The sounds you hear in a stethoscope when you listen to a normal heart sound like the syllables " lub " and " dup " repeated over and over in perfect rhythm. The " lub " is the sound of the contraction of the muscles of the ventricles and the closing of the auricular-ventricular valves. The " dup " is the closing of the semilunar valves at the base of the arteries.

During normal activity, the heart of the average adult man beats about 72 times per minute. The beat in the average woman is about 80 times per minute. However, many hearts beat faster or slower under normal activity.

Activity speeds up heart action. With the body at rest, the heart pumps about four or five pints of blood per minute. If your body contains 10 pints of blood, it would make a complete circulation through the body in less than a minute at this rate of heart action. However, mild exercise, such as walking, speeds the heart output to about 20 pints per minute and strenuous exercise may increase it to as much as 35 pints per minute. At this rate, blood may make a complete circulation in about 20 seconds. You could not possibly keep up with a heart under exertion using a hand pump to move the blood.

This will give you some idea of the efficiency of this organ which weighs only a quarter of a pound and works day and night all your life.

Movement of blood involves several kinds of blood vessels. They are classified as: (1) *arteries* and *arterioles;* (2) *capillaries;* and (3) *veins* and *venules,* according to their structure and function.

Arteries and arterioles carry blood *away* from the heart to the body tissues. We cannot classify them on the basis of the kind of blood they carry, for arteries leading to the body carry bright red blood, while those to the lungs carry dark red blood. The large **arteries** leaving the heart branch and become smaller as they reach the various body regions. The very small branches are called **arterioles.**

Arteries have elastic, muscular walls and smooth linings. They must be elastic to expand and absorb part of the pressure resulting from contraction of the ventricles. This expansion can be felt in the wrist and in other parts of the body where arteries are near the surface. It is known as the **pulse.** The muscles of the artery walls are controlled by nerves. When these muscles contract, they reduce the size of the artery and raise the blood pressure.

Blood pressure in the arteries. Blood leaves the heart ventricles under terrific pressure. Pressure in the aorta leading from the left ventricle to the body is greater than that in the pulmonary artery pumped by the smaller right ventricle. If the aorta were cut, blood would spurt out in a stream six feet or more.

With each contraction of the ventricles, blood surges through the arteries with a force so great it bulges their elastic walls. At this point, arterial blood pressure is greatest. We refer to this

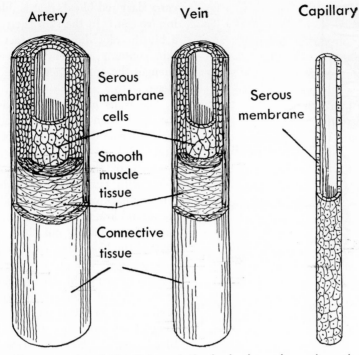

Fig. 37-6. The movement of blood through the body depends on these three types of blood vessels.

as **systolic** (sis-*tol*-ik) **pressure.** The recoil of the artery wall maintains part of this pressure while the heart is at rest. This is the time of lowest pressure in the arteries, or **diastolic** (dy-as-*tol*-ik) **pressure.** When you take a pulse at the wrist or temple, you feel the bulge in an artery wall caused by systolic pressure. The pulse taken at any part of the body has the same rhythm as the beats of the heart.

How a doctor measures blood pressure. He uses a simple device consisting of an air bag, a small pump, and a mercury gauge attached to the bag. He wraps the bag around your arm just above the elbow. Then he lays his stethoscope against the bend of your elbow and inflates the bag until he collapses the artery in your arm. While releasing air from the bag, he listens for the return of a pulse in the artery. At

this point, he reads his gauge and records the *systolic* blood pressure.

He continues releasing air from the bag until he hears a sudden change in the tone of the pulse or until the sound disappears completely. At this point the air bag is not collapsing the artery with the heart at rest. This is the *diastolic* blood pressure. He refers to the blood pressures as a fraction. The upper figure, usually between 110 and 140, is systolic pressure. The lower figure, or diastolic pressure, is usually between 70 and 90.

What are capillaries? As arterioles penetrate the tissues, they branch into still smaller vessels called **capillaries** (see Fig. 37-7). Capillaries differ from arterioles in that their walls are only one cell layer thick. Capillaries are only slightly greater in diameter than the red blood cells. Red corpus-

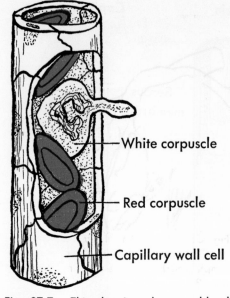

— White corpuscle

— Red corpuscle

— Capillary wall cell

Fig. 37-7. This drawing shows a blood capillary cut lengthwise and crosswise to show its structure.

cles must pass through them in single file and may even be pressed out of shape by the capillary walls. Various chemical substances, including *hista-mines* (*his*-tah-meens), cause the capillaries to enlarge, or *dilate,* and reduce the blood pressure.

Dissolved foods, waste products, and gases pass freely through the thin walls of capillaries, in and out of the tissue spaces. Tiny openings in the walls are penetrated by white corpuscles as they leave the blood stream and enter the tissue spaces. It is in the capillaries, too, that part of the plasma diffuses from the blood and becomes tissue fluid. Thus, all the vital relationships between the blood and the tissues occur in the capillaries and not in arteries and veins.

On leaving an organ, capillaries unite to form veins. These veins grow larger as they approach the heart. Veins always carry blood *toward* the heart. In the body circulation they

carry dark red blood; that is, blood lacking oxygen. In the skin the veins have a bluish color due to the fact that the skin contains a yellow pigment which changes the appearance of the dark red blood.

The walls of veins are thinner and less firm than those of arteries, and their internal diameter is proportionally larger.

Many of the larger veins are provided with cuplike **valves** which prevent the backward flow of blood. Veins are often close to the surface, as on the back of the hand, and show the dark color of the blood they carry.

Veins have no pulse wave and the blood pressure within them is much lower than that of arteries. Blood pressure resulting from heart action is almost completely lost in the capillaries. Blood from the head may return to the heart with the aid of gravity, but in the body regions below the level of the heart other factors are required. Venous flow from these regions is aided by the working muscles, the vacuum created in the chest during inspiration, and, to a small extent, by a sucking action caused by contractions of the heart.

Circulation in the body. In traveling through the body, blood may follow several different circuits.

The largest of these is the **systemic circulation.** It begins at the left ventricle of the heart where blood is pumped through the **aorta** (ay-*or*-tah), the largest artery in the body. Branches from this artery lead to the head and the arms and shoulders. It forms an arch above the heart and travels downward through the trunk, giving off branches to the various abdominal organs. In the lower part of the abdomen it branches to form the arteries which lead to the legs. All of the body tissues except the lungs and the heart are nourished by blood in the systemic circulation. Blood returns to the heart from this circulation through two great veins which enter the right auricle of the heart. The **superior vena cava** (*vee*-nah *cay*-vah) carries blood from the head and upper parts of the body. The **inferior vena cava** returns blood from the lower body regions.

The **renal circulation** is a short branch from the systemic circulation through the kidneys. The renal artery enters the kidneys as a branch of the aorta and the renal vein returns blood to the inferior vena cava.

The **portal circulation** includes the veins which leave the walls of the stomach and intestines and carry absorbed food to the liver. A branch of this circuit, the **hepatic vein,** carries blood from the liver to the inferior vena cava.

The **pulmonary circulation** is completely independent of the other circulations. It begins at the right ventricle, where blood is pumped through the pulmonary arteries to the lungs. It includes the lung capillaries, where exchange of gases occurs, and the pulmonary veins. These veins, the only ones which carry oxygenated blood, lead to the left auricle of the heart.

If you think of the pulmonary and systemic circulation as a figure " 8," the upper and smaller loop is the pulmonary circulation, the systemic circulation is the lower loop, and the point where the two loops join is the heart.

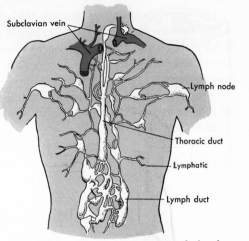

Fig. 37-8. The central parts of the lymphatic system are shown above. How does lymph reach the great veins near the heart?

The lymph circulation. As mentioned earlier, part of the plasma leaves the blood in the capillaries and enters the tissue spaces, where it bathes the cells. Lymph collects in *lymph tubes* which finally join the large, *thoracic duct*. This large duct joins the *subclavian vein* behind the collarbone and returns the lymph to the general circulation.

Lymph is circulated by pressure from the contracting muscles. Valves in the lymph tubes prevent backward flow. **Lymph nodes** are enlargements in the lymph tubes (*lymphatics*) which filter bacteria from the lymph. White corpuscles collect in the lymph nodes and destroy the bacteria.

In Conclusion

The circulatory system is the transportation system of the body. Blood is a fluid tissue, composed of a fluid called plasma and solid elements, the corpuscles and platelets. Plasma contains water, blood proteins, prothrombin, inorganic substances, digested foods, and cell wastes. The solid parts of the blood are of three types: red corpuscles, white corpuscles, and platelets.

The heart pumps blood through the arteries to all parts of the body. It consists of two auricles which receive blood from the veins, and two ventricles which force blood through the arteries by contractions. Arteries carry blood from the heart to the tissues, and veins return it. The arterial and venous systems are connected by the capillaries.

Lymph is a part of the blood plasma which passes through the capillary walls into the tissue spaces. It returns to the blood stream through lymphatics and the thoracic duct.

Our attention is directed next to a remarkable group of chemicals carried by the blood which have profound effects on the entire body.

Questions for Review

1. What materials are found in blood plasma?

2. What is the origin of the cells found in blood?

3. What condition in the body does a high white blood count usually indicate?

4. What are the various steps in the clotting of blood?

5. Why is plasma more quickly and easily used in a transfusion than whole blood?

6. What specifically is affected in the blood in cases of anemia, leukemia, and exposure to radioactivity?

7. Why has plasma in a readily usable form been so useful in modern medicine?

8. Trace the path of a drop of blood through the heart.

9. What are the four conditions which influence blood pressure?

10. Why can you feel the pulse in an artery and not a vein?

11. Trace a drop of blood through its complete route of the circulatory system beginning at the right ventricle and ending at the right auricle.

12. How does lymph differ in composition from whole blood?

Biologically Speaking

aorta	hemoglobin	renal circulation
arteriole	hemorrhage	*Rh* factor
artery	leukemia	septum
auricles	lymph	serum albumin
blood	oxyhemoglobin	serum globulin
blood bank	pericardium	systemic circulation
blood transfusion	plasma	systole
capillary	platelets	thrombin
coronary vessels	portal circulation	thromboplastin
diastole	prothrombin	vein
fibrin	pulmonary circulation	vena cava
fibrinogen	pulse	ventricles
hapten	red corpuscles	white corpuscles

 ——————— **Applying Facts and Principles**

1. Why does a doctor use a bone marrow sample in diagnosing leukemia?

2. In what ways is lymph an example of force filtration?

3. Under what conditions might blood plasma be used in a transfusion in preference to whole blood?

4. What is the basis for the following statement " Man is only as young as his arteries "?

5. Alcohol has a dilating effect on the skin arteries. What would be its effect, then, on the temperature control of the body?

6. (a) What could be the possible explanations for a blood pressure reading which was consistently low at both systole and diastole? (b) One high at systole but normal at diastole?

7. Why might a second transfusion with *Rh* positive blood in an *Rh* negative patient be fatal, while the first transfusion with *Rh* positive blood caused no complications?

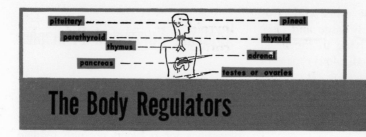

CHAPTER 38

The Body Regulators

Since the dawn of medicine in ancient Greece, men have searched for the strange and powerful chemical substances which regulate all vital activities of the body. Someone discovered that goiter could be treated successfully with a concoction of burnt seaweed and sponges. But it remained for scientists many centuries later, with a knowledge of iodine and the thyroid gland, to explain why this early treatment worked.

Now we know that an amazing system of glands, operating like the balance wheel of a watch, controls the vital activities of the body. It can cause your vital organs to function in perfect harmony, or struggle against each other in a desperate effort to survive. It can save your life in time of need, or lead to its destruction.

What are the ductless glands? You are already familiar with glands, like the salivary glands of the mouth and the gastric glands of the stomach. These pour their secretions into a digestive organ through a tube, or duct. However, the **ductless glands** which we will study in this chapter are entirely different from these digestive glands. The name *ductless* indicates that they have no ducts leading from them. Their secretions enter the blood stream directly. With blood as a transporting medium, they reach every part of the body and influence all the organs. Ductless glands are also called **endocrine** (*en*-doh-krin) **glands.**

We call the secretions of this group of ductless glands **hormones.** These powerful chemicals are formed from substances taken from the blood and control the activity of all the body processes. Thus the circulatory system is vital to the endocrine system, both in supplying the raw materials and in delivering the finished product. For the most part the endocrine glands are small. They are entirely out of proportion to the vital influence they exert on the body as a whole.

Endocrine glands operate in a state of *dynamic balance*. This means that the secretion of one gland may influence the activity of other glands. If one gland becomes overactive, the balance is upset and the other glands become overactive. For this reason, glandular disorders may be very complex.

Our study of endocrine glands will include the following six glands known to secrete hormones and their products: (1) *thyroid gland;* (2) *parathyroid glands;* (3) *pituitary gland;* (4) *adrenal glands;* (5) *pancreas;* and (6) *ovaries and testes.*

The *thymus* and *pineal* (*pin*-ee-al) *bodies* may also function as endocrine glands. However, we do not know too much about the part these structures play.

The thyroid gland. You are probably more familiar with the thyroid than with any of the other endocrine glands. It is relatively large and close to the body surface, lying in the neck, near the junction of the lower part of the larynx and the trachea. It consists of two lobes, connected by an " isthmus." The lobes lie on either side of the trachea and extend upward along the sides of the larynx. The " isthmus " extends across the front surface of the trachea. The complete thyroid gland somewhat resembles a butterfly with its wings spread.

The secretion of the thyroid gland is known as the **thyroid hormone,** but its exact chemical composition is not entirely known. We do know, however, that it contains two distinct chemical substances and that both of these are composed of amino acids, combined with large amounts of iodine.

The concentration of iodine in the thyroid gland is greater than in any other tissue of the body. This concentration is about one part of iodine to

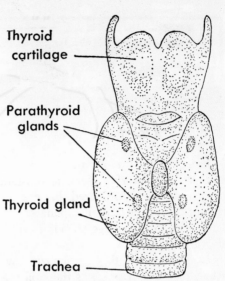

Fig. 38-2. Note the position of the thyroid gland in relation to the trachea. Note also the four parathyroid glands embedded in the back of it.

1,000 parts of thyroid tissue. While this may appear to be a very small amount, it is actually very high. Since both parts of the thyroid hormone contain large quantities of this element, you can understand why iodine is essential for normal functioning of the thyroid gland.

How is thyroid hormone prepared? Commercially, it is prepared by extraction from dried sheep thyroid glands. After being purified, it is called *thyroid extract* and is used in treating thyroid disorders. Thyroid extract is the least expensive of any commercial endocrine preparation.

What causes goiter? Iodine deficiency is the major cause of enlargement of the thyroid gland, known as *simple goiter*. This condition is rare along the seacoast where people include in their diet an abundance of sea foods containing iodine. It is more common in mountainous regions and in the Great Lakes basin where the iodine content of

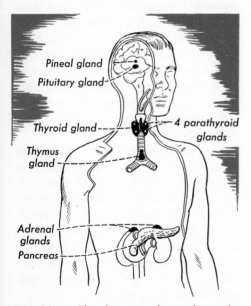

Fig. 38-1. The diagram above shows the location of the endocrine glands in the body. Why are they called ductless glands?

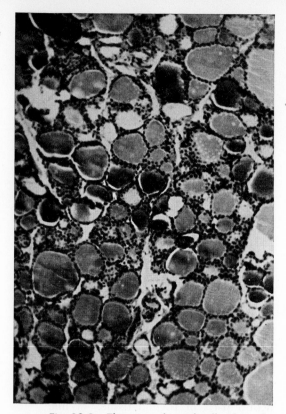

Fig. 38-3. These are thyroid cells of a rabbit as seen under a microscope and magnified 100 times.

the soil is low. The addition of iodine compounds to table salt and to the water supply in certain regions is an adequate preventive measure.

Thyroid hormone regulates rate of metabolism. In this way it influences growth and oxidation. Overactivity of the thyroid gland, or *hyperthyroidism* (hy-per-*thy*-roid-izm), increases the rate of oxidation and raises the body temperature. Heart action increases and blood pressure rises. Sweating, when the body should be cool, is a common symptom of this condition. In addition, the individual becomes extremely nervous and irritable. In some cases, victims may develop characteristic bulging eyes and a staring expression.

Underactivity of the thyroid gland, called **hypothyroidism** (hy-po-*thy*-roid-

izm), produces the opposite symptoms. The rate of oxidation is decreased and activity of the nervous system is reduced. This produces characteristic physical and mental retarding. Heart action decreases and in many cases the heart enlarges. Both overactivity and underactivity of the gland may be determined by measuring the rate of basal metabolism.

If the thyroid is defective during infancy, **cretinism** (*kree*-tin-izm) results. This condition produces a stunted body. The face usually becomes bloated, the lips greatly enlarged, and the tongue thick and protruding from the mouth. Cretins are mentally dull and stupid. If the condition is not corrected early in life by giving thyroid extract, the victim becomes a mental defective. However, if the cretin has passed from infancy to childhood without treatment, the dwarfism and certain other symptoms can never be corrected.

The parathyroid glands. The *parathyroids* (par-ah-*thy*-roids) are four small glands embedded in the back of the thyroid gland, two in each lobe. Their secretion, *parathormone* (par-ah-*thor*-mone), controls the use of calcium in the body. Bone growth, muscle tone, and normal nervous activity are absolutely dependent on a constant, stable calcium balance.

The pituitary gland. This small gland, about the size of an acorn or cherry, lies at the base of the brain. It was once thought to be the " master gland " of the body, since its secretions appeared to influence the activity of all other endocrine glands. However, it is now known that other glands, especially the thyroid and adrenal glands, influence the pituitary gland.

The pituitary gland consists of two lobes: *anterior* and *posterior*. The **anterior lobe** secretes several different hormones. One of these, the **somatotropic** (so-*mah*-toh-troh-pic), or growth hormone, regulates the growth of the skeleton. If an oversecretion of this hormone occurs during the growing years, tremendous height may be attained. This condition is called *giantism*. Circus giants over 8 feet tall, weighing over 300 pounds, and wearing size 30 shoes are examples of this disorder. If the oversecretion occurs during adult life, the bones of the face and hands thicken since they cannot grow in length. However, the organs and the soft tissues enlarge tremendously. This condition is known as **acromegaly** (ak-ro-*meg*-a-lee). Victims of this disorder have greatly enlarged jawbones, noses, and hands and fingers.

Somatotropic hormone deficiency results in a pituitary dwarf, or *midget*. These individuals are perfectly proportioned "men in miniature." They are quite different from the thyroid dwarf in having normal intelligence.

Another hormone secretion of the anterior lobe of the pituitary gland, the **gonadotropic** (gon-ad-oh-*trop*-ic) hormone, influences the development of the reproductive organs. It also influences hormone secretion of the ovaries and testes. The gonadotropic hormone, together with the sex hormones, causes the sweeping changes which occur during adolescence, when the child becomes an adult.

Other secretions of the anterior lobe of the pituitary gland include hormones which stimulate the secretion of milk in the mammary glands (*lactogenic hormone*), the activity of the thyroid gland (*thyrotropic hormone*), and the parathyroid glands (*parathyrotropic hormone*).

What is ACTH? *ACTH* (*adreno-cortico-tropic-hormone*) is a secretion of the *anterior lobe* of the pituitary gland

Fig. 38-4. If the pituitary gland produces too little of the somatotropic hormone, a midget may be the result. What happens when there is a oversecretion of this growth hormone?

and stimulates the outer part, or cortex, of the adrenal glands. The adrenals, in turn, secrete hormones which are responsible for the control of certain phases of carbohydrate, fat, and protein metabolism and the salt and water balance in the body.

The adrenal cortex also yields hormones which control the production of some types of white corpuscles, and the structure of connective tissue. When ACTH is given to patients with leukemia, a dramatic, but unfortunately temporary, improvement occurs. Its effects in arthritis treatment are somewhat more encouraging. Good results in the treatment of asthma and other allergies with ACTH have been reported. Even though ACTH may not give permanent cures to these diseases, its use may lead the way to the discovery of their actual causes.

The **posterior lobe** of the pituitary

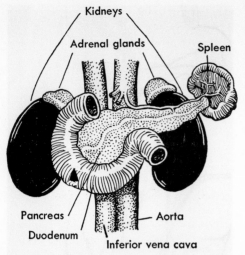

Fig. 38-5. The adrenal glands are vitally important members of the endocrine family. What are two important hormones that these glands secrete?

gland produces two hormones: (1) *pitressin* (pih-*tress*-in), which helps regulate the amount of water in the blood and the blood pressure; and (2) *pitocin* (pih-*toh*-sin), which stimulates smooth muscles. It is administered following childbirth to cause contraction of the muscles of the uterus, thus preventing blood loss.

The adrenal glands. The adrenal glands, also called *suprarenals,* are located on top of each kidney. They are composed of an outer region, the **cortex** and an inner part, the **medulla.** The adrenal cortex secretes a hormone-complex called **cortin** (*kor*-tin). These hormones were discussed in connection with ACTH.

The medulla secretes a hormone called *epinephrine* (eh-pee-*neh*-freen). The adrenal glands have been called the *glands of emergency* because of the action of this hormone. Many people have performed superhuman feats of strength during periods of anger or fright, which show the effects of epinephrine, or adrenalin, as it is sometimes

called. This strength of desperation results from a series of rapid changes in body activity:

1. The person becomes pale, due to constriction of the blood vessels in the skin. This rapid movement of blood from the body surfaces reduces loss of blood in case of a surface wound. It also increases the blood supply to the muscles, brain, heart, and other vital organs.

2. The blood pressure rises, due to constriction of surface blood vessels.

3. The heart action and output are increased.

4. The liver releases some of its stored sugar and provides material for increased body activity and oxidations.

Your life may have been saved on several occasions by these rapid changes in body activity.

The pancreas. The production of pancreatic fluid in connection with digestion is only part of the function of the pancreas. Special groups of cells called **islets of Langerhans,** secrete a hormone, *insulin.* This hormone enables the liver to store sugar as glycogen and regulates the oxidation of sugar in the tissues.

A person who lacks insulin cannot store or oxidize sugar efficiently. Thus the tissues are deprived of energy food, and sugar collects in the blood. As the blood sugar rises, some of it is excreted in the urine. Doctors call this condition *diabetes mellitus* (dy-ah-*bee*-teeze meh-*lye*-tuss).

However, diabetes mellitus is probably more complicated than simple failure of the islet cells of the pancreas to produce insulin. The pituitary, thyroid, and adrenal glands, as well as the liver, are known to play an important part in the disease. Body weight also influences the appearance of this condition. Diabetes mellitus is definitely hereditary. If you have it in your family, regular periodic checkups for sugar in the urine should be made by your family doctor. There is no cause for alarm if the disease appears, for once discovered, it usually can be controlled successfully. If treatment is begun in the early stages, the patient can lead a perfectly normal life without any fear of being an invalid.

The ovaries and testes. The **ovaries** of the female and the **testes** of the male have a dual function. We think of them primarily as organs for the production of eggs and sperms. However, certain cells of the ovaries and the testes serve as ductless glands. These ovary cells secrete the female hormone **estrogen** (*es*-troh-jen), while special cells of the testes produce the male hormone **androgen** (*an*-droh-jen).

Testosterone (tes-*tos*-ter-ohn), one of the active parts of androgen, can now be produced artificially, and is used in treating sex hormone disturbances in both males and females. Furthermore, the production of this hormone is not limited to the testes. It is secreted by the cortex of the adrenal glands in *both males and females.* In the female, the estrogen secreted in the ovaries normally neutralizes the effects of the androgen from the adrenal glands. However, if the estrogen secretion in the ovaries is reduced, the female may become mannish. Similarly, reduced production of androgen in the testes of the male can result in feminine tendencies. Thus different individuals may represent various degrees of maleness and femaleness.

Sex hormones control the development of secondary sex characteristics which appear in the change from childhood to adulthood. The time of the first appearance of these changes with the maturation of the ovaries and testes

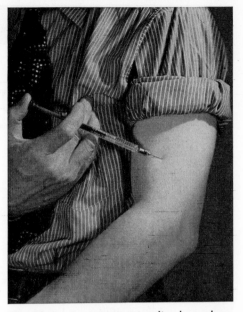

Fig. 38-6. By injecting insulin themselves, diabetics can control this disease and lead normal lives.

is called **puberty** (*pew*-bur-tee). In the animal world, these characteristics may appear as the large comb of the rooster, the bright plumage of most male birds, and the horns of the deer.

Many secondary characteristics are appearing or have appeared in your own body. As a boy approaches puberty, his voice cracks and then deepens. His beard appears along with a general increase in body hair. The chest broadens and deepens. Rapid growth of the long bones adds to his height. As a girl matures, her breasts develop, her hips broaden, her body contours become more rounded, due to the formation of fat deposits under the skin, and menstruation begins. These physical changes in both boys and girls are accompanied by sweeping mental and emotional changes. Compare your present personality with that of a child ten to twelve years old and you will see how these glands have influenced you.

DUCTLESS GLANDS AND THEIR SECRETIONS

GLAND	LOCATION	HORMONE	ACTIVITY STIMULATED BY HORMONE
Thyroid	Neck, below larynx	Thyroid hormone	Accelerates the rate of metabolism
Parathyroids	Back surface of thyroid lobes	Parathormone	Controls the use of calcium in the tissues
Pituitary	Base of brain		
Anterior lobe		Somatotropic hormone	Regulates growth of the skeleton
		Gonadotropic hormone	Influences development of sex organs and hormone secretion of the ovaries and testes
		ACTH	Stimulates secretion of hormones by the cortex of the adrenals
		Lactogenic hormone	Stimulates secretion of milk by mammary glands
		Thyrotropic hormone	Stimulates activity of the thyroid
		Parathyrotropic hormone	Stimulates activity of the parathyroids
Posterior lobe		Pitressin	Regulates water in blood and blood pressure
		Pitocin	Stimulates smooth muscles
Adrenal	Above kidneys		
Cortex		Cortin (a hormone-complex)	Regulates metabolism, salt, and water balance
			Controls production of certain white corpuscles and structure of connective tissue
Medulla		Epinephrine	Causes constriction of blood vessels, increase in heart action and output, stimulates liver and nervous system
Pancreas	Below and behind stomach		
Islets of Langerhans		Insulin	Enables liver to store sugar and regulates sugar oxidation in tissues
Ovaries	Pelvis		
Follicular cells		Estrogen	Produces female secondary sex characteristics; influences adult female body functions
Testes	Below pelvis		
Interstitial cells		Androgen	Produces male secondary sex characteristics

THE HUMAN TORSO

as seen by the "Trans-Vision" process

BY TURNING THE PAGES included in this dissection of the human torso, you can see the chief organs from front and back views. You can study each organ in relation to the other organs. Or, you can single it out and study it by itself. You can see also how the various systems are related to each other.

Ordinary drawings of single organs or small groups of organs do not show you this relationship of organs to each other. In addition, the three-dimensional depth of "Trans-Vision" plates allows you to see organs lying under other organs. The drawings are the work of Mr. Alfred Feinberg, Instructor of Medical Art in the Department of Pathology, College of Physicians and Surgeons, Columbia University, New York City.

The right-hand pages show the front view of the organs. The left-hand pages show the back view of the same organs. In other words, you're looking at the human torso from both sides at once. For easy identification, we have numbered the organs and blood vessels of most interest to you. These numbers appear in the descriptions at the bottom of each page.

On the last page of this "Trans-Vision" insert, you'll find a numbered key to all the organs shown. This will serve as a summary to check your knowledge of the names and locations of the chief organs of the human torso.

Transparencies reproduced by permission of the copyright owner.

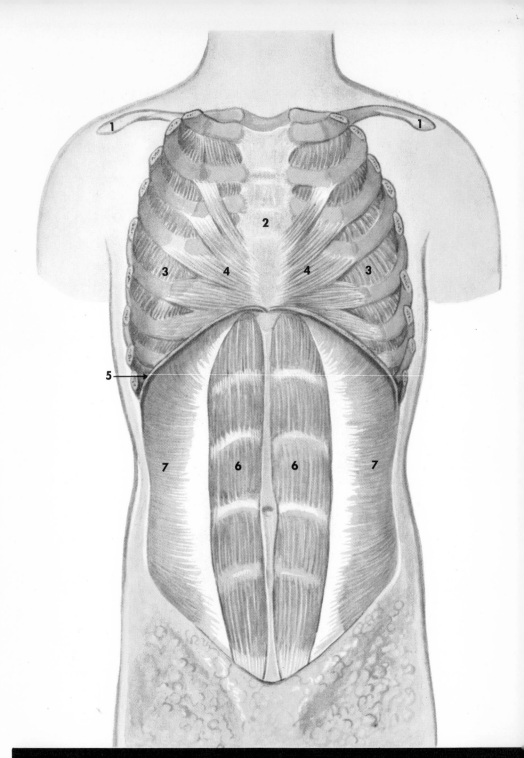

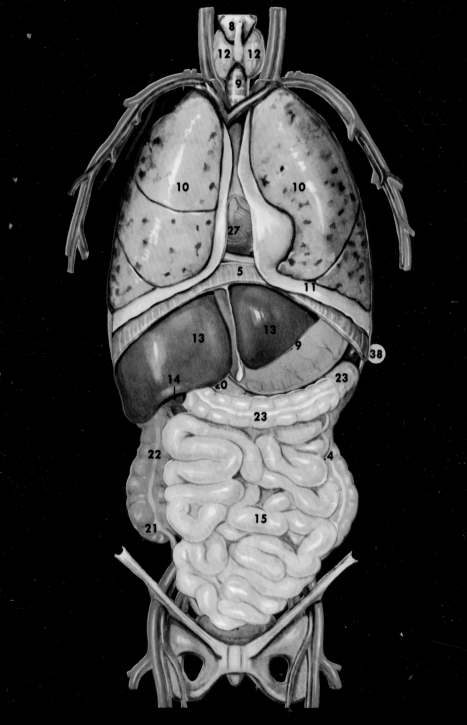

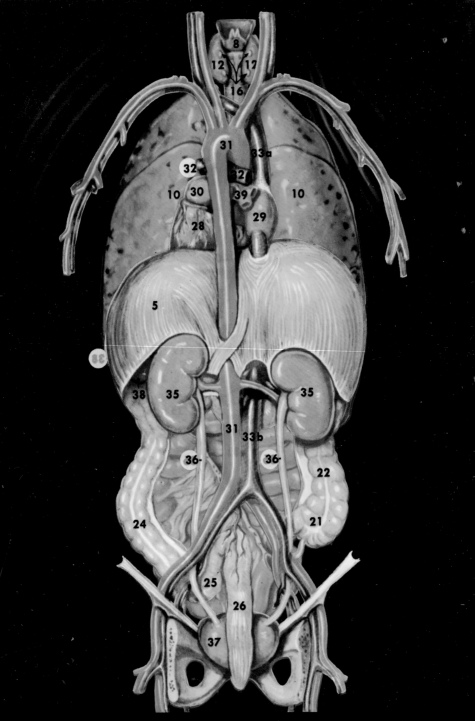

V CUTAWAY VIEW OF THE BACK SIDE OF THE FOLLOWING ORGANS: **(21)** caecum with appendix, **(22)** ascending colon, **(24)** descending colon, **(25)** sigmoid colon, **(26)** rectum, **(28)** left ventricle, **(29)** right auricle, **(30)** left auricle, **(31)** aorta, **(32)** pulmonary arteries, **(33 a and b)** venae cavae, **(35)** kidneys, **(36)** ureters, **(37)** bladder, **(38)** spleen. The **(39)** pulmonary veins are visible only in this back view.

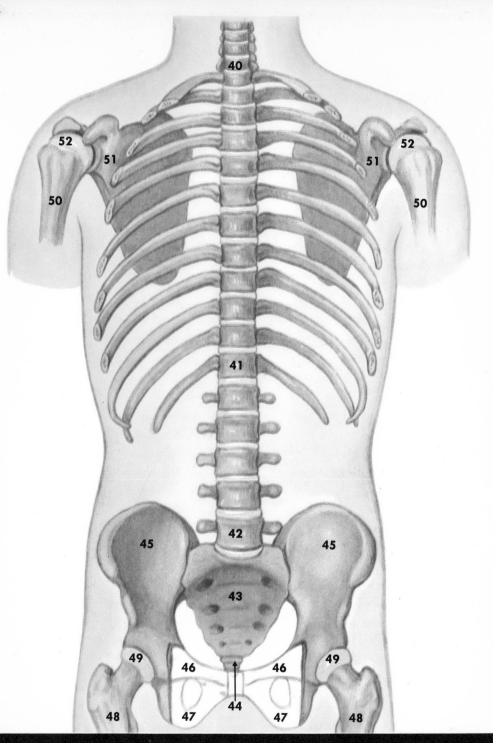

KEY TO THE
ORGANS OF THE HUMAN TORSO

1. Collar bone (clavicle)
2. Breast bone (sternum)
3. Intercostal muscles
4. Transverse thoracic muscles
5. Diaphragm
6. Vertical abdominal muscles
7. Transverse abdominal muscles
8. Voice box (larynx)
9. Windpipe (trachea)
10. Lungs
11. Pleura
12. Thyroid gland
13. Liver
14. Gall bladder
15. Small intestine
16. Parathyroid glands
17. Bile ducts
18. Mesentery
19. Stomach
20. Pancreas
21. Caecum with appendix
22. Ascending colon
23. Transverse colon
24. Descending colon
25. Sigmoid colon
26. Rectum

27. Right ventricle of heart
28. Left ventricle of heart
29. Right auricle of heart
30. Left auricle of heart
31. Aorta
32. Pulmonary arteries
33 a and b. Venae cavae
34. Adrenal glands
35. Kidneys
36. Ureters
37. Bladder
38. Spleen
39. Pulmonary veins
40. 7th cervical vertebra
41. 12th thoracic vertebra
42. 5th lumbar vertebra
43. Sacrum
44. Coccyx
45. Ilium
46. Pubis
47. Ischium
48. Thigh bone (femur)
49. Hip joint
50. Upper arm bone (humerus)
51. Shoulder blade (scapula)
52. Shoulder joint

TRANS-VISION

TRADE MARK REGISTERED U. S. PAT. OFFICE
U. S. PATENT NUMBERS
2,149,779-2,294,465-2,311,946
MILPRINT, INC., MILWAUKEE
PRINTED IN U. S. A.

The pineal body and thymus. The *pineal* (*pin*-ee-al) *body* is a mass of tissue, about the size of a pea, located at the base of the brain. It lies directly behind the junction of the spinal cord and brain tissue. As we stated on page 512, this body may or may not be a ductless gland. No hormone secretion from it has yet been discovered and we do not know what its function may be.

The *thymus,* too, may be a ductless gland but its function is unknown. It lies just above the heart, under the breastbone. At birth, the thymus weighs less than half an ounce. It increases in size during childhood and reaches its maximum size between the ages of 12 and 14.

During the time when it is of maximum size, the thymus gland usually weighs about one ounce, or twice its weight at birth. During adulthood, it gradually grows smaller and finally shrinks to the size it was at birth. The fact that it grows larger during childhood and then decreases in size shows that it may influence development of the reproductive organs. We have no real proof of this at the moment, but research workers with the assistance of prominent doctors are investigating this possibility.

Many questions regarding the action of these glands remain unanswered. However, a great deal of research on the endocrine glands and the specific effects of hormones is being done today to help find these answers.

In Conclusion

Ductless, or endocrine glands, secrete hormones directly into the blood stream. These hormones have a powerful influence over the activity of body organs, including the glands of the endocrine system themselves. Ductless glands function in a state of dynamic balance. Overactivity of any one gland may result from or may cause overactivity of other glands. This is especially true of the pituitary, adrenal, and thyroid glands. The pineal body and thymus may function as ductless glands, although the activity of neither one is understood.

The endocrine glands help to balance body activity. But there is much more than mere balance. Waste products accumulate and must be removed. Let's see how the excretory system takes care of this important body function.

Questions for Review

1. What are two very important relationships between the endocrine glands and the blood?

2. What do we mean when we say that the thyroid gland regulates the rate of metabolism?

3. In what ways may an improperly functioning thyroid gland affect the personality?

4. In what ways do the pituitary and thyroid glands influence growth?

5. How does the pituitary gland affect the sex glands?

6. Which ductless gland is stimulated by ACTH from the pituitary gland?

7. What do we mean by the " strength of desperation " during times of great fear or anger?

8. In what ways are puberty and adolescence a result of glandular activity?

9. Why does sugar appear in the urine of a diabetic?

10. Compare the body characteristics of a thyroid dwarf and a pituitary dwarf. How do they differ and in what ways are they similar?

Biologically Speaking

acromegaly	gonadotropic	pitocin
ACTH	hormone	pitressin
adrenals	hyperthyroidism	pituitary
cortin	hypothyroidism	puberty
cretinism	insulin	somatotropic
diabetes mellitus	islets of Langerhans	suprarenals
ductless gland	ovaries	testes
endocrine gland	parathormone	testosterone
epinephrine	parathyroid	thymus
estrogen	pineal body	thyroid

Applying Facts and Principles

1. Insulin is a protein. How does this fact enable you to understand why it must be given under the skin to diabetics rather than through the mouth?

2. What gland may have a hormone which influences intelligence?

3. How do you account for the fact that the heartbeat of a basketball player increases a great deal before the game as well as during it?

4. Why is a study of the endocrine glands often included with a study of the nervous system?

5. What hormone injected into the blood stream of a male rat will often result in a mothering instinct? Why?

CHAPTER 39

The Removal of Waste

If you could tag all the carbon, hydrogen, and oxygen atoms which compose the carbohydrates and fats in your diet, you would discover that none of them becomes directly part of your body substance. You have learned about the studies involving the ultimate fate of fats in the body by means of radioactive carbon (carbon 14) as a tracer element. Energy foods have served their purpose when the tissues have released the energy they contain during oxidation. Carbon dioxide and water, released as waste products, represent all the matter which composed the carbohydrates. Only the energy is utilized by the tissues.

Protein metabolism involves waste products. These result from the separation of the carbon and nitrogen parts of amino acids, before oxidation of the carbon part. Other waste products result from the organization of amino acids to form protoplasm during growth processes. These non-protein **nitrogenous wastes** include urea and uric acid.

Waste products must pass from the tissues to the blood, and from the blood to the organs of excretion. Accumulation of wastes, especially non-protein nitrogens, in the tissues causes rapid tissue poisoning, starvation, and suffocation. Tissues filled with waste products cannot absorb either food or oxygen. Fever, convulsions, coma, and death are inevitable if non-protein nitrogen wastes do not leave the tissues.

Further complications arise if the mineral acids and salts accumulate in the body because of excretory failure. This disturbs certain delicate acid-base balances in the body. It also upsets the osmotic relationships between blood and lymph and the tissues. When excess salts are held in the tissues, water ac-cumulates and causes a swelling in those tissues affected.

The kidneys are bean-shaped organs, about the size of your clenched fist. They lie on either side of the spine, in the " small " of the back. Deep layers of fat around the kidneys form a protective covering. They are situated in the body with the concave side toward the spine.

If you cut a kidney lengthwise (Fig. 39-1), you can see several different regions. The firm, outer region is called **cortex.** The cortex composes about one-third of the kidney tissue. The inner two-thirds, or **medulla,** contains conical projections called **pyramids.** The points of the pyramids extend into a sac-like cavity, the **pelvis** of the kidney. The pelvis, in turn, leads into a long, narrow tube (one for each kidney) called the **ureter** (you-*ree*-ter). The two ureters empty into the **urinary bladder.**

Blood enters each kidney through a large **renal artery,** which branches directly from the aorta. It is the largest artery in the body in proportion to the

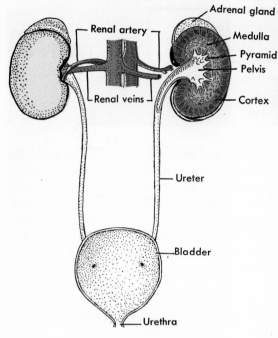

Fig. 39-1. This section of a kidney shows the different regions. Blood enters each kidney through a large renal artery and leaves through the renal veins.

size of the organ it supplies. In the kidney, the renal artery branches and re-branches to form a maze of tiny **arterioles,** which penetrate all areas of the cortex. Each arteriole ends in a coiled, knoblike mass of capillaries, the **glomerulus** (glow-*mur*-you-luss). Each glomerulus is surrounded by a **capsule,** which leads to a tiny *tubule.* If all of these tubules were straightened out and put end to end, they would extend over 200 miles.

The two kidneys have tremendous reserve power. When one is removed, its mate enlarges to twice its normal size and assumes the normal function of two kidneys.

The kidneys act as filters. In the first stage of removal of waste from the blood, far too much of the blood content leaves the blood stream and enters the glomeruli of the kidney. However, this is soon corrected in a second stage, in which valuable substances return to the blood.

The first stage takes place in the coiled capillaries of the glomeruli. Here water, nitrogenous wastes, glucose, and mineral salts pass through the walls of the capillaries and into the surrounding capsule. This solution resembles blood plasma without the blood proteins. Complete loss of this much water, glucose, and minerals would be fatal. However, after these substances leave the capsule through the tubules, they pass a network of capillaries. Here they are reabsorbed into the blood. Only the nitrogenous wastes, excess water, and excess mineral salts pass through the tubules to the pelvis of the kidney as *urine.*

Some recent studies of kidney function indicate that, for every 100 cc. of fluid which passes from the blood in the glomeruli into the capsules, 99 cc. are reabsorbed. Only 1 cc. remains as urine. The urine passes from the pelvis of each kidney through the ureters to the urinary bladder. Blood leaves the kidneys through the *renal veins* and returns to the general circulation by way of the *inferior vena cava.* The blood in these veins, while it is deoxygenated, is the purest blood in the body.

The formation of urine by the kidney is a constant filtration process. After this material leaves the kidneys through the ureters, it collects in the large muscular bladder. It is disposed of periodically from the bladder through the **urethra** (you-*ree*-thrah).

The skin. The skin helps the kidneys in the excretion of water, salts, and some urea in the form of sweat. However, this fluid is much more important in regulating body temperature than it is as an excretory substance.

Skin consists of an outer portion, or **epidermis,** composed of many layers of cells. (See Fig. 39-4). The outer cells are flattened, dead, and scalelike. The inner ones are more active and larger. The epidermis serves largely for protection of the active tissues beneath it. You rub off epidermis constantly, but active cells in the lower layers replace cells as fast as they are lost. Friction

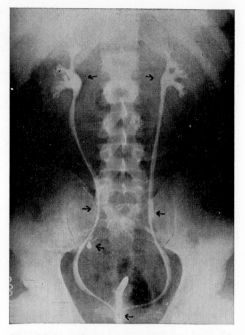

Fig. 39-3. This is an X-ray photograph showing the kidneys and ureters. The kidneys lie on either side of the spine. The ureters empty into the urinary bladder.

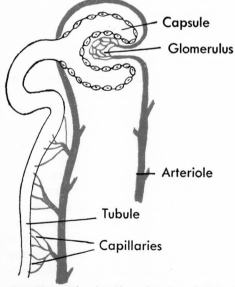

Fig. 39-2. Blood is filtered in the tubules of the kidneys. Above is a detailed structure of a tubule and its blood vessels.

Capsule

Glomerulus

Arteriole

Tubule

Capillaries

and pressure on the epidermis stimulate cell division, and may produce a *callus* more than a hundred cells thick. Hair and nails are special outgrowths of the epidermis.

The **dermis** lies under the epidermis. It is a thick, active layer, composed of tough, fibrous connective tissue, richly supplied with blood and lymph vessels, nerves, sweat glands, and oil glands.

The functions of the skin. The varied functions of the skin include:

1. Protection of the body from mechanical injury and bacterial invasion.

2. Protection of the inner tissues against drying out. The skin, aided by oil glands, is nearly waterproof. Little water passes through it, except out through the sweat pores.

3. Location of the nerve endings which respond to pressure, or touch, pain, and temperature changes.

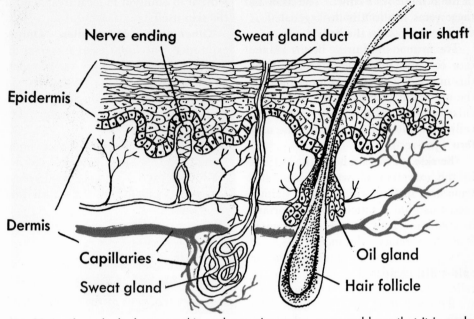

Fig. 39-4. If you looked at your skin under a microscope, you would see that it is made up of many layers of cells.

4. Excretion of wastes present in sweat.

5. Control of the loss of body heat through the evaporation of sweat.

This last statement needs further explanation. In an earlier discussion about water and its uses, we mentioned that heat is absorbed during the change of liquid water to water vapor. Thus as sweat evaporates from the body surface, heat is withdrawn from the outer tissues. The skin is literally an automatic radiator. It is richly supplied with blood containing body heat withdrawn from the tissues. As the body temperature rises, the skin becomes more flushed with blood, and heat is conducted to the surface. At the same time, secretion of sweat increases and bathes the skin. This increases the rate of evaporation and the amount of heat loss becomes greater.

The skin and its care. It is obvious that personal cleanliness is a vital part of being acceptable. We all expect to see clean hands and a skin free of dirt. However, there are certain unfortunate skin conditions which have a distressing effect on some people.

Acne (*ak*-nee) is a condition in which the skin erupts in numerous blackheads, pimples, and boils. It is especially prevalent among young people.

During the teen years, hormones, especially from the reproductive organs and the adrenal glands, are being secreted in greater quantity than at any previous time. This may result in a hormonic unbalance which often is expressed by acne and other disorders.

Acne is not a dangerous or permanent condition. But it does bring distress and embarrassment to a person at the time he is most sensitive about his personality and social acceptance. It may become a vicious circle. The condition causes emotional tension, and emotional tension increases hormone secretion and aggravates the condition.

There are several things to do to improve an acne condition. Eat foods that are low in fats. Avoid especially ice cream and butter. If chocolate aggravates the condition, stop eating it. Frequent washing of the spots with mild soap is helpful. By all means, do not squeeze or try to open any pimple.

Eczema (*ex*-zee-mah) is a condition of allergic or emotional origin which results in scaling of the skin. Such diseases require treatment for emotional

tension in addition to local treatment of the skin itself.

Other organs of excretion. During expiration, the *lungs* excrete carbon dioxide and considerable water vapor. The excretory function of the *liver* in forming urea has been discussed earlier. Bile, too, is a waste-containing substance.

The large intestine removes undigested food. This, however, is not really cell excretion, since food refuse has never actually been absorbed into the tissues.

In Conclusion

Various wastes are removed from the body through actions of the kidneys, skin, lungs, liver, and large intestine. The kidneys, the most vital organs of excretion, serve as blood filters. They are responsible for the removal of practically all the nitrogenous wastes resulting from protein metabolism, excess water, and mineral acids and salts. Skin has a complex role. It excretes large quantities of water as sweat. It also functions as the " radiator " of the body in eliminating heat during evaporation of sweat.

The controlling mechanism of all the complex activities of the human body is our next topic.

Questions for Review

1. In general, what type of waste material must be disposed of quickly?

2. What purposes does water serve in the excretory system?

3. In what way do the kidneys regulate blood content?

4. What are the differences in the glomerular fluid and the urine which finally leaves the kidney?

5. In what veins would you expect to find the purest blood in the body?

6. Why may a person who is not sweating in the hot sun be in danger of a sunstroke?

7. What are the chief functions of the skin?

8. Why is the skin considered to be an organ?

9. Why must the cells of the outer epidermis be dead rather than living?

10. Why does the skin act like an automatic radiator?

11. What is the function of the oil always found on normal skin?

12. What are other organs of excretion besides the kidneys?

13. Why can a person who has had one kidney removed still lead a normal life?

Biologically Speaking

capsule   medulla   urea
cortex   nitrogenous wastes   ureter
dermis   pelvis   urethra
epidermis   pyramids   urinary bladder
glomerulus   renal artery   urine
kidney   tubule

Applying Facts and Principles

1. Trace a molecule of nitrogenous waste from the renal artery to the urethra.

2. Trace a molecule of glucose from the renal artery to the renal vein.

3. Why is increased salt intake recommended in hot weather?

4. What happens to water in the blood if it does not enter the glomerulus? If it enters the glomerulus but is reabsorbed? If it enters the glomerulus but is not reabsorbed?

5. How is the urine changed by a great excess of sugar in the diet? Excess of water? During a hot, dry day? Under conditions of hypertension?

6. Explain what is probably wrong if, during an analysis of the urine, red blood cells are found? Albumin is found? Glucose is found? Excess of water is discovered?

7. What is the chief difference between the composition of sweat and of urine?

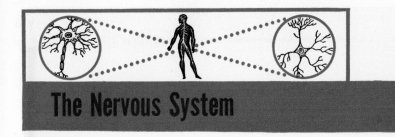

CHAPTER 40

The Nervous System

Today you can pick up your telephone and talk to 95 per cent of all the people in the world who have telephones. You can phone to or from a ship at sea, or a moving train. You can watch a World Series game in your own living room or hear Big Ben in London strike the hours.

Marvelous as are the telephone, radio, and television, none of them compares with the communication system of your own body. The nervous system receives impressions from your surroundings, stores them in the brain, originates activity, and carries impulses to all parts of the body. It coordinates the activity of several million cells into a single functioning unit.

The nervous system. This functions as a control of body activity and is closely associated with the endocrine system. You have already studied the hormone secretions of the ductless glands and their powerful chemical effect on body activity. Activity of the nervous system involves impulses carried along nerves. It is a two-way communication system. Impulses are sent from the body tissues and organs to nerve centers, and from these centers to the tissues and organs.

The brain and spinal cord comprise the *central nervous system*. They communicate with all parts of the body by means of the **peripheral** (peh-*rif*-er-al) **system**. Another division is the **autonomic** (ot-oh-*nom*-ik) **system** which regulates certain vital functions of the body almost independently of the central nervous system.

The brain and its regions. The brain is probably the most highly specialized and least understood organ of the human body. It weighs about three pounds and fills the **cranial** (*kray-*nee-al) **cavity.** It is composed of soft nervous tissues covered by three membranes called the **meninges** (meh-*nin*-geez). The inner membrane lies against the brain itself. It is richly supplied with blood vessels which carry food and oxygen to the brain cells. The

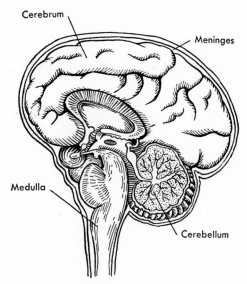

Fig. 40-1. The three regions of the brain are shown in this drawing.

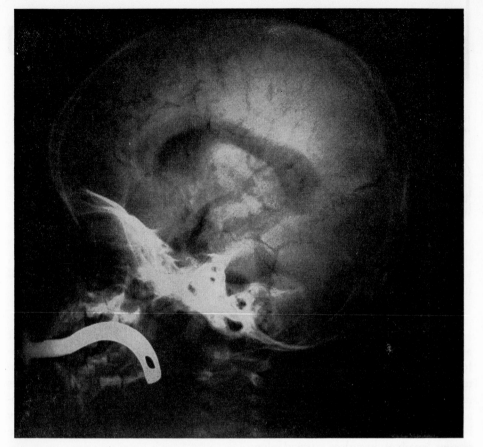

Fig. 40-2. An " air " X-ray photograph of the brain. The cerebrospinal fluid has been drained through the spine and replaced by air. Since the patient was under an anesthetic, the white " airway " was placed in the mouth to avoid swallowing the tongue. The convolutions of the cerebrum and large ventricular cavities are visible only because of the injected air. Notice the zigzag sutures of the cranial bones in the lower back area of the skull.

space between the inner and middle membranes is filled with a thin liquid, the **cerebrospinal** (*ser*-eh-bro-*spy*-nal) **fluid.** The outer membrane is the thickest and toughest of the three. The meninges and cerebrospinal fluid continue down the spinal cord.

The brain consists of three regions: (1) the *cerebrum* (*ser*-ee-brum); (2) *cerebellum* (ser-eh-*bel*-um); and (3) the *brain stem.* Only one part of the brain stem, the *medulla* (meh-*dull*-ah) *oblongata* will be discussed here.

The cerebrum is the largest of the brain regions. It is proportionally larger in man than in any animal. It consists of two halves, or hemispheres, securely joined by tough fibers and nerve tracts. The outer surface, or **cortex,** of the cerebrum is deeply folded in irregular wrinkles and furrows, called **convolutions.** This form of surface structure greatly increases the surface area of the cerebrum.

The cerebral cortex is composed of countless numbers of nerve cells not

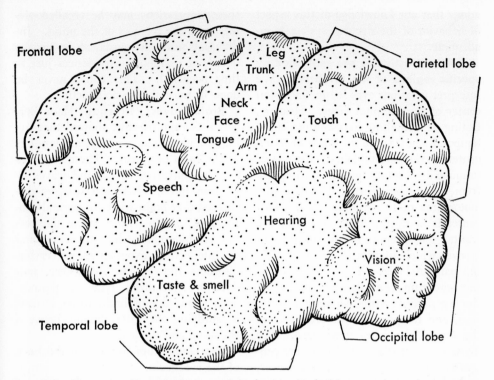

Fig. 40-3. These are the control areas of the brain. Each thing you do, such as seeing, hearing, speaking, or moving, is controlled by a certain part of your brain.

covered by sheaths. We frequently refer to this area as **gray matter** because of the color of these cells. The cerebrum below the cortex is composed of **white matter,** formed by masses of fibers covered by sheaths and extending from the nerve cells of the cortex to other parts of the body.

Deep grooves divide the cerebral hemispheres into lobes. The **frontal lobes** are situated on the front of the hemispheres and extend well back along the top of the cerebrum. These lobes are much more highly developed in man than in animals. The **parietal** (pa-*ry*-eh-tal) **lobes** lie behind the frontal lobes. The **temporal lobes** are below the frontal and parietal lobes, along the sides of the cerebral hemisphere. The **occipital** (ok-*sip*-ih-tal) **lobes** occupy the lower back region of the cerebrum. (See Fig. 40-3.)

The functions of the cerebrum. Through the cerebrum, we express our intellectual, moral, and spiritual values. However, even though we know that these qualities are centered in the cerebrum, we do not know how they are expressed. Thought is not secreted like bile or hormones. It is not a material substance. We can explain the activity of other body organs in terms of nervous and chemical stimulation and response. But the origin of thought is something quite different. We do not even know how thoughts originate. Nor can we explain how brain cells remember the things we have experienced, how they express emotion, or how they distinguish right from wrong. We must admit that our knowledge of this aspect of behavior of the nervous system is inadequate.

Different activities are controlled by specific regions of the cerebrum. We interpret what our eyes see in the vision center of the occipital lobes. Hearing, tasting, and smelling have centers in the temporal lobes, while the sense of touch centers in the parietal lobes. If we wish to move a voluntary muscle, an impulse from the cerebral cortex stimulates the motor area of the frontal lobes. This center is in the posterior region of the frontal lobes, close to the **fissure,** or groove, which divides these lobes from the parietal lobes. The motor area of the cerebrum controls the muscles of the legs, trunk, arms, shoulders, neck, face, and tongue (in this order) from the top of the lobes downward. We know also that the frontal lobes are centers of emotion, judgment, will power, and self-control. These functions, however, are shared by other areas of the cerebral cortex.

The things we see and hear and feel are registered as impressions in different areas of the cerebral cortex. These areas are, in turn, connected by a vast number of **association fibers.** Thoughts are the result of associations of these impressions. Your intellectual capacity is determined by the ability of your cerebral cortex to register impressions, the activity of your association fibers, and the sum of your past experiences.

The cortex of the brain never loses an impression. Many impressions of past experiences cannot be recalled in consciousness, but are retained in what we call the *subconscious mind.* In other words, these impressions are covered up by more recent or more outstanding impressions which dominate conscious activity. When, however, an individual is hypnotized and skillfully questioned,

these impressions may be recalled vividly from the recesses of the mind. Individuals under hypnosis can review the details of childhood experiences just as they occurred. This could never be done in normal conscious activity.

Brain waves. In 1929, Hans Berger, a German doctor, showed that living brains produce electrical impulses in the form of waves. These impulses may be converted into sound waves by vacuum tubes. Research workers discovered that brain waves in normal people may vary in pattern when the person is undergoing different emotional or intellectual experiences. Nervous disorders like epilepsy, however, produce a specialized type of pattern. This knowledge of brain waves is used in studying the interrelations between the mind and the body.

The cerebellum lies below the back of the cerebrum. Like the cerebrum, it is composed of hemispheres but its convolutions are shallower and more regular than those of the cerebrum. The surface of the cerebellum is composed of gray matter. Its inner structure is largely white matter, although it contains some areas of gray matter. Bundles of nerve fibers connect the cerebellum with the rest of the nervous system through the brain stem.

In a sense the cerebellum acts as an assistant to the cerebrum in controlling muscular activity. Nervous impulses do not originate here nor can one control its activities. The chief function of the cerebellum is to coordinate the muscular activities of the body. Thus, without the help of the cerebellum, the impulses from the cerebrum would result in disorganized body motions.

For example, you may decide to pick up a ball and throw it. Your decision in the frontal lobe of the cerebrum stimulates the motor area. This area in

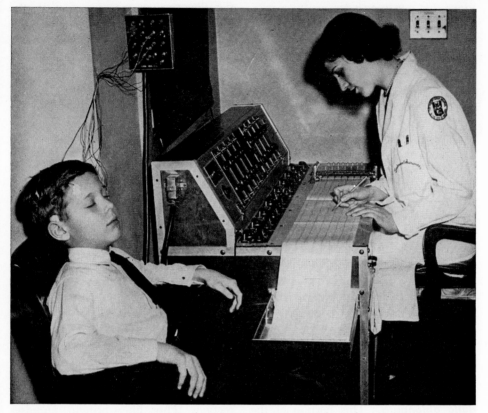

Fig. 40-4. Activities of the cerebral cortex can be measured as electrical impulses. The brain wave pattern appears on the paper which the assistant is examining.

turn sends a series of impulses to the cerebellum to notify it of the desired activity. By some amazing process, the cerebellum sorts out these impulses. It stimulates just the muscles involved in bending over, picking up the ball, and throwing it. It determines the time when the fingers should open to grasp the ball, when they should close to hold it, how the muscles of the arms, shoulders, and trunk work in throwing it, and how leg muscles maintain balance.

Other functions of the cerebellum. The cerebellum functions further in strengthening impulses to the muscles. This action is a little like picking up a weak radio or television signal and amplifying it before broadcasting it.

Another function of the cerebellum is maintenance of tone in muscles. The cerebellum cannot originate a muscular contraction, but it can cause the muscles to remain in a state of partial contraction. Otherwise you would collapse. You are not aware of this because the cerebellum is below the level of consciousness.

The cerebellum functions also in maintaining balance. In this activity, it is assisted by impulses from the eyes and from the organs of equilibrium, or semi-circular canals of the inner ears, which you will study in the next chapter. Impulses from both of these organs inform the cerebellum of your position in relation to your surroundings. The

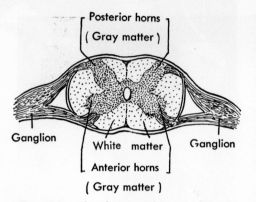

Posterior horns
(Gray matter)

Ganglion

White matter

Ganglion

Anterior horns

(Gray matter)

Fig. 40-5. This drawing shows a cross section of the spinal cord.

cerebellum in turn maintains contraction of the muscles necessary to balance your body. If you close your eyes, the task is more difficult and you may sway or lose your balance.

The brain stem. Nerve fibers from the cerebrum and cerebellum enter the brain stem, an enlargement at the base of the brain. It consists of three regions, the lowest of which is the **medulla oblongata.** This portion of the stem is about the size of a walnut. It is located at the base of the skull and protrudes from the skull slightly where it joins the spinal cord. The two other parts of the brain stem are the **midbrain** and the **pons.** Their functions are too specialized for our study here.

There are twelve pairs of **cranial nerves** connected to the brain stem. These act as direct connections with certain important organs of the body. One pair, for example, called the *optic nerves,* connects the eyes with the brain. Another important cranial nerve, the **vagus** (*vay*-gus), connects with the lungs, heart, stomach, and other abdominal organs.

The medulla oblongata controls the activity of the internal organs. It regulates the rate of respiration and heart action, muscular action of the walls of the digestive organs, secretion in the glands, and other automatic activities.

The spinal cord. This extends from the medulla oblongata through the protective bony arch of each vertebra, almost the length of the spine. Its outer region is white matter, made up of great numbers of nerve fibers. Nerve cells, composing the gray matter, lie inside the white matter in the form similar to the shape of a butterfly with its wings spread (Fig. 40-5). The pointed tips of the wings of gray matter are called **horns.** Two of them, the **posterior horns,** point toward the back of the cord while a pair of **anterior horns** point toward the front.

Thirty-one pairs of **spinal nerves** branch off the spinal cord. These nerves are large trunks, similar to a telephone cable in that each contains many nerve fibers. Some of them carry impulses into the spinal cord, while others lead away from it. Nerve impulses travel along these fibers in only one direction. Thus, fibers bringing impulses into the cord cannot carry outgoing impulses. Each spinal nerve divides just outside the cord. The fibers which carry impulses from the body into the spinal cord branch to the posterior horns of the gray matter. This branch of each spinal nerve has a swelling, or **ganglion** (*gan*-glee-un), near its point of entry to the cord. The other branch at the junction leads from the anterior horns of gray matter. These fibers carry impulses from the spinal cord to the body.

If the spinal cord were cut, all parts of the body controlled by nerves below the point of severing would be totally paralyzed. Such an injury might be compared to cutting the main cable to a telephone exchange. Anesthetics are now being used on the cord to temporarily deaden entire sections of the body by chemically blocking nervous impulses. Under these conditions, there is no effect on the brain or consciousness. In addition to linking the brain and the body, the spinal cord is the center of reflex actions, a type of nervous activity which will be discussed later.

The nerves. If all the other tissues of the body could be dissolved, the outline of the body would be preserved by the network of nerves which would remain (Fig. 40-7).

Nerve cells are called **neurons** (*nu*-rons). Each neuron has a rounded, star-shaped or irregular *cell body,* containing a nucleus and cytoplasm. Threadlike **processes** extend from the nerve body. The branching treelike processes which carry impulses *toward* the cell body are called **dendrites** (*den*-drytes). The number of dendrites entering a cell body may range from one to 200. Impulses travel *from* the nerve body along a single process enclosed in fatty sheaths. We call these outgoing processes **axons** (*ax*-ons). Dendrites and axons branch freely at their tips in tiny brushlike structures.

The bodies of nerve cells are most often found only in the gray matter of the brain and spinal cord in scattered masses called **plexuses** (*plek*-sus-ez) and in the ganglia of the spinal nerves. Sheathed fibers penetrate the body tissues and form the white matter of the brain and spinal cord.

Sensory and motor neurons. Sensory neurons carry impulses from the skin and other sense organs to the spinal cord and brain. These nerves have long dendrites with numerous branched endings. They may be short or very long, depending on their location. For example, an impulse from a sensory nerve in a toe travels along a dendrite from the toe to a nerve body in a ganglion just outside the spinal cord. It enters the cord through its axon.

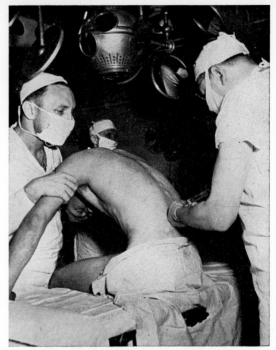

Fig. 40-6. Spinal anesthetics temporarily deaden entire sections of the body. This patient is receiving a " spinal " prior to an operation for appendicitis.

Motor neurons carry impulses from the spinal cord and brain to muscles and glands. When you wiggle a toe, impulses travel from the brain through the spinal cord and along an axon leading from the spinal cord to the toe muscles. The endings of sensory and motor nerves in the spinal cord and brain mingle with many association neurons with short processes. The processes of one nerve never join those of another nerve. The space between nerve endings is called a **synapse** (*sih*-naps). Nerve impulses must pass over these synapses as they travel from one nerve to another. Furthermore, an impulse never travels from one motor nerve to another. It is received by the dendrite of a sensory or an association neuron. The same applies to impulses received by sensory nerves. Look at Fig. 40-9 on page 535.

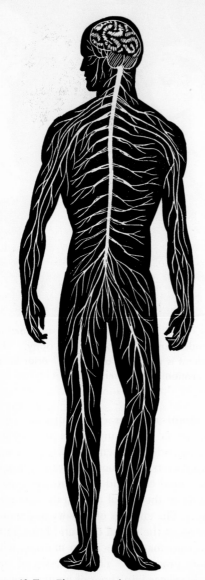

Fig. 40-7. The general arrangement of the nervous system of the human body.

impulse passes along a nerve, carbon dioxide is liberated. This indicates that a chemical reaction is involved.

For a long time scientists were in doubt as to how a nerve impulse causes a muscle to contract. Now we know that the stimulation is indirect. An impulse, traveling along the axon of a motor nerve, ends at the *motor end plates* at the tips of the brushlike structures.

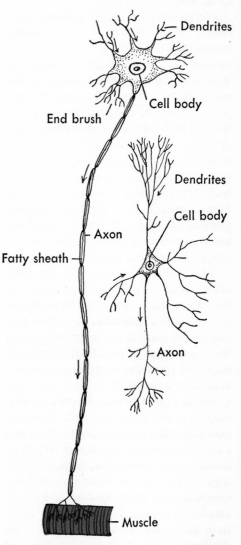

Fig. 40-8. Here are two types of nerve cells. Left: motor neuron. Right: neuron from the brain.

Nerve impulses. A nerve impulse is known to be an electrochemical impulse which brings about a change in the nerve processes. It is not a flow of electricity, for nerve impulses are much slower. A nerve impulse travels at a rate of about 272 miles per hour, while electricity travels at a rate of 186,000 miles per second. Also, when a nerve

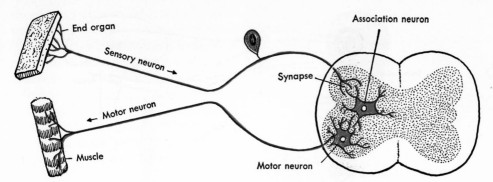

Fig. 40-9. Reflex actions are automatic. Trace the path of an impulse from the stimulus to the response.

Here the impulse causes the release of a minute amount of a chemical called **acetylcholine** (*as*-et-il-*ko*-leen). This substance forces the muscle to contract. Thus the direct cause of the contraction is chemical.

Nervous reactions. Nervous reactions vary greatly in form and complexity. The simplest of nervous reactions is the **reflex action.** It is an automatic reaction involving the spinal cord or the brain.

The knee jerk is an excellent example of a simple reflex action. If you allow your leg to swing freely and strike the area just below the kneecap with a narrow object, the foot jerks upward. This reaction is entirely automatic. Striking the knee stimulates a sensory nerve from the lower leg. An impulse travels along the dendrite to the spinal cord. Here the impulse is sent to an association neuron. This neuron, in turn, stimulates the dendrite endings of the motor nerve to the leg muscles, causing a jerk. The entire reflex takes only a split second.

When you touch a hot object, you experience a similar reflex. Your hand jerks away almost instantly. After the reflex is completed, the impulse reaches the brain and registers pain. However, if the muscle response had been delayed until the pain impulse had reached the brain and a motor impulse traveled down the spinal cord from the cerebral motor area, the burn injury would have been much greater. Other reflex actions include: sneezing, coughing, blinking the eyes, laughing when tickled, and jumping when frightened.

Voluntary activities involve the cortex of the cerebrum. When you learn to ride a bicycle, every movement is controlled by the cerebral cortex. You are aware of pedaling, guiding, and balancing. This is quite a muscular undertaking, and you may have fallen a few times during the learning period. As you practice riding, the pathways along the nerve fibers become well established. Furthermore, the cerebellum becomes more skilled in coordinating the muscular activity involved. After a time, riding your bicycle becomes a habit.

The motor area of the cerebrum and the cerebellum, after training, controls the impulses without any help from other areas of the brain cortex. You are no longer conscious of riding and can concentrate on other things. The same thing applies to playing a piano, after you have learned the fingering technique, the position of the keys, and the notes on the printed music.

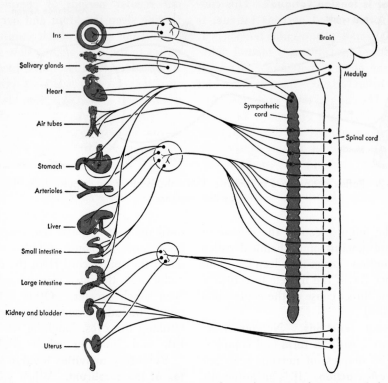

Fig. 40-10. The autonomic nervous system regulates the internal organs of the body. What is the function of the sympathetic system?

The autonomic nervous system. This division of the nervous system is entirely involuntary and automatic. It is partly independent of the rest of the nervous system. The autonomic system is, in turn, composed of two parts: (1) the *sympathetic system;* and (2) the *parasympathetic system.*

The **sympathetic system** includes two rows of nerve tissue, or *cords,* which lie on either side of the spinal column. Each cord has *ganglia,* which contain the bodies of nerve cells. The largest of the sympathetic ganglia is the *solar plexus,* located just below the diaphragm. Another is near the heart, a third is in the lower part of the abdomen, and a fourth is in the neck. Fibers from the sympathetic nerve cords enter the spinal cord and connect with

it and the brain, as well as with each other. The sympathetic nervous system helps to regulate heart action, the secretion of ductless glands, blood supply in the arteries, the action of smooth muscles of the stomach and intestine, and the activity of other internal organs. (See Fig. 40-10.)

The **parasympathetic system** opposes the sympathetic system and thus maintains a system of check and balance. The principal nerve of the parasympathetic system is the **vagus nerve,** one of the cranial nerves which extends from the medulla oblongata, through the neck, to the chest and abdomen. The check and balance system is illustrated by the fact that the sympathetic system speeds up heart action, while the vagus nerve slows it.

What is tension fatigue? This condition, often called nervous fatigue, is actually a state of muscular tension. It is produced by continued mental activity to the point of boredom. A person with tension fatigue is literally tense and tired. He cannot relax and sleep like a person who is physically fatigued. The obvious remedy for tension fatigue is change in mental activity or the substitution of enjoyable physical activity.

The human body needs sleep. It cannot endure continued activity without regular periods of complete rest. During sleep the brain and nerve cells, aside from those which continue impulses to the vital organs, slow their activity. Heart action slows, blood pressure decreases, secretion is greatly reduced, and tissue oxidation drops to a low rate. During this period, waste products are removed and body tissues undergo growth and repair without competition with rapid body activity. The amount of sleep a person needs often varies with the individual.

In Conclusion

The brain and spinal cord compose the central nervous system. They communicate with all parts of the body by nerves. The brain consists of the cerebrum, the cerebellum, and the brain stem.

The cerebrum controls conscious activities. It is the center of intelligence and contains both sensory and motor areas. Impulses from the cerebral motor area pass through the cerebellum, where coordination of impulses takes place. The medulla oblongata controls the activity of internal organs and is especially the center of control of respiration.

Remarkable nerve endings which are specialized to act as sense organs are the subject of the next chapter. We will see how some are organized so as to be sensitive to light, others to sound, some to pressure, and still others to chemicals. Without sense organs, our life would be quite dull.

Questions for Review

1. (a) What are the parts of the human nervous system? (b) Give the function of each part.

2. (a) What are the parts of the brain? (b) What are the functions of each?

3. What advantage do the convolutions of the cerebrum have?

4. What advantage does man have over animals in the greater development of his frontal lobes?

5. Why is it harder to maintain balance with your eyes closed than when they are open?

6. Why may a blow on the back of the head cause blindness?

7. What advantage would a spinal block have over other forms of anesthesia where complete unconsciousness results?

8. How do you account for the fact that brain waves during the time of sleep are so regular?

9. In what way is the autonomic system really two systems?

10. Why does the body need sleep?

11. How can a person overcome tension fatigue?

Biologically Speaking

association neurons
autonomic nervous system
axon
brain stem
brain wave
central nervous system
cerebellum
cerebral cortex
cerebrospinal fluid
cerebrum
conditioned reflex
convolutions
cranial nerves

dendrite
frontal lobes
ganglion
gray matter
medulla oblongata
meninges
motor neuron
motor end plate
nerve body
nerve processes
neuron
parasympathetic system
peripheral nervous system

plexus
pons
reflex
sensory neuron
solar plexus
spinal block
spinal cord
spinal nerve
sympathetic nervous system
synapse
vagus nerve
voluntary actions
white matter

Applying Facts and Principles

1. Compare the nervous system to a telephone exchange by tracing an incoming call, a connection by an operator, and a conversation with your party.

2. What is intelligence?

3. How can brain waves be accounted for by comparing the nervous system to an electronic calculating machine?

4. How can the brain store impressions below the level of consciousness?

5. Explain the activity which results when a chicken has its head cut off.

6. Explain the value of hypnosis in determining some kinds of mental illnesses.

7. How can a sample of cerebrospinal fluid aid in diagnosing diseases?

CHAPTER 41

The Sense Organs

Life without the sense organs would be as meaningless as that of a prisoner condemned to live and die in solitude in a dungeon. The nervous system would control the basic life processes, but for what purpose? Most of our pleasure in living results from being able to see, hear, feel, smell, and taste the things around us. These sensations are registered in the brain and are given meaning in the thought areas of our cerebral cortex. They provide the storehouse of impressions we associate with intelligent behavior. Indeed, there is some doubt whether the nervous system could operate without the sense organs.

Irritability is a fundamental process of living protoplasm. It is a quality possessed by every living organism. It may be expressed in the slow reaction of a stem to light or a root to water. In our study of plants, simple animals, and more complex animals, we have seen an increase in the efficiency of this life activity. In the higher animals certain cells are highly specialized by being sensitive to certain stimuli.

The sensations of the skin. The *skin* has five different types of nerve endings each associated with a different sensation. Certain of these nerve endings respond to *touch,* while others receive stimuli of *pressure, pain, heat,* and *cold.* No one nerve reacts to more than one stimulus, and thus the five sensations of the skin are distinct and different. The sensory nerves of the skin are distributed unevenly over the skin area in spots and lie at different depths in the skin.

If you move the point of your pencil over your skin very lightly, you stimulate only the nerves of *touch.* These nerve endings are close to the surface of the skin in the region of the hair sockets. The finger tips, the forehead, and the tip of the tongue contain abundant nerve endings which respond to touch.

Nerve endings which respond to *pressure* lie deeper in the skin. If you press the pencil point against the skin, you feel pressure in addition to touch. Since the nerves are deeper, a pressure stimulus must be stronger than a touch stimulus. We usually do not distinguish touch and pressure. However, the fact that you can distinguish the mere touching of an object from a firm grip on it indicates that separate nerves are involved. Pain receptors are distributed through the skin. If you press the point of your pencil firmly against the skin, you feel *pain.* Remember that a strong stimulus is necessary to register pain. If a light stimulus irritated these nerve endings, we would feel pain much of the time.

Heat and cold stimulate separate nerve endings. This is an interesting protective device of the body. Actually, cold is not an active condition. Cold results from a reduction in heat

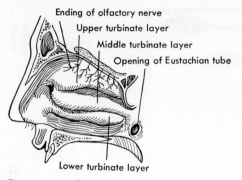

Ending of olfactory nerve
Upper turbinate layer
Middle turbinate layer
Opening of Eustachian tube
Lower turbinate layer

Fig. 41-1. This drawing shows the inner surface of the outer wall of the nose, including the turbinates. What is the function of the olfactory nerve?

energy. If temperature stimulated a single nerve, impulses would be strong in the presence of great heat and would become weaker as heat decreased. There would be no impulses in greatly reduced heat or intense cold. However, with some nerves stimulated by heat and others by the absence of it, we are constantly aware of both conditions.

Taste results from the chemical stimulation of certain nerve endings. Since nearly all animals prefer some food substances to others, we must assume that they can distinguish different chemical substances. Our sense of taste is centered in the taste buds of the tongue. These flask-shaped structures, containing groups of nerve endings, lie in the front area of the tongue, along its sides, and near the back. Foods, mixed with saliva and mucus, enter the pores of the taste buds and stimulate the hairlike nerve endings.

Our sense of taste is poorly developed. We recognize only four common flavors: *sour, sweet, salty,* and *bitter.* A fifth, *alkaline,* is difficult to describe but is not unlike salty. Taste buds are distributed unevenly over the surface of the tongue. Those sensitive to sweet flavors are at the tip of the tongue. Doesn't candy taste sweeter when you lick it than when you chew it far back in the mouth? The tip of the tongue is sensitive also to salty flavors. You taste sour substances along the sides of the tongue. Bitter flavors are detected on the back of the tongue. This explains why a bitter substance does not taste bitter at first. If a substance is both bitter and sweet, you sense the sweetness first, then the bitterness. Substances such as pepper and some other spices have no distinct flavor, but irritate the entire tongue and produce a burning sensation.

Much of the sensation we call "taste" is really smell. When you chew foods, vapors enter the inner openings of the nose and reach nerve endings of smell. If you plug up the external nasal openings, many substances lack the flavor we associate with them. Under such conditions, onions and apples have an almost identical sweet flavor. You have probably noticed the loss of what you thought was taste sensation when you had a head cold and temporarily lost your sense of smell.

Smell also results from the chemical stimulation of nerves. Odors are airborne. Some are strong and some are weak, but they must all make contact with our olfactory nerve endings before we can smell them.

Our sense of smell is poorly developed when compared to many animals. The nasal passages are arranged in three tiers, or layers, of cavities called **turbinates** (*tur*-bih-nates). The upper turbinate (Fig. 41-1) contains branched endings of the **olfactory nerve**. Stimulation of these endings by odors results in smell.

Smell involves several interesting factors. When you breathe cold air into the nostrils, air warmed in its pas-

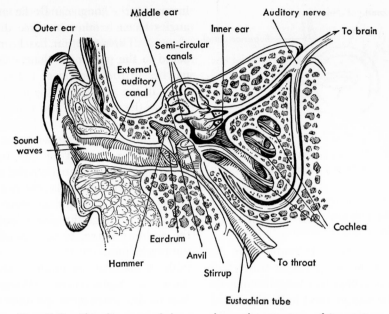

Fig. 41-2. This diagram of the ear shows the structure of its parts.

sage over the lower and middle turbinates is forced into the area above the upper turbinate, where smell occurs. This accounts for the fact that your ability to smell increases when you sniff several times in succession. Furthermore, nerve endings which are exposed to a particular odor over a long period of time become deadened to the odor, although they are receptive to other odors. Nurses are not aware of the odor of iodoform in a hospital, but a visitor notices it immediately.

Hearing. Hearing brings us into contact with our surroundings through the medium of sound waves carried in air. By means of this well-developed sense, we become aware of a large portion of our environment. Furthermore, it is along this avenue that we communicate with each other.

The structure of the human ear. Our ears, and those of other mammals, are wonderfully complex organs. The external ear opens into an auditory canal embedded in the skull (Fig. 41-2).

The canal is closed at its inner end by the **tympanic** (tim-*pan*-ick) **membrane,** or *eardrum,* which separates it from the middle ear.

The middle ear connects with the throat through the **Eustachian** (you-*stay*-kee-un) **tube.** This connection equalizes the pressure in the middle ear with that of the atmosphere. This prevents pressure from either side of the eardrum which would interfere with its vibration and, if too great or too little, would cause it to burst. Three tiny bones, the **hammer, anvil,** and **stirrup,** form a chain across the middle ear. They extend from the inner face of the eardrum to a similar membrane, covering the oval window which leads from the middle ear to the inner ear.

The inner ear is composed of two general parts. The **cochlea** (*kok*-lee-ah) is a spiral passage resembling a snail shell. It is filled with a liquid and is lined with nerve endings which receive the sound impressions. The **semi-circular canals** consist of three

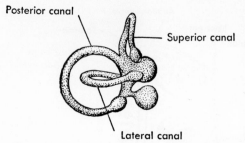

Fig. 41-3. The semi-circular canals of the inner ear function in maintaining equilibrium.

loop-shaped tubes each at right angles to the other two.

How we hear. If sound were visible, we would see irregular waves with peaks and valleys traveling through the air. The higher the pitch of a sound, the greater its wave frequency. This means that high notes have more peaks and valleys during a given unit of time, like a second, than low notes. When sound waves reach the ear, they are gathered by the external ear and directed through the canal to the eardrum. Here they cause the eardrum to vibrate in time with the peaks and valleys of the sound wave. As the drum vibrates, the hammer, anvil, and stirrup bones of the middle ear are vibrated. This sends the vibration to the membrane of the inner ear and causes the fluid in the cochlea to vibrate. Vibration of the fluid, in turn, irritates the nerve endings in the cochlea. Impulses travel through the auditory nerve to the cerebrum, where the translation of sound waves occurs. If the auditory nerves are destroyed, or if the auditory region of the cerebrum ceases to function, a person cannot hear, even though his ear mechanisms receive vibrations normally.

Equilibrium. Our sense of equilibrium, or balance, is centered in the semi-circular canals (Fig. 41-3) of the

inner ears. These canals lie at right angles to each other in three different planes. Their position has been compared to the parts of a chair. One canal lies in the position of the seat, another in the position of the back, and a third in the position of the arms.

The semi-circular canals contain a great number of nerve endings and a fluid similar to that of the cochlea. When the head changes position, the fluid rocks in the canals and stimulates nerve endings. Impulses travel from the nerve endings through a branch of the auditory nerve, to the medulla and the cerebellum. In the cerebellum, the brain is made aware of the position of the head. Since the canals lie in three planes, any change in position of the head moves the fluid in one or more of them. If you spin around rapidly, the fluid is forced to one end and strong impulses travel to the brain. This results in dizziness. Regular rhythmic motions produce unpleasant sensations that involve the whole body. This is motion sickness. Disease of the semi-circular canals results in temporary or permanent dizziness and loss of equilibrium.

Care of the ears. Fortunately, the most important parts of our ears are situated within the protection of the skull. However, you can injure the eardrum by probing the ear canal with hard instruments. Excess wax can accumulate in the eardrums but it should not be removed by probing. Only a physician should attempt to remove any excess wax.

Earache and discharge from the middle ear indicate an infection. Such a condition should receive the immediate attention of your doctor. Middle ear infections may occur during a head cold, especially if you blow your nose too hard and force mucus and infectious organisms into the Eustachian tubes.

The structure of the human eye. The normal eye is spherical and slightly flattened from front to back. The wall of the eyeball is composed of three distinct layers. The outer, or **sclerotic,** (skle-*rot*-ick) **layer** is tough and white. This layer shows in front as the white of the eye. It bulges and becomes transparent in front. We call this circular bulge the **cornea** (*kor*-nee-ah).

The second, or **choroid** (*ko*-roid) **layer,** is richly supplied with blood vessels and color cells. This layer forms the colored **iris** (*eye*-ris) in the front part of the eye. The opening through the iris is called the **pupil.** Change in size of the circular pupil is accomplished by muscles of the iris. This adjustment in size of the pupil opening to the intensity of light is an automatic reflex. When the light is reduced, the pupil becomes large, or *dilates.* In bright light, it *constricts* and becomes small. When you look through the pupil into the eye, you see the black pigment of the choroid layer in the eyeball. This black pigmentation prevents reflection of light rays within the eye.

The inner layer, or **retina** (*ret*-ih-nah), is the most complicated and delicate of the eye layers. It is really the expanded end of the *optic nerve.* This large nerve extends from the back of each eyeball to the vision center of the cerebrum. The nerves cross as they lead to the cerebrum, so that your right eye sends impulses to the left lobe of the cerebrum, while the right lobe receives impulses from the left eye.

A convex, crystalline **lens** lies behind the pupil opening of the iris. The lens is supported by the **ciliary** (*sill*-ee-ary) **muscles** fastened to the choroid layer. Contraction of these muscles changes the shape of the lens and focuses light

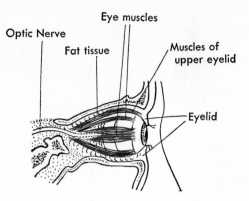

Fig. 41-4. A diagram of the human eye. This shows the muscles that move the eye.

on the surface of the retina in the eye.

The space between the lens and the cornea is filled with a thin, watery substance, the **aqueous** (*ay*-quee-us) **humor.** A thicker, jellylike transparent substance, the **vitreous** (*vit*-ree-ous) **humor,** fills the interior of the eyeball. This fluid aids in keeping the eyeball firm and preventing its collapse.

The eye rests in its socket against layers of fat which serve as cushions. Movements of the eyeball are accomplished by pairs of muscles (Fig. 41-4) which attach to its sides and extend back into the eye socket. The sclerotic layer is supplied with nerve endings which register pain when a foreign object touches it. It is further protected by its location deep in the recesses of the eye socket, by bony ridges, by the eyelids, and by the tear glands which keep its surface moist. Tears wash over the eye and drain into the tear ducts in the lower corner of the eye socket which leads to the nasal cavity. Because of their high salt content, tears are mildly antiseptic.

The structure of the retina. The retina is less than $\frac{1}{80}$ of an inch thick. Yet it is composed of seven layers of cells, nerve endings, ganglia, and nerve

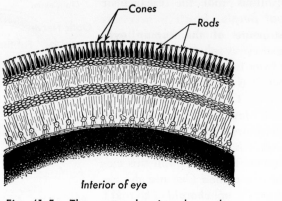

Interior of eye

Fig. 41-5. The center drawing shows the arrangement of rods and cones which are nerve endings on the retina of the eye. The drawing on the left (A) shows a highly magnified cone. The drawing on the right (B) shows a highly magnified rod.

A

B

fibers. The cells which receive impulses from light rays are of two types, **cones** and **rods** (Fig. 41-5). They lie deep in the retina, pointing toward the back surface of the eyeball. Impulses from the cones and rods travel through a series of short nerves with brushlike endings to ganglia near the front part of the retina. More than half a million nerve fibers lead from the ganglia over the surface of the retina to the optic nerve. There are no rods or cones at the point where the end of the optic nerve joins the retina. Thus there is no vision at this point. This is called the blind spot.

How we see. *Cones* are sensitive to bright light, and are responsible for color vision. *Rods* act in reduced light but do not respond to color changes. Cones occur through the retina, but are especially abundant in a small sensitive spot called the **fovea** (*fo*-vee-ah). When we see in daylight, light rays pass through the pupil, the aqueous humor, the lens, and the vitreous humor to the cones of the retina. The lens focuses rays on the fovea, the point at which we see an object clearly. As light rays pass through the lens, they cross and strike the retina in an inverted position (Fig. 41-6). Cones outside the fovea receive light rays and register vision, but not distinctly.

Thus, if you focus your eyes on an object, you see it clearly. In addition, you see objects contained in a hemisphere of vision indistinctly, or out of the corner of your eye.

During the late evening or at night, the light is too reduced to stimulate the cones. This quality of light stimulates

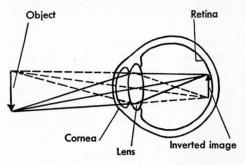

Fig. 41-6. Light rays enter the eye, cross in the lens, and focus on the retina. Why is the image inverted on the retina?

the rods. Rods produce a substance we call **visual purple,** which is necessary for their proper functioning. Bright light removes visual purple and prevents activity of the rods. This explains why, when you leave a bright room at night, you are temporarily night-blind. As visual purple is restored, the rods begin to function, and you can see objects in dim light.

The human eye contains fewer rods than many animal eyes, and so our night vision is relatively poor. The cat, deer, owl, and many other animals see well at night because they have many rods. The owl, however, lacks cones and is day-blind.

The fovea of your retina contains many cones, but no rods. This explains why you can see an object out of the corner of your eye at night but when you focus on it, it disappears.

The eye and the camera. By understanding the eye and how it produces vision, we have been able to compare it to a camera in certain respects (Fig. 41-7). There are, however, several fundamental differences between an eye and a camera. In a camera the image of a picture is recorded on the film in the back of the

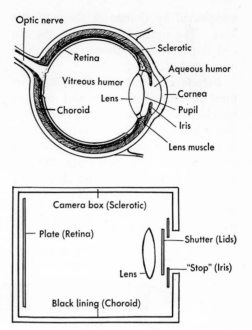

Fig. 41-7. Explain how the parts of the eye (upper drawing) correspond to those of a camera (lower drawing) and how they differ.

camera. In the eye, this image is recorded on the retina and in the brain. Furthermore, when you focus light rays on a film, you change the distance between the lens and the film surface. In the eye, focusing on the retina is ac-

COMPARISON OF THE EYE AND THE CAMERA

PART OF THE EYE	CORRESPONDS TO		PART OF THE CAMERA
Eyeball	"	"	Camera box
Lens	"	"	Lens
Lids	"	"	Shutter
Iris	"	"	Stops or diaphragm
Pupil	"	"	Lens opening
Lens muscles	"	"	Focusing devices
Pigment of choroid and retina	"	"	Black lining
Retina	"	"	Plate or film

complished by change in shape of the lens. The similarities between the eye and the camera are shown in the table on page 545.

Defects of the eye. Certain structural defects of the eye and changes which occur as you get older result in incorrect vision. Many defects result from improper shape and irregularities of the eyeball. In such cases, the lens is unable to focus light rays sharply on the surface of the retina. These conditions may be remedied by altering the path of the light rays to the retina by means of glasses. However, only an expert can diagnose the defect properly and restore proper vision by means of glasses.

The doctor of medicine who specializes in the treatment of eye defects, the correction of improper vision, diseases of the eye and their treatment, and eye surgery, is called an **oculist** (*ock*-you-list). The **optometrist** (op-*tom*-uh-trist) is a specialist in the diagnosis of vision defects and the correction of these. His work requires extensive training in a school of optometry. It is

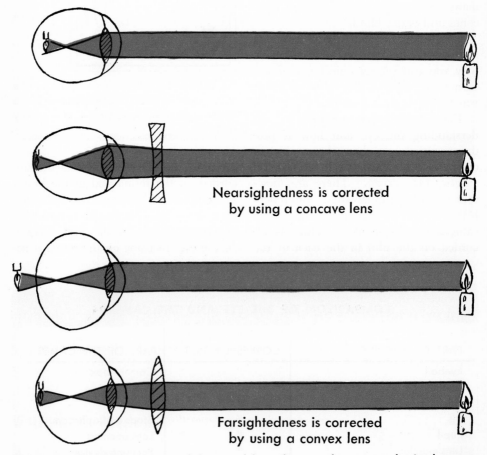

Nearsightedness is corrected by using a concave lens

Farsightedness is corrected by using a convex lens

Fig. 41-8. This shows two eye defects and how they can be corrected. In the nearsighted eye, the image is focused in front of the retina. In the farsighted eye, the image is focused behind the retina. Proper lenses in eyeglasses are used to correct these conditions.

very important for you to have your eyes examined at regular intervals.

The table on this page summarizes certain common eye defects and their causes, and the type of lens used to correct each.

SOME COMMON EYE DEFECTS		
CONDITION	DEFECT OF THE EYE	CORRECTIVE MEASURE
Nearsightedness	Eyeball lengthened from front to back, or lens too curved.	Concave lens glasses
Farsightedness	Eyeball shortened from front to back, or lens too flat	Convex lens glasses
Astigmatism	Irregularities in the shape of the lens or cornea	Special prisms or cylinders in lens glasses
Old age	Loss of lens flexibility, resulting in farsightedness	Convex lens glasses

In Conclusion

Sensory nerves carry impulses from their endings in sense organs to the central nervous system. The endings involved in the sense of smell contact gases in the upper turbinate region of the nasal passages. The ears are highly developed sense organs which receive air-borne vibrations and carry them to the nerve endings of the cochlea in the inner ear. The eardrum receives vibrations through the ear canal and sends them by way of the bones of the ear to the membrane of the inner ear where they cause waves in the fluid in the cochlea.

The eye is the most highly specialized of the sense organs. It receives light rays through the pupil and directs them to the retina by means of the lens.

Questions for Review

1. (a) The pleasure of living partially results from the possession of how many senses? (b) Name these senses.

2. What differences are there in the nerve endings for touch, pressure, and pain?

3. Why is it important to have both heat and cold receptors in the skin?

4. Account for the fact that we believe we distinguish more than the five flavors the tongue can perceive.

5. Why do you often sniff in detecting an odor?

6. How can an infection in the middle ear produce temporary deafness?

7. Is there any advantage in having the organs of balance located with the organs of hearing?

8. Why is our vision at night relatively poor?

9. Why is the owl " day-blind "?

10. What structures of the eyeball do light waves pass through as they enter the eye and finally reach the retina?

11. Name the structures of the ear through which sound waves pass as they enter the ear and finally reach the nerve endings.

12. Compare the parts of the eye with those of a camera.

Biologically Speaking

anvil bone	fovea	retina
aqueous humor	hammer bone	rod
auditory nerve	iris	sclerotic layer
choroid layer	lens	semi-circular canals
cochlea	olfactory nerve	stirrup bone
cone	optic nerve	turbinate
cornea	pupil	tympanic membrane
Eustachian tube	receptor	vitreous humor

Applying Facts and Principles

1. Why is it that you become so used to warm water in which you put your arm that you soon cannot tell whether it is warm or not?

2. How does the ear transmit sound waves so that there is a difference in the pitch, the quality of the tone, and the volume of the sound?

3. How would you go about designing an experiment to prove whether or not the eye really receives an image upside-down, and our brain interprets it oppositely?

4. How do optical illusions indicate the ability of the brain to interpret what we really see?

5. What hearing illusions can you recall to prove the statement that the brain interprets what we hear?

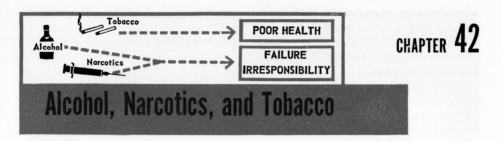

CHAPTER 42

Alcohol, Narcotics, and Tobacco

Problems resulting from alcohol and narcotics are as old as civilization. But the problems are more acute today because automobiles, firearms, and other mechanical devices become implements of destruction in the hands of an intoxicated person.

It is unfortunate that the use of alcohol and tobacco are often referred to together as though they had much in common. Young people seeing a large proportion of adult society smoking without any apparent effect on the body might assume that the effects of alcohol are no more serious. While there is no real justification for the use of tobaccco, its influence on the human mechanism is not to be compared with the physical, emotional, and mental damage resulting from the habitual and excessive use of alcohol.

Is alcohol a food? We defined food in Chapter 35 as any susbtance which, when taken into the body, yields material valuable for the growth and repair of tissue, production of energy, or regulation of the life processes without harming the organism. Alcohol yields no material which can be used in growth and repair of tissues. Actually, its presence in tissue may interfere with growth and repair involving protein foods. While large amounts of heat are released during oxidation of alcohol in the tissues, this heat cannot be used as energy for carrying on the life processes. In fact, energy derived from real foods must be used up in ridding the body of the excess heat from the alcohol. Even if there were energy value from alcohol, the anesthetic effect of alcohol on the body would rule it out as a food classification. Thus we must rule out any possible nutritional value of alcohol.

Is alcohol a stimulant? Many people excuse moderate drinking on the grounds that it stimulates them. A

" shot " before an important conference does not sharpen the mental processes. In fact, it dulls them. Actually, *alcohol is a depressant,* a substance which dulls the senses. Any feeling of uplift a person may claim to feel is a mistaken impression or an attempt to justify the act in his own mind.

What happens when alcohol enters the body? When alcohol is consumed, it passes to the stomach and starts to enter the blood within two minutes. No change in form or composition occurs before absorption begins. This explains why absorption is so rapid.

Absorption continues in the stomach and in the upper region of the small intestine until all the alcohol has reached the blood. This absorption is more rapid when the stomach is empty than when it contains food. The blood carries it to all body tissues. Here the alcohol is combined with water in the tissue spaces.

Oxidation begins immediately and large amounts of heat are released. The

549

Fig. 42-1. The "drunkometer," being demonstrated above, is one of several breath-test devices used to determine the amount of alcohol in a person's blood.

rate of oxidation of alcohol has no relation to the energy needs of the body tissues. This is evidence that the heat has no value. Otherwise the oxidation rate would be in proportion to energy needs in the tissues. As heat is released, it is picked up by the blood and delivered to the skin. This causes the flush in the body surface associated with the presence of alcohol in the system. The heat is released from the skin. The body tissues oxidize alcohol at the rate of approximately one ounce in three hours.

The rush of blood to the skin gives the false impression of warmth in the body. This is quite explainable, for the receptors of heat are in the skin. During this feeling of warmth, however, the internal organs are deprived of adequate blood supply and become chilled. A person who is in danger of chilling or freezing increases his chances of freezing to death by drinking alcohol.

Some effects of alcohol on the body organs. Since alcohol is absorbed by all the body organs, all of them are affected by its presence. However, certain organs seem to be affected more than others. The kidneys are overworked in eliminating excess water consumed with certain beverages. In other cases, alcohol dehydrates the tissues and causes the skin to excrete large quantities of water during heat elimination. This loss of water concentrates nitrogenous wastes in the kidneys and interferes with normal elimination.

Cirrhosis (si-*ro*-sis) of the liver is often associated with heavy drinking and alcoholism. Probably alcohol does not produce the liver degeneration directly. This is indicated by the fact that many habitual drinkers do not develop cirrhosis, while the condition may appear in people who have never consumed alcohol.

When beverages with high alcoholic content are taken into the stomach and intestine, damage may occur in the linings. Inflammation of the stomach lining causes a painful condition called *gastritis* (gas-*try*-tis).

Effects of alcohol on the nervous system. Alcohol has an anesthetic effect on the nervous system. The influence may appear as temporary impairment of the mental faculties and abnormal behavior. Or it may exert an influence over a period of time which will lead to permanent mental illness. It can even cause death.

The first effects of alcohol occur in the brain cortex. *Reaction time* for muscular activity is increased. The association of sensory and motor impulses is retarded due to the drug effects of alcohol on brain tissue.

Another early effect is loss of judgment, will power, and self-control. These qualities of man are centered in the brain cortex. With loss of judgment, cares seem to vanish and the person becomes gay and lightheaded. Influence on the frontal lobe alters emotional control and may lead to a feeling of great joy, shown by foolish laughter or sadness and weeping. As the effects of alcohol progress through the brain tissue, the vision area of the cerebrum and the eyes themselves become involved. Blurred vision, double vision, and lack of ability to judge distance occur.

As the cerebellum becomes involved, coordination of the muscles is affected. The victim becomes dizzy when standing, and if he is able to walk at all, does so with a clumsy, staggering gait. Even the muscles of the tongue become involved, and speech becomes thick and hesitant.

In the final stages of drunkenness, a person becomes completely helpless. The brain cortex ceases activity, resulting in complete unconsciousness. The skin becomes pale, cold, and clammy. Body oxidation is reduced and alcohol remains in the tissue fluids. Heart action, digestive action, and respiration slow up and the victim lies near death.

Addiction to alcohol. There is a sharp distinction between a habit and an addiction. We may make a habit of eating candy, chewing gum, or carrying on some type of activity. By exerting self-control, we can break the habit. It may cause some nervous tension and a temptation to resume the activity. Other than this, however, there is no serious effect upon the body.

An *addiction* is much more serious and acute. If a person is addicted to alcohol, his system reacts violently if he is deprived of it. Nervous reactions may be acute, resulting in hallucinations and violent craving, conditions we refer to as *withdrawal symptoms.*

Alcoholism is a disease. It produces both mental and physical symptoms. It results also in complete destruction of the personality.

Six to seven per cent of the adult users of alcohol develop into alcoholics. Alcoholism may begin with occasional social drinking. As distressing situations and problems arise and life seems temporarily unpleasant, the individual uses alcohol as an escape from reality. The problems remain unsolved, and alcohol is used for a definite purpose — to try to escape from the problems.

With loss of judgment and will power, the chances of solving them are further reduced. The alcoholic then resorts to solitary drinking for the pure effects of alcohol.

Alcohol becomes the tool and not the underlying cause of alcoholism. Thus the alcoholic seeking a cure must first find the reason for his problem drinking. Then he must solve the problem and not resort to alcohol as an escape from it. Sympathetic understanding and cooperation of his family and friends will help greatly in overcoming the problem.

Twenty-six states and the District of Columbia have clinics and hospitals to assist alcoholics in curing their condition. They supply both medical treatment and counseling necessary to deal with the problem.

If alcoholism is allowed to progress to an acute condition, serious deterioration of brain tissue may result. This may cause terrifying hallucinations known as *delirium tremens,* or " D.T.'s." The victim has visions of snakes, rats, and other vermin crawling over his body, and becomes violent with fear. By this time, his alcoholism has reached the proportions of alcoholic insanity.

Frequently, the heart muscle degenerates and the arteries harden. Almost constant digestive upsets occur due to the damage caused to the stomach walls by large quantities of alcohol. Such a person is extremely ill and requires medical care and hospitalization.

Alcohol and the length of life. Life insurance companies ask applicants for information about their use of alcohol and drugs. This is evidence that heavy drinkers are poorer risks than those who abstain.

It is difficult to say that limited or moderate use of alcohol shortens life. However, no one can deny that even moderate drinking of alcoholic beverages increases the possibility of accidental death. It also lowers body resistance and increases the possibility of death from infectious disease, especially tuberculosis. There is no question that heavy drinking shortens life considerably.

Alcohol and society. The effects of alcohol are much more far-reaching than damage to the habitual drinker himself. His family and all society pay a price for his short-sightedness.

Often a man or woman addicted to alcohol will neglect a family to satisfy the desire. Child neglect, home neglect, divorce, and other acute domestic problems frequently result. Anxiety, frustration, and insecurity in children are a terrible price to pay for alcoholism.

Alcohol must also answer for much of the crime committed in America. In a recent study of the records of 13,402 convicts in 12 states, alcohol was found to be a contributing factor in 50 per cent of the crimes committed, and a direct cause in 16.8 per cent of the crimes.

Alcohol and driving. Automobile accidents, resulting from driving while intoxicated, take a huge toll of life on our highways. Many people think a drink or two could not possibly affect their driving. In fact, such a person may feel that he is even more skilled in driving than usual. As a result, he takes chances because he is so sure of himself.

Important experiments have recently been carried on in Pennsylvania to test thoroughly, under actual road conditions, the relation of drinking to driving a car. Motorists who have been given measured amounts of alcohol but who were not drunk (all but one passed the standard police sobriety tests) were found to make all sorts of accidental errors. Not only did most of these drivers have a slower braking reaction time, but they were also inaccurate in performance. Yet every one of these drivers thought that he was doing well. The fundamental trouble, graphically proved by psychological tests, was found to be the *impairment of judgment after only one or two drinks.*

The death toll from automobiles is approaching 100 per day with 2,500 more injured per day. Safety officials attribute from 7 to 10 per cent of fatal highway accidents directly to the use of alcohol, while competent traffic officials state that one-third of these accidents are indirectly caused by alcoholic indulgence by the driver.

The effects of alcohol on a driver of a car are:

1. Less attention to signals and driving hazards.

2. Slower responses of eyes, hands, and feet, due to increased reaction time.

3. Increased self-assurance which causes a driver to take chances and be less considerate of other drivers.

Narcotic drugs. In discussing problems relating to alcohol and narcotic drugs in the same chapter, we do not mean to imply that the problems are similar. Many people consume alcoholic beverages without becoming habitual drinkers or alcoholics. However, continued use of narcotic drugs results in both mental and physical addiction. That is, the victim becomes dependent on the mental and emotional effects of the drug and his body develops a need for it. When not under the influence of a narcotic, the addict develops violent withdrawal symptoms. These include sleeplessness, difficulty in breathing, irregular heart action, and acute suffering. Mental symptoms include severe depression and derangement. Withdrawal sickness

Fig. 42-2. " If you drive, don't drink; if you drink, don't drive " is good advice. Accidents like this may result when drinking and driving are mixed.

may be severe enough to cause death. The longer an addict uses a narcotic, the greater amount he must take to ward off the withdrawal sickness. The situation becomes so desperate an addict will commit a crime to get a supply of a narcotic drug.

It is hard to define a narcotic accurately. Generally, we include a group of drugs classified as *narcotics* by the federal government. They have a powerful effect on the nervous system and are dangerous to use except under strict medical supervision. For this reason, the sale of narcotics, except on a doctor's prescription, is illegal.

Opium (*oh*-pee-um) is the source of a family of narcotic drugs. It is extracted from the juice of the white poppy. *Morphine* (*mor*-feen), *codein* (*ko*-deen) are derived from opium. *Heroin* (*hair*-oh-in) is a synthetic compound prepared from morphine. Morphine is used to reduce pain. Codein has similar uses and is an ingredient in special kinds of medicines, including some cough

HOW ALCOHOL AFFECTS A DRIVER

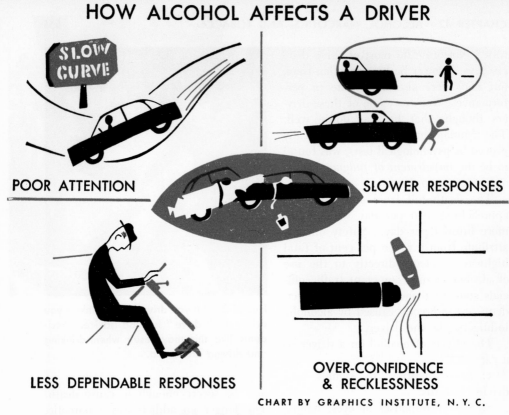

POOR ATTENTION

SLOWER RESPONSES

LESS DEPENDABLE RESPONSES

OVER-CONFIDENCE & RECKLESSNESS

CHART BY GRAPHICS INSTITUTE, N. Y. C.

Fig. 42-3. Alcohol lowers driving efficiency.

syrup. Heroin is so dangerous and addiction-forming that its possession or use, even medicinal, in the United States is illegal.

Cocaine (ko-*kane*) is a narcotic drug extracted from the leaves of the South American coca plant (not connected with the beverage cocoa). Cocaine deadens skin and mucous membranes. A doctor may use it to deaden the area around a wound before he cleanses it or takes stitches. When taken internally, cocaine causes a temporary stimulation of the nervous system and a feeling of pleasure. Later, the victim is seized by a feeling of great fear and may become violent.

Recently a weed called *marijuana* (mar-ih-*wah*-nah) has received considerable attention in the newspapers as a narcotic. Its strength is so great that it is mixed with tobacco before being smoked. The marijuana user develops an emotional addiction to the effects of the drug, but does not experience physical addiction. However, marijuana addicts usually continue down the narcotic road to ruin and turn to opiates.

People may become narcotic addicts in several ways. In some cases, they become addicted during an illness in which a narcotic drug was used medically to relieve pain. Highly nervous or distressed people may use certain narcotics as depressants and continue purchase of the drugs illegally. Still others who are emotionally disturbed or maladjusted deal with dope peddlers who are associated with organized crime engaged in the unlawful sale of narcotics. This has become a serious problem in certain sections of the country.

Tobacco is the nation's leading habit. Recent surveys show that about 60

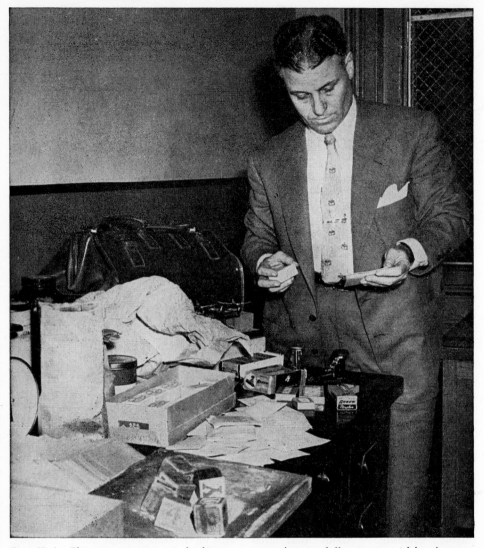

Fig. 42-4. This narcotic agent is looking over pure heroin, following a raid by the narcotics squad.

million people in the United States use tobacco in some form. More than 50 million of these are cigarette smokers.

We cannot say that the use of tobacco is injuring the health of all these people, especially the light and moderate smokers. But we can say that it is not improving the health of any of them and excessive use of tobacco certainly leads to poor health.

Tobacco is strongly habit-forming. In fact, the smoker becomes a slave to two habits. One is the *smoking habit*. He becomes accustomed to reaching for a cigarette at regular intervals, lighting it, and going through the various movements associated with smoking. Heavy smokers often light a second cigarette before finishing the first one through habit. Heavy smokers especially ac-

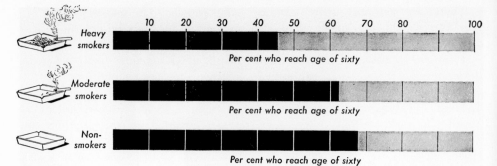

Fig. 42-5. Statistics indicate that nonsmokers live longer than heavy smokers.

quire the *nicotine habit.* This is a physiological habit in that the body craves tobacco.

Most young people who start smoking feel that it makes them seem more mature. Yet, if they asked the advice of an older person who has smoked for several years, his advice would probably be not to start. Certainly several things should be considered before deliberately starting a practice as habit-forming as smoking.

Tobacco contains a strong alkaloid, nicotine. In its pure form nicotine is very poisonous. The nicotine present in a single cigar, injected into the body and absorbed at one time, is sufficient to cause death.

Fortunately, about 60 per cent of the nicotine in a cigar or cigarette is burned during smoking. About half that amount is exhaled with the smoke, and about 10 to 12 per cent is absorbed by the body.

The harmful effects of tobacco are not as definite as those of alcohol and narcotics. The harm depends on: (1) the amount one smokes; (2) the depth to which the smoke is inhaled; and (3) the nervous make-up and general health of the individual.

The principal damage to the body as a result of smoking includes:

1. *Throat irritation.* The fact that smoke is irritating to the eyes indicates that it is irritating also to the throat membranes. This may lower the resistance of these membranes to invasion by bacteria.

2. *Depression of heart action* for a period and increase in the rate of beat following this period. This effect varies in different people.

3. *Constriction of arteries and increase in blood pressure.* This condition also varies in different people. It is the result of tension due to the effect of nicotine on the nervous system.

4. *Stomach discomfort.* Smoking increases the flow of gastric fluid at a time when it is not required. This is especially injurious to a person with a stomach ulcer. Many people develop spasms of the stomach wall as the result of nervous tension due to smoking.

People who smoke can give several reasons to justify their habit. They say that it quiets their nerves. This condition would probably not exist if they did not smoke. Others say it gives them something to do. This is quite apparent in the case of chain smokers who light a cigarette, smoke it a few minutes, then lay it down and forget it. Perhaps the tension which requires them to do something is aggravated by the fact that they use tobacco for that purpose.

There are certainly more reasons why you should *not* smoke than excuses for smoking.

1. *It is expensive.* The average moderate smoker smokes a package of cigarettes per day. At a cost of about 24 cents a package, this amounts to $1.68 per week, or $87.36 per year. The cost of tobacco to the entire population is well over $3,500,000,000 each year.

2. *Smoking is often annoying to other people.* The smoker is sometimes nervous if he finds himself in a place where smoking is forbidden. Or, if he insists upon smoking, he is being discourteous to those around him.

3. *Tobacco may mar the appearance.* Teeth may become stained and discolored. Breath can become strong and objectionable. Certainly, no one's appearance is improved by a cigar or cigarette hanging from the mouth. And good appearance is worth a great deal.

In Conclusion

All your ambitions, plans, and hopes for the future depend on good health. You have every reason to look forward to many years of health and happiness. The highly advanced medicine of modern times is at your service.

As you assume more and more of the responsibilities of adult life, you will feel the pressure of the complex age in which we live. Hustle and bustle — hurry and worry — these are signs of the times. Maybe they account for a large number of the millions of smokers. They might explain too why many become maladjusted and emotionally disturbed and seek an escape in problem drinking.

Certainly, tobacco is a blind alley leading nowhere. Alcoholism is a dangerous detour which leads only to misery and failure. The narcotic road leads all too suddenly to complete physical, moral, and mental ruin.

Your opportunities for success are almost unlimited today if you have the desire, the drive, the ability, and the good health to claim your place.

 **Questions for Review**

1. Why is alcohol not considered to be a stimulant?

2. Why is alcohol not considered to be a food?

3. What happens when alcohol enters the body?

4. What organs of the body are especially affected by cirrhosis?

5. Where in the body do the first effects of alcohol occur?

6. (a) Is there a difference between habit and addiction? (b) If so, what is the difference?

7. Why is it dangerous for a person who has had an alcoholic drink to drive an automobile?

8. Name six definite narcotic drugs as defined by the federal government.

9. In what ways is it possible to become a narcotic addict?

10. What are the harmful effects of using tobacco?

Biologically Speaking

addiction	delirium tremens	narcotic
alcohol	depressant	reaction time
alcoholism	gastritis	stimulant
cirrhosis	habit	withdrawal symptoms

Applying Facts and Principles

1. Why does the presence of alcohol in the body give a person a feeling of warmth?

2. The narcotic addict follows a definite pattern. What are the steps in the narcotic road to ruin?

3. Why do life insurance companies always ask the applicant if he drinks or smokes, and to what extent?

4. Why is drinking alcohol on an empty stomach more injurious than drinking with meals or after eating?

5. Why is inhaling smoke more injurious than not inhaling?

6. Explain the possible relationship between drug addiction and juvenile delinquency. How do drug addicts and alcoholics show weakness in character?

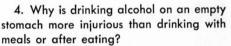

Research On Your Own

1. Bring in two chicken drumsticks. Clean off any muscle or ligaments clinging to them. Put one in a jar containing enough dilute solution of hydrochloric acid to submerge the bone. Leave the bone in the acid two or three days. Then remove it, wash off the acid, and examine its texture. Lay the other bone on a piece of wire gauze and heat it with a burner until it becomes red hot and no more smoke and vapor come off. Cool it and examine its texture.

2. Using either prepared slides or fresh mounts, examine several kinds of muscle tissues. Record your results in sketches. If fresh mounts are made, use fibers of heart muscle and lean beef as skeletal muscle. Stomach or intestine wall is a good subject for smooth muscle. Spread the fibers apart and stain them with methylene blue.

3. Keep an accurate check on all of your meals for one week. Calculate the number of Calories you take in each day by consulting a Calorie chart. Calculate the number of Calories you need each day, based on your weight and activity. Make a bar graph showing the number of Calories consumed each day and draw a line across the graph to show what your intake should have been.

4. Test various foods, such as apple, potato, cane sugar, raisins, lean meat, etc., for simple sugar, starch, fat, and protein. Use Fehling's solution, iodine, carbon tetrachloride, and the nitric acid—ammonia test for the various foods. Be sure to review the procedure for using each of these before making the tests.

5. Fill a quart jar with water and submerge it, mouth down, in an aquarium or a large, deep pan. Put the end of a rubber hose into the mouth of the jar. When you

blow through the hose, the air you exhale will displace water in the jar. Exhale normally, then blow all of the air you can into the jar. Mark the level of water in the jar. Fill the jar again and repeat, blowing out all the air you can after normal inhalation. Repeat after a forced inhalation.

6. Place a drop of blood on a microscope slide and stain it with Wright's blood stain. Examine it under high power of your microscope.

7. Have each member of your class take his pulse for one minute. Determine the class average for girls and boys.

8. Prepare a set of corks (about six) with a pair of pins stuck through each one. One cork should have the pins touching each other. The second should have them slightly separated, the third still farther apart, etc. Have someone touch the pins to various areas of your skin to see how far apart the points must be before you feel both of them and to discover if all areas of the skin have similar reactions to touch.

 ———————————————— **More About Biology**

Beck, Lester. *HUMAN GROWTH.* Harcourt, Brace and Co., New York. 1949

Behrman, Howard T. and Levin, Oscar L. *YOUR SKIN AND ITS CARE.* Emerson Books, Inc., New York. 1948

Berman, Louis, M.D. *GLANDS REGULAT— ING PERSONALITY.* The Macmillan Co., New York. 1928

Carlson, Anton Julius and Johnson, Victor. 4th Ed. *MACHINERY OF THE BODY.* University of Chicago Press, Chicago. 1953

Eisenbert, Philip. *WHY WE ACT AS WE DO.* Alfred A. Knopf, Inc., New York. 1947

Emerson, Haven. (Ed.) *ALCOHOL AND MAN.* The Macmillan Co., New York. 1932

Glynn, John H. *THE STORY OF BLOOD.* A. A. Wynn, Inc., New York. 1948

Goodman, Herman. *YOUR HAIR.* Emerson Books, Inc., New York. 1950

Pattee, Alida F. and Munsell, Hazel E. *VI— TAMINS FOR EVERYONE.* G. P. Putnam's Sons, New York. 1942

Pollack, Luby. *YOUR NORMAL MIND: ITS TRICKS AND QUIRKS.* Wilfred Funk, Inc., New York. 1951

Pomeranz, Herman. *YOUR RESPIRATORY SYSTEM.* The Blakiston Co., Philadelphia. 1944

Ravielli, Anthony. *WONDERS OF THE HUMAN BODY.* The Viking Press, New York. 1954

Riedman, Sarah R. *FOOD FOR PEOPLE.* Abelard-Schuman. New York. 1954

Riedman, Sarah R. *THE WORLD THROUGH YOUR SENSES.* Abelard-Schuman, Inc., New York. 1954

Riedman, Sarah R. *YOUR BLOOD AND YOU.* Henry Schuman and Co., New York. 1952

Schloat, Warren G., Jr. *YOUR WONDER— FUL TEETH.* Charles Scribner's Sons, New York. 1954

Sherman, Henry Clapp. *CHEMISTRY OF FOOD AND NUTRITION.* 8th Ed. The Macmillan Co., New York. 1952

Vail, Derrick. *TRUTH ABOUT YOUR EYES.* Farrar Straus, New York. 1950

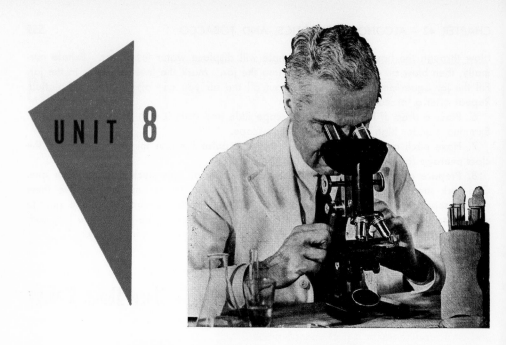

Biology and the Problems of Disease

Can you imagine an epidemic sweeping through your community and killing half the population? What if you lived in constant fear of smallpox, typhoid fever, or diphtheria?

You have been spared the dread of smallpox because an English country doctor made a great discovery and dared to defend his idea in the face of ridicule. We have waged a successful war against the microbe world because a French chemist discovered bacteria and a German doctor devoted his life to the study of germ diseases. An English biologist discovered penicillin, a German scientist gave us sulfa drugs, and an American produced a polio vaccine.

Step by step, scientists of the world have developed a highly organized medical science. As new discoveries are made, more and more infectious diseases are brought under the control of your doctor. Years are added to life expectancy.

You, your doctor, the staff of your hospital, your public health workers, and all the others who deal with the prevention and treatment of disease form a team. You have a part in this vital undertaking. To do your part, you need an understanding of the problems.

CHAPTER 43

Microbes—Mighty Mites of Infection

A few tiny bacteria, so small that thousands can live on the point of a needle, are able to multiply in your body and give you an infectious disease. They can be carried through the air in a drop of spray from a cough or sneeze, be present in the food you eat, or enter a wound you did not wash and treat.

You can perhaps understand why infectious diseases swept through whole communities years ago before microbes were finally tracked down. No one thought of looking for an invisible, living organism as the cause of scarlet fever, tuberculosis, or typhoid fever. Actually, bacteria were discovered by a chemist, not a biologist, and he found them in a beet sugar solution.

But this was only about 100 years ago. Let's go back many centuries before the microbe was unmasked and see how ancient people struggled to find an answer to the riddle of infectious disease.

Medicine among the ancients. In ancient Greece, during the fourth century B.C., one early physician, Hippocrates (hih-*pah*-krah-teez), began to look for natural causes for disease. His great wisdom in dealing with the sick marks him as the *father of medicine.*

Hippocrates had many mistaken ideas about the body and about disease. He thought the brain was a radiator to cool the head, and that food was cooked in the digestive system. He believed that health was determined by four body fluids. He named these fluids blood, phlegm, black bile, and yellow bile. But while he was wrong in some of his ideas, he was amazingly right in others. He recognized that pain, cough, and fever were reactions of the body to disease. He noticed that hollow eyes, sunken temples, and dry skin, especially on the forehead, were signs of grave illness and usually approaching death. He emphasized the need of proper diet, rest, fresh air, and exercise in maintaining good health. When patients came to him, he made careful records of their symptoms, his treatment of the disease, and the progress of the case. While he made mistakes, he tried not to repeat them.

The wisdom of Hippocrates established a new era in medicine. His influence remains today in the *Hippocratic Oath* taken by young doctors when they receive their M.D. degrees. This is an oath to uphold the high ethical standards of the medical profession, and to give all knowledge they acquire to new generations of doctors.

In the second century, another famous Greek physician, Claudius Galen (*gay*-len), came upon the scene. Galen was appointed surgeon to the Roman gladiators following his study of medicine in Alexandria. Later he went to Rome where he served as a doctor, teacher, and medical experimenter.

Fig. 43-1. This is an artist's conception of the plague in Florence, Italy in the 14th century which killed over 100,000 people.

Galen was the most honored physician of his time. Galen's writing became the basis for medical instruction and his influence lasted for hundreds of years.

Disease in the Middle Ages. Following the decline of Rome in the 5th and 6th centuries A.D., the civilized world entered the Dark Ages. Progress in medicine as well as in other fields was halted until the 15th and 16th centuries. Epidemic diseases stalked the civilized world. Rats swarmed through the streets and in open sewers carrying the fleas which harbored the deadly microbes of Black Death, or Bubonic Plague. One epidemic of the Plague between 1347 and 1350 killed 60 million people in Europe, Asia, and Africa. Over 100,000 people died in Florence, Italy alone during a single year of this dreadful epidemic. As the Plague spread through France, it took the lives of 50,000 people. A short time later,

it killed half of the population of London. Influenza, cholera, smallpox, and typhus fever swept through the civilized world in other epidemics.

Many theories of disease came out of the Middle Ages. Doctors believed that bad blood was the chief cause of infectious diseases. They referred to it as " bad humor," referring back to the humors of Hippocrates. This belief led to the practice of blood letting, or bleeding, as a means of removing " bad blood " and allowing the body to produce more " good blood." Blood letting was done by barbers, who also performed surgical operations. The barber opened a vein in the patient's arm which was held over a basin to catch the flowing blood. Blood spiraled down the arm in wide, red streams — a living duplicate which even today stands before the barber's shop as a symbol of his trade. At the end of the treatment,

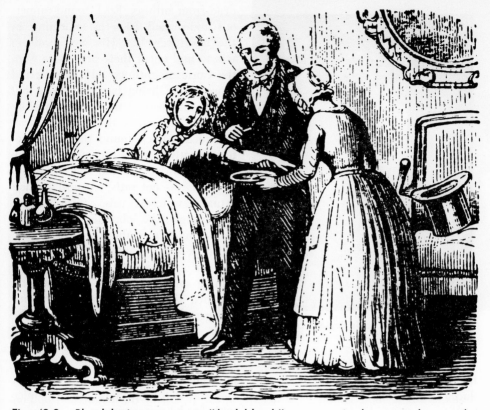

Fig. 43-2. Blood letting to remove "bad blood" was practiced even as late as the 19th century in this country.

the patient was sent home, weak from loss of blood and with the probability of infection from the wound in his arm made by the barber's dirty knife.

Such were conditions in the middle of the 19th century when one of the outstanding scientists of all time made a startling discovery.

Louis Pasteur, the father of bacteriology. Our scene now shifts to France in the year 1854. Louis Pasteur, a young chemist, was a professor of chemistry. One day a local distiller asked him to investigate the process during which alcohol is produced in the fermentation of sugar in beet pulp. As part of the investigation, Pasteur examined sugar solutions in various stages of fermentation. He was amazed to

find numerous rod-shaped bodies which seemed to be alive. He noticed, too, that the number of rods increased during fermentation. Thus, in his study of the fermentation of a beet sugar solution, Pasteur discovered bacteria. He made one of the greatest scientific contributions of all time.

He continued his study of fermentation with the souring of milk. He found similar organisms in sour milk and discovered that they changed milk sugar to lactic acid during the souring process. When he transferred some of the organisms to a sugar solution, he found that they soured the solution and produced acid just as they had in milk. He reasoned that microorganisms caused fermentation and disproved the

Fig. 43-3. Why is Louis Pasteur called the father of bacteriology?

theory that fermentation and decay produced living things by *spontaneous generation.*

He found that bacteria in milk could be destroyed by boiling and that sterile, sealed liquids did not ferment. His process is used today in the heating of milk to reduce its bacterial content. We call this **pasteurization.** The world respects Louis Pasteur today as the *father of bacteriology.*

Robert Koch, the father of bacteriological technique. Robert Koch (1843–1910) was born in Germany, the son of a poor miner and one of 13 children. His first outstanding contribution to medicine was in the study of **anthrax,** an epidemic disease of animals and often contracted by man. From early times, anthrax had spread through sheep, cattle, and other herds in epidemics. Anthrax was the first disease definitely linked to bacteria. In the examination of the organs of animals

dead from anthrax, Koch found numerous rod-shaped bacteria swarming in the blood vessels. His next problem was to find out if these organisms were the cause of anthrax. He transferred some of the living bacteria into a cut made at the base of the tail of a healthy mouse. The mouse developed anthrax and died. Koch found the same bacteria greatly increased in number in the blood stream of the dead mouse.

Koch was not satisfied until he had actually watched this multiplication. Accordingly, he obtained a drop of sterile fluid from the eye of a freshly killed ox and put into the drop a small portion of the spleen of a mouse containing anthrax germs. He patiently watched through his microscope until the germs spread entirely through the drop. He transferred germs from one drop to another and succeeded in growing them in the complete absence of any mouse spleen or blood. His next step was to try inoculating healthy mice with his laboratory-grown organisms to see if they would produce the disease. The mice died soon after inoculation and microscopic examination of the blood disclosed the same abundant rod-shaped organisms.

Koch's brilliant procedure is summarized in four steps called the **Koch postulates:**

1. Isolate the organism probably causing the disease. (Koch found anthrax organisms in the blood stream of infected animals.)

2. Grow the organisms in laboratory cultures. (Koch used sterile fluid from the eyes of oxen.)

3. Inoculate a healthy animal with the cultured organisms. (Koch inoculated mice with the eye fluid containing germs.)

4. Examine the diseased animal and recover the organisms which produced

the disease. (Koch found that the organisms with which he had inoculated the mouse had multiplied enormously in the blood stream.)

Koch's discovery of tuberculosis organisms. Koch discovered the causative organism in the lungs of victims of this disease. In 1882 he announced that tuberculosis was caused by a tiny, rod-shaped organism. His announcement was based on long hours of research during which he inoculated experimental animals with the disease by using pieces of infected lung tissue.

He had trouble growing tuberculosis organisms in his laboratory, for they failed to grow on any of the many kinds of media he had perfected. Finally he produced a successful medium by adding blood serum to agar. Thus, he was not only the first person to see the tuberculosis organism, but the first to grow it under laboratory conditions.

Forms of disease. We may define *disease* as any condition which actively impairs the health or interferes with the normal functioning of the body of an organism. It may be due to various causes which can be classified in distinct groups. They are:

1. Diseases caused by microorganisms (*infectious*).

2. Organic diseases due to abnormalities in body organs, abnormal growths, etc. (*noninfectious*).

3. Functional diseases due to abnormalities in the functioning of body organs (*noninfectious*).

4. Diet deficiency diseases due to a lack of proper diet, especially of vitamins (*noninfectious*).

5. Glandular diseases due to an improper functioning of the glands (*noninfectious*).

Organisms which cause disease. We use the term *pathogenic* to distinguish disease-causing organisms from

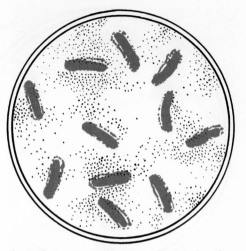

Fig. 43-4. To Koch is attributed the discovery of the rod-shaped organisms that cause tuberculosis.

harmless forms. These pathogenic organisms include various kinds of plants as well as certain minute forms of animal life. The following types of organisms may be associated with disease: (1) viruses; (2) Rickettsiae; (3) bacteria; (4) spirochetes; (5) protozoans; (6) molds and moldlike fungi; (7) yeasts; and (8) parasitic worms.

We will limit our discussion to viruses, Rickettsiae, bacteria, and spirochetes and the infectious diseases associated with them.

Viruses may be extremely small forms of living matter. The first virus was isolated from tobacco plants infected with leaf mosaic in 1935. Until the development of the electron microscope, no one had ever seen a virus. Even now scientists are not sure just what a virus is. It may be a tiny protein molecule which assumes the properties of life only when it invades a living cell. We do know that viruses are much smaller than any other organisms and that they cannot be grown outside living tissue. These characteristics have made viruses difficult to study.

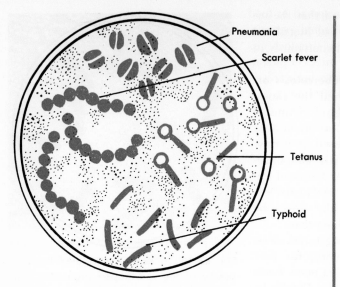

Fig. 43-5. Pathogenic bacteria may be of the coccus, bacillus, or spirillum types. Four different pathogenic bacteria appear in this drawing.

Better known virus diseases include smallpox, chickenpox, rabies, influenza, mumps, measles, German measles, polio, and yellow fever.

The *Rickettsiae* (rick-*ett*-see-ee) seem to be midway between the viruses and bacteria. They are like viruses in that they cannot live outside a host organism. They resemble bacteria in form, but are much smaller. These microorganisms were named in honor of Dr. H. T. Ricketts who first found them in cases of Rocky Mountain spotted fever and typhus fever. Dr. Ricketts died of typhus fever in 1910 while trying to find the cause of the disease. For some strange reason, Rickettsiae seem to be carried only by various arthropods, including the human body louse, rat flea, tick, and mite.

By far the largest number of pathogenic microorganisms are *bacteria* of various types. They may be coccus, bacillus, or spirillum forms. Pathogenic bacteria do not differ in appearance from the harmless forms you studied in Chapter 18. They cause disease when they invade a living host with damaging effects. Among the well-known bac-

terial diseases are: diphtheria, scarlet fever, tetanus, typhoid fever, tuberculosis, pneumonia (lobar), and anthrax.

Spirochetes (*spy*-roh-keets) resemble both bacteria and protozoans and seem to be forms of life midway between the two. They are long, spiral forms resembling corkscrews. The syphilis organism is probably the best known of these.

The spread of infectious organisms. Bacteria and other pathogenic organisms may be transferred from one person to another almost instantly during a cough or sneeze or contact with an infected person. Or they may float through the air, lie on objects, or live in water or food a long time before reaching a new victim.

Food-borne infections. Food, contaminated with pathogenic bacteria, Protozoa, and other organisms, is a common agent of infection. The organisms enter the digestive organs with food and multiply rapidly during an incubation period in the intestine. In some cases, they reach the blood and lymph. Symptoms of infection appear following the incubation period.

Typhoid fever may be spread in food through handling by infected persons. Tuberculosis and various streptococcus infections may travel in milk. Epidemics of undulant fever have been traced to raw milk from cows suffering from a specific infection of cattle.

Food poisoning. We must be careful to distinguish between food infection and food poisoning. In *food infection,* food is merely the agent in which bacteria enter the body. In *food poisoning,* bacteria grow in the food and produce poisonous products. The poisons are absorbed into the blood stream from the digestive organs. They act on the body suddenly and within a period of a few minutes to a few hours after eating.

Botulism (*bot*-u-liz-um) is the most deadly of all food poisoning. Most cases result from home-canned foods, especially string beans, which are eaten before thorough cooking. The botulism organism, a close relative of the deadly tetanus bacterium, thrives in an airtight container. It gets into the food as a spore before canning and multiplies during the period of storage. Powerful poisons are released from the bacteria into the food. Symptoms of botulism usually appear within 12 to 36 hours after the food is eaten. They include double vision, weakness, and paralysis which creeps from the neck region to other parts of the body. Death may result from respiratory failure or heart failure. Mortality occurs in about 65 per cent of cases. Since the poison is destroyed by heat, botulism can be avoided by cooking home-canned vegetables before eating them.

Water-borne infections. Certain bacteria remain alive for days or even weeks in water. Most water-borne infections are intestinal and are introduced into water through sewage con-

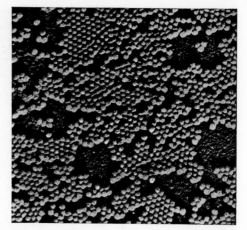

Fig. 43-6. The above is the polio virus as seen under an electron microscope.

tamination. Many lakes and streams near heavily populated regions are dangerously contaminated with typhoid, dysentery, and other intestinal parasites. Shallow wells are especially dangerous because they are usually located in low areas and are exposed to surface drainage. You should be careful to drink water only from deep, tested wells. If you have to use water from a spring or a stream, be sure to boil it for at least ten minutes.

Droplet infection. Fig. 43-7 shows a photograph of a sneeze. Each of those tiny *droplets* could contain bacteria and viruses which were dislodged from the nasal membranes, throat, and respiratory passages. They might be diphtheria, scarlet fever, tuberculosis, pneumonia, measles, mumps, influenza, or common cold organisms.

Diseases spread through droplet infection are most common in winter and spring. This is due partly to the fact that people are confined indoors at these seasons. The air in buses, stores, theaters, and other public places becomes heavily laden with droplets from coughing and sneezing as well as from normal breathing. Many of the drop-

Fig. 43-7. Every time anyone sneezes, he throws out a spray that fills the air with droplets of mucus. This is one way colds and other diseases can be spread.

lets are inhaled. Others settle on objects where the microbes remain alive. These objects may be handled and later transferred to the mouth by someone who did not wash his hands before eating or perhaps by someone who puts his fingers to his mouth or bites his nails.

Various health measures have cut the number of droplet-borne infections greatly. Sanitary disposable cups have replaced the public drinking cup. Paper towels are far more sanitary than the old " family " towel. Even the pocket handkerchief has given way to disposable tissues which can be thrown away and burned after use.

Diseases spread by contact. Certain diseases produce sores or lesions on the skin and mucous membranes. Di-

rect contact with material from these lesions or sores spreads the infection. Ringworm of the scalp and barber's itch, or impetigo, may be spread in this manner. In earlier times, smallpox was spread rapidly by contact with the virus present in skin lesions. Chickenpox virus may be transmitted by direct contact or through the air. Diseases spread by direct contact include syphilis, gonorrhea, and other venereal diseases.

Wound infections. The unbroken skin is an effective barrier against the entrance of bacteria. However, breaks in the skin caused by wounds frequently become infected unless they are cleansed by bleeding and properly treated with antiseptic. Puncture wounds are especially dangerous because of the possibility of tetanus. These anaerobic bacteria enter the wound as spores, clinging to some object. When the wound heals on the surface, it leaves an airtight cavity ideally suited to the tetanus organisms.

Various staphylococci commonly infect wounds and produce a characteristic yellow pus. Streptococcus infections in wounds are highly dangerous and may lead to general blood poisoning and death. Wounds resulting from animal bites are sometimes dangerous. Rabies, or hydrophobia, is a dreaded virus disease transmitted through wounds resulting from the bites of rabid animals, most commonly dogs. Any serious or extensive wound should be treated by a doctor immediately. Minor wounds should be washed, treated with antiseptic, and covered.

Human carriers of disease. Certain diseases are spread by *human carriers* who are themselves immune but who harbor the organisms in their bodies. In some cases patients who recover from an infectious disease carry the organisms in their bodies for weeks or even months. This sometimes happens in diphtheria. The patient recovers from the illness, but diphtheria organisms continue to grow in infected tonsils or in nasal passages.

The carrier problem is especially great in the case of typhoid fever. Certain apparently healthy people harbor typhoid bacteria in their gall bladders and intestines and spread them through intestinal waste. When a carrier is found, his family is given immediate typhoid immunization treatments and he is not permitted to handle food or eating utensils.

Diseases spread by insects. Insects spread disease in two entirely different ways. The housefly carries germs on its sticky feet and hairy body. When it

Fig. 43-8. The Aedes mosquito is a host of the virus that causes yellow fever.

flies from sewage to your home, it can be carrying typhoid fever organisms, dysentery, or other intestinal infections. Respiratory infections can be carried by flies when they lap up droplets. Houseflies, roaches, and certain other insects are agents of infection.

Other insects carry bacteria internally and transmit them in bites. Typhus is associated with the human body louse, Bubonic Plague with the rat flea, and African sleeping sickness with the tsetse fly. As we mentioned earlier, Rocky Mountain spotted fever is carried by ticks which are relatives of the spider. Yellow fever virus is carried by the Aedes mosquito of Central and South America.

Still other insects serve as hosts of infectious organisms. Malaria organisms spend part of their life cycle in the body of a female Anopheles mosquito and part in the human blood stream.

How microbes cause disease. Various microbes damage the body in several ways. The damage may be mechanical or chemical. It may occur at the place of the infection or in other parts of the body, depending on the kind of pathogen present and the ability of the body to control the infection. Direct causes of body damage due to the activity of infectious organisms include: (1) *tissue destruction;* (2) *production of soluble toxins* (exotoxins); and (3) *production of insoluble toxins* (endotoxins).

Tissue destruction is illustrated by tuberculosis. The organisms usually infect the lungs, although other organs may be affected. As tuberculosis bacteria multiply in the lung tissue, they destroy cells and produce lesions. These allow blood to seep from the capillaries into the air passages, resulting in the hemorrhages (*hem*-oh-rages) characteristic of advanced tuberculosis.

Many organisms, including streptococci, destroy blood cells. During meningitis, the membranes covering the brain or spinal cord are attacked by bacteria.

Viruses act chiefly through tissue destruction. The polio virus attacks the cell bodies of motor nerves in the spinal cord. This damage may be temporary or it may be permanent. The deadly virus of rabies attacks the brain substance.

Many bacteria produce powerful chemical substances which are absorbed by the surrounding tissue or are transported through the blood stream with damaging effects. We refer to these poisons as **exotoxins.** Such toxins may cause serious damage far from the seat of the infection. For example, tetanus organisms living in a wound in the foot produce toxins which cause paralysis in the upper regions of the body. Other diseases involving exotoxins include scarlet fever, diphtheria, streptococcus infections, as well as botulism food poisioning.

Endotoxins remain inside the bacterial cells which form them. However, these toxins are released with deadly effect when the bacteria die and disintegrate. Endotoxin diseases include typhoid fever, tuberculosis, cholera, Bubonic Plague, and dysentery.

In Conclusion

We have considered the various kinds of microbes which cause infectious diseases, the many ways in which they enter the body, and several ways in which they cause disease.

To produce an infection, the germs must be able to multiply in the body. Undoubtedly, you have pathogenic bacteria in your mouth, sticking to your nasal membranes, and lurking in your respiratory passages at the present moment. Many enter your body with the food you eat. Why aren't you sick with an infection? They have not been able to multiply in enough numbers to overcome the body's natural defenses.

Your body has a marvelous system of defense. It keeps out most of the microbes you contact and destroys many others before an infection develops. How does it do these things? This is the subject of the next chapter.

Questions for Review

1. Explain why primitive people turned to magic and superstition in an effort to deal with infectious diseases.

2. Name four body fluids described by Hippocrates.

3. Which of the Greek physicians, practicing in Rome, was most influential in medicine through the Middle Ages?

4. Name several infectious diseases which swept through the civilized world in epidemics during the Middle Ages.

5. Upon what theory of disease was blood letting practiced?

6. Explain the principle of pasteurization.

7. List the Koch Postulates and explain how Robert Koch used these steps in his investigation of anthrax.

8. List eight groups of infectious organisms.

9. In what ways are the Rickettsiae similar to both viruses and bacteria?

10. Distinguish between a food-borne infection and food poisoning.

11. Explain why deep puncture wounds are especially dangerous.

12. Name four insect carriers of disease and the diseases they carry.

13. What are the five various causes of diseases in the body?

Biologically Speaking

carrier	food poisoning	noninfectious diseases
contact infection	hemorrhage	pasteurization
droplet infection	Hippocratic Oath	pathogenic
endotoxin	infectious diseases	spontaneous generation
exotoxin	Koch Postulates	tissue destruction
food infection	lesion	wound infection

Applying Facts and Principles

1. Explain how Pasteur's work in investigating the causes of fermentation disproved the idea of spontaneous generation.

2. Give reasons for the prevalence of colds, influenza, pneumonia, and other droplet-borne infections during the winter.

3. What measures have been taken in your community to protect you from water-borne infections?

4. Why may exotoxins cause damage far from the seat of infection?

CHAPTER 44

Body Defenses and Aids Against Diseases

With bacteria and viruses present outside and inside your body, you may wonder how anyone escapes infection to live to a ripe old age. True, some do lose the battle of infection, but the human body has marvelous defenses against disease. When microbes invade, the tissues set up a counterattack and usually win — for they can only lose once.

Today the doctor knows how to mobilize defenses against some diseases before they strike. He can send reserves into the blood stream to aid the body's natural defenses by means of a hypodermic needle, as well as drugs and antibiotics.

In this chapter, we will examine the body's defenses against disease and tour the doctor's arsenal of defensive weapons with which he prevents many infections and deals effectively with others when they strike.

The first line of defense. The most effective way of avoiding an infection is to prevent the organisms from entering the body. This is the function of the first line of defense. **Skin** covers all the external parts of the body and, if unbroken, is bacteria-proof. Unfortunately, it is not virus-proof, hence we have little protection against the entry of this group of pathogenic organisms. The openings of the body are lined with **mucous membranes,** which serve as a protective lining. Mucous membranes are much thinner than skin, usually consisting of a single layer of cells. Those membranes lining the trachea and nasal passages are covered with cilia which sweep foreign particles, including bacteria, upward toward the throat. When the foreign particles irritate the throat membranes, a cough results and the particles are blown out into the air. Irritation of the membranes of the nasal passages results in sneezing.

Other first-line defenses include the *acid* of the stomach which destroys large numbers of bacteria taken in with food. *Tears* which protect the eyes are slightly antiseptic and cleanse the eyeballs continually, washing foreign matter through the tear ducts into the nasal passages.

Normally these first-line defenses

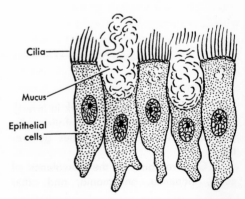

Fig. 44-1. The structure of the mucous membrane, one of the first lines of defense, is shown above.

prevent bacteria from gaining entrance into the body. However, skin may be broken or mucous membrane may become irritated, thus allowing the organisms to enter the body. An unknown factor called *general resistance* seems to play an important part in maintaining the defenses against disease. It concerns not only the first line, but the other lines as well.

We know that exposure to cold air or wet weather may cause irritation of the mucous membranes and permit cold germs, pneumonia organisms, or even tuberculosis organisms to gain entrance and start an infection. General resistance seems to affect this first-line defense too, because lack of sleep and a general run-down condition makes the entrance of disease germs much easier.

The second line of defense. Once the bacteria have passed the first line of defense, they are met with a second line which operates within the body. This line is defended by cells from the blood stream called **white corpuscles.** They originate in the bone marrow and normally are present in the blood in an approximate proportion of one to 1,000 red corpuscles.

When disease-producing bacteria pass the first line of defense, as, for example, through a break in the skin, the white corpuscles leave the blood vessels and migrate through the tissue fluids to the site of infection. They make a wall around the invading germs and begin to engulf them. It then becomes a race between the multiplication of bacteria and their destruction by the white corpuscles. During the infection, which is still local, the tissues involved often swell and become inflamed. Redness often results from the increased flow of blood to the area to promote healing. The lymph aids in the struggle by carrying bacteria to nodes, where they are

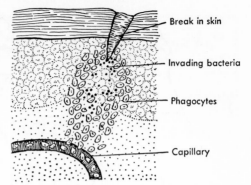

Break in skin

Invading bacteria

Phagocytes

Capillary

Fig. 44-2. The body fights harmful bacteria by sending armies of white corpuscles to the area of infection. This is a second line of defense.

filtered out and destroyed by white blood cells.

This struggle with the second-defense line may cause a fever (rise in the body temperature). **Fever** is a body reaction against infection, and is beneficial unless it becomes too high for too long a period. The dead bacteria and white corpuscles collect at the site of the infection as *pus.* This is later discharged externally, or carried to the organs of excretion for elimination.

The third line of defense. If the bacteria overcome the army of white corpuscles, a "break through" occurs and the organisms enter the blood stream. The infection then becomes general and the patient begins a fight for his life. Bacteria or their poisons are carried by the blood throughout the body with damaging effects. The fever usually rises sharply and the patient becomes increasingly weak.

The infection becomes a battle between bacteria and their products and various substances which are produced by the blood to destroy the bacteria or neutralize the effect of their poisons. These blood substances are generally called **antibodies.** Antibodies are of an extremely complex nature and are not

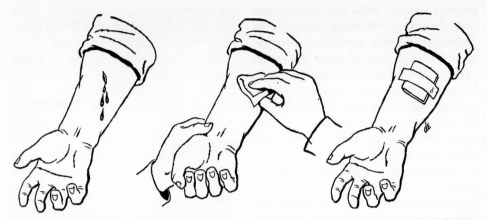

Fig. 44-3.   These three drawings show ways you can strengthen your own body defenses. Bleeding helps to wash out microbes.   Antiseptics help reduce infections.   A bandage serves to keep a wound clean and prevent the entrance of germs.

entirely understood.   They seem to be *specific* — that is, a single kind of antibody is effective against a specific kind of organism or its products.

The types of antibodies.   While antibodies are numerous, the principal types include: (1) *antitoxins;* (2) *agglutinins* (ag-*glue*-tin-ins); (3) *bacteriolysins* (bak-*ter*-ee-oh-*lye*-sins); (4) *precipitins* (pre-*sih*-pih-tins); and (5) *opsonins* (*op*-so-nins).

Antitoxins serve to neutralize toxins. In the case of diphtheria, for example, the organisms in the throat pour toxins into the blood stream which cause most of the symptoms of diphtheria.   The blood is stimulated by the infection to produce diphtheria antitoxin which neutralizes the effect of the toxins.   If the blood produces antitoxin faster than toxins are formed, recovery is assured.

Agglutinins are substances formed in the blood which cause bacteria to gather in clumps.   When they are congregated, white corpuscles may surround them and devour them.   **Bacteriolysins** are strange chemical substances formed in the blood which cause bacteria to dissolve.   **Precipitins** are little under-

stood, but seem to cause bacteria to settle out of the blood.   This makes it easier for the blood stream to filter them in the lymph glands and various organs and for the white corpuscles to destroy them.   **Opsonins** are peculiar substances which prepare bacteria for ingestion by white corpuscles.

Immunity to disease.   We call the resistance of the body to disease by the term **immunity.**

Immunity may be of several types. It may be *natural* or *acquired* within the lifetime of the organism.   Acquired immunity may be more or less permanent (*active*) or only temporary (*passive*).

Natural immunity.   Man is not subject to most animal diseases, due to differences in structure.   A different type of environment exists in the human body than in other kinds of animals. Consequently, we are not usually plagued by diseases of horses, cattle, swine, and other animals.   This type of immunity is *species immunity* since it includes all members of a species.   Notable exceptions to species immunity are: *tuberculosis* and *undulant fever,* which may be transmitted from cattle to man through milk; *anthrax,* which may cause lesions on the human body in addition to infecting animals; *tularemia,* which may be carried from rabbits to man; and *psittacosis* (sit-ah-*koh*-sis) from parrots.

Acquired immunity. As the name implies, *acquired immunity* is established during the lifetime of the individual. It may be *active* or *passive,* depending on the way in which it is acquired.

Active immunity results from having had a disease. The infection stimulates the body to form its own specific antibodies against the germs or their products, depending on the type of the disease.

For example, a person with diphtheria produces diphtheria antitoxins, while one who has typhoid forms typhoid agglutinins. Active immunity may be acquired artificially by using biological preparations consisting of weakened or dead bacteria or products removed from living cultures. In this way, the body is stimulated to form its own antibodies without actually having the disease.

Passive immunity is acquired artificially by the injection of antibodies that have been formed by the blood of other individuals or from animals. For example, tetanus antitoxin is taken from the blood of the horse and may be injected into the blood of man to give immediate immunity in the case of deep wounds. The horse antibodies remain only temporarily and, when destroyed, no longer make the individual immune. In the same manner, human blood serum containing antibodies for scarlet fever may be used to give immediate, but only temporary, immunity.

Immune therapy. One vital phase of the treatment and prevention of infectious diseases is based on the bolster-ing of the body's natural defenses. We refer to it as *immune therapy*. It involves two kinds of weapons and a two-pronged attack. One weapon is **serum** (*seer*-um), a blood protein containing specific antibodies against disease. A serum is used to reinforce the body's production of antibodies during an infection. It is also used to give an immediate passive immunity to someone who has been exposed to a disease. The other weapon is **vaccine** (*vack*-seen), a product which stimulates the blood to produce antibodies and to develop active immunity against a specific disease.

Serum production. Serum usually comes from the blood of an animal which has been inoculated with a disease and has produced antibodies against it. Horses, cattle, sheep, goats, and rabbits are frequently used in serum production. In general, serums are of two types; (1) some contain antibodies, such as agglutinins or precipitins, which act against the bacteria themeslves; and (2) others contain antibodies (antitoxins) against their toxins.

The production of diphtheria antitoxin is an excellent example of serum production. The horse is used because it has a powerful resistance to the disease and produces a large quantity of antitoxin in its blood. The horse is given a large dose of diphtheria toxin. It responds with the immediate production of antitoxin. After several days, blood is drawn from the external jugular vein in the neck into sterile containers. It is then processed to remove the serum containing the antitoxin from the rest of the blood. This method of producing antitoxin is quite painless to the horse.

Similar antitoxins are prepared against scarlet fever and tetanus. They are given to patients who have been exposed to one of these infections. In the

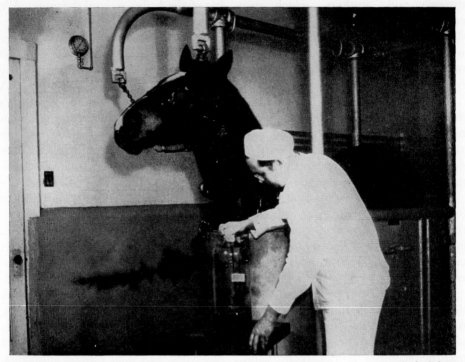

Fig. 44-4. Diphtheria antitoxin is prepared by first injecting quantities of diphtheria toxin into the blood of a horse. After removal of the blood from the external jugular vein in the neck, it is processed to remove antitoxins from the rest of the blood substances.

case of diphtheria and scarlet fever, they are used to assist the recovery of a victim of the disease.

Vaccine production. Vaccines are prepared by biological companies under carefully controlled conditions. The vaccines must be strong enough to cause blood to produce antibodies, yet weakened sufficiently to be safe to use. Vaccines vary with the nature of the organisms or products involved. They may contain:

1. Virus weakened by growth in an animal (animal passage), aging, heat, or chemical treatment.

2. Bacteria killed by heat or chemicals (bacterins or bacterial vaccines).

3. Living bacteria in small numbers.

4. Bacteria weakened by adding weak antiseptics.

5. Bacterial products which have been weakened, as in the case of toxin-antitoxins and toxoids.

The toxin-antitoxin, used until recent years to produce active immunity against diphtheria and other toxin diseases, was made by weakening toxin taken from cultures of bacteria with antitoxin from horse blood serum. Doctors found it hard to give products containing serum to some patients because of a serious reaction caused by sensitivity to the protein in serum. This problem has been solved by using a newer product called a *toxoid*. A **toxoid** is a toxin which has been weakened by treatment with heat and chemicals so it is safe to inject into human tissues.

Chemotherapy. The conquest of disease is not a war of biology alone, for chemistry plays a very significant part. **Chemotherapy** is a rather recent field in which specific chemicals are used to destroy germs. This is of great importance because it assists the natural body defenses.

The development of chemotherapy is associated with the work of a brilliant German chemist, Paul Ehrlich, in connection with his long search for a cure for syphilis. Ehrlich spent many years attempting to discover a drug which would kill the organisms in the blood stream without damaging the blood or other parts of the body. After 605 unsuccessful attempts, he finally succeeded. His 606th drug was an arsenic compound called *salvarsan*. It was used in treating venereal disease until the discovery of penicillin.

Other scientists began experimenting with chemicals in the treatment of disease. Dr. Gerhard Domagk (*doh-mag*), another German scientist, discovered in 1932 that a red dye called *prontosil* had remarkable germ-killing powers. Soon after his discovery of prontosil he tried it on his own daughter who was dying with a streptococcic infection which had progressed beyond medical control. It proved to be effective in halting the infection and saved the child's life by what seemed at the time to be almost a miracle.

Further investigations on prontosil proved that only a part of the drug had germ-killing powers. This part was isolated and called *sulfanilamide* (sul-fa-*nil*-ah-myde). It was the first of an important family known as the **sulfa drugs.** There are many different ones now, and they are used in the treatment of certain infectious diseases. These drugs should be taken only on the advice and recommendation of a physician. They are by no means cure-alls and are often dangerous.

Fig. 44-5. The white ring which you see in this culture of bacteria is the mold called *Penicillium*. A substance produced by this mold, penicillin, has become a powerful weapon against certain pathogenic bacteria.

Antibiotic therapy. Powerful chemical substances, called **antibiotics** (an-tee-by-*ot*-icks), are now quite commonly used in the treatment of disease. Antibiotics are products of living organisms. In this respect they are different from the drugs used in chemotherapy. We can sum up the use of antibiotics by saying, "bugs produce drugs which kill bugs," for our supply of these substances comes from bacteria, molds, and mold-like organisms.

Penicillin. The "wonder drug" of World War II was the first of the antibiotics. It was discovered accidentally by Sir Alexander Fleming, a British bacteriologist, in 1929. Fleming was working with staphylococcus bacteria in a London hospital. While examining plate cultures of staphylococci, he noticed that several of them contained fluffy masses of mold. Later the mold colonies turned dark green and were identified as *Penicillium notatum*, a relative of the mold found on oranges.

In the opening days of World War II, Dr. Howard Florey and a group of Oxford workers began a search for antibacterial substances which would be use-

Fig. 44-6. This is a culture of *Streptomyces griseus* which produces streptomycin. It is quite effective in fighting tuberculosis.

ful in combating wound infections. Their attention turned to Fleming's work and, in cooperation with him, penicillin was developed and thoroughly tested. The result of this work is history.

Today a penicillin ten times as powerful as Fleming's is available in unlimited quantity and at low cost. New strains of *Penicillium notatum,* produced by exposure to X-rays, yield far more penicillin than earlier strains. Biological companies have devoted vast plants to penicillin production. It is given effectively in large doses by injection with a slowly absorbing procaine salt. It can be taken by mouth in tablet form and inhaled into the nasal passages in powder form. Ointments are available for use locally and in the eyes. However, it should *never be used in any form unless recommended by a physician.*

Streptomycin. Dr. Selman Waksman became interested in the soil and its relation to life when he was a boy in Europe. Later he came to the United States and enrolled in Rutgers

University. His interest in soil led him to New Jersey Agricultural Experiment Station at Rutgers. While still a student, Waksman discovered a filamentous soil fungus which he named *Streptomyces griseus.*

After graduate study, Waksman returned to Rutgers as a member of the faculty. With the aid of students, he continued the investigation of soil organisms. They studied the problem of the disappearance of disease organisms when the body of a diseased animal is buried and found that products of soil organisms destroyed them. After years of testing the effect of soil organisms on various pathogens, *streptomycin* (strepto-*my*-sin), an antibiotic substance produced by *Streptomyces griseus,* was discovered.

Streptomycin proved to be an effective drug against tuberculosis. In addition, it is partially effective against whooping cough, some forms of pneumonia, dysentery, gonorrhea, and syphilis. The streptomycin industry grew rapidly, and this valuable antibiotic took a place with penicillin.

Other antibiotics. Today, many new antibiotics have been added. Among these are *aureomycin* (*aw*-ree-oh-mysin) and *chloromycetin* (kloh-roh-mysee-tin), both of which are effective against a wide range of diseases including the Rickettsia diseases, typhus fever, Rocky Mountain spotted fever, and virus pneumonia. *Terramycin* (*ter*-ahmy-sin), another recent addition, promises to be of great value because of its wide range of effectiveness and low toxicity in the body.

Study the table on page 579 which shows the effectiveness of five antibiotics.

Bacteriophage. Scientists believe that there is a form of minute virus, called a **bacteriophage** (bak-*tee*-ree-oh-

USE AND EFFECTIVENESS OF FIVE IMPORTANT ANTIBIOTICS

	PENICILLIN	STREPTOMYCIN	CHLOROMYCETIN	AUREOMYCIN	TERRAMYCIN
How administered:					
By injection	√	√			
By mouth	√		√	√	√
By inhalation	√	√		√	√
Externally	√			√	√
Effective against:					
Boils	X	O	O	X	X
Bone infection (staphylococcus)	X	?	O	X	X
Colon bacillus infections	O	X	X	X	X
Common cold	O	O	O	O	O
Gonorrhea	X	O	X	X	X
Influenza (virus)	O	O	?	?	?
Measles	O	O	?	?	?
Mumps	O	O	?	?	?
Pneumonia (pneumococcus)	X	?	?	X	X
Pneumonia (virus)	O	O	X	X	X
Poliomyelitis (polio)	O	O	O	O	O
Rocky Mountain spotted fever	O	O	X	X	X
Scarlet fever	X	O	?	X	X
Streptococcus blood poisoning	X	?	?	X	X
Streptococcus throat	X	?	?	X	X
Syphilis	X	O	?	X	X
Tetanus	X	O	O	?	?
Tuberculosis	O	X	?	?	?
Typhoid fever	O	O	X	?	?
Typhus fever	O	O	X	X	X
Undulant fever	O	?	X	X	X
Whooping cough	O	?	?	X	?

Key to the above symbols:

√ indicates that the antibiotic is usually administered by that method.

X indicates that the antibiotic has proved effective against the diseases. Where several are listed as effective against a disease, one may be more so and in more general use than the others.

? indicates that the antibiotic is of limited or questionable effectiveness, or that tests are incomplete.

O indicates that the antibiotic seems not to be effective against the disease. However, it may be effective in controlling secondary infections which are associated with certain of the diseases listed, or in combination with other antibiotics.

fage), which enters the cells of bacteria and destroys their contents. When solutions of bacteriophage are added to cultures of bacteria, the colonies dissolve and disappear. It is possible, therefore, that bacteriophage might be used against infectious diseases. To some extent, this has been done by applications of the bacteriophage to external infections. However, this phase of the treatment of disease is still in the experimental stages.

In Conclusion

You might think of your body as a fort, with defenses set up against sneak attacks by invading microbes. Your skin is the outer wall. Mucous membranes, tears, and other first-line defenses guard the entrances. If microbes break through these defenses, white corpuscles rush to the attack and engage the invaders in a local battle. If the battle grows and becomes a general war, the reserves are called out in the form of antibodies in your blood stream.

With the doctor as your ally, you can be spared much of this desperate struggle. When an infection strikes, he can send you immediate help against some enemies in the form of a serum army, fully equipped and ready to fight beside your natural antibody soldiers. Better still, he can send a preventive vaccine to prepare and train a horde of defensive soldiers to be ready without delay if a certain microbe strikes.

These are the weapons with which we have moved forward in the conquest of disease.

 ————————————— **Questions for Review**

1. List various first-line defenses of your body. Would you say that one is more important than another? Why or why not?

2. Explain the role of white corpuscles in the second line of defense.

3. What is the content of pus which forms at the site of an infection?

4. (a) List five specific blood antibodies. (b) Explain briefly the function of each kind in combating bacteria or their products.

5. Explain why a serum gives immediate passive immunity against a specific disease.

6. List five different products contained in various vaccines.

7. Which disease was first controlled by a specific drug discovered by Paul Ehrlich?

8. What important family of drugs was isolated from the red dye, prontosil?

9. In what respect are antibiotic drugs different from those used in chemotherapy?

10. Name four widely used antibiotics other than penicillin.

Biologically Speaking

acquired immunity	fever	pus
active immunity	general resistance	serum
agglutinin	immune therapy	species immunity
antibiotic	immunity	specific antibodies
antibody	mucous membrane	sulfa drugs
antitoxin	natural immunity	toxin
bacteriophage	passive immunity	toxoid
chemotherapy	precipitin	vaccine

Applying Facts and Principles

1. Explain why exposure to the weather, getting wet, overtiredness, or improper eating may bring on a cold, sore throat, or other infection.

2. A fever is considered beneficial unless it gets too high or lasts too long. Of what benefit might a fever be in the struggle against an infection?

3. Why is active immunity more permanent than passive immunity?

4. How did World War II speed the dawn of antibiotic therapy?

5. Explain the principle of the bacteriophage in dealing with infections.

6. What is the chief limitation in the use of the sulfa drugs?

CHAPTER 45

The Conquest of Disease

Less than 200 years ago, infectious diseases swept through cities and across the countryside in terrifying epidemics. Few escaped the scourge of smallpox. A face which did not show deep pockmarks as a grim reminder of a life-and-death struggle with the deadly smallpox virus was unusual. Diphtheria, scarlet fever, and pneumonia were fatal to many children. Typhoid fever, influenza, tuberculosis, and other dangerous infections took a heavy toll of those who were fortunate enough to escape the infections common during childhood.

Today many of the infectious diseases your ancestors feared a few generations ago rarely appear in communities with high standards of health. Smallpox, diphtheria, whooping cough, tetanus — your doctor probably sees to it that you will never have these infections. How is this possible? He has the knowledge and products of nearly 200 years of work contributed by scientists of all nations, teamed together in the conquest of disease.

In this chapter you will review some of the well-known infectious diseases and the measures we can take to control them.

Edward Jenner — country doctor. It was during one of the most dreadful smallpox epidemics in England that Edward Jenner, a country doctor, made a discovery which was to alter the course of history. Epidemics took their greatest toll in cities. Jenner noticed that the disease seldom struck people who lived in rural areas and worked around cattle. Most farmers and dairy workers had contracted cowpox and had recovered with nothing more serious than a pustule which left a scar. Did this make them immune to smallpox? If so, why not vaccinate people with cowpox to protect them from smallpox?

The first vaccination. On May 14, 1796, Dr. Jenner had a chance to test his vaccination theory. His patient was James Phipps, a healthy boy about eight years old. James's mother, with

great confidence in Dr. Jenner, allowed her son to be used in the test with the hope that he could be spared the danger of smallpox. Dr. Jenner took his young patient to a dairy maid, Sarah Nelmes, who had a cowpox pustule on her hand resulting from an infection from one of her master's cows. Dr. Jenner made two shallow cuts about an inch long on James Phipps's arm and inoculated them with matter taken from the cowpox sore. A pustule developed on the boy's arm, formed a scab and healed, leaving only a scar. Was James Phipps now immune to smallpox? There was only one way to find out. He must be inoculated with smallpox.

In July of the same year, Dr. Jenner deliberately inoculated James with matter from a smallpox pustule. During the next two weeks, the doctor watched

Fig. 45-1. This scene, taken from the movie based on Dr. Jenner's life, shows him ready to inject cowpox into James Phipps's arm. Dr. Jenner's discovery of artificial immunity to smallpox marked a milestone in the history of medicine.

his patient anxiously for signs of small-pox. They did not appear. Several months later he repeated the inocula-tion. Again, the disease did not devel-op. The vaccination was successful. James Phipps was definitely immune to smallpox!

Following this famous experiment, Dr. Jenner wrote a paper explaining his method of vaccination. At first, the doctors were hostile and would not listen to such a ridiculous procedure. Many townspeople even organized anti-vacci-nation campaigns. Gradually, how-ever, the doctors and their patients ac-cepted vaccination and smallpox epi-demics were eliminated.

Smallpox immunization. Smallpox and cowpox, or *Vaccinia* (vak-*sin*-ee-ah), are closely related viruses. Cow-pox virus produces a mild infection in humans. But even a single cowpox pus-tule is enough to stimulate the body to produce active immunity against small-pox.

Young heifers are used in the com-mercial production of vaccine virus used in vaccination. Before inoculating the animals with virus, they are examined thoroughly by a veterinarian for signs of disease. Then, the abdomen is shaved and sterilized. Cowpox virus is placed in numerous scratches made on the ab-domen. The virus is grown on the

Fig. 45-2. Louis Pasteur's control experiment with anthrax vaccine on sheep proved active immunity could be produced against the disease.

heifer for six or seven days, after which the animal is killed under anesthetic. The virus, growing in the scratches in white, pulpy patches, is scraped off and put into sterile containers. After harvesting the virus, the animal is examined internally for symptoms of any other disease.

The pulp containing cowpox virus is frozen temporarily before processing. Later, it is ground and mixed with 50% glycerin and salt solution in a ratio of one part virus to four parts glycerin and salt solution. In this condition, the processed virus can be held at subzero temperature. The virus preparation is placed in sealed capillary tubes for distribution to the doctor. After being tubed, it can be stored for three months. This is the vaccine the doctor rubs in scratches on your arm or leg when he vaccinates you to protect you from smallpox.

Pasteur's famous immunization experiment. About 80 years after Jenner vaccinated James Phipps, Louis Pasteur conducted his famous immunization experiments. Previous to these experiments, Pasteur had made a vaccine containing the weakened microbes of chicken cholera. He found that he could inject the vaccine into healthy chickens and produce active immunity against the disease. This led him to try a similar procedure against anthrax at about the same time Robert Koch was conducting his famous work on the disease.

Pasteur made an anthrax vaccine from weakened bacteria taken from the blood of infected animals. He claimed this vaccine would immunize animals against the disease. Scientists challenged him to prove his theory. This was the opportunity he had waited for. He selected 48 healthy animals (mostly sheep) and divided them into two groups. He gave the animals in one group injections containing five drops of anthrax vaccine. Twelve days later, he gave the same animals a second injection of vaccine. Fourteen days later he gave all 48 animals an injection of living anthrax bacteria. Two days later the scientists met at the pens to laugh at Pasteur. Imagine their amazement to find all Pasteur's immunized animals alive and healthy and all the untreated animals dead or dying of anthrax. This famous experiment was an important milestone in the conquest of disease.

Pasteur's greatest contribution to mankind. During the latter years of his life, Pasteur turned his genius to experimentation with one of the most dreadful of all diseases, *rabies* (*ray-bees*), or *hydrophobia* (hy-droh-*foh-bee-ah*). This disease was common among dogs, wolves, and other animals during his time. If the virus was transmitted to a human by a bite, a human victim was certain to suffer an agonizing death after an incubation period of a few weeks to six months or more. During this time the virus slowly destroyed brain and spinal cord tissue.

The restlessness, convulsions, great thirst, and throat paralysis which climaxed a rabies infection led Pasteur to believe that the infection centered in the brain. However, microscopic examination of the brain tissue of an animal victim did not reveal any microorganisms. We can understand this today for the rabies virus is invisible under the microscope.

Pasteur found that he could transmit rabies by injecting infected brain tissue from a rabid dog to a healthy one. He repeated the inoculations with rabbits and discovered that the virus gained strength as it was passed from one animal to another. However, if spinal cord tissue taken from a dog or rabbit was dried for 14 days, the virus lost its strength and could no longer produce the infection. Thirteen-day-old virus was only slightly stronger. The discovery that the virus weakened with drying and aging led to experiments to find out if rabies immunity could be produced. Pasteur injected 14-day-old brain tissue into a healthy dog, then followed this injection with 13-day-old material.

The injections were continued day after day until the dog was given an injection of full-strength virus in the 14th injection. The animal suffered no ill effects. The series of injections with material of increasing strength had produced immunity to rabies. The question now was whether he dare try the series of injections in human victims. A decision was forced on Pasteur a short time later.

Pasteur's treatment of rabies. On July 6, 1885, a frantic mother brought her son to Pasteur's laboratory, pleading that he use any method to save her boy's life. The boy had been attacked by a rabid dog. This had happened two days before they reached Pasteur's laboratory. Pasteur had no time to lose, and no choice except to give the boy the treatment which had worked on dogs. The physicians and laboratory assistants he consulted agreed with his decision. On the evening of this important day, the boy was given an injection of rabbit-grown virus which had aged 12 days. Injections were repeated each day, using successively fresher virus. On the 12th day he received full-strength virus. After several weeks of observation, he was sent home, the first human being immunized against rabies.

The conquest of diphtheria. From the earliest times, diphtheria was one of the worst epidemic killers, especially among children. The effects of diphtheria on the body are twofold. The germs grow in a thick, grayish-white membrane on the back wall of the throat. As the membrane spreads, it may block the glottis opening and cause death by strangulation. In addition, powerful toxins are given off by the living bacteria and are absorbed through the infected tissues into the blood. They often cause severe damage to the heart, the nervous system, and other body organs.

The conquest of diphtheria some 50 years ago involved the work of several scientists. One found the rod-shaped bacteria growing in the throats of patients with diphtheria. Another worker cultured the bacteria in a medium containing blood serum and developed a stain used in microscopic study of the organisms. However, much of the

Fig. 45-3. This scene in Pasteur's laboratory shows a child being vaccinated against rabies. This was once one of the most dreaded of diseases until Pasteur made his contribution toward conquering the disease.

credit for the conquest of this disease belongs to Emil von Behring (*bay*-ring), a German bacteriologist.

Von Behring was puzzled by the fact that, even though diphtheria organisms remained in the throat, the effects of the disease appeared in distant organs. When bacteria were grown in culture media, they produced a toxin which, when injected into guinea pigs, produced the symptoms of diphtheria even though no germs were present.

While conducting such experiments with diphtheria toxin, von Behring discovered that guinea pigs and rabbits could be used only once. They developed immunity to the disease. Could this immunity be transferred to animals which had never been given doses of

toxin? Von Behring was about to find out. He took blood from immune animals, separated the blood serum from other substances in the blood, and injected it into other animals. They too were made immune to diphtheria toxin. Von Behring named this immune body present in serum **antitoxin.**

Sheep were used first in the production of diphtheria antitoxin. After extensive testing of the antitoxin in guinea pigs, it was first used with great success in the Children's Hospital in Berlin. As we mentioned earlier, the antitoxin used today is produced in greater quantity in the blood of the horse.

Von Behring found that immunity resulting from injections of sheep antitoxin lasted only a few weeks. Appar-

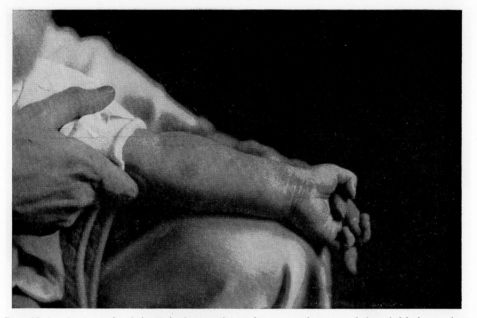

Fig. 45-4. As a result of the Schick test, the red spot on the arm of this child shows that he is not immune to diphtheria.

ently, the antitoxin is destroyed slowly in the human blood stream. If children could be made to produce their own antitoxin, immunity would be as lasting as though they had recovered from diphtheria. To give diphtheria toxin would be as dangerous as inoculating them with the disease itself. Von Behring reasoned that a mixture of toxin and antitoxin might be safe to use. World War I prevented von Behring from finishing his work. However, it was completed in the United States by Dr. William H. Park and other workers. Until the recent development of the toxoid, *toxin-antitoxin* was used in producing active immunity against diphtheria.

The Schick test for diphtheria. The *Schick test* is used to determine the presence of immunity to diphtheria. A small amount of dilute diphtheria toxin is injected under the skin on the inside of the lower arm with a hypodermic needle. If the test is negative, there is no reaction. Diphtheria antitoxin in the blood neutralizes the toxin. A positive test shows as a reddened area with a raised, dark red center at the point of injection. This indicates that the patient is susceptible to diphtheria and that he should have toxoid immunization. The wide use of the Schick test in small children as well as those of school age has nearly eliminated diphtheria.

Tetanus immunization. The tetanus organism is an anaerobic spore-forming bacillus. The cells are not active in the presence of air, but remain alive as resting spores. Tetanus organisms live normally in the intestinal tract of horses and other animals. The spores are therefore most abundant in soil on which manure has been used as a fertilizer. Some of these spore forms may live 60 or more years in contaminated soil.

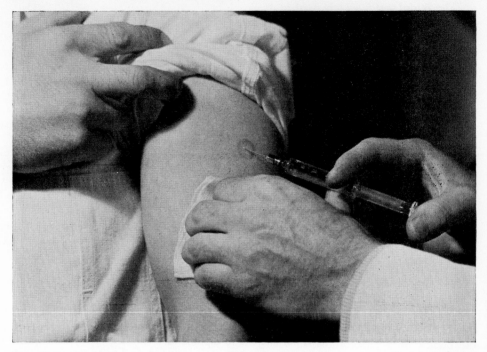

Fig. 45-5. Typhoid inoculations, made from dead bacteria, are usually injected into the arm.

When spores are introduced into the body in a deep puncture wound, they germinate and become active cells. Within a short time they multiply and pour powerful toxins into the tissue and blood. The toxin causes grave illness, including fever, chills, and paralysis, usually first evident in the jaw, face, and neck muscles. This led to the name "lockjaw." Mortality is over 50 per cent. Many cases do not respond to any treatment after the symptoms have appeared, following a three- to five-day incubation period.

Horse antitoxin serum is used immediately to give passive immunity to a victim of a deep wound. However, the use of serum involves the possibility of serum sickness or may cause development of allergy to serum which would make the use of a serum in treating another disease difficult and dangerous. Today tetanus toxoid is widely used to produce active immunity against tetanus. Injections are given as a preventive measure and not at the time of an injury. If an immune person has an injury which requires further immunization, it is given in the form of a toxoid booster shot. Everyone should have toxoid immunization as a safe prevention against this dangerous infection.

Typhoid fever. The typhoid fever organisms live in the intestine, causing lesions in the intestine wall. They reach the lymph nodes of the mesentery from the intestine and enter the general circulation. From the blood, they may invade the spleen, lungs, bone marrow, liver, and gall bladder.

Typhoid vaccine, used in immunization, is made from dead bacteria. The vaccine is usually injected into the arm. A slight redness appears and may remain for a few days. Active immunity lasts for about three years.

The **Widal test** is widely used in diagnosing typhoid and in locating immune carriers. A typhoid patient or carrier has typhoid agglutinins, the principal defense against the disease, in his blood stream. A small drop containing typhoid bacteria is put on a microscope slide. A drop of the patient's blood is added. If agglutinins are present, the typhoid germs clump together, or agglutinate. This is a positive reaction and shows that typhoid fever is present, or that the patient is immune.

Tuberculosis — its treatment. Until recently, *tuberculosis* was the most fatal disease, causing one-seventh of all deaths. While we usually think of it as an infection of the lungs, it may infect the bones, glands, and other organs, too. Tuberculosis is caused by tiny rod-shaped organisms which may enter the body with food or travel down the air passages. Damage to the body is slight at first and usually goes unnoticed. The bacteria destroy tissue at the place of the infection and produce a lesion. Endotoxins, released into the blood from dead bacteria, cause general weakness, loss of weight and appetite, fever, and other symptoms of the disease.

When Koch grew tuberculosis organ-

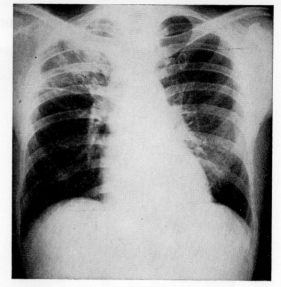

Fig. 45-7. The chest X-ray picture of the lungs of a patient shows moderately advanced tuberculosis.

isms on blood agar, he discovered the endotoxin, which he named *tuberculin*. He had hoped to use this product to produce active immunity, but discovered that it produced a dangerous abscess when injected into the body. However, we use tuberculin today to test for active tuberculosis. If a small square of filter paper, saturated with tuberculin, is laid against the skin, a red spot appears within two or three days if the patient is sensitive to tuberculin. Such a positive patch test means that a person has, or has had, active germs in his body. It does not mean that he has active tuberculosis.

A positive patch test is followed by an X-ray of the chest to check for a lesion in the lungs. A sputum test may also be made to see if the organisms are present in fluid from the lungs. Many people develop a slight tuberculosis infection following a severe cold, influenza, pneumonia, or some other condition which lowers their resistance to infection. They recover without knowledge of the infection. For this reason many people have a positive reaction to a

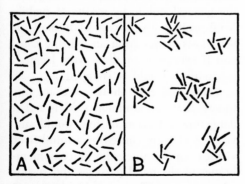

Fig. 45-6. A. Bacteria before an agglutinin has been added. B. The addition of an agglutinin causes the bacteria to gather in small clumps.

Fig. 45-8. The patch test is widely used in testing for tuberculosis. If the test is positive, an X-ray of the chest should be taken.

patch test and show no evidence of tuberculosis in X-ray and other tests.

The prevention of tuberculosis. Sparked by the untiring efforts of the National Tuberculosis Association and numerous county associations, a campaign has been conducted for several years to prevent tuberculosis. The work of these organizations has been financed through the sale of the familiar Christmas seals as well as private donations. The associations have sponsored educational campaigns and measures to remove conditions which lead to tuberculosis. They have stressed the importance of adequate rest, proper food, sanitation, healthful working and living conditions, and other measures to prevent tuberculosis. One of the most

effective weapons has been the mass X-ray examination of the chests of large numbers of school children, employees in many industries and professions, and the general public by means of mobile X-ray units. Every case of human tuberculosis comes from an existing case, and if every one of these were located, tuberculosis would be stamped out.

Colds and cold shots. We are fortunate that the common cold is not a dangerous infection or few would survive. Colds are caused by a number of viruses which attack the mucous membranes of the nasal passages and respiratory tract. They are highly contagious in most cases and usually follow a period of weakened resistance. After recovery, there is a brief period of im-

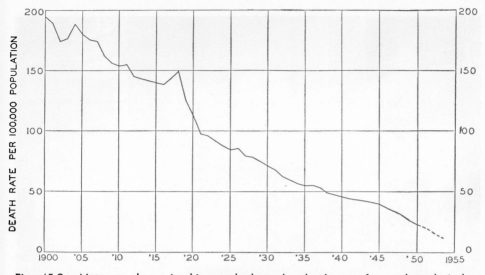

Fig. 45-9. Note, as shown in this graph, how the death rate from tuberculosis has steadily declined since 1900.

munity to that virus which caused the particular infection. But a cold caused by another virus may follow. Streptococcus infections, pneumonia, and other diseases may follow a cold.

Many investigations of colds and their causes have been made in recent years in an effort to produce a vaccine. One problem is the distinction between a cold and a noninfectious nasal allergy. Another is isolation and classification of the many cold organisms. Oral vaccines, to be taken by mouth, have not proved effective. The best preventive measure seems to be adequate rest, proper diet, and other health practices. These insure a maximum amount of resistance to the virus.

A group of drugs called **antihistamines** (an-tih-*his*-tah-meens) has become popular during the past few years because of their possible relief of nasal congestion during a cold. Success with antihistamines has been reported in some cases, while others seem not to respond. In any event, they should never be taken without a doctor's prescription.

Influenza, a highly contagious virus infection. Influenza, or " flu " as we commonly call it, is a respiratory infection caused by a virus. It may occur in epidemic form, spreading rapidly from one person to another. Symptoms appear suddenly with fever, general weakness, aching pain in the back, arms, and legs, and inflammation of the mucous membranes of the respiratory passages.

One reason for the rapid spread of influenza during an epidemic is the fact that many people continue their daily work and mingle with others. The greatest danger from influenza is secondary complications which often follow. These include bronchitis, pneumonia, and other respiratory infections. Treatment includes rest in bed, abundant fluids, and protection against possible sources of secondary infection.

An influenza vaccine is prepared by growing the virus in hen eggs. Three injections of the virus vaccine are given at intervals of a week.

Various forms of pneumonia. *Lobar pneumonia* is an infection of the

Fig. 45-10. The National Tuberculosis Association, working closely with the medical profession and public health agencies, have sponsored mass X-ray chest examinations by mobile X-ray units.

lungs by a specific pneumonia organism known as *pneumococcus* (new-moh-*cock*-us). This bacterium is a tiny ball-shaped organism, often found in pairs and frequently enclosed in a thick, slimy capsule. At least 30 types of the pneumococcus organism are known to exist.

Specific sera have been replaced by the use of penicillin and various sulfa drugs in recent years. These new drugs are highly efficient in the treatment of pneumonia and bring about a dramatic response. When given at the start of the infection, penicillin usually brings the infection under control within 12 hours, and promotes a crisis with sudden lessening of symptoms within 48 hours.

Bronchial pneumonia results from invasion of the lungs by a variety of organisms which infect the respiratory tract. *Virus pneumonia* is an infection of the lungs by a single virus, or group of viruses. It usually is not as serious as other forms of pneumonia, but it may last much longer. Aureomycin, one of the antibiotic drugs, seems to be the most effective treatment in this case.

Childhood diseases. Certain infections are so common during childhood that we often think of them as *childhood diseases*. However, they are by no means limited to children, nor is it necessary that all children have them.

Whooping cough is a bacterial disease most common in childhood. About half of the cases occur in chil-

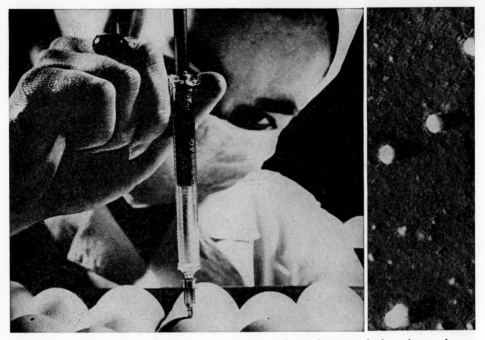

Fig. 45-11. By injecting influenza virus (shown at the right) into chick embryos, large-scale production of the vaccine is made possible.

dren under two years of age. The disease is most common during the winter and spring. Epidemics occur at two- to four-year intervals. Severe coughing, vomiting, and the characteristic gasping "whoop" are common symptoms. The disease is very dangerous in infants under one year of age. In fact, it is one of the most fatal diseases because they may strangle due to an accumulation of mucus. For this reason, three injections of whooping cough vaccine are given one week apart to infants within a few months after birth.

Chickenpox is a highly contagious virus infection of children. The disease is usually mild, starting with a slight fever, weakness, and nasal congestion. Within 24 to 48 hours, raised areas appear over the trunk, shoulders, and face. These open, and fluid seeps out a short time later. If a child scratches these small pustules it may leave a permanent scar of the skin. The most common complication is infection of the skin eruptions.

Measles and *German measles* are virus infections. Both diseases are spread rapidly through nasal discharges. Serious complications, including ear infections and pneumonia, may follow measles. Serum may be given to provide passive immunity to an exposed child or to reduce the seriousness of the disease if it develops. Complications from German measles are less frequent.

Mumps is a virus infection of the salivary glands, although it may involve other tissues, especially the reproductive organs. It is more serious in an adult than in a child.

What is polio? Polio is a shortened name for poliomyelitis, a disease well-known to the public today. Its common name, infantile paralysis, is poorly chosen for it is not a disease of infants,

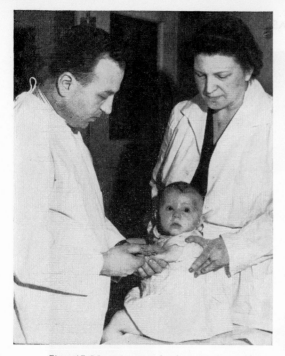

Fig. 45-12. Cases of whooping cough, a so-called childhood disease, have greatly diminished due to vaccine injections at an early age.

nor does it always cause paralysis. From 40 to 60 per cent of polio cases result in no permanent damage. There is a slight paralysis in 25 to 35 per cent of the cases, and extensive, permanent paralysis in 14 per cent of cases.

The polio virus attacks the anterior motor nerve roots of the spinal cord. These are the great nerve trunks which lead to the muscles. If there is destruction of nerves by the virus, the muscles they control become paralyzed. In some severe cases of polio (*bulbar type*), the virus attacks the spinal bulb at the base of the brain. This causes paralysis of the breathing muscles. When this occurs, the victim has to be put into an " iron lung," a mechanical breathing device.

The polio virus lives only in the tissue of primates and was first transmitted from humans to monkeys in 1908. The path of the virus into the body has been a subject of study for several years. Until recently it was thought to enter the nasal cavity and travel along the olfactory nerves to the brain. More recent research seems to indicate that it enters the alimentary tract with food or water. It then passes into the blood stream and finally reaches the nerve tissue of the spinal cord where it starts to grow. Three specific types of polio virus are known to exist.

A patient who recovers from polio has a lifetime immunity to the type, or types, he has experienced. Many adults appear to have immunity to polio without being aware of having had a mild polio infection. For some years, scientists have worked frantically to find either a serum which would give temporary passive immunity or a vaccine which would give permanent active immunity. These efforts have been supported through the tireless work of the Polio Foundation and other health agencies and an interested, generous public. The battle may be won. If so, it will be as important as any medical triumph of past years. This may well be the greatest contribution of our age to the conquest of disease.

The conquest of polio. The first major victory came a few years ago with the production and first use of GG, or **gamma globulin.** It resulted from the work which had been done in the pooling and preservation of blood in blood banks during World War II. Gamma globulin, containing antibodies against polio, is separated from other parts of blood by quite complicated chemical processes. A large pooling of blood is necessary to be sure that antibodies against all three types of polio virus are present. These come from many adults who have experienced mild and probably undiagnosed polio infections. Gamma globulin serum gives a short

Fig. 45-13. The virus-containing tissue culture of polio vaccine is reincubated for four days to allow further growth of the virus.

passive immunity against polio, which lasts about five weeks. For this reason, its use is limited to the protection of children during a polio epidemic and to members of a family who have been exposed to polio.

The long-awaited polio vaccine was announced in the spring of 1953. While many scientists had an important part in developing the vaccine, much of the credit for its discovery has been given Dr. Jonas Salk and his colleagues at the University of Pittsburgh. The Salk vaccine is not the first polio vaccine produced. As early as 1933, vaccine had been produced from virus grown in the brain and spinal cord of monkeys. Tests of these earlier vaccines indicated that they were not safe for general use.

The production of Salk vaccine was possible because of advances in the area of tissue culture, or the growing of animal tissues in nutrient solutions outside of the animal's body. During the latter part of 1953, biological companies started the production of the vaccine in tissue cultures made from the kidneys of monkeys. Kidney cells are used because they are more successfully cultured than nerve cells, and because certain proteins present in nerve tissue might be introduced into the vaccine. These cause serious reactions in a few people.

The production of the vaccine starts with thorough examination of a monkey to be used to determine whether it has tuberculosis. If the tuberculin test is negative and the monkey appears to be in good health, it is given a fatal anesthetic during which time the kidneys are removed. This is followed by a complete examination of the internal organs for evidence of disease. If the animal is healthy, the kidneys are cut into fine pieces and put into flasks containing a nutrient solution to which antibiotics have been added to prevent bacterial growth. These tissue cultures are incubated for six days at 98.6° F. Then the nutrient solution is drained off and replaced with new solution containing all three types of polio virus. Incubation continues four more days, during which the virus multiplies rapidly in the kidney cells. The cultures are filtered three times to remove all cells and any bacteria which may be present. The virus is then made inactive by treating it with a weak solution of formaldehyde. The inactive virus is then tested in another tissue culture as well as in monkeys. Before the vaccine is released for use, the manufacturing company's tests are duplicated in the laboratories of the National Institute of Health in Washington.

Several years will be required to determine the effectiveness of the Salk polio vaccine. However, evidence now points to great success. With the possibilities of even further improvement, it may protect new generations from the ravages of the disease. This will then be another victory for medical science.

In Conclusion

In the lobby of a mid-western children's hospital, bronze tablets bearing the names Edward Jenner, Robert Koch, Louis Pasteur, and other great men of science are set among the stone slabs of the floor. Because these men lived, few if any cases of smallpox, diphtheria, rabies, and other dangerous infectious diseases need be admitted to this hospital. One ward is assigned to the treatment of polio cases. Some day, perhaps this ward can be reassigned to some other medical problem because of the work of Dr. Jonas Salk and the many others who contributed to the work in tissue culture and the production of polio vaccine.

The conquest of infectious diseases continues. But only part of the battle is fought in doctors' offices, clinics, hospitals, and research centers. Prevention of disease is equally important. We will explore this phase in the next chapter.

Questions for Review

1. Why is the fact that Edward Jenner was a country doctor important in the discovery of vaccination against smallpox?

2. What false belief regarding the danger of vaccination in Jenner's time led to violent objections and campaigns against it?

3. Discuss modern methods in producing and processing smallpox vaccine.

4. Against what disease of poultry did Pasteur make a successful vaccine before making his famous anthrax vaccine?

5. What characteristics of rabies led Pasteur to believe that it centered in the brain?

6. Describe the treatment Pasteur gave the boy who was bitten by a mad dog. Do we use the same treatment today?

7. Describe the two-fold effect of diphtheria on the body.

8. What condition in a patient is indicated by a positive reaction to the Schick test for diphtheria?

9. Describe the Widal test for typhoid fever.

10. Of what medical use is tuberculin?

11. Describe the several different forms of pneumonia.

12. What medical use is made of antihistamine drugs?

13. What living host is used in growing influenza virus?

14. Explain why muscle paralysis occurs in some cases of polio.

Biologically Speaking

antihistamines	inoculation	sputum
antitoxin	patch test	tuberculin
bulbar polio	Salk vaccine	vaccination
gamma globulin	Schick test	Widal test

Applying Facts and Principles

1. Explain how the production of virus for smallpox vaccination illustrates the weakening of a virus by animal passage.

2. Why is a person who is immune to scarlet fever deprived of important warning signs in the case of a later infection?

3. Explain why the patch test for tuberculosis, while valuable for children, is of little value in testing adults.

4. Under what conditions might gamma globulin be used against polio?

5. Why did the production of a vaccine for polio (Salk vaccine) depend on advances in the field of tissue culture?

CHAPTER 46

The Prevention of Disease

It is reassuring to know that your doctor is standing by to help you with effective biological products and powerful drugs and antibiotics if infection strikes you. He is highly trained in the use of these weapons of *curative medicine,* but the cure of infectious disease is only one phase of the health program today. *Preventive medicine* fights infection at the source by removing the cause. It is in this phase of the health program that you, your doctor, and others concerned with maintaining the health of the community work as a team in protecting your health and the health of others.

In this chapter we will discuss the prevention of infection in various areas of your community. Then we will explore the problems of heart disease and cancer to find out what you may be able to do to prevent these major killers of our time.

Lister and antiseptic surgery. A hundred years ago few patients survived the ordeal of major surgery. Anesthetics were just coming into use. Because of the high mortality rate, operations were avoided, except in cases of severe wounds or those requiring amputation of limbs. Doctors often performed operations with unscrubbed hands and instruments which had not been sterilized. Wounds were covered with nonsterile dressings and bandages. Under conditions like these serious infection almost always followed surgery. The mortality rate was at least three out of four patients, if not from shock and loss of blood during surgery, then from infection a few days later.

These conditions in hospitals were alarming to a famous English surgeon, Sir Joseph Lister, a century ago. Lister had studied Pasteur's accounts of air-borne organisms and the possibility of infection during surgery. He applied this knowledge to his surgical proce-dures. He scrubbed the walls and floor of his operating room and covered his operating table with clean linen. Splints and bandages were soaked in a carbolic acid solution and surgical instruments were boiled in water. Those present in the operating room were required to scrub thoroughly. He even devised a carbolic acid spray which produced a fine germ-killing mist over the area of operation. By these methods Lister introduced **antiseptic surgery.** His success in reducing surgical infection changed the practice of surgery all over the world.

The modern hospital operating room uses germ-free methods known as **aseptic surgery.** The rooms are scrubbed with germicides. The air is sterilized with lamps which give off germ-killing rays. All linens, dressings, and bandages are sterilized. The surgeon and his assisting doctors and nurses wear sterile gowns, head covers, and face masks. Those actually performing the

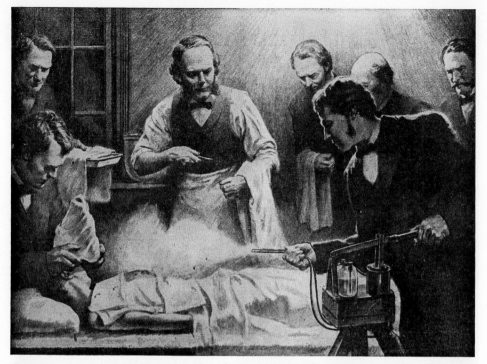

Fig. 46-1. Lister was the first to realize the importance of antiseptic surgery. His assistant is spraying carbolic acid on the skin of a patient just before an operation to prevent infection.

surgery and handling instruments and dressings wear sterile gloves over thoroughly scrubbed hands. These aseptic conditions have removed much of the risk of an operation and now most surgical wounds heal with no infection whatever.

Antiseptics and disinfectants. Since Lister's first use of carbolic acid as a **disinfectant** (germicide), many chemical substances have been developed for use in the destruction of microbes. They are of two general types. **Antiseptics** destroy some bacteria and prevent the growth of others. They are used locally in contact with body tissues, and must not be of such strength that they damage the tissues. Do not confuse antiseptics with **disinfectants,** which are powerful germ-killers used in chemical sterilization.

The perfect antiseptic with powerful effect on germs without injury to living tissue has not been found. Iodine is reliable for treating ordinary wounds and cuts. A 1% iodine solution is good. Solutions up to 3½% are used as antiseptics. Hydrogen peroxide (if fresh), potassium permanganate, camphor, thymol, and even common salt and soap are of definite antiseptic value. Some of the most recent antiseptics work on the cleansing principle rather than chemical destruction.

Disinfectants are used in sterilizing instruments, utensils, bedding, clothing, and walls and floors of rooms which have been exposed to infection. Some disinfectants may be used in diluted form on hands, but only with extreme care. They should never be used on other parts of the body without specific

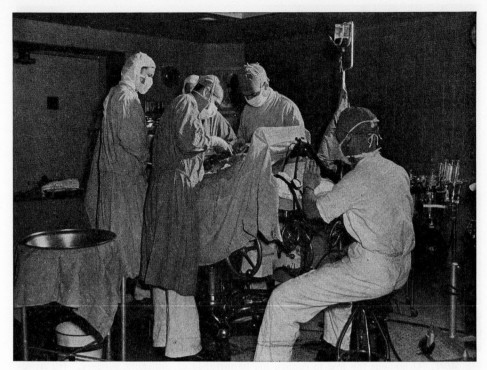

Fig. 46-2. The modern hospital operating room uses the aseptic method. All parts of the room are made as sterile as possible during an operation.

medical instructions. Among the widely used disinfectants are: 5% carbolic acid (phenol) solution, creosol, lysol, creolin, and formaldehyde. All of these are used in solution, according to directions supplied.

Preventive medicine in the community. Much of the responsibility for protecting the community from infectious disease is assigned to the local and state boards of health. One of the major activities of these organizations is protection of the community through the enforcement of quarantine in certain contagious diseases. When a doctor discovers a case of scarlet fever, measles, whooping cough, or certain other contagious diseases, he reports it to the Board of Health. A health officer puts a sign on the patient's house as a warning to people not to enter un-

til danger of contagion has passed. This work of the Board of Health prevents contagious diseases from sweeping through the community in epidemics as they did in earlier times.

The Board of Health gathers statistics on diseases in a community which are valuable to doctors. These data serve further in tracing epidemics and removing the cause whenever possible. The local food supply, water supply, public restaurants, hotels and motels, and other public places are under the Board's constant observation.

Inspection of the food supply. Almost every city and state has regulations in regard to food inspection. The stores, bakeries, meat-packing plants, and milk companies are under supervision of official inspectors. Meat which is to be sold outside the state must be

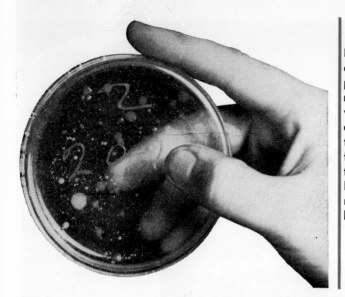

Fig. 46-3. Public health officers constantly inspect public eating places to make sure that china, silverware, and glassware are sterilized. Here a culture of bacteria, taken from eating utensils, shows that proper sterilization has not been used. Such restaurants may lose their licenses to operate.

inspected by the Bureau of Animal Industries of the United States Department of Agriculture. You have probably noticed the purple stamp of the inspector on meat you buy.

Milk can be a dangerous source of infection, especially in small children. Many cases of tuberculosis, undulant fever, streptococcus infections, intestinal infections, and typhoid fever have been traced to contaminated milk. For this reason, every precaution is taken to be sure the cows of a dairy herd are free of disease and that milk does not become contaminated during milking, handling, and bottling for delivery.

Safeguarding our water supply. The water supply is one of the most critical factors, especially in cities where great numbers of people use a common source. Under such circumstances, infected water could cause an epidemic almost overnight. The water supply for a large city represents an enormous investment. The watershed, or original source of the water supply, the streams or lakes from which the water is obtained, and the wells driven deep into the ground must be checked continually.

Chemical and bacteriological tests are run almost constantly. Thus, one living in a large city may be sure that his water supply is a safe and healthful one.

In smaller communities and individual farms, wells usually serve as water supply. Water from these sources should be checked regularly by the Board of Health to guard against infection.

Sewage and garbage disposal. Disposal of waste products, especially of sewage and garbage, is an important problem in most cities. The old way was to dump the garbage in special areas outside the city and carry the sewage through sewers to rivers and streams. Both measures created serious health hazards. Garbage dumps created breeding places for flies and general offensive conditions. Streams and beaches polluted by sewage became dangerous areas of infection for bathers. It also made water unfit for other uses, even to the extent of killing fish and other aquatic animals.

The best method of garbage disposal consists of converting it into useful fer-

Fig. 46-4. Local health departments and water purification plants are responsible for keeping drinking water safe for consumption. This laboratory technician is testing samples of water from a reservoir.

tilizer for distribution to agricultural regions for use on fields. In the same way, sewage may be treated and either reduced to fertilizer or treated to stimulate the growth of bacteria of decay. This is done to destroy its harmful properties before it is piped into rivers and streams.

Other agencies concerned with the fight against disease. To some extent, disease is an individual problem. But the effects of disease are much more far-reaching. The life of every individual has a direct bearing on his community, his state, and even the nation as a whole.

In 1912 the United States Public Health Service was established as a national agency to assist in the control of disease. It grew out of a much older organization, the Marine Hospital Service.

In addition to national and state agencies, numerous local and private agencies are doing extremely important work in the control and prevention of disease.

Insurance companies have made exhaustive studies in connection with the life expectancy of their insured. This information is available to the public in the form of numerous pamphlets and is valuable in health education. The Rockefeller Foundation maintains an extensive program of research in the fields of medicine and prevention of disease. Public health nursing associations, both privately and in connection with the local boards of health, provide nursing care to those who could not otherwise afford it. In most cities, public health nurses are available for people of all economic circumstances and no one is denied proper care during illness because of inability to pay for nursing care.

Patent medicines. Home prevention of disease is highly desirable, but home treatment of disease is an entirely different matter. In this day of highly advanced and efficient medicine, one is extremely foolish to attempt self-diagnosis and treatment of disease.

The Federal Food, Drug, and Cosmetic Act has done much to eliminate quack medicines. While it does not forbid the sale of these medicines, it does require that the manufacturer:

1. Put on the label the amounts of alcohol, and other ingredients in the medicine.

2. Make no false or misleading statement about cures or other virtues in using the medicine.

Effectiveness of recognized drugs and antibiotics is proven in large numbers of clinical tests, performed under medical supervision. Curative value is not determined by testimonials of private users. If a drug is found to be of questionable value, it is withdrawn from public use.

Organic and functional diseases. These diseases present quite a different problem from infectious diseases. They are not due to microorganisms and cannot be treated like infectious diseases.

Organic and functional disorders are increasing today. At the present time, diseases of the heart are the leading cause of death. Cancer and other malignant tumors, cerebral hemorrhage, arteriosclerosis (hardening of the arteries), and diseases of the nervous system also have become prominent.

These diseases are of a personal nature. They cannot be prevented through efforts of public agencies the way infectious diseases can. The individual must understand them and use every possible precaution against their occurrence.

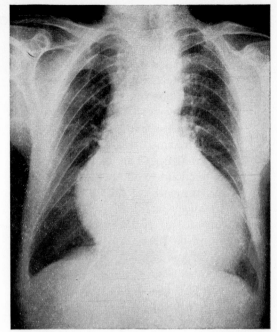

Fig. 46-5. This X-ray photograph shows the greatly enlarged heart of an elderly person.

Diseases of the heart and related organs. Heart disease leads all others today as a cause of death, especially among people of middle and old age. We usually think of heart disease as developing suddenly because death from certain forms of this ailment is almost immediate. Actually, heart disease develops over a long period of time and often involves other organs.

Various kinds of heart damage and diseases are associated with different periods of life. We can divide them according to age and cause as follows: (1) childhood and adolescence — rheumatic fever; (2) middle age — hypertension, or high blood pressure, and coronary heart disease; and (3) old age — hardening of the arteries, or arteriosclerosis.

Heart disease can result from rheumatic fever. Rheumatic fever develops as a complication in approximately three per cent of the cases of scarlet fever and related streptococcic throat infections. The powerful exotoxins absorbed from the infected throat tissues cause an allergic reaction in the connective tissues of certain people. This reaction is most common in the joints where the tissues become inflamed, reddened, and painfully swollen. The condition travels from one joint to another during several weeks or months of the illness.

In about one-third of the cases of rheumatic fever, the valves and ligaments of the heart, especially on the left side, become similarly inflamed. This may cause scar tissue to develop and leave the valves defective. The bicuspid, or mitral valve, between the auricle and ventricle on the left side of the heart, is most frequently involved. In some cases, the valve does not open enough to allow a normal flow of blood from the auricle to the ventricle. In others, the valve does not close properly and allows blood to flow back into the auricle each time the ventricle contracts. This lowers the blood pressure and adds greatly to the work of the heart.

The use of penicillin and other antibiotics, as well as sulfa drugs, has reduced the amount of heart damage in rheumatic fever. These drugs lessen the seriousness as well as the duration of streptococcic infections.

Children who have valvular heart damage resulting from rheumatic fever should be taught to live with their heart conditions as normally as possible, and should not become over-cautious heart invalids. A heart specialist should be consulted. He may advise nothing more than a little more rest and a little less exertion than usual.

Hypertension is the great enemy of middle age. This condition has been increasing in recent years. It is far more common in men than in women.

Hypertension, or high blood pressure, is commonly related to emotional stress resulting from worry, fear, and anxiety. Emotional stress causes various body changes, including constriction of the artery walls and increase in blood pressure. When arteries remain in this condition for long periods of time, their walls die slowly and harden with internal deposits. This situation reduces the internal diameter of the arteries and also reduces the flow of blood, just as lime deposits in a pipe reduce the flow of water. As a result, the blood pressure remains high.

In some cases, hypertension results in slow destruction of the tiny arteries of the kidneys, resulting in *chronic nephritis.* In others, the coronary arteries of the heart become involved. For this reason, hypertension is sometimes referred to as **cardiovascular-renal disease,** referring to the heart, blood vessels, and kidneys.

Coronary heart disease. Constriction and hardening of the coronary arteries which supply the heart muscle reduces the blood supply to the heart. This condition may not be noticed at first, especially if the person does not exert himself physically. However, as the condition grows worse, he may experience a crushing pain in the chest which extends into one or both arms at times of exertion. The pain and feeling of pressure in the chest at these times result from insufficient circulation to the heart muscle when the work of the heart is increased because of body exertion.

In some cases of coronary heart disease, a sudden flow of blood into the constricted coronary arteries at a time of exertion may cause a clot to form and block one of the arteries. Such a stoppage in a coronary artery is called a **coronary occlusion.** When the clot

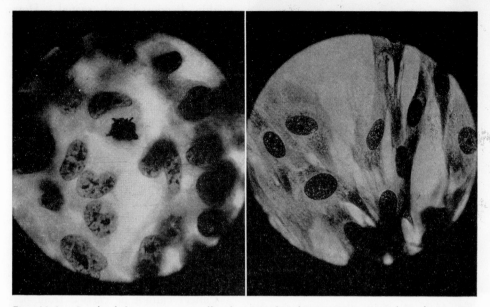

Fig. 46-6. On the left are cancer cells, showing the characteristic growth and arrangement. On the right is healthy tissue, showing regular cell outlines and an orderly distribution of the cells.

causing the occlusion forms in the heart vessel, we refer to it as a **coronary thrombosis.** Occasionally, a clot may form in a vessel in some other part of the body, travel through the circulation, and lodge in a coronary artery. This results in a **coronary embolism.**

When a coronary artery becomes blocked, the portion of the heart muscle it supplies dies. This results in a " heart attack." The seriousness of the condition depends on the location of the occlusion and the amount of heart muscle involved. Absolute rest is necessary during the period the heart is repairing the damage. A doctor can determine the amount of heart damage by means of an instrument known as an **electrocardiograph** (e-lek-tro-*kar*-dee-oh-graf).

Hardening of the arteries. This condition, known medically as arteriosclerosis, is primarily a disease of older people. It results from permanent change in the artery walls. In some cases, calcium deposits form in the walls of the vessels and make them rigid. The arteries do not expand freely with the surge of blood following each contraction of the ventricle of the heart. This causes a rise in blood pressure. Hardening of the arteries puts the heart under constant strain and may cause it to enlarge and, in time, go into failure.

We are in the midst of extensive research in an effort to find the causes of heart diseases. When they are eventually found, many years will be added to the present human life span.

Cancer is one of the chief killers today. The difficulty in dealing with cancer is that it is a " normal abnormality." It seems to be a mass of tissue in which cell division has gone wild, resulting in an abnormal growth which soon invades other organs.

Cancer appears most frequently in the colon, stomach, throat, and liver,

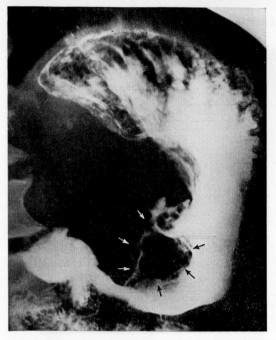

Fig. 46-7. An X-ray photograph showing cancer of the stomach. Much of the wall along the inner curvature (toward the spine) is replaced by cancer tissue.

and in the case of women, in the uterus and breast. Cancer is rare in people under 30 and seems to be most common between the ages of 40 and 60.

The disease can be treated effectively if found in its early stages. Consequently, one should report any suspicious symptoms to the doctor immediately. The following symptoms *may* mean cancer, although they are not necessarily indications and should not cause undue alarm: (1) any sore that does not heal in a few weeks; (2) bleeding from any body opening; (3) a lump on the surface of the body which changes shape or becomes enlarged; (4) persistent indigestion; (5) alternate periods of diarrhea and constipation; (6) progressive change in the color of a wart or mole; and (7) continued hoarseness or cough.

The diagnosis and treatment of cancer. External cancers of the skin are readily diagnosed and treated. However, internal forms are often very difficult to detect. X-rays are used to determine the extent and location of the growth, although even this method is not positive evidence. The proof of cancer is based on the presence of characteristic giant cells in the abnormal growth.

There are *only three recognized methods of treating cancer.* (1) The entire growth may be removed by *surgery;* (2) *X-ray* may be used to destroy the rapidly dividing cells; and (3) treatment with *radium* and other radioactive substances which give off radiations that destroy cancerous cells more rapidly than normal ones.

Cancer cannot be carried from person to person because it does not involve microorganisms. It cannot be inherited directly, although statistics seem to indicate that certain types of cancer are more prominent in some families than in others. An individual may inherit a constitutional make-up which tends toward cancer, although the disease is never inherited as such. Furthermore, cancer tendency in a family may be altered in offspring through marriage with individuals in which the tendency is not present.

Mental diseases. The average individual today lives under great stress and strain which is apt to affect his nervous system in some way or other. Although mental disorders may result from disease in other parts of the body or from organic conditions, by far the greatest number of cases are the result of purely functional disturbances.

We look on mental disease as we would on any other disease, except that in affecting the nervous system it necessarily influences the actions of the individual. We know now that by far the majority of cases may be cured and

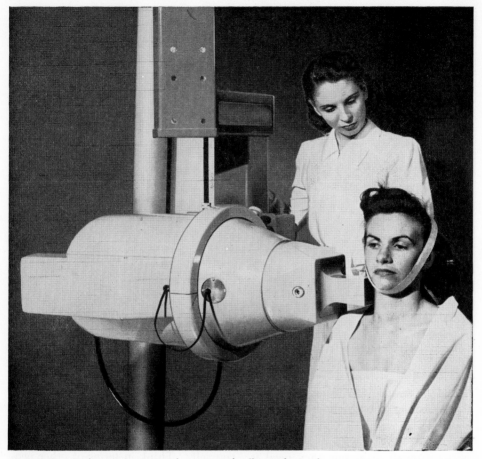

Fig. 46-8. Radioactive materials are used effectively in the treatment of cancer in its early stages. This patient has a good chance for complete recovery because her case was diagnosed early enough.

restored to normal life if treatment is begun early. While some forms of mental disorders may require institutional care for long periods of time, seven out of ten patients could avoid institutional commitment if treated in time.

The great need in the country now is for more mental hospitals with emergency wards where critical mental cases of short duration may receive extensive treatment.

If a patient who has "cracked up" could be sent to a hospital *at once,* he would have the skilled care of a psychiatrist. A **psychiatrist** (sy-*ky*-ah-trist) is a physician who has been specially trained to handle mental cases. The mentally ill patient who can be put under the care of a psychiatrist immediately will seldom have to return to an institution later in life.

Our trouble has been in disregarding early symptoms of mental and nervous disease and then committing the patient to an institution when he is advanced beyond anything private care can do. Consequently, many patients fail to re-

Fig. 46-9. Bowling is a recreational sport that anyone can enjoy either alone or in a group. Having a hobby and engaging in sports help maintain good mental and physical health.

ceive treatment at a time they need it most and are put into overcrowded mental hospitals or state or local institutions.

Mental diseases can be prevented. Most cases of mental illness could be avoided if the individual understood something about the cause of these disorders. Frequently, mental disease begins with attitudes on the part of the individual. These attitudes, in turn, put a strain on the nervous system which may affect the mental processes. Even as high-school pupils you should guard against damaging attitudes and types of behavior. Study the following list carefully. Then see if you are tending toward any of the attitudes which may possibly lead to trouble in later life:

1. Avoid thinking too much about yourself. Think in terms of other people and make their happiness your chief goal. Avoid selfishness and self-pity.

2. Don't allow all your activity to center around one thing. The person with varied interests may change activities from time to time and be able to relax.

3. Strive to get satisfaction from your work. Don't look on things you must do as chores, but rather as opportunities.

4. Maintain hobbies which have little to do with your routine life. These activities are as important to you as your chief occupation.

5. If possible, engage in sports and other outdoor activities which tend to tire you physically.

6. Develop adaptability. Learn to adjust yourself to new friends and situations. Don't exclude new acquaintances and live in a rut.

7. Learn to accept disappointments willingly and cheerfully. Always look beyond present reverses to future successes.

8. Develop admiration for those who are more successful in certain things than you are. Avoid the attitude that some people get all the breaks and that you have more than your share of bad luck.

9. If you have any handicaps, disregard them and develop superiority in some other line. If you have no physical handicaps yourself, be sure to disregard them in others. Don't stare at a physically handicapped person and embarrass him.

10. Be conscientious in what you do, but don't worry excessively.

When nervous and mental disorders are treated with the same degree of efficiency as infectious diseases, we will have reached a high standard in the conquest of disease.

In Conclusion

One reason the percentage of deaths from heart disease, cancer, and other diseases of middle age and beyond, has been increasing in recent years is the reduction in the number of deaths from infectious diseases earlier in life. Most of the dangerous killers of childhood have been eliminated. Tuberculosis and pneumonia, which once took a heavy toll of young people and adults, are under control. When we finally conquer heart disease and cancer, the average life span will rise suddenly from the present 68–70 years to perhaps 100 or more. Some day, perhaps soon, science will make this possible.

Questions for Review

1. List various methods Lister used in creating antiseptic conditions in his surgery.

2. What practices in a modern surgery produce an even more desirable aseptic condition?

3. List several commonly used antiseptics and disinfectants.

4. List various health regulations observed by dairies in protecting the milk supply.

5. Why must drinking water be pure?

6. Classify the major forms of heart and blood vessel diseases according to age groups.

7. What specific parts of the body are involved in cardiovascular-renal disease?

8. How can a coronary occlusion cause heart damage or death?

9. Explain how hardening of the arteries may cause high blood pressure, heart strain, and heart failure.

10. Name several body organs in which cancer frequently develops.

11. What are the three recognized treatments for cancer?

12. Discuss several of the various ways of maintaining good mental and emotional health.

Biologically Speaking

antiseptic	coronary thrombosis	mental disease
antiseptic surgery	curative medicine	organic disease
aseptic surgery	disinfectant	preventive medicine
cardiovascular-renal	electrocardiograph	psychiatrist
disease	functional disease	public health
coronary occlusion	hypertension	radium

Applying Facts and Principles

1. What are some of the methods various communities use in disposing of sewage and garbage? Point out good and bad practices.

2. Discuss problems relating to the use of patent medicines.

3. In what respect are organic and functional diseases more personal and difficult to control than infectious diseases?

4. Discuss the relation of valvular heart disease and rheumatic fever.

5. Make a list of suggestions that you think could possibly help prevent mental illness.

Research On Your Own

1. Using prepared slides of pathogenic bacteria which cause well-known diseases, make drawings of the organisms under high power of your miscroscope. Prepared slides of pathogenic bacteria can sometimes be supplied through your local Board of Health or a hospital.

2. Make a table of insect carriers of disease, listing the insect, the disease carried, the way in which the insect carries the disease, and the way in which it transmits the organisms to man.

3. Make a diagram showing three lines of defense against disease and include as forts in each line the proper agents of defense.

4. Send to a biological supply company for a culture of *Penicillium notatum*. Grow it in a moist chamber or a large covered dish containing a recommended culture medium. The mold is started in the culture dish by transferring spores and fragments from the stock culture. After about two weeks at room temperature, the mold should have grown enough for microscopic examination.

5. Assume that you are investigating an unknown disease. Outline the procedure you would follow in conducting your research according to the Koch postulates.

6. Get figures showing the five diseases causing the greatest numbers of deaths today. Make a block graph, showing the number of deaths resulting from each disease last year, or in the most recent year you can show. In each case, indicate whether the disease is infectious, organic, or functional.

 More About Biology

Buckler, Helen. *DOCTOR DAN: PIONEER IN AMERICAN SURGERY.* Atlantic Monthly Press, Boston. 1954

Chandler, C. A. *FAMOUS MEN OF MEDICINE.* Dodd, Mead and Co., New York. 1950

Cooley, Donald G. *THE SCIENCE BOOK OF WONDER DRUGS.* Franklin Watts, Inc., New York. 1954

Fox, Ruth. *GREAT MEN OF MEDICINE.* Random House, Inc., New York. 1947

Fox, Ruth. *MILESTONES OF MEDICINE.* Random House, Inc., New York. 1950

Garland, Joseph. *STORY OF MEDICINE.* Houghton Mifflin Co., Boston. 1949

Lariar, Lawrence (Ed.) *YOU'VE GOT ME IN STITCHES.* Dodd, Mead and Co., New York. 1954

Marriott, Henry L. *MEDICAL MILESTONES.* The William and Wilkins Co., Baltimore. 1952

Millman, Milton, M.D. *PARDON MY SNEEZE.* Frye and Smith, Ltd., San Diego. 1952

Montgomery, Elizabeth Rider. *THE STORY BEHIND THE GREAT MEDICAL DISCOVERIES.* Robert M. McBride and Co., New York. 1946

Rapport, Samuel and Wright, Helen. *GREAT ADVENTURES IN MEDICINE.* Dial Press, Inc., New York. 1952

Spencer, Steven M. *WONDERS OF MODERN MEDICINE.* McGraw-Hill Book Co., Inc., New York. 1954

Traux, Rhoda. *TRUE ADVENTURES OF DOCTORS.* Little, Brown and Co., Boston. 1954

Waksman, Dr. Selman A. *MY LIFE WITH THE MICROBES.* Simon and Schuster, Inc., New York. 1954

Wasserug, Joseph. *YOUR COUGHS, COLDS AND WHEEZES.* Wilfred Funk, Inc., New York. 1949

The Biology of Heredity

Have you ever wondered why people resemble their parents? The answer to this, and other questions about inheritance lies in a specialized branch of biology called *genetics* (je-*net*-icks). This is one of the most recently developed branches of biology.

Knowledge of the heredity or inheritance of plants and animals is important in many phases of modern life. The gardener and horticulturist apply the principles of heredity to plant breeding in the production of new varieties of garden flowers, crop plants, and fruit trees. The agriculturist has used them in developing his beef cattle and dairy cattle, hogs, sheep, and other highly productive farm animals.

The Basis of Heredity

Perhaps you have never stopped to realize that no other hand is quite like your right hand — except the left one! Nor will there ever be another face just like yours, or a body, or a personality like the one you have.

At one time people believed that all characteristics were controlled by the blood. Doubtless you have heard some of your friends say that they are related by blood to some famous person. And we all know that breeders of dogs, cats, and farm animals always refer to " blood lines."

Actually, the blood has nothing to do with the qualities an organism inherits from its parents. A child's blood frequently is quite unlike that of either its father or mother. Neither are the characteristics of an individual changed in any way by receiving blood from another person during a blood transfusion.

Heredity is the tendency of organisms to resemble their parents. In this chapter you will see how the determiners of heredity are included in every cell. You will learn how they are passed on to new cells during cell division, and how they are paired with one another in forming a new organism.

Heredity and environment. Two sets of controlling factors determine the make-up of an individual. The first is **heredity.** Such traits as: body size, hair color, skin color, eye color, and even some traits which contribute to his personality may be inherited.

The second set of factors is **environment.** It is hard to say, however, where hereditary influences end and environmental ones begin. Biologists and sociologists have been debating this for years. Apparently, no one can draw a definite line between the two. For example, body size is controlled by heredity. But isn't it also determined partially by diet, by the action of the glands, and by the type of activity in which the person engages?

We speak of " born criminals," but no one is really born with a tendency toward crime. Rather, it is developed because of bad social influences in a poor environment. Perhaps these arguments seem pointless. However, they are really of tremendous importance because environment can be changed, while heredity is fixed.

What kinds of characteristics are inherited? In certain respects, all members of a single species are alike. For example, man normally inherits the characteristics of the human race which make him like other human beings. These **species characteristics** include hands with fingers for grasping, the ability to walk erect, and a highly developed nervous system with a brain that is superior to all other organisms.

In addition to species characteristics, he inherits **individual characteristics** which make him different from all other

613

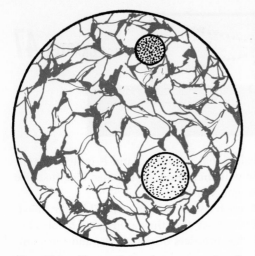

Fig. 47-1. The nucleus, the center of cell heredity, contains chromatin which is the substance of heredity. This nucleus has two nucleoli.

people. Many of these individual characteristics are passed on from parent to offspring. The result is that the individual resembles his parents to a certain degree, but differs from each because he has inherited characteristics from both.

The cell is the unit of heredity. You know that the cell is the unit of structure. Similarly, the cell is the unit of function, for it is the seat of all the activities of the organism. We now come to the cell as the center of another phase of the life of an organism — *the unit of heredity.* The characteristics of an organism are expressed through its cells. That is, every cell is controlled individually by the factors of heredity.

The nucleus is the center of cell heredity. As you recall, the nucleus is a spherical body of protoplasm usually lying near the center of the cell. It consists of a *nuclear membrane,* one or more small bodies called *nucleoli,* and a mass of living substance called *nucleoplasm.* When you add special

stains to the nucleus, you can see a twisted mass of threadlike material in the nucleoplasm. This material is called **chromatin** (*kroh*-mah-tin), the substance of heredity. The mass of threads is termed the **chromatin net,** or **nuclear net.** (See Fig. 47-1.) This substance seems to control the characteristics of the individual cell as well as the organism as a whole. Furthermore, *the chromatin in all the nuclei of the body cells of a single organism is identical.* Thus, the individual functions as a single unit and carries the same hereditary characteristics in all parts of his make-up.

Chromosomes and genes. The chromatin material in the nucleus becomes more apparent during division of the nuclear substances prior to division of the cell. The chromatin then changes so as to form several rod-shaped bodies called **chromosomes** (*kroh*-moh-soams). Chromosomes appear as dark, elongated pieces inside the nucleus when it is treated with special stains. They frequently vary in shape. When certain chromosomes are photographed under the high-powered electron microscope, numerous small granules are visible. Thus chromosomes consist of large numbers of tiny particles arranged in strands, somewhat like a string of beads. The individual particles are **genes** (*jeens*), and have been shown to be the bearers of heredity.

The number of chromosomes often varies in different plants and animals, but is constant for *every organism in a particular species.* For example, all corn plants always have 20; all pigeons, 16; all bullfrogs, 26; and all humans, 48. Furthermore, chromosomes always appear as pairs. Man has 48 chromosomes which actually represent 24 pairs. A pair consists of duplicate chromosomes and genes. Thus, not one but two genes or several pairs of genes control each hereditary characteristic. Perhaps you have already figured out that one chromosome of each pair comes from one parent, while the other comes from the other parent.

The formation of body cells is called mitosis. Immediately after it has been formed, a cell enters a period of growth and other activities. We refer to this period in the life of a cell as the ***interphase stage.*** The length of the interphase depends largely on the rate of growth. In some cases, such as in the embryonic region of a root and other rapidly growing tissues, it may last only a few hours. On the other hand, some cells of the human body grow very slowly and may spend a year or more in the interphase stage.

At the close of the interphase stage, the cell begins its nuclear division by a process called **mitosis** (my-*toh*-sis). The chromatin material of the nucleus is divided. Thus, the two new cells resulting from the division of the old one will have an identical hereditary makeup. Division of the chromatin material of the nucleus occurs during this remarkable process of mitosis. Mitosis always precedes division of a body cell. You can see it in many plant and animal tissues under the microscope. It is very easily seen in rapidly growing embryonic tissue, such as the tip of a root or stem, or in an animal embryo.

The stages of mitosis. While mitosis is a continuous process, we often group the changes which occur into four stages, or phases, as follows: (1) *prophase;* (2) *metaphase;* (3) *anaphase;* and (4) *telophase.* (See Fig. 47-3.)

1. ***Prophase.*** The first evidence that nuclear division is about to occur is the gradual condensing of the chromatin net into double ribbons. These are

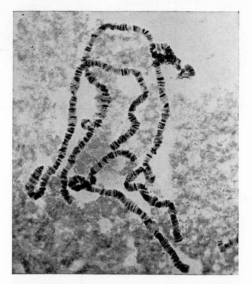

Fig. 47-2. These chromosomes are from the salivary gland of the fruit fly (*Drosophila*) magnified many times.

chromosomes and this stage is called the *early prophase,* the first of the stages of mitosis. The chromosomes then become shorter and thicker until they appear as distinct rodlike bodies. We refer to this stage in the process as the *middle prophase.* With the shortening of chromosomes, the nuclear membrane gradually disappears and *numerous* fine threads composing the **spindle** form from poles above and below the nucleus. During *late prophase,* the nuclear membrane and other parts of the nucleus are no longer visible.

2. **Metaphase.** This is an easy stage to identify, but the hardest to find in tissue prepared for microscopic study because it is the shortest of the four stages. The chromosomes arrange themselves along the imaginary center of the cell in the region referred to as the **equator.** As though attracted by some mysterious force at each of the opposite poles, the chromosomes are pulled apart lengthwise into two identical halves. The separation occurs first

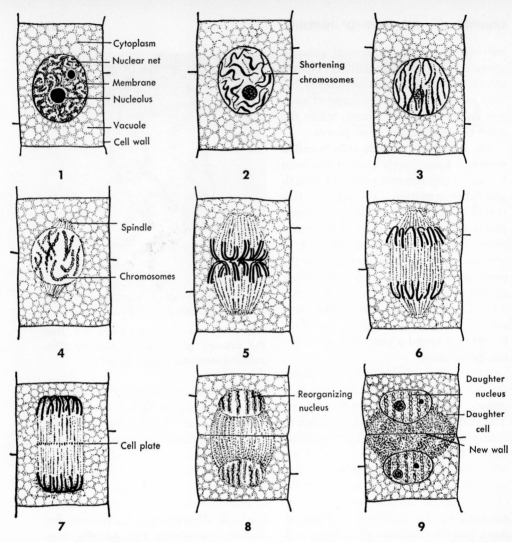

Fig. 47-3. The four stages of mitosis as it occurs in a plant cell are shown here. **1:** resting cell in interphase; **2–4:** various prophase stages; **5:** metaphase stage; **6:** anaphase stage; **7–8:** telophase stages; and **9:** the two new daughter cells.

at the ends, then in the middle. The metaphase stage is now complete.

3. *Anaphase.* During the anaphase stage, the two sets of chromosomes move along the spindle threads in opposite directions toward the respective poles. Bear in mind that each group of chromosomes is a full set, identical with the set which is moving in the opposite direction toward the other pole. Late in the anaphase stage in a plant cell, a **cell plate** begins to form across

the middle of the spindle. This splits the cell into two halves. During the next stage, each of the new cells will form a wall along this cell plate. In an animal cell, indentations appear in the outer membrane and gradually deepen, cutting the cell in half. The anaphase stage ends when the chromosomes have reached their respective poles.

4. *Telophase.* The final, or telophase stage, includes the formation of two daughter nuclei. The spindle fibers

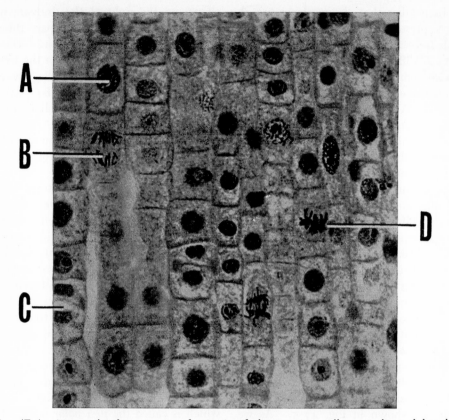

Fig. 47-4. Name the four stages of mitosis of these onion cells as indicated by the letters, A, B, C, and D.

disappear gradually. The rod-shaped chromosomes reverse the process of shortening and become long, loosely tangled threads that have the appearance again of a chromatin network. The other nuclear contents reappear and become surrounded by a nuclear membrane. As each daughter nucleus is reorganizing, division of the cell in the region of the equator is completed.

Each daughter cell enters an interphase period during which it will carry on its normal activities, including growth. When maturity is reached, the process will start again.

Chromosome content of germ cells. During sexual reproduction, a *sperm,* produced in a testis of the male parent,

combines with an *egg,* formed in an ovary of the female parent. The two germ cells unite and produce the new individual as a result of fertilization. The sperm and egg carry hereditary characteristics of both parents and combine them in the offspring. Both germ cells contribute equally to the heredity of the new individual.

Perhaps you have already wondered why, with both parents contributing to the heredity of the offspring, it does not receive twice the number of genes and chromosomes either parent possessed. That is, if both parents had 48 chromosomes in all of their cells, like all other humans, why doesn't the offspring have 96 chromosomes?

Remember that chromosomes are always present in pairs. Human body cells have 24 pairs of chromosomes and not 48 different ones. One set of 24 chromosomes came from one parent, while the other set came from the other parent. A sperm with its 24 chromosomes is only half an individual. The egg with the other set of 24 chromosomes is the other half. You can see already that a child is equally related to both parents even though it may resemble one more than the other.

The cells of the testes which form human sperms have 48 chromosomes (24 pairs) like all other body cells of the human being. Similarly, the cells of the ovaries which form eggs have 48 chromosomes (24 pairs). What happens to the missing set of chromosomes not present in an egg or sperm?

Reduction division is called meiosis. Eggs and sperms are formed as a result of a complicated series of cell divisions in the ovaries or testes. These divisions are shown in Fig. 47-5. As we describe each division, study the diagram closely to note the chromosome changes. We will start with a cell in an ovary or testis which contains a full set of chromosomes with both numbers of a pair present.

The biologist refers to this, the double number, as the **diploid** (*dip*-loid) **number** of chromosomes. During one of the divisions, the chromosome pairs will separate so that each new cell receives only one chromosome of each pair. This is *reduction division,* or **meiosis** (my-*oh*-sis). We refer to this chromosome content, with only one of each pair present, as the **haploid** (*hap*-loid), or **half number.** In order to make it easier to show the changes in the chromosomes, only three pairs of chromosomes have been shown. The various stages in egg formation are shown on the right of the drawing in Fig. 47-5. You should compare these carefully with the stages in the formation of the sperms as shown on the left.

1. The original germ cells divide and form many oogonial cells. (We have shown only one such cell in Fig. 47-5.) These oogonial cells have the same chromosome composition as the germ cells because they were formed by mitosis.

2. Each oogonial cell matures and then becomes a **primary oocyte** (*oh*-oh-syte). An **oocyte** is an egg before maturation, which includes the formation of the polar bodies. Important changes in the chromosomes take place during this growth. Pairs come together. Then each chromosome divides and becomes double. This division thus produces groups of four, or *tetrads,* of chromosomes.

3. The primary oocyte then divides unequally. This division forms a large secondary oocyte and a smaller cell which is called the *first polar body.* It is this division which is the real *reduction division.* The pairs of divided chromosomes separate from each other. One member of each pair goes to the secondary oocyte. The other member of each pair goes to the first polar body.

4. The secondary oocyte divides to form an **oötid** (*oh*-oh-tid), which will mature into the egg and a second polar body. During this division, the halves of each divided chromosome separate from each other, one-half going into each of the new cells. Thus the ootid and second polar body each have a haploid set of chromosomes, with only one member of each pair present. The first polar body divides similarly to form two other polar bodies. None of the polar bodies is involved in fertilization.

5. The ootid matures into the egg, ready for fertilization.

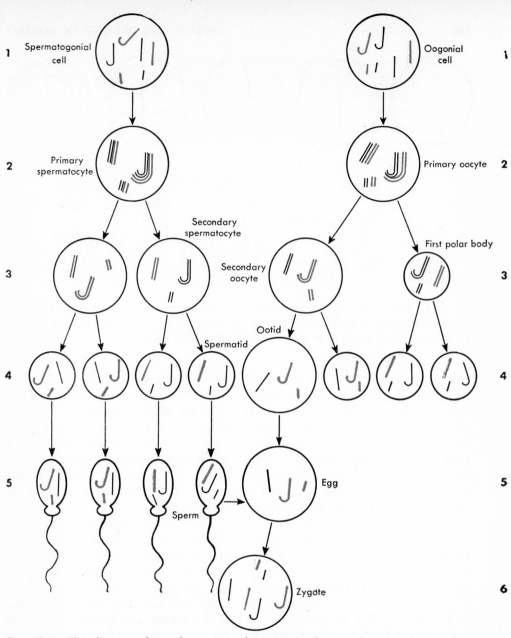

Fig. 47-5. This diagram shows the various chromosome changes during reduction division, or meiosis, in the formation of eggs and sperms.

6. A mature sperm unites with a mature egg during fertilization, each contributing a set of chromosomes. This restores the original diploid number of chromosomes, with a pair of each kind present in the fertilized egg, or zygote.

Notice that sperm are formed as a result of similar divisions. However, the primary spermatocytes form two functioning secondary spermatocytes by meiosis. The secondary spermatocytes give rise to four *spermatids,* all of which mature into sperms.

From fertilized egg to many-celled organisms. Immediately after fertili-

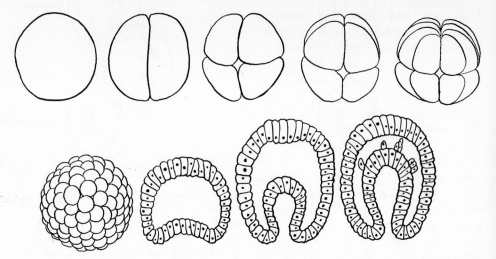

Fig. 47-6. Cells divide repeatedly (as shown in the top drawings) to form a hollow ball, or blastula (shown in the lower left). The last three stages, or gastrula, develop to form germ layers which give rise to organs and tissues of the embryo.

zation, the zygote begins a period of rapid division. The cell divides by mitosis to form a two-celled stage. Since chromosomes are split in the process, both cells of the two-celled stage have identical chromosome make-up. Soon these cells divide to form a four-celled stage, then an eight-celled stage, and so on until a large number of cells forming a hollow ball are produced. We refer to this hollow sphere of cells as the **blastula** (*blas*-tyoo-luh). A short time later, the wall of the blastula folds inward on one side, forming a deep pocket. This produces an inner layer, or *endoderm,* as well as the outer layer, or *ectoderm.* A third layer, or *mesoderm,* forms between these layers. We refer to the stage in which the germ layers are formed as the **gastrula** (*gas*-truh-luh). As development continues, the various layers form the organs and tissues of the embryo.

Note that all the cells are related to the original zygote and have descended from it by the process of mitosis. Each new cell receives part of the chromo-

somes which were present in the original fertilized egg. Thus, the hereditary make-up of the individual is determined the instant the egg and sperm unite. From that moment on it cannot be changed, except through disease or injury which might destroy certain genes. This would be a very rare occurrence, however.

Variation in offspring. We know that the same parents may produce several offspring with quite different characteristics. It is evident, therefore, that the eggs or sperm formed by a single individual may vary. This is due to the **chance distribution** of genes on the chromosomes in the germ cells.

This chance distribution is shown in Fig. 47-7. Two pairs of genes on separate chromosomes are shown. These pairs are shown as *Aa* and *Bb.* During reduction division in forming eggs or sperms, these pairs may separate in several ways. *A* may segregate with *B.* *A* and *b* may go together, or *a* and *B,* or *a* and *b.* When you consider the fact that man has 48 chromosomes in all and that each chromosome has numerous genes, the possibilities of gene combinations in eggs and sperm following reduction division are almost without limit. According to mathematical calculations, 48 chromosomes can be separated off in 16,777,216 different haploid combinations during reduction division in egg and sperm formation. All of these different eggs and sperm can unite in 281,474,976,710,656 different combinations during fertilization. These figures are based on chromosome combinations alone. Consider that each chromosome bears many genes and you can easily understand why no two people are alike.

It is on this chance distribution of genes during reduction and resulting variation in characters of offspring that the science of genetics is based. It is this same chance distribution of a large

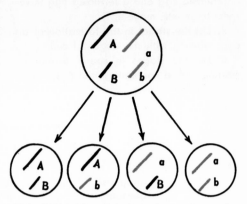

Fig. 47-7. The diagram above shows the chance distribution of chromosomes and genes during reduction division, or meiosis.

number of genes which makes you different from any other person. This particular combination of genes will never occur again, so there will never be another you.

In Conclusion

It is in recent years that we have known how family traits were passed on from parent to offspring. "Like father, like son," is only a very small part of the story. You might have your grandfather's nose or certain artistic talents neither parent had but which resemble some aunt's.

As you continue the study of genetics, you will discover how genes can be carried without indicating their presence for several generations, then they may appear at a later time in some member of the family.

There is nothing strange about inheritance. It follows definite laws, the first of which were discovered by an Austrian monk, about whom you will learn in the next chapter.

Questions for Review

1. What is the difference between hereditary and environmental characteristics?

2. Why is the cell the unit of heredity?

3. What is the relationship between chromatin, chromosomes, and genes?

4. (a) How many chromosomes are present in every human body cell? (b) How many do eggs and sperm contain?

5. Describe the migration of chromosome halves from equator to poles during mitosis.

6. What is the difference between an

unfertilized egg and a fertilized egg in respect to genetic make-up?

7. List the stages in the formation of an egg, starting with the oogonial cell.

8. List the stages in sperm formation, starting with a spermatogonial cell.

9. Name three cell layers which form during the gastrula stage.

10. List four possible gene combinations which may result from chance distribution of two pairs, *AaBb*, during reduction division in egg or sperm formation.

Biologically Speaking

anaphase	fertilization	oocyte
blastula	gastrula	ootid
cell plate	gene	prophase
chance distribution	genetics	reduction division
chromosome	haploid	sperm
diploid	heredity	spermatid
ectoderm	meiosis	spermatocyte
egg	metaphase	spindle
environment	mitosis	telophase

Applying Facts and Principles

1. To what false idea of early times does the term " blood line " refer?

2. Account for the fact that all of your cells have identical genetic make-up.

3. In terms of chromosome number and structure, explain why unrelated organisms cannot be crossed.

4. You know that a single oocyte gives rise to only one egg whereas a single spermatocyte gives rise to four sperms. Explain why.

5. Explain, in terms of chance distribution of genes, how the same parents can produce a wide variety of offspring.

CHAPTER 48

The Principles of Heredity

In 1865, Gregor Mendel, an Austrian monk, published the results of a masterful piece of work on the laws of heredity. He was not the first to experiment in the field of inheritance, but his findings were the first of any scientific consequence. His paper, representing years of work with garden peas, was published by the Natural History Society of Brünn, Austria. Mendel had been dead for 16 years when three other scientists discovered his work and began to make use of his findings. It is unfortunate that Mendel could not have lived to see his work acclaimed. It is, however, the greatest tribute to Mendel that the laws he formulated from his experiments with garden peas stand today practically unchanged as the basis of the science of genetics.

Mendel's experiments with the garden pea. There were good reasons why Mendel selected the garden pea for his experiments. Mendel noticed that garden peas differed in certain definite characteristics. Some plants were short and bushy, while others were tall and climbing. Some produced yellow seeds, some green seeds; some had colored flowers and some white ones. Altogether, Mendel discovered that garden peas differed in seven respects. He also found that the characteristics of any one kind of pea were preserved in generation after generation because the plants normally carried on self-pollination. However, cross-pollination could be performed easily by transferring pollen from the stamens of one flower to the pistil of another. With seven different characteristics to follow, and cross-pollination easy to perform, Mendel selected an ideal subject.

His first task was to find out whether or not the seven characteristics which he observed were always handed down from parent to offspring. To establish this fact, Mendel collected seeds from different plants of all the various types and arranged them in his garden. He collected seeds from each different type to establish a second generation. The second generation proved that the seven characteristics he was considering were transmitted from parent to offspring. Tall plants produced other tall ones and those with yellow seeds produced others with yellow seeds. He called each of these a *pure characteristic* because it was carried from one generation to another.

Mendel illustrates the Law of Dominance. His next step was to determine what would happen if he crossed two plants with contrasting characteristics. Accordingly, he selected one tall parent and one short one. He took pollen from the tall one and put it on the pistil of the short one. When the seeds matured on the short plant, he sowed them to find out the results of his cross. Would they be short like one parent,

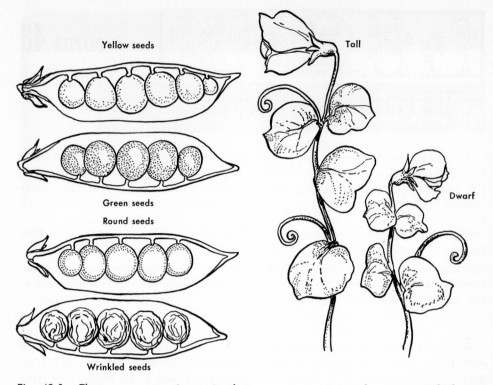

Fig. 48-1. These are contrasting traits that may appear in garden peas. Which are dominant and which are recessive traits?

tall like the other, or of medium height with characteristics of both? He discovered that all the plants were tall like the plant from which he had taken the pollen in making the cross.

His next step was to determine if it made any difference which plant he used for pollen and which he used to produce seeds. Accordingly, he reversed the process of pollination, using a short plant for pollen and a tall one for seed production. The results were as before — all the second generation were tall.

Mendel then experimented with crosses involving other characteristics. He crossed plants which had yellow seeds with those which had green seeds. He found that all of the second generation had yellow seeds. Similarly, he discovered that round-seeded varieties

crossed with plants with wrinkled seeds produced a generation with round seeds. He repeated these experiments until he had tested all seven characteristics. Then he drew his first conclusion. One character *dominated* the other. The offspring resembled *one* of the parents but not *both*. In drawing this conclusion, Mendel established the first of his laws of heredity, the **Law of Dominance.**

Mendel called the trait that appeared in the first generation of offspring, the **dominant** trait, and the one that seemed to be lost, the **recessive** trait. In keeping track of his generations of crosses, he designated the parent generation in which the characters were *pure* as P. The second generation, resulting from the cross, he called **F_1,** which stands for **first filial.** The individuals in the **F_1** generation appeared

MENDEL'S LAW OF DOMINANCE

THE SEVEN PAIRS OF CONTRASTING TRAITS	DOMINANT TRAIT IN OFFSPRING (F$_1$ HYBRIDS)
1. Round seeds, wrinkled seeds	Round seeds
2. Yellow seeds, green seeds	Yellow seeds
3. White seed coat, colored seed coat	Colored seed coats
4. Inflated pod (unripe), constricted pod	Inflated pod
5. Green pod, yellow pod	Green pod
6. Axial flowers, terminal flowers	Axial flowers
7. Tall stem, short stem	Tall stem

like the parent possessing the dominant characteristic. Actually, however, they were not identical. The plants of the first generation were not *pure* tall because they had been crossed with a short parent. Rather, they were *hybrid* tall peas. **Hybrids** are the offspring from a cross between two parents which differ in one or more traits.

Mendel's experiments with hybrid tall peas. Having produced tall peas as a result of crossing pure tall and pure short parents, Mendel's next step was to determine what would happen if he crossed two *F$_1$* hybrid tall peas. Would they produce all tall plants like the pure tall parent, or would the recessive character for shortness again appear? To determine this, he selected two *F$_1$* hybrid tall plants, cross-pollinated them, and planted the seeds for another generation which he called *F$_2$*, or **second filial.**

The results of this cross were quite striking. Some plants were tall, while others were short. None was in between. Furthermore, ¾ of the plants were tall, while only ¼ were short. He later found that ¼ of the plants were pure tall and always produced tall plants when crossed with each other, ½ were hybrid tall, and ¼ were short.

Exactly the same results were obtained in crossing hybrids showing other traits. The yellow peas which had been produced by crossing plants having pure yellow seeds and pure green seeds, when crossed with each other, produced peas of which ¼ were pure yellow, ½ hybrid yellow, and ¼ pure green.

This sorting out and reappearing of the seemingly lost recessive trait in the offspring of hybrids Mendel called **segregation.** The principle is referred to as the **Law of Segregation.** (See Fig. 48-2.)

TABLE TO ILLUSTRATE DOMINANCE AND SEGREGATION

PARENTS	PURE TALL × PURE SHORT
F$_1$ Generation	Tall hybrids × Tall hybrids
F$_2$ Generation	¼ pure tall ½ tall hybrid ¼ pure short

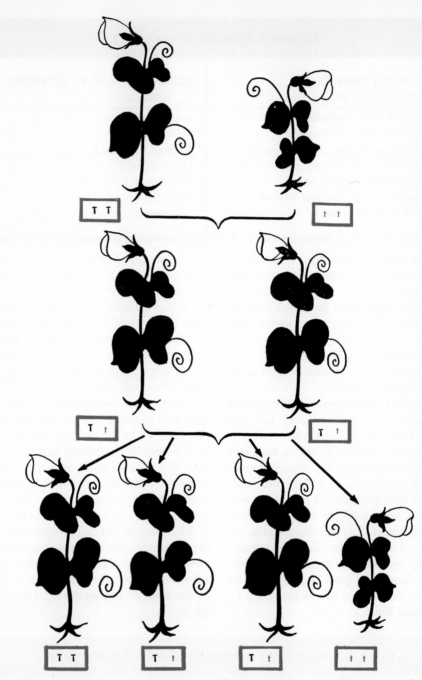

Fig. 48-2. Mendel's Law of Segregation is illustrated here. A tall pea crossed with a short pea produces an **F₁** generation in which all plants are tall. When these tall plants are crossed with each other, the plants in the **F₂** generation will show a ratio of three tall to one short.

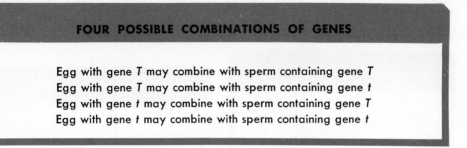

FOUR POSSIBLE COMBINATIONS OF GENES

Egg with gene *T* may combine with sperm containing gene *T*

Egg with gene *T* may combine with sperm containing gene *t*

Egg with gene *t* may combine with sperm containing gene *T*

Egg with gene *t* may combine with sperm containing gene *t*

In the study of genetics, we use special charts resembling checkerboards to determine the results of various crosses. Mendel's work with tall and short peas can be made clear by diagraming his various experiments.

You will recall that chromosomes are always present *in pairs* and that as a result of fertilization each parent contributes *one number of each pair.* In dealing with tallness and shortness in peas, Mendel was actually concerned only with *one pair* of genes. If we let the letter *T* stand for tallness, a *pure tall* plant would be written *TT,* indicating that both its genes for this character were tall. The capital *T* indicates that tallness is dominant over the contrasting character, shortness. In like manner, the small letter *t* stands for short, and a *pure short* individual would be designated as *tt.*

While all the body cells contain diploid sets of chromosomes and genes, you remember that reduction division occurs only during the formation of sex cells. Consequently, the egg cell in the pea ovule and the sperm nuclei formed from the pollen grain have only one gene for each character. When eggs or sperm are formed by a pure tall pea plant, one sperm nucleus receives one *T* and the other receives the other *T.* In like manner, the *tt* genes present in all body cells are separated in reduction division to *t* and *t* in the formation of eggs or sperm. Therefore, we may diagram a

cross between pure tall, *TT* and *tt* pure short, as follows:

TABLE TO SHOW RESULTS OF CROSSING TT AND tt		
Female → Genes Male ↓	*t*	*t*
T	*Tt*	*Tt*
T	*Tt*	*Tt*

All the offspring are hybrids, with a gene for tall, *T,* and a gene for short, *t.* They appear tall, however, because tall is dominant over short.

If the *Tt* hybrids are bred together, it is easy to see that four possible combinations of genes may occur.

Thus the chance combination of the genes *T* and *t* of hybrid parents make it logical that the offspring should be ¼ pure dominant (*TT*), ½ hybrid (*Tt, Tt*), ¼ pure recessive (*tt*).

TABLE TO SHOW RESULTS OF CROSSING Tt AND Tt		
Female → Genes Male ↓	*T*	*t*
T	*TT*	*Tt*
t	*Tt*	*tt*

The same scheme explains the other ratios.

TABLE TO SHOW RESULTS OF CROSSING TT AND Tt		
Female → Genes Male ↓	T	t
T	TT	Tt
T	TT	Tt

TABLE TO SHOW RESULTS OF CROSSING Tt AND tt		
Female → Genes Male ↓	t	t
T	Tt	Tt
t	tt	tt

Dominant and recessive genes in guinea pigs. The same results Mendel obtained in crossing tall and short peas are shown in the inheritance of color in guinea pigs. In this case, *black* is dominant over *white*.

Now see what happens when we cross a *pure black* guinea pig (*BB*) with a *pure white* (*bb*) one. All the offspring in the F_1 generation are black. They differ in genetic make-up, however, in that they are *hybrid blacks* (*Bb*). When two hybrids are crossed, the F_2 generation will show a ratio of ¼ pure black (*BB*), ½ hybrid black (*Bb*), and ¼ pure white (*bb*). The cross between two hybrids of the F_1 generation to produce the F_2 generation may be diagramed as on this page (see also Fig. 48-3). The same applies to the cross-

ing of rough and smooth-coated guinea pigs. In this case, rough coat is dominant over smooth coat.

TABLE TO SHOW RESULTS OF CROSSING Bb AND Bb		
Female → Genes Male ↓	B	b
B	BB	Bb
b	Bb	bb

Crosses involving two characters. Crosses involving two characters become more complicated than simple crosses in which only one pair of contrasting characters is considered. The same principles apply, but the possible gene combinations are increased. When two pairs of characteristics are involved, the individuals possessing mixed genes for both characters are called **dihybrids** (*dy-hy-brids*).

If a pea with round green seeds (two characters) is crossed with a pea having wrinkled yellow seeds, all members of the F_1 generation have round and yellow seeds. The recessive characters of *greenness* and *wrinkledness* are overshadowed by the two dominant traits. In this cross, *R* will stand for a gene for round, *r* for wrinkled, *Y* for yellow, and *y* for green. The F_1 hybrids would all possess the genetic make-up *RrYy*, a gene for *round* (*R*) having come from one parent, and a gene for *wrinkled* (*r*) having come from the other. In like manner, one parent supplied a gene for *yellow* (*Y*), while the other supplied a gene for *green* (*y*).

When the two hybrid round yellow peas are crossed, the situation becomes more complicated. Each hybrid with

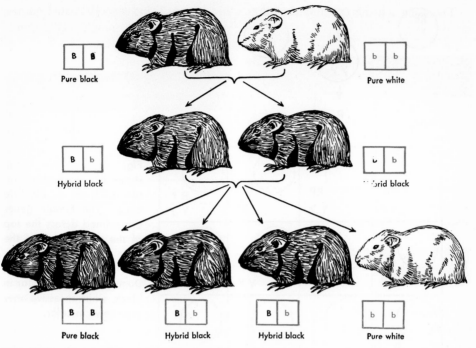

Fig. 48-3. By crossing a pure black guinea pig with a pure white, the **F₁** generation produces hybrid black animals. What results are obtained when the two hybrid black guinea pigs are mated?

the genetic make-up *RrYy* may produce four kinds of eggs or sperm. During reduction division, the pairs *R* and *r* as well as *Y* and *y* must separate and go into different cells. *R* may pair with *Y* to form *RY* or *R* may pair with *y*, resulting in *Ry*. Similarly, *r* may pair with *Y* to form *rY* or with *y* to form *ry*. The nature of the offspring in such a cross depends on which eggs and sperms happen to unite during fertilization.

The possible offspring which may result from such a cross and the ratio of their occurrence may be diagramed as in the case of a single character, except that space must be provided for more possible crosses. The diagram in Fig. 48-4 shows the result of such a cross. One of the parents was pure round green (*RRyy*), while the other was pure wrinkled yellow (*rrYY*). You will note

that all the **F₁** generation are alike, being hybrid round yellow (*RrYy*). In the **F₂** generation, however, four different kinds of individuals have been produced as follows:

Nine have seeds which are round and yellow (both dominant traits).

Three have seeds which are round and green (one dominant and one recessive trait).

Three have seeds which are wrinkled and yellow (one recessive and one dominant trait).

One has seeds which are wrinkled and green (both recessive traits).

You will note, too, that yellow seeds may be either *pure yellow* or *hybrid yellow;* also that round seeds may be either *pure round* or *hybrid round.* The only case where a recessive character shows is when both genes for the reces-

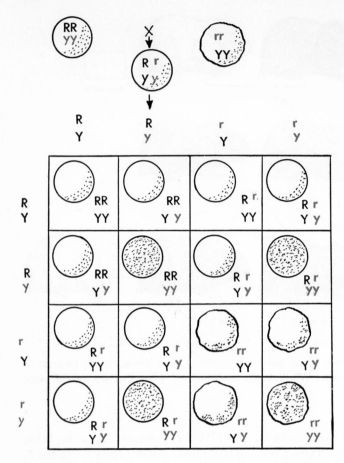

Fig. 48-4. This table shows two generations resulting from a dihybrid cross. The female genes are printed across the top of the table, those of the male are printed down the left side of the table. Dominant genes appear in black, while recessive ones are shown in color.

sive character are present. Both recessive characters appeared only once in the 16 possibilities.

When hybrid black, rough-coated guinea pigs are crossed (black and rough are dominant), similar results are obtained. Nine are black and rough, three are black and smooth, three are white and rough, and one is white and smooth.

Mendel's Law of Unit Characters. In working with more than one set of contrasting characters involving more than one pair of determiners, Mendel found that characteristics are *units* and that different ones bear no relationship to each other. For example, a pair of factors controlling color, as yellow and green in pea seeds, operates entirely in-

dependently of those which control tallness and shortness or the wrinkled and smooth seed coats. In other words, a pea which is hybrid for color but pure for tall (*YyTT*) will show a 3:1 ratio for color when crossed, even though all individuals will be tall. Thus, the individual determiners, and not the group as a whole, illustrate dominance and segregation. Mendel established this fact in his *Law of Unit Characters.*

Blended characters. Genes are not always dominant or recessive. In some cases, different genes of a pair may both appear in a blended character. This blending, or *incomplete dominance,* as it is called, may be illustrated in crossing the flowers of four-o'clocks, zinnias, and some other plants.

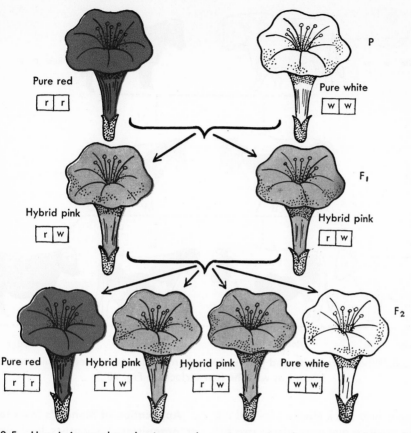

Fig. 48-5. How is incomplete dominance shown in crossing these pure red four-o'clocks with pure white ones?

When *pure red* four-o'clocks (*rr*) are crossed with *pure white* (*ww*) varieties, all of the first generation are *pink* (*rw*). Neither red nor white is completely dominant. The result is that both colors appear in the hybrid ***F₁*** as a blend which is pink. However, when two of these hybrid pink (*rw*) flowers are crossed, the next generation includes ¼ red, ½ pink, and ¼ white individuals. The fact that red and white genes actually did not mix in the pink hybrid is indicated in the fact that both appear again as pure genes in the second generation (see Fig. 48-5).

Similarly, color in shorthorn cattle is inherited in this way. A *pure red* ani-

mal crossed with a *pure white* animal results in a mixture of red and white called *roan*. When two roan animals are crossed, ¼ of the offspring are red, ½ are roan, and ¼ are white. This again illustrates the 1:2:1 ratio. (See Fig. 48-6.)

Ratios are based on averages. The ratios obtained in breeding experiments represent *averages* and not definite numbers that will always appear if the group is small. They are accurate *only when large numbers of individuals are considered*. For example, two roan shorthorns bred four times will not necessarily produce one red calf, two roan ones, and a white one.

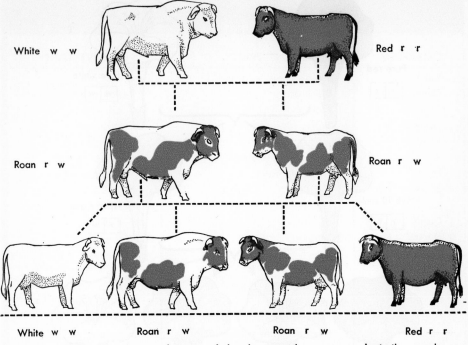

White w w   Red r r

Roan r w   Roan r w

White w w   Roan r w   Roan r w   Red r r

Fig. 48-6. When pure white and pure red shorthorn cattle are crossed, similar results are shown as with the four-o'clocks in Fig. 48-5.

Two hybrid black guinea pigs will not always produce one pure black, two hybrid blacks, and one white. If only four eggs and four sperms were involved in the process, the ratio would work out. But actually, the eggs may be more or less than four in number and the sperms usually number in the millions. Thus it becomes entirely a matter of chance as to how the eggs and sperms will unite.

Chance ratios may best be illustrated with two coins. If you flip two coins, they will light in these possible combinations: two heads, one head and one tail, or two tails. There is twice the chance of one head and one tail appearing as two heads or two tails. Consequently, if you flip them many times, they should appear in a ratio of 1 (two heads) :2 (one head and one tail) :1 (two tails). The exact ratio will only appear after flipping many times.

Application of Mendel's laws to other organisms. Scientists have worked with numerous traits of plants and animals, and the truth of the Mendelian laws is beyond question. There is overwhelming evidence that in humans, too, inheritance follows the Mendelian laws. But it is impossible to experiment on humans. Therefore, geneticists have difficulty in finding purebreds and in knowing what traits are the contrasting ones. The table on page 633 lists some of the observations which have been made concerning characteristics of various organisms.

Determination of sex. Sex is determined at the time of fertilization. This is shown by the fact that identical twins, which began life as one individual but became separated in the two-celled stage, are always of the same sex.

Determination of sex is *purely the re-*

CHARACTERISTICS OF VARIOUS ORGANISMS		
ORGANISM	DOMINANT TRAIT	RECESSIVE TRAIT
Corn	Yellow grain	White grain
Corn	Black grain	Yellow grain
Tomato	Tall stem	Short stem
Tomato	Spherical shape	Oval shape
Wheat	Late ripening	Early ripening
Wheat	Susceptibility to rust	Immunity to rust
Fowls	Black plumage	Yellow plumage
Fowls	Crest	No crest
Cattle	Hornless	Horned
Cattle	Black coat	Red coat
Horses	Trotting	Pacing
Humans	Brown eyes	Blue eyes
	Curly hair	Straight hair
	Fused fingers	Normal fingers
	Extra digits	Normal digits
	Normal growth	General dwarfing
	Normal pigmentation	Albinism
	Normal mentality	Mental defectiveness
	Normal hearing and speech	Deaf-mutism
	Normal sight	Blindness at birth

sult of a chance union of sperm and egg. Actually, in human beings and many animals, it is determined by the sperm alone. Two of the chromosomes in the cells of females are called **X-chromosomes.** The cells of males, however, have only one X-chromosome, and, in addition, have what is called a **Y-chromosome.**

When an oocyte becomes an egg, there is a reduction in the number of chromosomes due to meiosis. Each egg cell receives an X-chromosome. A similar reduction occurs when sperms are formed. Since each spermatocyte always contains one X-chromosome and one Y-chromosome, half of the sperms will receive an X-chromosome, while the other half will lack the X and will receive the Y-chromosome. If the egg is fertilized by a sperm with an X-chromosome, the fertilized egg will have two X-chromosomes and will be female. If, however, the sperm happens to be lacking an X-chromosome, but has a Y-chromosome, the fertilized egg will develop into a male.

Sex determination may be shown easily by the following diagram.

SEX DETERMINATION		
Female → Chromosomes Male ↓	X	X
X	XX	XX
Y	XY	XY

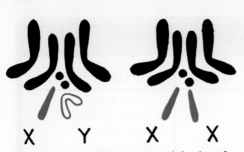

Fig. 48-7. Sex chromosomes of the fruit fly, *Drosophila*. There are two groups of chromosomes in the fruit fly. The sex cells of the female (right) include two straight X-chromosomes. The sex cells of the male (left) have one straight X-chromosome and one bent Y-chromosome. In mating, combinations of XX-chromosomes produce females. Combinations of XY-chromosomes produce males.

Although sex is *determined* at the time of fertilization, it may be altered under certain unusual conditions. These are due to stimuli called **primary sex determiners.** Destruction of an X-chromosome would most certainly alter sex. Sometimes chemical changes occur in the egg due to variations in temperature, nutrition, or other causes which affect an X-chromosome and thus change the sex. Occasionally, sex reversal occurs in animals during embryonic development, or even later, due to changes in the sex glands or variations in hormone production. These instances are, however, all very rare.

Sex-linked characters. Certain characters seem to be carried in the X-chromosome by means of genes which are recessive in the presence of a normal X-chromosome. These characters may be carried in a female without appearing because only one of the X-chromosomes is carrying the gene. In the male, however, such a gene causes a characteristic to appear because only one X-chromosome is present. *Color blindness* and "*bleeder's disease*," or *hemophilia*

(hee-moh-*fee*-lee-ah), are examples of sex-linked characters. They appear much more frequently in males than in females.

Mutations. Occasionally an offspring appears with a characteristic which was not inherited, but which can be passed on to future generations. This new characteristic is called a **mutation,** and the individual possessing it is called a **mutant.**

One of the most common examples of mutation is illustrated in albino organisms which are completely lacking in color. Apparently the genes for color are destroyed or altered in such a way that they do not function. This characteristic will remain and can be passed on to new generations, although it may not reappear immediately due to its recessive nature.

Albino animals are always white and have pink eyes. The white body covering is normal except that it lacks any pigmentation. The eyes, too, are normal but lack coloring in the iris so that the blood in the capillaries will give them a reddish appearance. You have seen albinos in the form of white rabbits, white rats, and white mice. All these animals, if they are true albinos, have pink eyes. In addition to these forms which are well-known, albino squirrels, woodchucks, raccoons, deer, robins, crows, sparrows, and other kinds of animals have been found although they are very rare. Albino humans are characterized by having very light skin, pure white hair, and pink eyes.

Other mutations have occurred from time to time in cattle. Occasionally, a calf belonging to a horned breed is born without horns. From such mutations, hornless, or polled, breeds have been developed, including the Aberdeen-Angus and polled shorthorn. Other mutations include tailless dogs, and hogs with

Fig. 48-8.   New variations, or mutations, due to changes in genes appear in plants and animals.   The albino robin has white feathers and pink eyes.

" mule " feet, that is single hoofs rather than normal split hoofs.

Causes of mutations.   The principles of mutation, in which genes may be lost or new combinations of genes may appear, were discovered by a famous biologist of recent years, Thomas Hunt Morgan.   Much of his work was done with the fruit fly (*Drosophila*), a tiny insect which has been used extensively in research in genetics since his time.

In 1946, the Nobel Prize was awarded to another American scientist working in the field of genetics, Dr. H. J. Muller of Indiana University.   Dr. Muller discovered that exposure of fruit flies to X-rays caused various mutations. One mutation he produced was a change in eye color.   A normal fruit fly with red eyes produced offspring with white eyes after exposure to X-ray.   In further studies, Dr. Muller produced mu-

tants with entirely different body hair, wings, and eye structure.   In fact, he produced a series of monstrosities the like of which has never been seen.   And having produced the change, he found that all offspring bore the new characteristics, since the X-rays had altered the gene structure.

The rays given off by radium and other radioactive substances also influence or destroy genes and cause mutations.   This creates a serious problem for those who work in atomic installations where they might be exposed to radiation.   In most cases, human mutations are fatal, causing death of a baby before birth.   A mutation may result if radiation penetrates the ovaries or testes. For this reason, people who work with radioactive material and X-rays should use extra precaution to shield their bodies from radiation.

Lethal genes. Occasionally, characteristics appear which result in death of the organism. For example, geranium and corn seedlings have been discovered which are entirely lacking chlorophyll. Normally they could not live because the lack of chlorophyll means lack of the ability to make food by photosynthesis. However, if such colorless seedlings are partly woody and are grafted to normal plants as in the case of geranium, food may be obtained and the colorless plants may even bloom. This lethal character has been proved to be recessive in every case which has been studied.

Other lethal characteristics have been found in animals. When they appear, usually during its period of development, the animal dies suddenly. The characters are transmitted as recessive ones. They appear only when both of the parents are carrying recessive genes for the trait and the offspring happens to receive a recessive gene from each one of the parents.

Biologists have discovered lethal characteristics in many different kinds of animals. Among them are mice, chickens, hogs, and certain breeds of cattle. They have also been known to occur in man.

In Conclusion

Who would have thought that an Austrian monk, working with peas in a monastery garden, would have made a discovery important enough to introduce a new branch of biology? This was the genius of Gregor Mendel. Among his tall peas and short ones, those with round seeds and wrinkled ones, green pods and yellow pods, he discovered that variations appeared in an orderly manner. Laws seemed to control the heredity of those peas — laws which were so exact, he could even predict the particular kind of peas which might grow from a handful of seeds.

Remarkable indeed was this pioneer in genetics. We have gone far beyond Mendel, but we have never revised his understanding of the Laws of Dominance, Segregation, and Unit Characters.

As we continue our study of genetics, we will apply the principles of heredity to our own inheritance.

Questions for Review

1. (a) List seven pairs of contrasting traits Mendel found in garden peas. (b) Which ones are dominant?

2. Black is dominant in guinea pigs. How is a pure black different from a hybrid black, even though the guinea pigs look alike?

3. When two hybrids are crossed, pure dominant, hybrid dominant, and pure recessive individuals appear. How does this illustrate the Law of Segregation?

4. When two parents which are hybrid for one character are crossed, what ratio of offspring will show the dominant character and how many will show the recessive character?

5. In breeding experiments, why do the ratios obtained represent averages rather than definite numbers?

6. How does the Law of Unit Characters operate in heredity?

7. In what way is blending or incom-

plete dominance an exception to the Law of Dominance?

8. Why do red-green color-blindness and hemophilia occur much more frequently in males than in females?

9. Give an example of mutation and distinguish a mutation from an inherited character.

10. Name some of the most common causes of mutations.

11. When lethal genes are present, death of the organism usually results. Why?

Biologically Speaking

albino	incomplete dominance	mutation
blended character	Law of Dominance	primary sex determiner
dihybrid	Law of Segregation	pure characteristic
dominant character	Law of Unit Characters	recessive character
F_1	lethal gene	sex-linked character
F_2	monohybrid	X-chromosome
hybrid	mutant	Y-chromsome

Applying Facts and Principles

1. Outline a possible cross to determine whether a black guinea pig is a pure black or a hybrid black.

2. How can you disprove the idea that some people have that the father determines the sex of a male child, while the sex of the female is determined by the mother?

3. Why have scientists been concerned about people who work in atomic research having children?

4. Why should a hybridizer know which traits are dominant or recessive?

5. Lethal genes are rare in plants and animals. Give at least one reason to account for this.

CHAPTER 49

Genetics Applied to Human Inheritance

The same laws and principles which govern heredity in plants and animals apply to human inheritance. However, human inheritance, in many instances, is far more difficult to study. For one thing, being thinking and reasoning organisms we respond more to environmental conditions than other forms of life. Genes may determine certain of our facial characteristics, but cares and worries, satisfaction and contentment leave their mark, too. Similarly, genes may influence certain characteristics of the form and size of the body. But so do the diet, the general health, and other environmental influences. None of your genetic make-up is quite as simple as tall or short in peas, or black or white in guinea pigs. Factors are often complex, and environmental influences make them even more so.

Much attention has been given to human inheritance in recent years. A specialized branch of genetics, called **eugenics** (you-*jen*-icks) is now an organized science. It deals entirely with human inheritance.

Galton, the founder of eugenics. Eugenics dates its beginnings from 1883 when Sir Francis Galton pointed out the need for such a science. He even gave it the name, *eugenics,* which means literally " good birth." Galton himself defined it as " the science which deals with all influences that improve the inborn qualities of a race."

He studied the family records of many English families and concluded that mental ability, scholarship, moral strength, and weakness were subject to heredity just as were physical traits, such as *size* and *eye color.* He based these ideas on the results of numerous case histories and mathematical investigations he had conducted in the field of heredity.

Today we know that a good many of Galton's ideas were incorrect since he did not have the benefit of Mendel's work. While Galton was mistaken in some of his conclusions concerning human inheritance, he was correct in others.

The nature of human heredity. The heredity of man is essentially like that of any other organism. Characteristics of the human race are carried by genes which are borne on the *48 chromosomes* present in every cell. Furthermore, the genes are always paired in the same way as chromosomes are paired. A pair of genes concerned with a particular characteristic is located in identical places on corresponding chromosomes.

Human inheritance is difficult to trace for several reasons. For one thing, human characters are frequently not controlled by a single pair of genes as in the case of tallness and dwarfness in peas. In the human eye, for example, two colors seem to be involved. The infant's eye is blue, but in many individuals a brown layer appears later, resulting in a change in eye color. It seems that the number of genes present for brown determines the shade of the eyes. They may range from deep brown to shades of hazel, and greenish-blue to pure blue. This would indicate the presence of numerous genes, each exerting a definite influence on the color of the eyes.

Another complicating factor in human inheritance is the fact that most people come from a mixed ancestry. This means that few, if any, characters are pure. Therefore, it is almost impossible to trace one characteristic through a family. Each time a marriage occurs, two families of entirely different genetic background are combined in the offspring.

The use of case histories in studying human inheritance. Mendel was able to trace the inheritance of garden peas through several generations within a few years. Other investigators have used fruit flies, rabbits, and guinea pigs because they, too, mature rapidly and can produce several generations of offspring in a relatively short time. But any one person can observe only three or four generations of human beings within a lifetime. Many times that number of generations would be necessary to demonstrate the principles governing human inheritance.

For this reason, the *eugenist* (you-*jen*-ist) makes use of case histories in the study of human families. Eugenics is a young science and a case history soon outdates the science itself. Many descriptions of individuals of several generations ago may have been inaccurate and unreliable. The eugenist must take this into consideration in tracing various physical and mental characteristics through a family by the case history method.

Much has been learned from the study of twins. Twins are of two types. *Fraternal twins,* the more common type, are two entirely different individuals. Often they are brother and sister. They develop from separate eggs which were fertilized by different sperm. They are no more closely related than any other brothers or sisters in a family. Fraternal twins usually live in identical environments. Yet they may be totally different in physical characteristics, personality, emotional make-up, and mental ability. These variations are valuable in helping to find out just what kinds of characteristics are hereditary and which ones are environmental.

Identical twins have been the subject of many interesting studies in human inheritance. Identical twins are nearly the same person *in duplicate.* They started life as the same fertilized egg. But after the first division, the two cells separated and started growth over again. Sometimes this happens several times, resulting in identical triplets, quadruplets, or quintuplets.

Having started life as the same cell, identical twins have the same genetic make-up. Consequently, the similarities in identical twins indicate, for the most part, characteristics controlled by genes. Identical twins show a marked likeness not only in appearance, but in temperament, abilities, likes and dislikes, and many other personality traits.

Several studies have been made of identical twins who were separated early in life and reared in different environments. In cases like these, home and family life, education, day-to-day experiences, friendships, and other environmental influences leave their mark on the personality of each. But the two persons usually remain amazingly alike in appearance, basic personality traits, and capacity for learning.

Fig. 49-1. Since identical twins started life as the same cell, they show many physical and mental similarities.

Can acquired skills be inherited? Man, more than any other organism, adjusts his life to his surroundings. High mentality makes these adjustments possible. The complex nature of human society requires that each individual develop his inherited abilities in the form of trades, skills, and professions. One may become a lawyer, a doctor, a musician, a carpenter, or a mechanic as a result of a long period of training and practice. The question is whether these acquired skills are transmitted to the offspring in any degree.

To answer this question, we must examine very carefully the nature of the skill. Certain individuals inherit tendencies which lead them toward a particular kind of activity. Certain characteristics such as coordination of finger movements essential in musical ability may be inherited, but a musician is the product of long hours of practice. Only the inherited, or native ability, may be passed onto the next generation. If such an ability is inherited but, for some reason, never developed further during life, the same ability may still be passed on to the next generation.

If on the other hand, the individual uses his inherited ability to become a great musician, he will have in no way improved the inheritance of his children in that respect. In like manner, the acquired skills of great lawyers or expert mechanics cannot be passed on to the next generation. However, certain inborn characteristics, which had an important influence on the success of these individuals, may be passed on.

Is prenatal influence possible? Have you ever heard of a baby supposedly being "marked" before birth because of some thought or experience of the mother during its development? This idea has been handed down from early times as part of the superstition associated with human inheritance.

Many people today believe in such *prenatal influence.*

According to this belief, prenatal influence could be either good or bad. If a mother wanted her child to be a musician, she might cause him to acquire musical genius by listening to music and attending concerts before his birth.

Thoughts, emotional upsets, and experiences, either good or bad, can in no way alter the heredity of a developing child. The heredity was determined at the time of the union of the egg and sperm before development started.

Inheritance of desirable and undesirable traits. Among the traits known to be inherited in the human race are eye color, skin color, and body stature. Others include the structure and color of the hair, length of the limbs, shape of the hands, finger length, facial features, and other factors which determine the form of the body. It is features such as these that we notice in family resemblances. In addition to these physical traits, there is evidence that personality traits, native intelligence, and aptitudes may be inherited. These characteristics are more difficult to determine and to trace than physical traits.

Finger deformities, including extra fingers, fingers grown together, and fingers lacking one bone occur as dominant traits. Other unfortunate defects include blindness from birth and deaf-mutism. These characteristics are carried by recessive genes or by genes which express a characteristic more in some people than in others. When paired with normal genes, the traits usually do not appear. For this reason, many undesirable traits in humans do not appear when genes are mixed in the offspring of unrelated people. On the other hand, close intermarriage tends to

Fig. 49-2. Six fingers are an inherited dominant characteristic. In certain areas of the world, there are instances where all members of a family have inherited this trait.

make these characteristics appear more frequently.

Sex-linked characteristics in the human race. The genes for certain characteristics are carried on the X-chromosomes which function also in the determination of sex. Several abnormal characteristics are carried by recessive genes on the X-chromosomes.

Red-green color blindness, a condition in which these colors appear as shades of gray, is a sex-linked characteristic. The gene for color blindness is carried on an X-chromosome, but it is recessive to a normal gene on another X-chromosome. Thus, a female can carry a gene for color blindness (X') on one chromosome and a normal gene on the other (X). Such an individual (X'X) will not show the characteristic,

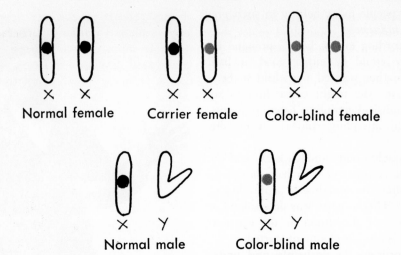

Fig. 49-3. Color blindness is a sex-linked characteristic. The gene for color blindness is carried on an X-chromosome.

but will transmit it to offspring. In the case of a male, however, only one X-chromosome is present. Hence, a single color-blind gene combined with a Y-chromosome, lacking a gene for the character (X'Y), will produce the defect. This explains why red-green color blindness is much more common in males than in females.

Fig. 49-3 shows the genes on X-chromosomes of a normal female, one carrying color blindness, and a color-blind female as well as a normal male and a color-blind male. The diagram below shows how a female parent, carrying a gene for color blindness but not showing the trait, may produce a color-blind

son even though the male parent is not color-blind.

The ratio in such a cross will be one female carrying color blindness; one normal female; one color-blind male; one normal male.

If a color-blind male marries a normal female, color blindness will not appear in any of the offspring, although all the females will carry the trait as a recessive gene. The diagram is below.

INHERITANCE OF SEX—LINKED CHARACTERS		
Female → Sex chromosomes Male ↓	X	X
X'	XX'	XX'
Y	XY	XY

INHERITANCE OF SEX—LINKED CHARACTERS		
Female → Sex chromosomes Male ↓	X'	X
X	X'X	XX
Y	X'Y	XY

By diagraming a cross between a color-blind male and a female carrying a recessive gene for the character, you will discover how color blindness may appear in a female. Similarly, a color-blind female crossed with a normal male will produce all color-blind males, but with no females showing the trait, although all are carrying it. Two color-blind individuals will have all color-blind offspring.

Hemophilia, or bleeder's disease, operates in the same way as color blindness.

Hemophilia is the result of an inherited abnormality in the character of the blood. Normally, blood clots when exposed to the air. Clotting causes formation of a scab which stops the flow of blood through severed blood vessels. In the case of hemophilia, the blood does not clot properly due to the absence of fibrinogen, and bleeding may continue for a long time. Death from loss of blood may occur as a result of slight wounds.

Hemophilia tends to run in families and to appear in males. It can appear in a female only when the father is a bleeder and the mother either has the disease or is a carrier.

Other characteristics associated with sex. Certain genes produce a character in one sex or the other, but not in both, even though they are carried in both sexes. In this respect, *sex-limited characters* are different from *sex-linked characters*. It seems that sex-limited characters develop only in the presence of sex hormones. The characteristics of the beard is a good example. A boy may inherit a heavy beard with a coarse growth around his chin and upper lip from his mother's side of the family. The mother never developed the trait. Nor did the son until he reached sexual maturity and started producing male hormones in his reproductive organs. Other examples of sex-limited characters include the bright plumage of certain male birds which does not appear in females of the same species. The roosters of most breeds of chickens develop a large comb and wattles and characteristic male plumage, while hens of the same breed develop a different kind of female plumage. Both result from the influence that sex hormones have on genes for these characteristics that are present in the variety.

Baldness is an example of a human *sex-influenced character*. In this case, the gene for baldness is dominant in males but recessive in females. Thus a mother may transmit baldness to her son without showing it herself. If we represent a gene for baldness as *B* and normal growth of hair as *b,* then a *Bb* male would be bald, while a *Bb* female would have normal hair. However, *BB* would represent a male or female with baldness, while *bb* would produce a normal male and female. This explains why baldness is more common in men than in women.

Inheritance of blood type. In the mention of blood types in Chapter 37, we referred to them as type *A, B, AB,* or *O.* These letters refer to a protein substance known as an **antigen** (*an*-tih-jen). Some people have type *A* antigen, while others have type *B.* Some have both (*AB*) while others have neither (*OO*). Blood type is an inherited characteristic, controlled by three kinds of genes.

If you have type *A* blood, you could have received an *A* gene from each parent (*AA*) or an *A* gene from one parent and a recessive gene (*O*) from the other (*AO*). Similarly, a person with type *B* blood may have *BB* genes or *BO* genes. If one parent transmits an *A* gene and the other a *B* gene, the offspring (*AB*) will produce both antigens, since neither is dominant over the other. Type *O* blood, lacking both antigens, results when neither dominant gene is present (*OO*).

Inheritance of the *Rh* factor. At least four pairs of genes are involved in inheritance of the *Rh* factor. There is evidence that as many as six pairs of genes may be involved. An *Rh* negative person lacks all dominant genes which produce the various *Rh* antigens. *Rh* positive persons have various combinations of dominant genes which produce the *Rh* antigens. For this reason, it is difficult to diagram the results of crosses between various *Rh* types.

Inheritance of mental ability. This phase of eugenics is complicated. For one thing, mental ability is difficult to determine. How much of what we call intelligence is hereditary and how much environmental is hard to measure.

One of the modern methods of determining mental ability is by the administration of *intelligence tests.* These are intended to evaluate the mental processes of the individual in various ways. The score on the intelligence test is used to calculate the *mental age.* Intelligence is then determined by dividing the mental age by the actual, or *chronological,* age. The result, multiplied by 100, is the *intelligence quotient,* or *I.Q.* A normal, or average, I.Q. is considered to be 100.

Actually, this method contains many flaws due to variable factors. The general physical and mental conditions such as slight illness or mental strain of the person taking an intelligence test may affect his mental processes temporarily. Furthermore, no test has yet been devised which will eliminate completely the effects of environment.

We must consider, too, that the mental age and I.Q. of a person may change through the years. Many children are late in maturing, both physically and mentally, but finally " catch up " with their chronological ages. Thus, a child may have a below normal I.Q. in ele-

mentary school, a normal I.Q. in high school, and a superior I.Q. in his college years and adult life.

Man's intelligence allows him to expand his environment. Man's intelligence has enabled him to solve many of his own problems and even to modify his environment to suit himself. He has worked constantly toward a better understanding of his life, his world, and his universe. For example, man has extended his habitat from a localized area to a nation, to the world, and is on the verge of extending it into outer space. Each time man expands his environment, he encounters new problems. Now that we are in the **Space Age,** let's look at the biological problems to be solved for the space traveler.

Effects of acceleration upon leaving the earth's atmosphere. In order for a vehicle to leave the gravitational field of the earth, a speed of about 25,000 miles per hour must be attained. We know that the problems of physics and chemistry involved in such a feat are being solved when we recall that the first attempt to propel a rocket to the moon was made with *Pioneer* in October, 1958.

One of the biological factors involved in man's conquest of space is that of the effects of acceleration, or the rate of change of speed. When you are taking off in an airplane or even starting up your car, you can feel your body press slightly into the back of the seat. This force that you feel is measured in units called **G's,** which have the effect of increasing your weight. At a force of two G's, for example, your body would weigh twice what it normally does. A pilot making diving or gunning runs usually blacks out between five and seven G's because the heart cannot pump sufficient blood to the brain against the extreme force of acceleration. However, recent experiments indicate that men lying down can take from 14 to 20 G's without blacking out. The rockets now in use seldom exceed 10 G's during their greatest acceleration, so that physicists now think acceleration in space is not the problem it was once thought to be.

Respiration — a vital problem. Respiration problems at high altitudes were discussed on pages 495 and 496. The space traveler would encounter the same problems, but to a greater degree, because after an altitude of about 70 miles there is no atmosphere and therefore no oxygen. Either the entire cabin of the space ship must be supplied with oxygen or masks connected to oxygen tanks must be worn. Also, the carbon dioxide which results from respiration will have to be disposed of.

A decrease in pressure. At sea-level, the weight of the great ocean of air presses on us to the extent of 14.7 pounds per square inch. We are not aware of this weight because our bodies are adapted to it. When we climb a mountain or fly in an airplane, however, the pressure is less than that on the surface of the earth, as there is less air above us. In a rocket, the results of this decrease in pressure could be drastic, because at altitudes above 60,000 feet, the blood would boil at normal body temperature. This means that the gases, normally dissolved in blood, would form bubbles. These bubbles would tear through capillaries and damage delicate brain tissue, resulting in death. This particular problem of our space adventure might be solved by having a pressurized cabin such as is used in modern aircraft, or pressurized suits which would maintain a nearly normal pressure, in order that the physiological processes might continue.

Extreme temperature changes. The temperature on the earth seldom falls below 0° F or rises above 100° F, because of the water vapor in the atmosphere which exerts a moderating effect. Throughout the year the average temperatures on the earth's surface are between 50 and 60° F. The space ship, on the other hand, would encounter very high temperatures on the surface nearest the sun, and extremely low temperatures on the side away from the sun. But physicists believe that imparting a slight spin to the ship might distribute these temperatures evenly. The greater temperature problem might well come in trying to insulate the ship against the extreme heat generated by friction between the ship and the atmosphere of the earth or other planets.

Radiation problems. In outer space there is no atmosphere to protect the space traveler from the ultraviolet rays of the sun or from cosmic rays which constantly bombard objects. The earth satellites are at present giving us more data on the extent of these radiations, so that we may learn how to protect the space traveler from them.

Psychological effects. Men traveling in space will need sufficient food to sustain them until the return to earth. However, instruments and fuel to allow for a return trip must make up the greatest weight of the rocket. Hence the food supply will have to be basic nutrients in their most condensed form — not a very tasty menu!

The sense of weightlessness experienced outside the earth's gravitational field, cramped quarters, and the long period of time needed for space travel will require only well-adjusted, very stable crew-members in perfect physical condition. These requirements and other problems are now being studied by physicians and scientists who are conducting exhaustive research on the factors involved in space travel.

In Conclusion

There never was a combination of genes just like those you carry in the chromosomes of every cell of your body. Each of those billions of cells is distinctly you. Each is carrying your potential as an individual. What use will you make of your heredity? It is largely up to you. Lying in those tiny chromosomes may be genes bearing artistic talent, mechanical aptitude, athletic ability, or the qualities of great leadership. But genes alone will never produce the fine quality. This requires education, training, practice, and experience.

 ## Questions for Review

1. What contribution did Sir Francis Galton make to the science of genetics?

2. Why are case histories essential to the study of human inheritance?

3. How does inheritance of human eye color and skin color indicate the presence of several pairs of genes?

4. (a) Can acquired skills be inherited? (b) Explain your answer.

5. How can an apparently normal mother transmit color blindness to her son?

6. Under what conditions might a female with hemophilia be produced?

7. Explain the relation of sex hormones to sex-limited characters.

8. How many kinds of antigens are involved in the common blood groups, A, B, AB, and O?

9. How might a space traveler be affected by the decrease in pressure?

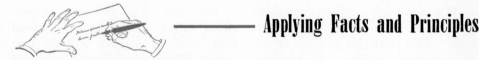 ## Biologically Speaking

acceleration	fraternal twins	mental age
acquired skill	G's	sex-influenced character
antigen	hemophilia	sex-limited character
chronological age	identical twins	sex-linked character
eugenics	intelligence quotient	

 ## Applying Facts and Principles

1. How have identical twins supplied valuable data in the study of human heredity?

2. Distinguish between musical ability and musical skill and discuss the possible inheritance of either or both.

3. Using what you have learned about heredity, prove that prenatal influences from the external environment do not exist.

4. Explain how baldness is a sex-influenced character.

5. Why would a space traveler experience a sense of weightlessness? What might be done to decrease this sense?

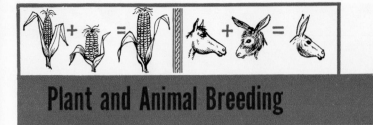

CHAPTER 50

Plant and Animal Breeding

Selective breeding of plants and animals is an old practice. For centuries, man has made a constant effort to improve the varieties of plants and animals which supply his daily needs. Wheat was grown as a cereal crop by the early Egyptians. Garden flowers, fruit trees, domestic fowl, sheep, goats, cattle, and many other plants and animals have been domesticated longer than recorded history.

Genetics originated largely to explain the phenomena which resulted from plant and animal breeding. Selective breeding was a practice of chance selection rather than scientific application of principles. With the development of genetics as a science, established laws have greatly improved the efficiency of the process.

The laws of heredity when applied directly to plant and animal breeding are not always exact because of the extreme complexity of the inheritance of organisms. Not one or two, but hundreds of different characteristics are involved in each cross.

Luther Burbank, the genius of California. Plant breeding will always be associated with the genius of Luther Burbank. He produced many new and different plants on his farm in California.

Burbank's brilliant work began in the summer of 1871 in his native Massachusetts. While a young man, he was examining a crop of potatoes one day and happened to notice a fruit maturing on one of the plants. This was an unusual occurrence because the potato plant flowers regularly but seldom bears fruit. New plants are grown from cuttings rather than from actual seeds. Burbank saved that fruit.

When the seeds ripened, he planted each one in a separate hill. After the plants matured, he dug the potatoes and discovered that those from each plant were different. Some were large, some were small. Some hills had many tubers, while others had only a few. One hill had far better potatoes than any of the others. These were large, smooth, and numerous. Burbank sold them to a gardener for $150 — his first profit from plant breeding. They were named Burbank potatoes in his honor, and were the first of a strain which was destined to become popular all over the country.

With the profit from his first achievement, Burbank bought a ticket to California where he established the farm that made him famous. From his experimental gardens came such varieties as the Shasta daisy and a new strain of poppies. By combining various fruits, he produced the plumcot, pitless plum, and the improved beach plum. Another of his famous developments is the thin-shelled walnut. The spineless cactus, used as fodder for cattle, is still another of his achievements.

Fig. 50-1. The cabbage plants on the left are affected with the disease known as " yel-lows " or " wilt." The plant on the right is healthy. The development of disease-resistant plants has greatly helped to increase our food supply.

Objectives in plant breeding. The plant breeder has several purposes in producing new strains or varieties of plants. One of the chief objectives is the production of *more desirable varieties*. Such characteristics as large fruit, large and abundant seeds, vigorous growth, early maturation of fruit, large leaf area in leafy vegetables, and vigorous root growth in root crops are highly profitable. Plant breeders work constantly to improve the quality and quantity of the yield of all crop plants. In addition to the nature of the yield, resistance to disease is highly important. Plant breeders also have been able to produce many varieties of *disease-resistant crops*.

A third objective is an *extension of crop areas* through the production of new varieties. Wheat is an example of this extension through plant breeding. Varieties of spring wheat grow well in the northern sections of the nation, while winter wheat favors the climate of the central states. Wheat growing has been extended even to the Great Plains by the production of varieties of hard wheat. In a similar way, other crops which were once limited to small areas because of climatic requirements or soil conditions have now been ex-

tended to many other regions in the form of new varieties.

By means of hybridization, entirely *different kinds of plants* have been developed. The hybrid may be the result of crossing two strains or varieties or two closely related species.

Mass selection is widely used in obtaining desirable varieties. As the name implies, *mass selection* consists of the careful selection of parent plants from a great number of individuals. Burbank practiced mass selection when he discovered his famous potato. He selected the most ideal plant from all those he grew from seed. The farmer who selects seed from his own crop always picks the most desirable plants for propagation. Thus he takes advantage of any natural, desirable variations which occur.

Mass selection is important, too, in the production of disease-resistant strains of plants. To show how mass selection operates, let us assume that a cabbage disease has swept into an area, resulting in the destruction of almost all the crop. Field after field of cabbages have become victims of the disease. As we examine the acres of diseased plants, we find two or three plants which, for some unknown reason, have withstood

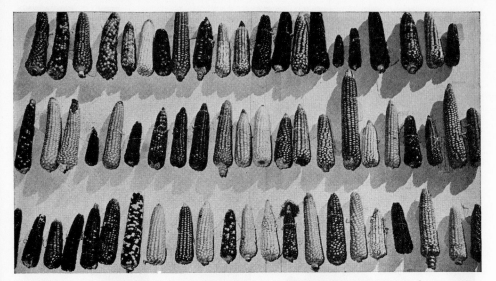

Fig. 50-2. Plant breeders have developed many varieties of corn. Notice the variation of grains which appear on certain ears of corn shown above.

the disease. We carefully preserve the seeds from these plants and sow them the following season. Disease again strikes the crop, but a few more plants remain than the year before. Again, we use these plants for seed in the following season. Each year, more and more plants withstand the disease. The character of disease-resistance, present in the original plant, becomes more and more strongly established in the offspring. Finally, an entire strain is developed in which this character appears.

What is hybridization? We define *hybridization* as the crossing of two different varieties to obtain a new one. It is like mass selection in some ways because desirable traits are always sought. But it is a more rapid way of getting the desired results than selection of natural variations.

In hybridization, characteristics of two unlike, but closely related, parents are combined in a new individual by artificial cross-breeding or outbreeding. In getting a new hybrid strain, we might choose one parent because of

vigorous growth. The other one might be selected because of the fine quality of its fruit or flower. Often a hybrid possesses qualities not shown in either parent due to a new combination of genes.

Another advantage of hybridization is *hybrid vigor* in the offspring. Often the new hybrid has a natural vigor which neither parent had.

Line breeding is the opposite of hybridization. After the desired characteristics have been obtained by mass selection or hybridization, it then becomes a matter of propagating these new and different plants. This is a simple matter when vegetative multiplication in no way affects the hereditary make-up.

After Burbank had discovered his potato, propagation was simple. He used cuttings from the potato in order to produce more plants exactly like the parent. Had he been forced to grow more potatoes from seed, the situation would have been quite different. In the same way, the grower can propagate a new variety of apple, peach, iris, or rose by

Fig. 50-3. These two photographs show controlled pollination of corn for the production of inbred lines required for hybridizing. Top: The tassel is being covered by a bag. The pollen will then collect in this bag which is fastened at its base. Bottom: Pollen collected from a tassel is blown onto the silks. The ear is then covered with a bag before and after pollination to prevent contamination with pollen of other strains of corn.

grafting, cutting, or budding without altering its hereditary make-up.

In the case of plants like corn and wheat where seeds must be used for propagation, the problem is more difficult. Seed production involves a mixing of numerous characters. Plants produced from seeds are not necessarily like the parent, especially when they are crop plants which have been crossed by man for centuries.

The way you can overcome this difficulty is by generations of **line breeding**, or inbreeding. This is the opposite of hybridization, or **outbreeding**. Self-pollination is carried on to avoid introducing any new characteristics from a new plant. Seeds resulting from self-pollination are planted and all individuals of the new generation are carefully sorted. Only those with the desired characteristics of the parent are selected as seed plants for the next generation. Again, self-pollination is carried on, after which the resulting plants are carefully sorted.

As you repeat this breeding method generation after generation, more and more plants bear the desired characteristics. Eventually, a pure strain which will be true to seed is established and is ready for the market. Even then all plants may not produce the pure strain characteristics, but these individuals can be readily sorted out.

The production of hybrid corn. Years ago a farmer saved some of the best ears from his corn crop as seed for the next year. By the process of mass selection, he tried to produce more corn like his best plants of the previous season. But the plants which bore these ears were so mixed in their heredity that only part of the kernels bore the genes which had made them productive. And with no control over pollination, the farmer had no idea about the quality of

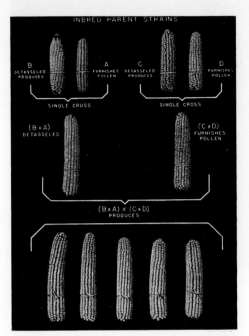

Fig. 50-4. This shows a cross in producing hybrid corn. Strain A is crossed with strain B, and strain C with strain D. The products of these crosses are then crossed to produce the hybrid corn seed. The ears at the bottom are representative of the crop produced.

the other parent. The seeds on a single ear might produce many different varieties of corn, some good and some poor. Some of the kernels might have resulted from self-pollination, while others were the result of cross-pollination from fields some distance away. It was not unusual to find ears of corn with a mixture of yellow, white, and red kernels. Often sweet corn and popcorn were mixed with kernels of field corn. Under conditions like these, a yield of 20 to 40 bushels per acre was all that could be expected.

Today hybrid varieties, produced under scientific control methods, produce from 60 to 80 bushels of corn per acre. These hybrids have large root systems, sturdy stalks, broad leaves, and large

Fig. 50-5. Selective breeding resulted in the Beltsville small turkey. It meets the needs of small families for small birds with plenty of white meat.

ears. The energy which once produced the towering stalk now produces the full, long ear.

Much of hybrid corn planted today is the result of a double-cross in which four pure line parents are mixed in two crosses. Each pure line parent has been selected because of its vigor, resistance to disease, or some other desirable trait. However, plants resulting from the double-cross are superior to any of the parent strains.

Fig. 50-4 shows how hybrid corn is produced by the double-cross method. Four inbred plants, designated as A, B, C, and D, serve as the foundation. These varieties are the result of controlled self-pollination or line breeding. This is accomplished by covering the developing ears with sacks until the silks are ready to receive pollen. Then pollen collected from the same plant is dusted onto the silks. The plant breeder carefully avoids hybridization in these inbred varieties. During the first cross, plant A is crossed with plant B.

This produces a single-cross hybrid plant $A \times B$. In making this cross, the tassel from plant B is removed and the ear is covered with a bag. When the silks are mature, they are dusted with pollen from plant A. A similar first cross is made between plant C and plant D, resulting in a single-cross hybrid, plant $C \times D$. The following season, plant $A \times B$ is detasseled. The developing ear is covered. This plant is cross-pollinated with $C \times D$. Kernels resulting from this double-cross are designated as $A \times B \times C \times D$.

This seed is sold to the farmer for planting. However, he cannot plant the seed produced by this hybrid corn because the genes will sort out in new combinations. He might get plants which would have different characteristics from those of the hybrid parents.

New plants are produced by crossing different species. One of the best known of Burbank's plant varieties is the Shasta daisy. He produced this beautiful garden flower by crossing a native ox-eye daisy with a European variety. In a cross between a plum and an apricot, he produced the plumcot. Another hybrid plant was produced by crossing the squash and the pumpkin. One of Burbank's last experiments was an attempt to cross a tomato and a potato to produce a dual purpose plant which would bear fruit above ground all season and form tubers which could be dug at the end of the season. Unfortunately, such a cross was never perfected. Many crosses of closely related species have been made in animals as well as plants.

Plant varieties resulting from mutations. While examining a bed of white tea roses one day, a grower happened to notice a branch which had produced a pink flower. He carefully removed the branch and set it in a cutting bed. The

Fig. 50-6. Selective breeding has improved livestock as well as plants. The Guernsey cow has been bred as a milk producer.

plant which grew bore all pink flowers. These were budded onto understock and propagated as a *bud-mutant,* or *sport,* of the white rose. This happens from time to time in roses and other plants. For some reason, a mutation occurs in a cell which gives rise to the tissue of a branch. If the branch is propagated vegetatively, the mutation will remain.

Other varieties which have resulted from a *bud-mutation* include the California navel orange, the Delicious apple, and the smooth-skinned peach, or nectarine.

Plants with increased chromosome numbers. Have you ever noticed blueberries on a fruit counter which are twice as large as native blueberries? These blueberries have a double set of chromosomes. Other fruits that have been produced by plants with multiple chromosome numbers include varieties of plums, cherries, grapes, strawberries, and cranberries. A similar increase in the chromosome number occurred in the McIntosh apple. Apple trees usually

have 17 pairs, or 34 chromosomes. The normal McIntosh has this number. However, one variety with a fruit more than twice as large as the normal McIntosh has four sets (tetraploid) of chromosomes, or 68 in all.

Now that breeders have *colchicine* (*kol*-cheh-seen), a chemical which artificially increases the chromosome number in plant cells, it is hard to tell how many new fruits and vegetables will be available in future years.

Animal breeding. The principles used in plant breeding apply to animal breeding as well. Mass selection has long been a method of producing highly desirable breeds of animals.

The results of years of selective breeding are well-illustrated in the modern breeds of poultry. The Leghorn, for example, has been bred for its ability to lay large numbers of eggs. All its energies are directed toward egg production rather than body flesh. The Plymouth Rock has been developed as a dual-purpose fowl and is ideal for egg-production and meat. Large breeds, like the

Fig. 50-7. The Hereford steer, with its low, broad, stocky body, provides prime beef for the consumer.

Brahma, Cochin, and Cornish, are famous for their delicious meat rather than for egg-production.

The modern turkey, with massive body and broad breast covered with thick layers of white meat, is quite a contrast to the slender bird the Pilgrims found in the New England forest. The modern turkey has been bred for the highest possible flesh production. It spends its life, often on wire, eating a scientifically prepared diet and building up large, little used muscles, better suited to the dinner table than to flying and perching high in trees.

Improvement in livestock. Using similar selective breeding methods, domestic cattle have been developed along two entirely different lines. Aberdeen-Angus, Hereford, and Shorthorn are breeds of beef cattle. Their low, broad, stocky bodies provide high-quality steaks

and roasts for the nation's markets. Dairy breeds, including the Jersey, Guernsey, Ayrshire, and Holstein-Friesian, have been bred as milk producers. A breed of Shorthorns, known as " milking Shorthorns," as well as Brown Swiss and Redpoll cattle, are classified as dual-purpose breeds because they were developed for milk production as well as beef.

Swine raising is one of the most important divisions of American agriculture, especially in the mid-west corn-belt. Heavy, or lard type, breeds include the Poland China and Berkshire, Hampshire, and Duroc-Jersey. The Yorkshire and Tamworth hogs have long slender bodies and are classified as lean, or bacon, type hogs.

In livestock breeding, the records of outstanding individuals used in breeding are kept in pedigree and registration

Fig. 50-8. The man above is timing the breathing rate of a Brahman cow, as compared to that of a half Aberdeen Angus and Brahman cow, both of which were exposed the same length of time to Gulf Coast heat and sunlight. Brahman cattle, unlike Aberdeen Angus, have sweat glands to carry off excess moisture, thus keeping the body temperature from rising too high.

papers. Purebred animals may be registered at the headquarters of their respective breed. Papers must include the names and registration numbers of both *sire* (male) and *dam* (female) as well as part of the ancestry. In this manner, different strains of the same breed may be crossed without the danger of introducing undesirable characteristics or losing any good qualities.

True hybrid animals. Plant and animal breeders use the term hybrid loosely. They use it to indicate crosses between different strains of the same species as, for example, hybrid corn. A **true hybrid,** in the strict sense of the word, is the result of crossing two different species.

The mule is an example of a true hybrid animal. This hardy, useful animal is produced by crossing a female horse with a male donkey. The size is inherited from the horse. From the donkey the mule inherits long ears, sure-footedness, great endurance, and the ability to live on rough food and endure hardships. However, with all of its hybrid vigor, the mule in most cases is sterile — that is, unable to reproduce.

Successful hybrids have resulted from crosses between the Brahman cows introduced years ago from India. Tourists in the southern and southwestern states are often surprised to see in pastures these large gray or brownish animals with long, drooping ears and shoulder humps. Brahman cattle can endure the hot, humid climate of the Gulf States as well as the dry summer heat of the Southwest much better than domestic breeds of beef cattle. In addition, they resist disease and insect attacks.

A cross between Brahman and Aberdeen-Angus cattle produced *Brangus cattle,* one of the most popular of the Brahman crosses. The *Bradford* is another cross breed with Brahman and Hereford cattle as parent stock.

In Conclusion

Plant and animal breeding may seem far removed from you if you live in a large city. Actually it is no more removed than your next trip to the grocery store.

Scientific breeding has brought rust-resistant asters to flower beds of your home and city parks. Roses in clusters, long-stemmed tea roses, and climbing roses in great variety leave the growers by tens of thousands each season to beautify our gardens. Just name a size and color of tomato and the time in the summer you want it to ripen and a grower will supply it to you. Beef cattle and dairy cattle, fat hogs and lean hogs, horses for work and horses for pleasure — we have all.

Questions for Review

1. What are four objectives of plant breeding?

2. When is line breeding practiced in plant and animal breeding?

3. Compare hybridization and line breeding as to methods and purposes.

4. How many pure line parents are involved in the production of hybrid seed corn by the double-cross method?

5. Name several hybrid plants produced by the genius of the late Luther Burbank.

6. How is natural cross-pollination prevented in growing hybrid corn?

7. Name three general types of chickens and a breed representing each type.

8. Name a dual-purpose breed of cattle.

9. In what respect is the mule a true hybrid animal?

10. Why are Brahman cattle good parent stock for breeding purposes?

Biologically Speaking

artificial pollination
bud-mutant
disease resistant
double-cross

hybrid vigor
hybridization
inbreeding
line breeding

mass selection
outbreeding
sport
true hybrid

Applying Facts and Principles

1. If line breeding is practiced too long, offspring may become weak and inbred. How might this condition be remedied?

2. A farmer does not use seed from his hybrid corn for the next year's crop. Explain why.

3. Outline the method by which poultry breeders have produced 300 egg strains of chickens.

4. What is the importance of pedigrees and registration papers in breeding livestock?

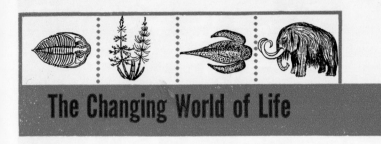

CHAPTER 51

The Changing World of Life

This is a changing world. It changes from day to day, from year to year, and from age to age. Rivers deepen their gorges as they carry more land to the sea. Mountains rise, only to be leveled by winds and rain. Continents rise and sink back into the sea. Such are the gradual changes of the physical earth as the days add into years and years combine to become ages.

During these ages, many species of plants and animals have appeared, have flourished for a time, and have then perished as new species took their places. As surroundings changed, life also changed. When one race lost the struggle for survival, another took its place.

The idea that all life in the world has some type of unity and relationship is an ancient one. Man throughout the ages has noticed among living things many similarities as well as differences. In our previous chapters concerning plants and animals we have tried to tell of some of the differences. But if you will briefly review these chapters, you will find that some similarities and relationships have been shown with other plants and animals.

How old is the earth? It probably doesn't matter too much, and certainly never will be settled. Scientists have expressed its age in staggering figures. We who appear during only a brief scene in the total drama are inclined to underestimate the length of time our planet has existed.

There are several methods used in determination of how long the earth has existed. For one thing, the rate at which solid materials are deposited in water to form *sedimentary rocks* can be measured (see Fig. 51-1). We can also measure the thickness of the layers of these rocks which have built up the earth's crust. *Geologists* (scientists who study rocks and their formation) have found layers of sedimentary rock ten miles thick. To form such a layer would require nearly two billion years.

In such calculations a mistake of a million years or so is trivial! Whatever its actual age is, we may be sure that the earth is extremely old, that it has changed from age to age, and that those changes are still continuing very gradually.

Evidence that living things have changed through the ages. Science has turned to various sources to obtain evidence that organisms have become more complex through the ages and that plant and animal populations have changed with time. These sources include: (1) fossil evidence; (2) homologous structures; (3) vestigial organs; (4) evidence in embryology; (5) physiological similarities; (6) geographical distribution; (7) results of breeding; and (8) experiments in plant and animal genetics.

Fig. 51-1. How do sedimentary rocks help geologists estimate the age of the earth?

Fossil evidence. Perhaps the best indication of the nature of plants and animals of past ages has been found in the form of *fossil remains.* **Fossils** might be likened to "footprints in the sands of time" except that the footprints may be entire organisms or their parts and the sands are hardened sediments. Each age, from the beginning of life, has left evidence of its existence in the sediments of the earth. These sediments are found originally on the surface of the land in the form of mud or other soft material. As plants and animals die, their remains sink into the soft sediment. As layers of sediments are formed, one above the other, these plant and animal remains are gradually replaced by mineral matter to remain for all time. The sediment gradually changes form to become deposits of rock arranged in layers.

This process has been going on for ages. As a geologist breaks through successive layers of sedimentary rock, each new layer he reaches represents a *geological era* older than the one immediately above. Fossils embedded in these sedimentary layers are arranged in their order of existence.

Where rivers have cut through layer after layer to form deep canyons, rocks which are millions of years old lie exposed in the walls of the stream. Fossils in the deepest layers are remains of some of the oldest forms of life.

The lowest layers, which probably represent the earliest era of life, contain few fossils. Above these ancient layers, fossils occur in considerable numbers. Typical ones are marine invertebrates such as sponges, coral, and long extinct animals known as **brachiopods** (*brack*-ee-oh-pods) and **gastropods** (*gas*-troh-pods).

Through the next layers fossils of higher invertebrates appear. **Trilobites** (*try*-loh-bytes), insects, armored fish, and amphibians are abundant, together with traces of tree ferns whose stems and leaves have for the most part been converted into coal. In later sedimentary rocks, one finds the remains of huge dinosaurs and other reptiles. As we approach more recent rocks, the land reptiles seem to be giving place to flying reptiles and to true birds. The plants and trees of this era begin to look like the living forms of today. Finally, in the most recent layers, fossils of mam-

Fig. 51-2. Geologists who study the fossils found in sedimentary rock can estimate how long plants and animals have lived on the earth.

mals, the highest form of animal life, can occasionally be found.

We know some strains or races of animals perished in the struggle for existence. That ended their line, but those groups which lived must have been the forebearers of modern organisms. These are the descendants of those remote forms which we know only from fossil evidence. When we find likenesses, we know they show relationship.

Homologous structures. In both plants and animals we find parts evidently of similar origin and structure, although they may be adapted for very different functions in different species. These are *homologous structures*. Among plants leaves can be altered to become petals, tendrils, or thorns. Roots may likewise act as organs for climbing, anchorage, or storage.

Epidermal tissue of animals may be modified as hoofs, scales, nails, claws, feathers, and hair. The various appendages of the crayfish are greatly changed for different functions in its relatives, yet the correspondence of these parts is evident. The bones of the bird's wing, the front leg of a horse, and the paddle of a whale are so similar in structure that, with slight exceptions, they are given the same names. Likewise, the muscles and internal organs of mammals are, with certain modifications, basically alike.

The way in which comparative organs are modified for different uses throughout the animal kingdom indicates clearly how new species have resulted from structural variations.

Vestigial organs. In certain animals, structures may be well-developed, yet in one of its relatives the corresponding structure may be very inadequate. For example, the abdomen of the crayfish and the lobster is the largest divi-

Fig. 51-3. Fossils are a living record of the past. Here you see skeletal remains of a fish and that of a plant preserved in stone.

sion of the body. But in the crab the abdomen has been reduced to a V-shaped part so tiny that it is sometimes entirely overlooked. In the foot of the horse there are unused bones which in its ancestors were used to support separate toes.

The theory is that such inadequate structures are remains of corresponding organs well-developed in ancestors or living relatives. These are called **vestigial** (vess-*tij*-ee-al) **organs.** (See Fig. 51-4.) In tailless primates there are, nevertheless, distinct tail bones at the end of the spinal column. In rodents, the appendix is the largest part of the intestine. On the other hand, in those organisms which belong to the primate group, it has become a small and apparently useless vestige.

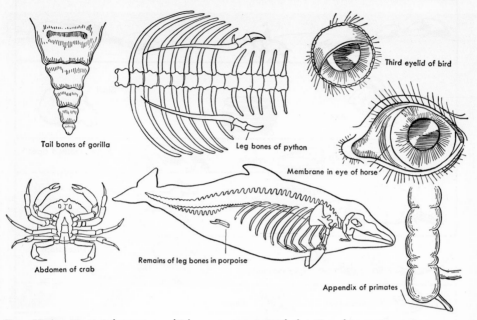

Fig. 51-4. Vestigial organs which serve no actual functional purpose are common among animals.

Evidence from embryology. It is amazing that the embryos of mammals which are never aquatic, such as cows and dogs, nevertheless possess gill arches. As mammalian embryos develop, the gill arches are modified or obliterated, but two of them later become the Eustachian tubes in the adults. Tailless, as well as tailed mammals, have a distinct tail in early embryo stages (see Fig. 51-6). All land vertebrate embryos have a two-chambered heart and circulatory system like that of a fish, even though later they may have a heart with three or four chambers.

The evidence seems to be that each animal in its individual development passes through stages which resemble its remote adult ancestors. The similarity of vertebrate embryos shows relationship through common ancestry. With this in mind we can understand the *embryological evidence* showing that vertebrate lungs have developed from the swim-bladder or air-bladder of fishlike animals. It explains the teeth in the embryos of whalebone whales, which as adults lack teeth.

Physiological similarities. Not only do the various classes of vertebrates resemble one another in structure, as the three preceding discussions have indicated, but in functions there is also marked similarity. For instance, internal secretions of mammals show a striking resemblance.

The digestive enzymes are so similar that many commercial products such as *pepsin,* extracted from cows, sheep, and hogs, are used in medicine. The tremendous use of *insulin* and *thyroid hormone,* endocrine products taken from animals for use in human treatment, suggests relationship. Antitoxins produced by the horse are used in immunity treatments for human diseases like diphtheria, scarlet fever, and tetanus.

Evidence from geographical distribution. It is known that animals on isolated islands usually differ from cor-

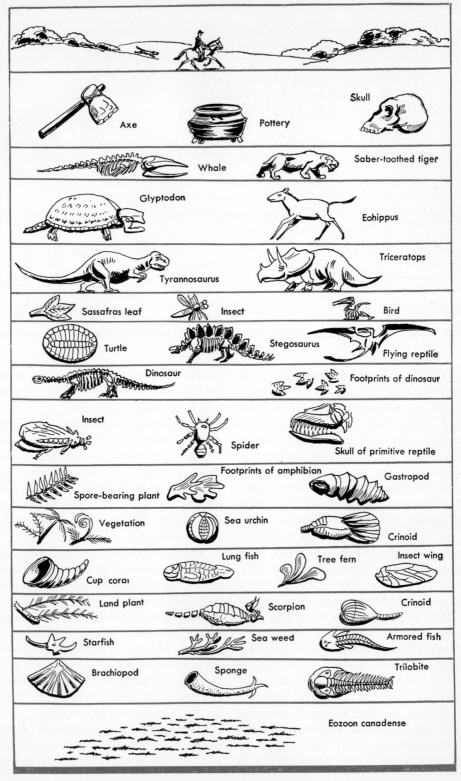

Fig. 51-5. The geological timetable.

	PSYCHOZOIC ERA — 26,000 years
Recent Period	Beginning of man's dominance; domestication of animals
	CENOZOIC ERA — 60,000,000 years
Pleistocene Period	Ice ages; extinction of mammoth and mastodon; rise of modern horse; man uses fire and makes implements
Pliocene Period	Rise of man; Pliohippus
Miocene Period	Saber-toothed tiger; Protohippus; whale
Oligocene Period	Primitive anthropoids and Mesohippus
Eocene Period	Primitive forms of modern mammals: sloths, armadillos, marsupials, Eohippus, rhinoceros
	MESOZOIC ERA — 125,000,000 years
Cretaceous Period	*Tyrannosaurus* and other dinosaurs become extinct
Comanchean Period	Flowering plants; true trees; modern insects; true birds
Jurassic Period	Giant dinosaurs dominant; birds with teeth; turtles and flying reptiles; egg-laying mammals
Triassic Period	Rise of dinosaurs
	PALEOZOIC ERA — 368,000,000 years
Permian Period	Rise of insects, spiders, and primitive reptiles; extinction of trilobites and other forms; glacial period
Pennsylvanian Period	Spore-bearing plants; sharks and large amphibians (first land vertebrates); coal formed
Mississippian Period	Rise of crinoids, brachiopods, and sea urchins; dense vegetation on land
Devonian Period	Tree ferns and other land plants; lung fish and primitive amphibians; fish and invertebrates dominant
Silurian Period	First air-breathing animals; crinoids; primitive sharks; scorpions; first land plants
Ordovician Period	Corals and clams; armored fish; starfish; first seaweeds
Cambrian Period	Marine invertebrates: sponges, jellyfish, trilobites, gastropods, brachiopods

Proterozoic Era and Archeozoic Era — 1,450,000,000 years — Origin of life in form of one-celled organisms; few fossil remains

Total number of years since life began — 2,003,026,000 years

Fish	Salamander	Turtle	Bird	Pig

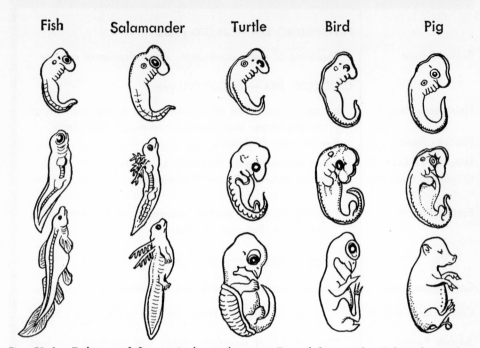

Fig. 51-6.   Embryos of five typical vertebrates.   From left to right: Fish, salamander, turtle, bird, and pig.   Note the long tails and gill slits in the earliest stages, as well as other structural similarities.

responding forms on the mainland.   Yet both must have descended from common ancestors.   One scientist investigated snails on Tahiti, a South Sea island.   He found that isolation seemed to produce special varieties.   These differed from the crosses or hybrids that developed on the mainland where they had a chance to breed with snails possessing many characters different from their own.

Animals which find themselves in an environment markedly unfavorable face three possibilities: (1) migration to a new territory; (2) death; or (3) survival of individuals which through mutations can adapt themselves to new conditions.   Presumably there have been many cases in prehistoric times where marine fish, for instance, became landlocked and died in fresh water.   Yet a few mutants must have lived on to give

rise to the types of fish we find today, such as the fresh-water herring and others.   These living forms are distinctly different from, though necessarily the descendants of, their marine ancestors.

Results of breeding.   Domesticated plants and animals are examples of racial development.   The facts show that over 25 kinds of dogs have been developed by man from wild wolflike progenitors.   A dozen kinds of chickens have a common ancestor in the jungle fowl of India.   The Percheron horse has been bred for draft purposes and the Arabian steed for riding and racing.   In these cases the skeletons show striking differences in size and weight of bones and hoofs.   Domestication and man's control of certain characteristics preserve variations arising as mutations or as the result of hybridization.

The story of plant and animal breeding, while it does not prove that similar developmental changes have taken place in past ages, does prove the possibility of such changes in nature.

Experiments in genetics. Rapid growth of genetics has established heredity as one of the chief causes for the modification of life forms. When the eggs of fruit flies are exposed to X rays, alterations in the flies which hatch from the treated eggs occur. As more of this work is carried on with X rays, more knowledge will probably become available concerning the artificial alteration of heredity.

If plants or seeds are sprayed with a chemical which is called *colchicine,* the chromosomes per cell may be doubled or even quadrupled. As you will remember in Chapter 48, mutations do occur in nature from time to time. It is quite possible that many new species and varieties may have originated more or less suddenly as a result of this peculiar hereditary phenomenon.

Theories to explain racial development. As evidence was accumulated, indicating that living things may have changed through the ages, scientists turned to the problem of explaining theories to account for **racial development.**

One of the first was presented by the French biologist Jean Baptiste Lamarck, in 1801. Later, in 1859, the famous English scientist, Charles Darwin published his theories. In 1901, just 100 years after Lamarck, a third great scientist, Hugo De Vries, announced another explanation for racial development.

Lamarck's theories. Lamarck proposed three theories as follows:

1. *Theory of need.* The production of a new organ or part of a plant or animal results from a need.

2. *Theory of use and disuse.* Organs remain active as long as they are used, but disappear gradually with disuse.

3. *Theory of inheritance.* All that has been acquired or changed in the structure of individuals during their life is transmitted by heredity to the next generation.

While some of Lamarck's ideas are still acceptable, most of them have been discarded. We know today that organisms cannot develop new organs as they are needed.

Another fallacy in the Lamarckian theory is in regard to inheriting acquired characteristics. As organisms change, gradual modifications seem to be passed on to new generations, but not the way Lamarck suggested. No environmental variation which has occurred in the lifetime of a single organ is inherited.

Lamarck's idea of use and disuse has little if any scientific basis. However, we must admit that man's appendix has no real use. The same may be said of the third molars, or " wisdom teeth."

Darwin's theory of natural selection. In 1859 Charles Darwin, an English scientist, published his *Origin of Species by Natural Selection.* His theory is not confined to biology alone, but has influenced other branches of science. In its broader features it is accepted generally although there are many details which still fail to account for all the known facts.

The chief factors assigned by Darwin to account for the development of new species from common ancestry are: (1) overproduction of individuals; (2) struggle for existence; (3) variation among individuals; (4) survival of the fittest; (5) inheritance of favorable characteristics; and (6) new forms better adapted to survive, thus " naturally selected " as new species.

ORIGIN OF DOMESTIC ANIMALS

ANIMAL	PROGENITOR
Dog	An animal resembling the wild wolf, jackal, or possibly the fox. The first animal to be domesticated
Horse	Diminutive, five-toed *Eohippus*, progenitor of the *Orchippus*.
Ox	Sacred cattle of India
Sheep	Domestic so long that previous history is lost; probably same type in Asia, possibly China
Goat	Of uncertain origin. Wild relatives still alive: Angora of Asia Minor, Kashmir of Tibet, Egyptian goat of Nile
Pig	European wild boar; Indian wild boar
Cat	Some wild type like European wildcat
Hen	Jungle fowl of India, a kind of pheasant
Goose	Graylag goose of north British Isles. Long domesticated
Dove, Pigeon	Rock pigeon of England
Duck	Original wild progenitor unknown. Many wild species still living
Turkey	American wild turkey
Peacock	Some pheasant in Asia

Overproduction. A fern plant may produce 50 million spores each year. If all matured they would nearly cover North America the second year. A mustard plant produces about 730,000 seeds annually, which in two years would occupy 2,000 times all the land surface of the earth. The dandelion would accomplish the same thing in about ten years.

The English sparrow lays six eggs at a time and breeds four times a year. In the course of a decade, if all survived, there would be no room for any other birds. The codfish produces over a million eggs per year. If all survived this would fill the Atlantic solidly with fish in about five years. There is, however, no such actual increase.

Struggle for existence. We know that the number of individuals of a species usually changes but little in its native environment. In other words, only a small minority of the potential number of offspring reaches maturity. Each seeks food, water, air, warmth, and space, but only a few can obtain these needs in struggling to survive.

Variation. No two individuals of any plant or animal are exactly alike. Slight variations in structure or function occur in all. This furnishes the material for nature to use in her selection; and those forms whose variations tend to adapt them best to their environment survive, while the others perish.

Survival of the fittest. If, among the thousands of dandelion seeds produced, some have better dispersal devices, these will be carried to a distant place where they will be less crowded, and so will survive. Those having poorer adaptations will perish by overcrowding. In so severe a struggle where only a few out of millions may hope to live, very slight variations in speed, or sense, or protection may turn the scale in favor of the better fitted individual. Those with unfavorable variations sooner or later will be wiped out.

Inheritance. It is common knowledge that in general the offspring resembles the parents. If the parents have reached maturity because of special fitness, those of their descendants which inherit most closely the favorable variation will in turn be automatically selected by nature to continue the race.

New and better adapted species. A continuation of this process of natural selection will in time produce such differences in structure and habit that the resulting forms must be regarded as new species, genera, and finally higher groups. This process may be aided when developing species are separated by distance, mountain ranges, bodies of water, or climatic differences, and so do not lose their favorable variations by interbreeding.

Conclusions from the theory. Natural selection, while recognized today as an important factor in the development of plant and animal life, does not seem to account for all the known facts. Scientists are turning to other theories to help explain things that natural selection fails to cover. This does not mean disbelief in Darwin's general conclusions nor their abandonment. The main facts are being more strongly intrenched every year. The interpretation of these facts will continue to vary with new discoveries.

Mutation theory. Hugo De Vries, the Dutch botanist, in 1901 startled the scientific world by announcing his *mutation theory.* De Vries had found among a group of evening primroses two plants which were definitely different from the common type. He experimented for many years, finding that

Fig. 51-7. This group illustrates overproduction. Note the hordes of marine organisms which crowd this wharf pile. Mussels below and hydroids above occupy almost every inch, and even attach themselves to each other.

from 50,000 specimens of evening primroses at least 800 plants showed striking differences and that these characteristics were hereditary. To such new forms arising suddenly and breeding true for the new characteristic, De Vries assigned the name of *mutants.*

Most mutants are weaker than the normal stock because mutations are usually defects. But some mutations are advantageous. The result is that such mutations become permanent and a new variety is thus formed. Thus natural selection begins to operate.

Science and religion. Some people are concerned because they think science interferes with religion. There is nothing in all of science that in any way opposes a belief in God and religion.

Thomas Huxley the famous English biologist who lived in Darwin's time wrote:

" Science seems to me to teach in the highest and strongest manner the great truth which is embodied in Christian conception of entire surrender to the will of God.   Sit down before the fact as a little child, be prepared to give up every preconceived notion, follow humbly wherever and to whatever abysses nature leads, or you shall learn nothing.

I have only begun to learn content and peace of mind since I have resolved at all risks to do this."

A famous physician, the late Major W. W. Keene, M.D., whose professional training gives him a different point of view from that of Huxley, wrote: " With the passing years I am more and more impressed with the wonderful mechanism of nature, which to me bespeaks God."

In Conclusion

Through periods and eras representing millions of years, life on the earth has undergone gradual changes.   This modification of life forms is termed racial development.   Evidence has been accumulated through the study of fossils, homologous organs, vestigial organs, embryology, physiological similarities, geographical distribution, results of breeding, and experiments in genetics.

Three theories have been advanced to explain the way racial development occurs.   Lamarck expressed the idea of use and disuse, in which the organism was thought to modify its structure to fit its needs and to pass these changes on to the next generation.   Darwin's theory of natural selection based on overproduction, struggle for existence, and survival of the fittest was developed more on demonstrated facts than was Lamarck's theory.   De Vries applied the knowledge of heredity in advancing his theory of mutations.   Modern theory uses many of the genetic principles we have discussed.

In this Unit we have studied the changes and inheritance of life.   Now we shall study how we can preserve the best we now have.

Questions for Review

1. What methods have scientists used to determine the approximate age of the earth?

2. How are fossils formed?

3. What significance is attached to the order of the layers in which fossils are found in the earth?

4. How do homologous organs help explain the variety of forms found in related organisms?

5. Name several vestigial organs and discuss their probable origin.

6. How does embryology show the possible ancestry of organisms?

7. What are some of the physiological similarities found in animals?

8. Using your knowledge of genetics, discuss briefly how isolation is an important factor in forming new varieties of organisms.

9. How have the results of breeding shown that organisms may change because of variations in heredity?

10. What is meant by " the fittest "?

Biologically Speaking

acquired characteristics	homologous structure	racial development
brachiopods	isolation	sedimentary rock
embryological evidence	Lamarck's theories	struggle for existence
fossil	mutation theory	survival of the fittest
gastropods	natural selection	trilobite
geological era	overproduction	variation
geologist	physiological similarities	vestigial organs

Applying Facts and Principles

1. How do you account for the fact that squirrels found on the north rim of the Grand Canyon differ in many respects from the squirrels found on the south rim?

2. How is it possible for the fossil remains of salt-water organisms to be found many hundreds of miles from the ocean?

3. "Goose pimples" are caused by the action of little muscles attached to the hairs of the skin. Under what general heading of the evidences for change would you place this fact?

4. How do you explain the fact that many plants and animals found in England and Japan resemble each other more than plants and animals found in Africa and Madagascar?

5. Explain the long neck of the giraffe according to Lamarck, according to Darwin, and according to modern theory.

Research On Your Own

1. Prepare a list of eight sketches showing successive stages of mitosis. Include the following: a cell at the close of the interphase and ready to start mitosis, early prophase, middle prophase, late prophase, metaphase, anaphase, telophase, and the beginning of a new interphase stage in the two daughter cells. If prepared slides showing mitotic stages are available, see how many you can find using high power of your microscope.

2. Construct an imaginary cell containing three pairs of chromosomes. Make each pair a different shape and color. Diagram a mitotic division by drawing lines from the mother cell to two daughter cells. Show the three pairs of chromosomes in each of the cells.

3. Using the cell you constructed in Question 2, diagram egg formation (oogenesis) and sperm formation (spermatogenesis). Show the chromosome content of all of the cells produced during the series of divisions.

4. Diagram a cross between two trihybrid guinea pigs with the genetic formula *BbRrSs*. The parents are black, rough-coated, short-haired guinea pigs, with black (*B*) dominant over white (*b*); rough (*R*) over smooth (*r*); and short hair (*S*) over long hair (*s*). Each parent can produce eight different types of eggs or sperm. Sixty-four squares will

be needed to diagram all of the possible egg and sperm combinations. Tally all of the offspring into various groups on the basis of appearance.

5. Make a study of eye color of the members of your class. List such colors as brown, hazel, green, blue, etc. Tabulate all colors represented and determine ratios of occurrence of each color.

6. Bring in a pedigree, or registration paper, for a dog, a cat, a horse, or some other purebred animal. Examine the ancestry shown and explain why this is important. Explain how this information can be used in either line or cross-breeding.

 ——————————— **More About Biology**

Andrews, Roy Chapman. *ALL ABOUT DINOSAURS.* Random House, New York. 1953

Andrews, Roy Chapman. *MEET YOUR ANCESTORS.* Random House, New York. 1953

Beaty, John Y. *PLANT BREEDING FOR EVERYONE.* Charles T. Branford Co., Boston. 1954

Burbank, Luther. *PARTNER OF NATURE.* D. Appleton-Century Co., New York. 1939

Edel, May. *STORY OF PEOPLE: ANTHROPOLOGY FOR YOUNG PEOPLE.* Little, Brown and Co., Boston. 1953

Fenton, Carroll Lane. *PREHISTORIC WORLD: STORIES OF ANIMAL LIFE IN PAST AGES.* John Day and Co., Inc., New York. 1954

Billet, Ray Oren and Yeo, John Wendell. *GROWING UP.* D. C. Heath, Boston. 1951

Museum of Science and Industry. *MIRACLE OF GROWTH.* Univ. of Ill. Press, Urbana, Ill. 1952

Grobman, Arnold B. *OUR ATOMIC HERITAGE.* University of Florida Press, Gainsville. 1951

Martin, Charles. *MONSTERS OF OLD LOS ANGELES.* The Viking Press, New York. 1950

Reed, W. Maxwell and Lucas, Jeanette May. *ANIMALS ON THE MARCH.* Harcourt, Brace and Co., New York. 1937

Scheele, William E. *PREHISTORIC ANIMALS.* The World Publishing Co., Cleveland. 1954

Scheinfeld, Amram. *THE NEW YOU AND HEREDITY.* J. B. Lippincott Co., Philadelphia. 1950

Schneider, Herman. *ROCKS, RIVERS AND THE CHANGING EARTH.* Scott, Foresman and Co., New York. 1952

Weyler, Rose and Ames, Gerald. *RESTLESS EARTH.* Abelard-Schuman, Inc., New York. 1954

Williams, Henry L. *STORIES IN ROCKS.* Henry Holt and Co., Inc., New York. 1948

Wyler, Rose. *LIFE ON EARTH.* Henry Schuman and Co., New York. 1953

UNIT 10

Safeguarding Our Natural Resources

The prosperity of a city depends on productive farms and ranches. Agriculture springs from the soil. Isn't soil, then, the basis for the prosperity of a whole nation?

If this is true, soil conservation is vital to all of us. But good soil means much more than prosperous agriculture. Conserve the soil, and you control the water problems which can result in two major disasters — floods and droughts. Soil conservation is closely related to forest conservation. And forests provide the requirements for a large portion of our wildlife population.

An active program of total conservation is vital to the future of our nation. Regardless of the brilliance of our scientists, the wisdom of our statesmen, the ingenuity of our industrialists, and the skill of our workmen, our country cannot continue in its role as a leading nation with its soil exhausted, its forests leveled, and its wildlife destroyed.

Conservation is everybody's business — yours, your state's, and your nation's. We are charged with the responsibility for preserving our natural heritage — the land and all it contains.

CHAPTER 52

Conservation of Soil and Water

When the first settlers came to America, they found a land of almost unbelievable opportunity. Climate, geographical location, and soil were ideal for crop production. Trees in almost endless quantity were at hand to supply materials for building a new nation. The greatest problem was the clearing of the land for agriculture. For generations, it was man against nature. The eastern forests fell to the woodsman's axe. Trains of covered wagons bore pioneer families through the eastern forest lands, across the prairies and Great Plains, and finally across the Rocky Mountains to the Pacific Coast.

The soil was the basis of all this prosperity. It grew forests and grasslands where game abounded. As planted crops replaced native stands of timber, the soil yielded its fertility to fields of grain and vegetables. Herds of cattle and flocks of sheep fattened on the rich grasses of the prairies and plains.

The land today. What of our land today? Can our soil continue to support such a rapidly growing nation? Can it supply the demands of a nation in which the average citizen enjoys a standard of living far above that of inhabitants of any other country? Unless large-scale conservation measures are taken immediately, the answer to these questions is definitely *no!* It can if we rebuild it more rapidly than we deplete it and restore natural controls against its removal by forces of nature. Our task in rebuilding the land is doubly hard today. We must not only guard against further depletion in our age, but must repair the damage caused by past generations.

Soil and where it comes from. Think of the earth as a gigantic ball of rock. Soil lies in a thin film on the surface of this great ball. Season after season, running water, freezing and thawing, wind, and other forces of na-ture crumble the rocks and form gravel, sand, or clay. This becomes mineral soil, or **subsoil.** In most regions, the subsoil forms a layer several feet in thickness, representing thousands of years of the slow disintegration of rock.

The organic part of the soil comes from the slow decay of roots, stems, leaves, and other vegetable materials and the remains of animals. We refer to the organic remains of land plants as **humus,** while sphagnum moss and other aquatic plants form *peat* in lakes and bogs.

A mixing of mineral matter from the subsoil and organic matter combine to form **topsoil,** or loam. This is the most vital part of soil, the nutritional zone of plants both large and small. Topsoil forms very slowly, at a rate of about one inch in 500 years.

Topsoil supports great numbers of bacteria, molds, and other fungi which we refer to as the **soil flora.** Activities

Fig. 52-1. These two plots show the difference in corn growth resulting from soil treatment. The plants on the right received lime and fertilizer. The plants on the left have had no special soil treatment. All plants are the same age.

of the many soil organisms are essential to fertility of the soil. Decay, ammonia production, nitrate formation, and many other chemical processes condition topsoil for the growth of higher plants.

If you examine a soil profile along a bank or the side of a ditch, you can see the dark topsoil and the lighter subsoil below. Under natural conditions, a small quantity of topsoil washes away or is blown away each season. This is replaced by additional topsoil formed by decaying vegetation added to the upper surface. Thus, topsoil formation is a continuous process. Remember, however, that this is an extremely slow process.

The original topsoil in America averaged nine to ten inches in depth. Today it averages about five inches. When topsoil is gone, land becomes a desert. In other words, we are now living within five inches of a desert. This is what the conservationist means when he says we have lost half the battle to save our soil. This is an extreme-

ly serious problem, but it can be solved.

Various kinds of soil loss. In some cases, soil is deprived of its essential minerals through continued planting of agricultural crops. We refer to such mineral exhaustion as **depletion.** Often, water seeping through deeply cultivated soil carries the soluble minerals far below the topsoil. We refer to this loss of fertility as **leaching. Erosion** is loss of the entire topsoil, due to water or to wind. This is the most critical of all the forms of soil loss.

In discussing various kinds of soil loss, we will refer to **row crops** and **cover crops.** As the name indicates, row crops are planted in rows in cultivated fields. The soil lies exposed between the rows. Corn, beans, tobacco, and tomatoes are examples of row crops. Wheat, oats, rye, clover, alfalfa, and various grasses are grown as cover crops. Here the close-growing plants form a dense mat of roots which bind the soil and an aerial cover which protects the soil surface from wind and water. The relation of row crops and cover crops to the soil is very important in soil conservation.

Depletion of soil minerals. A century ago, abundant fertile land was still available to anyone who would "go West" and claim it. The soil contained a rich store of minerals, accumulated through centuries of the growth and decay of native vegetation. Year after year, corn, cotton, and other field crops were grown in the same fields with little thought about the condition of the soil. *Overproduction* was the order of the day. The object seemed to be to produce as much as possible in as short a time as possible. After a few seasons, the loss of fertility began to show in the form of reduced crop yield. Rather than heeding this danger signal, many farmers pushed the land even harder. When the soil finally became exhausted, the field was abandoned for a new and more profitable area.

A scientific view of the mineral depletion problem. It stands to reason that agricultural crops with a high food value would draw heavily on soil minerals. The most critical of these minerals are nitrates, phosphates, and potash. In a natural cycle, plants draw minerals from the soil and organize them into the various parts of the plant body. When the plant dies, these are returned to the soil through the process of decay. But a crop plant is harvested for its food value. The minerals contained in the crop are removed from the soil permanently. This can continue only a few seasons before the soil shows evidence of depletion of the most heavily used minerals.

Soil which is badly depleted of minerals usually becomes acid, or sour. To correct this condition, the farmer uses lime. Other minerals are restored by heavy applications of commercial fertilizer, especially superphosphate. In addition to this rapid method of restoring minerals, the scientific farmer avoids depletion by practicing **crop rotation.**

Principles of crop rotation. Various crops differ in the minerals they take from the soil. Furthermore, some crops must be grown in rows, while others are grown as cover crops. Many farmers prevent mineral depletion as well as serious erosion by rotating crops in each growing area. Many rotation plans follow a three-year cycle. The first crop might be corn, followed by wheat or oats, then by grass or clover. Clover, alfalfa, cowpeas, lespedeza, and other legumes are important in a rotation cycle because they support nitrogen-fixing bacteria on their roots. As we mentioned in the discussion of the nitrogen cycle, these bacteria produce nitrates from atmospheric nitrogen.

Mineral depletion and health. Have you ever heard a doctor speak of "hidden hunger"? It could happen to you without your knowing it. We assume that vegetables, meats, and other foods contain certain nutrients and minerals essential in our diets. But did you know that one bunch of carrots may be rich in mineral content, while another which looks just the same may be largely cellulose and water? It all depends on the soil where the carrots grew.

"Hidden hunger" is a kind of hunger you do not feel because you have eaten sufficient bulk of food. But your body cells are not satisfied by the proteins and minerals the foods contained.

The problem of leaching. Before a field is planted, it is plowed and disked. This turns the weeds under the soil and conditions the soil for planting. Rains soak into the pulverized soil easily. This is ideal for young plants, but it may cause a serious problem, especially in loose sandy loam. If the soil is properly cared for, the topsoil should be rich

Fig. 52-2. This farmer is plowing under clover to add organic matter to the soil.

in minerals. These minerals must be dissolved in water or plants cannot absorb them. As water runs through the topsoil, it dissolves minerals and carries them down below the reach of the roots of many crop plants. By such leaching action, valuable fertility is lost.

We have always assumed that frequent cultivation is good for crops. But this may not be true. Row crops especially leave much of the soil exposed to soaking rains. One method of reducing leaching is minimum cultivation. Another is the planting of cover crops between row crops. Deep-rooted crops, like alfalfa, absorb minerals from the subsoil and bring them into the plant body. If such a crop is turned under, the minerals are thus returned to the topsoil.

Loss of organic matter. In a natural environment, the organic matter present in topsoil decays slowly as it is acted upon by bacteria and other soil organisms. In time it would disappear entirely were it not for the leaves, roots, and other plant parts which are added to the soil each season. However, when hay crops are harvested or when stalks of wheat or oats are used for straw, little organic matter is left to return to the soil. In some cases, weeds and native grasses are burned off fields before plowing. This is a waste of valuable organic matter which should be plowed into the soil.

If fields are cleared season after season, the organic part of the topsoil may disappear to the extent that much of the soil flora dies out. When these organisms are gone, many of the processes necessary for maintaining soil fertility cease. There are several ways in which organic matter can be added to soil. One is the addition of manure and decayed straw. An even better

Fig. 52-3. Rill erosion has already started on this hillside, causing gullies to form.

method is sowing grass or clover in a field, then plowing it under.

Erosion, the loss of topsoil. Of all forms of soil loss, erosion is the most advanced and the most destructive. Precious topsoil from millions of acres of our most productive land now lies in riverbeds and ocean bottoms. Some has been blown thousands of miles in violent dust storms. This is the tragic result of man's carelessness and shortsightedness.

Some erosion has always occurred. We refer to this slow blowing away or washing out of soil as **geologic erosion.** Before any land was cultivated, soil formation kept pace with this type of erosion. But when land was stripped of its natural vegetation and poor farming methods exposed it to forces of water and wind, **accelerated erosion,** a far more dangerous condition, began.

Much of the land which is badly eroded today was abandoned for agriculture when the minerals became de-pleted. This resulted from *overcultivation*. With the rapid expansion of agricultural industry, more and more areas were cultivated for crops. In eagerness to make every inch of land pay, many farmers began cultivating hillsides, river bottoms, and all other available locations rather than increasing yields from land already cultivated.

In hilly forest lands, where oak and hickory trees were thriving in shallow topsoil, native vegetation was cleared to make more tillable ground. Such lands were excellent for forests but entirely unsuitable for crops. Soon they were abandoned to the ravages of erosion or were left for families to eke out an existence from a few patches of dwarfed corn and vegetables.

Water erosion. One form of water erosion, known as **sheet erosion,** occurs when water stands in a field during a flood, then flows away gradually. The standing water dissolves a sheet of soil and becomes muddy. As it flows away slowly, it takes the soil with it. When the water is gone, the land is left that much nearer the sterile subsoil. A few such floods may leave the land totally worthless.

In rolling and hilly sections where the rain falls on exposed soil, raindrops dissolve the soil and form tiny channels or rills as they trickle down the slope. This is the beginning of **rill erosion.** Each time water flows down the slope, it follows the same rills. These deepen and widen much as a stream increases the size of its bed. This may lead to a more advanced stage known as **gully erosion.** If the gully isn't checked, it may in time become a yawning canyon, like the one pictured in Fig. 52-4. This can be avoided even on cultivated hillsides when proper conservation methods are used.

Contour farming. When land is cultivated up and down a slope, the furrows act as man-made rills and start rill erosion. Each time it rains, water pours down the furrows and enlarges them. They can become gullies in a short time.

The solution to this problem is logical. Plow around the hill rather than up and down. This method is called **contour farming.** When furrows are plowed around the slope, each one serves as a small dam to check the flow of water. Water stands in each furrow and then soaks into the ground. If this simple practice had been followed long ago, our lands today would be richer and our rivers deeper and clearer.

Strip cropping. This extremely valuable soil conservation practice frequently combines two important measures. Broad strips are cultivated on the contour of a slope for growing *row crops* such as corn, cotton, potatoes, or beans. These strips alternate with strips in which *cover crops,* such as wheat, oats, clover, alfalfa, or grass, are grown.

Fig. 52-4. If unchecked, severe erosion can result in gullies as large as canyons, such as you see below.

Fig. 52-5. Strip cropping. Whole fields are not planted with a single crop. Cotton still grows on this South Carolina farm, but it is planted in strips that follow the contour of the land. Small grain is sown in between the strips of cotton. How does this practice help in conserving the soil?

These cover crops completely cover the surface of the soil and hold it securely. As water runs from the strip of row crop, it is checked upon entering the strip of cover crop.

Frequently, clover is used as a cover crop. In this way, strips may be rotated within a single field. Nitrogen-fixing bacteria, associated with roots of clover, alfalfa, and other legumes, return the various nitrogen compounds to the soil. Strips may be alternated every few years with the result that water erosion is checked continually and fertility of the soil is maintained.

Terracing. This is used extensively to check the flow of water on steeply sloping land. A long slope is broken into numerous short ones by forming a series of banks. A type of machine, the terracing grader, is used to form flat strips on the contour of the slope. Each strip is divided from another by a bank. Drainage ditches at the base of each bank conduct the water around the slope.

Gully control. When large gullies have already formed, measures other than those discussed previously must be used. One of these is planting the slopes of the gully with trees, grass, or other plants to act as soil binders and prevent further widening. Deepening may be prevented by building a series of small dams. The dams slow the flow of water and soil gradually fills the gully.

The problem of wind erosion. Wind erosion is a critical factor in western Texas, Kansas, and Oklahoma. The prevailing strong winds blow from the south, especially during the spring and summer months. Originally, native grasses and other plants bound the soil firmly in place with their extensive, shallow root systems. Much of this land was extremely fertile and suitable for growing cereal crops and, as a result, extensive areas were plowed for agriculture.

During the spring and early summer months the soil was moist enough to

Fig. 52-6. These terraces on a steep hillside were made with a special tractor-drawn plow and finished with a grader. Trees will be planted in these terraced channels.

hold its place, but with the late summer drought the strong hot winds blew the dry topsoil away. This process of wind erosion increased. Entire fields were covered with fine particles of topsoil carried in dense clouds during a dust storm. Abandoned fields added to the growing desert. The farmer who was fortunate enough to hold his soil in check was powerless to stop the tons of soil which blew onto his land from other areas. There was nothing left but to abandon the homestead with its half-buried houses and barns and join the procession of landowners out of the growing "Dust Bowl." This is wind erosion on a large scale.

Control of wind erosion. Wind erosion is especially difficult because it involves such large areas. Any local wind erosion control could be wiped out in a single dust storm. Consequently, these projects must be undertaken on a very large scale and with the aid of the state and national agencies. One such measure is the planting of windbreaks, or *shelterbelts.* Extensive experiments have been conducted to find trees which can be planted at intervals to break the force of the wind. In addition to windbreaks, plants are needed as soil binders. Every inch of exposed land not used regularly for crop production must be anchored firmly by the roots of grasses and other soil-binding plants.

When land is cultivated, furrows should be *plowed at right angles to the prevailing wind.* Thus the wind does not blow down the furrows, but blows across them. Each furrow helps to stop the movement of soil. In sections where *irrigation* is possible, diversion of water into the fields during dry periods will check wind erosion because moist soil does not blow.

Problems in administering soil conservation. In 1935 the United States Soil Conservation Service was established as part of the Soil Conservation Act. This agency became a permanent part of the Department of Agriculture. This division of the Department of Agri-

Fig. 52-7. These rock-check dams were used in a ditch to conduct road water around the gully on a farm.

culture has embarked on an extensive program of soil conservation. Expert agricultural engineers are investigating all phases of the problem. They travel throughout the country studying various problems and offering aid where needed.

Farmers have the opportunity to examine demonstration farms where soil conservation measures are in operation. If the farmers of a community wish to use these methods on their farms, they must first form a local soil conservation district under local control. Engineers from the Soil Conservation Service will then cooperate with the local district in applying soil conservation methods to the problem.

Soil problems and water problems — a vicious cycle. Disastrous floods and droughts, the two extremes in water problems, are inevitable results of misuse of soil and its plant cover. Rains which should soak into the ground and supply plant roots during drier periods pour off the surface of eroded land in torrents. Streams flood with muddy water from nearby fields. Now there is too much water. Later in the season, plants may die for want of ground water lost during the floods. During floods, water washes soil away and the wind blows it away. Soil erosion, floods, and droughts — these three disasters form a vicious circle. Yet if we solve the soil problems, we will help in correcting the water problem.

The wide flood plains of the streams and rivers of the Mississippi River drainage basin indicate that high and low water stages have always occurred. Rivers of this enormous system drain the land from the Appalachian Mountains in the east to the Continental Divide in the Rocky Mountains.

Prolonged droughts and desert conditions are normal in some sections of the country, too. This is because of uneven distribution of rainfall. But it remained for the past few generations to make the mistakes which increased this natural condition to the proportions of major disasters.

The water cycle. The *water cycle* is a continuous movement of water from the atmosphere to the earth and from the earth to the atmosphere. The movement in the water cycle from the atmosphere to the earth is **precipitation.** Eventually this water will return to the atmosphere by **evaporation.**

When it rains, some of the water evaporates while falling or evaporates quickly from the surface of the ground. Much of it runs off the surface of the ground and enters the drainage system. This **runoff water** feeds the rivulets, streams, and rivers, and eventually reaches a pond, lake, or the ocean where it is stored. Water also evaporates constantly from the surface of these drainage systems and storage basins.

A large amount of the precipitation normally enters the soil and becomes **ground water.** This water will reach the drainage system through springs or underground streams or it will move upward through the soil during dry periods and pass into the atmosphere as *water vapor.* Our greatest problem in water conservation is the reduction of the amount of *runoff water,* and at the same time an increase in the amount of *ground water.*

Precipitation. The water vapor which passes from the earth to the atmosphere collects as mist in clouds. As warm air containing water vapor rises through the atmosphere, it cools. The mist then condenses as drops of water. The drops fall from the clouds as *rain.* If they freeze in falling, they reach the earth as *sleet.* Sometimes strong updrafts force falling sleet upward so that layers of ice deposit around the frozen drops, resulting in *hail.* *Snow* is frozen and crystallized mist which falls gently to the earth.

Ground water. Topsoil acts as a sponge in receiving and holding water during precipitation. As the topsoil be-

Fig. 52-8. Notice the sand drift and the hard surface of blown land. Wind erosion is one of the factors involved in soil loss and depletion.

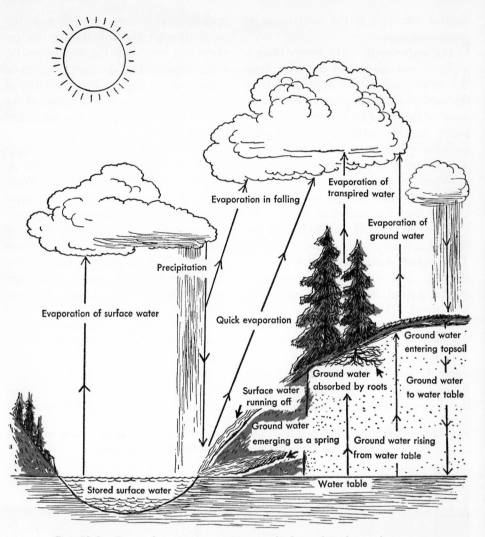

Fig. 52-9. Trace the steps in a water cycle from the above diagram.

comes saturated, water moves into the subsoil, where it is held around the rock particles and in soil spaces. Some of the water moves downward and reaches the **water table,** the point at which water is standing in the ground.

The depth of the water table depends on the amount of precipitation, the condition of the soil surface for receiving water, and the nature of the rock and clay layers under the soil. Where depressions occur, as in basins of lakes and ponds, the water table is above the surface.

In hilly regions, ground water may strike a shelf of rock and travel along it to the side of the hill. Here it emerges as a *spring*. **Dug wells** are holes which reach to the water table. As the water table lowers during dry spells, these wells can become dry. **Driven wells** reach water far below the danger of surface drainage. They are quite expensive to dig.

Fig. 52-10. Because of past misuse, large areas of land now support only a sparse cover of poor soil-binding plants. The soil is raw and hard. Topsoil has been washed away.

Movement of ground water. You may wonder why plants do not wilt between rains. This is because water moves from the water table up through the soil. Much of this water is absorbed by roots and passed to the atmosphere during transpiration. Some of it reaches the surface of the soil and evaporates into the atmosphere. This movement of water upward from the water table is an important part of the water cycle.

Depletion of ground water. The water table is lowering dangerously in many sections of the country. This is due largely to loss of water as runoff water during rainy periods. It is due, too, to the increased use of ground water in cities. Numerous wells, necessary to supply drinking water, draw heavily on the supply of ground water. Industries require large quantities of water. Large cities must supplement this supply with treated surface water taken from rivers, lakes, and artificial reservoirs.

However, in recent years, these cities have tapped the supply of ground water heavily in supplying cold water for air-conditioning systems. After the water has been used to remove the heat in buildings, it enters the sewer system and adds to the amount of surface water. It cannot be returned to the ground from which it was taken.

Runoff water. The water problem in America can never be solved until we have succeeded in reducing the amount of runoff water. To do this, we must correct costly mistakes of the past and restore part of the original wilderness.

This is what *should* happen when it rains. Rain which falls in level areas strikes the plant cover and drips to the surface of the soil. Most of the water which falls enters the soil and becomes ground water. Only when the soil is thoroughly soaked does it run off the surface or collect in pools.

In hilly and mountainous regions

Fig. 52-11. This farmstead was flooded by the Missouri River. Building dams and reservoirs are effective control measures against floods.

called **watersheds,** some of the water soaks into the topsoil, protected by trees and other vegetation. Much of it follows rivulets which lead down the slope to streams. Streams, in turn, carry the water to rivers. As rivers rise, water overflows channels and spreads into flood plains. Much flood water is received by sloughs and backwaters. As the crest of the flood passes, the flood plains feed water back to the channel. With the end of the rainy season, water is maintained in the river by the sloughs and backwaters and by numerous springs which feed streams in the watersheds. Thus the ground and natural surface reservoirs receive excess water during rainy periods and maintain the water supply during dry periods.

This condition is altered somewhat in the Great Plains where there are no forests or tall grasses to help hold water back during brief but heavy rainy periods. Flash floods and some soil loss cannot be avoided in these regions. This explains why De Soto saw muddy flood water in the Mississippi River.

Much of this mud came from the Great Plains region. Further east, the original tall grass prairies were dotted with sloughs and marshes during the rainy season.

But what *does* happen when it rains today? The spongy topsoil is gone in many regions. Rains pour onto hard subsoil clay, rush through deep gullies, and choke the streams. In watersheds where forests have been cut away, nothing stops the rush of water downhill in flash floods. Rivers rise rapidly and have no place to store the excess water. Long ago we reclaimed their backwaters and swamps and extended our fields and cities to their very banks. Storm warnings go out and people flee from their lowland homes. As much of our water supply roars to the sea, drought later in the season is inevitable. River channels which were swollen with flood waters during the rainy period become narrow, winding trickles when the rain stops. Crops bake in the fields.

Water conservation. We can summarize the measures necessary to control floods and prevent seasonal droughts as follows:

1. Control soil erosion and restore topsoil.

2. Restore forests, especially in watersheds.

3. Restore sloughs and backwaters along the rivers.

4. Prohibit cultivation of lowlands and flood plains of major rivers and restore the forests of these areas.

5. Build dams and reservoirs to hold back flood waters and store water for dry periods.

6. Control the use of ground water, especially in cities.

7. Maintain dikes and levees along major rivers. This measure, although the major flood control project in past years, is probably the least effective of all.

Dams and water power projects. As another means of controlling water, the government has constructed enormous dams in several sections of the country. These dams and the great reservoirs they form are important in preventing floods. In addition, they are the site of hydroelectric plants which use the water rushing over the dam to turn turbines attached to generators. In this way water power is converted into electricity for use in large areas of the nation. By raising the water level in the rivers, dams have made them navigable for long distances. In the west, water from reservoirs formed by dams is used for irrigation, and has made many semi-arid regions ideal for crop production. Deep, clear lakes which lie above the dams are ideal places for swimming, boating, and fishing.

In Conclusion

A soaking rain is a welcome sight to a farmer whose crops are flourishing in fertile fields. But to a family fleeing the flood waters of a river on a rampage, the sight of more rain only adds to their misery. It would seem that nature can be both kind and cruel. But when you examine our soil and water problems more closely, you discover that man cannot destroy nature's balance without paying a terrible price. Almost every dust storm, advancing gully, and disastrous flood is related somehow to man's carelessness or indifference. The forces of nature are powerful. They can produce a rich harvest or tremendous destruction. They can provide us with great wealth or great poverty.

Conservation is everybody's business. No nation can prosper on poor soil. Our economy depends on agriculture, and agriculture is geared to the water cycle.

Questions for Review

1. What are the several forces in nature which crumble rock and form subsoil?

2. From what sources are humus and peat formed?

3. Distinguish between depletion, leaching, and erosion. Mention the particular kinds of soil loss and the special cause of each.

4. Give several examples of row crops and cover crops.

5. How did overproduction in past years lead to soil depletion?

6. How can deep plowing and cultivation cause leaching, especially in sandy areas?

7. What are various methods of restoring organic matter to soil?

8. How can rill erosion lead to gully erosion?

9. Why are row crops alternated with cover crops in strip cropping?

10. In which kind of situation would terracing be used?

11. What are two methods of stopping the advance of a large gully?

12. What various methods can be used to prevent wind erosion? Can these be used in all parts of the country or are they adapted only to local situations?

13. Outline various phases of the water cycle.

14. List seven or more measures to reduce seasonal floods and prevent severe droughts.

 # Biologically Speaking

accelerated erosion	irrigation	soil exhaustion
contour farming	leaching	strip cropping
cover crop	peat	subsoil
crop rotation	precipitation	terracing
erosion	rill erosion	topsoil
evaporation	row crop	water cycle
geologic erosion	runoff water	water erosion
ground water	sheet erosion	water table
gully erosion	shelterbelt	watershed
humus	soil binder	wind erosion

 # Applying Facts and Principles

1. Discuss the various parts of topsoil and the importance of each to plant life.

2. Outline a crop rotation program and explain why each crop is included.

3. How can loss of soil organic matter lead to the loss of another vital part of topsoil?

4. Discuss the combination of strip cropping, contour farming, and crop rotation in hilly agricultural areas.

5. Discuss various mistakes in past years which have led to disastrous floods and droughts. How do you think they might have been avoided?

CHAPTER 53

Forests and Conservation

As you drive through many of our forest states, you may get the impression that timber trees are still abundant. The highways cut through grove after grove. And even in heavily farmed areas scattered woodlots and forested hillsides stretch across the horizon. But take a closer look. How far do unbroken forests extend from the highways? Do you still see extensive stands of large timber trees? How many trees are too small to cut or too crooked or damaged to be valuable as timber? How many are species which can never be used for saw logs or forest products? We have drawn heavily on our vast forest resources. Can our forests continue to meet these increased demands and still assure a supply of wood for the future, too? The idea of growing trees as a carefully regulated crop has been spreading rapidly in recent years. Foresters agree that we can produce all the wood we need if we get all of our forests under good management.

Some forest facts. The original forests covered nearly half our land — a total of more than 822 million acres. Forests occupied the eastern and western parts of our country. Prairies, plains, and arid lands covered much of the large central area.

The two great forest belts of the east and west were in turn divided into distinct types of forests. Then, as they are today, forests were greatly influenced by temperature, rainfall, soil, topography, and other physical factors of environment.

Today all of these same forest areas exist, although, for the most part, vigorous young second and third growth forests have replaced the original virgin stands. We will take a brief trip into each forest area, so as to get a picture of the total forest lands of America.

Forest areas of America. Foresters divide our nation's forests as follows:

1. Northern forest

2. Central hardwood forest
3. Southern forest
4. Tropical forest
5. Rocky Mountain forest
6. Pacific Coastal forest

Northern forest. We shall begin our journey in the region of the Great Lakes and the St. Lawrence River Valley in the **northern forest**. This forest continues into Canada where it broadens out and extends from the Atlantic to the Pacific Ocean. It is the only forest extending completely across the continent. The Canadian section of the northern forest differs somewhat from the portion in northern United States. However, both are dominated by evergreen (coniferous) trees. The Canadian forest consists largely of Canadian or white spruce, black spruce, and balsam fir. Foresters call this the **boreal** (*boh*-ree-al) **forest** and distinguish it from the *lake forest* region of the Great Lakes and the St. Lawrence River Valley.

Fig. 53-1. Deciduous trees, like these sugar maples and buckeye above, occur in the central hardwood forest.

The **lake forest** extends from Minnesota, through northern Wisconsin and Michigan northeast to Maine. Much of the lake forest grows on sandy soil. It is here that white pine, red or Norway pine, and jack pine grow in nearly pure stands and mingle with the spruce and fir of the Canadian forest. Lakes and bogs are abundant in this forest area. Their shores and the surrounding lowlands are often ringed with white cedar and larch, or tamarack. In open places, the paper or canoe birch and aspen are abundant. In more fertile soils, giant eastern hemlocks mingle with beech, maple, linden, yellow birch, and other hardwoods. Northern hardwood forests would probably crowd out the pine in time if they could adapt to the barren sandy soils of the area.

The northern forest has a long narrow arm which follows the mountain ridges from southeastern Canada, across the New England states, New York and Pennsylvania, through West Virginia, Virginia, and North Carolina, to Tennessee and into northern Georgia. At altitudes of from 3,000 to 5,000 feet, conifers of the northern evergreen forest mingle with hardwood trees in a mixed forest. Among the conifers are white pine, hemlock, and red spruce. Hardwood species are represented by red maple, oak, black gum, black birch, beech, linden, and yellow birch. In the Allegheny Mountains of Pennsylvania, the wild black cherry, one of our most valuable hardwood trees, grows in great abundance.

Trees of the northern evergreen forest, especially the white pine, have supplied the nation and much of the world with highly valuable timber in past years and are one of our major sources of pulpwood.

Central hardwood forest. Continuing southward from the lake forest, we enter one of the largest of forest areas. It extends from the prairies west of the Mississippi River to the Atlantic coastal states and from the lake forest nearly to the Gulf. We call it the **central hardwood forest.** Most of the trees are **deciduous** (dee-*sid*-you-us). That is, most of the trees growing in it drop their leaves each fall.

The central hardwood forest area is a region of rich, deep soil for the most part. The climate is moderate. The rainfall averages about 40 to 50 inches each year. Trees towering more than 150 feet and with trunk diameters at eight feet or more were common in the original hardwood forest, especially in the Ohio River Valley. Among the many tree species found in this forest are beech, oak, the maple, buckeye, hickory, elm, ash, walnut, sycamore, cottonwood, tulip or yellow poplar,

Fig. 53-2. This beautiful stand of loblolly pine is one of the common trees found in the southern forest.

sweet or red gum, shortleaf pine, and red cedar. Much of this forest was cleared early in our history because its soils were so fertile. Today, it is the center of very productive farmland.

Southern forest. The coastal plain extending from New Jersey to eastern Texas lies in a narrow belt along the Atlantic and Gulf Coasts. Its sandy soils support pine trees more than any other type. In the rich soils of the bottomlands and swamps, however, many commercially important deciduous, or hardwood trees, are found. The four principal species of pine which compose this forest are: (1) loblolly pine; (2) shortleaf pine; (3) longleaf pine; and (4) slash pine.

The leading hardwoods are black gum or tupelo, bald cypress, red and white oak, water oak, live oak, coast white cedar, willow, cottonwood, ash, and pecan. The black gum, or tupelo, water oak, and live oak form much of this broad-leaved forest. The bald cypress, a conifer which drops its needles each year, stands in the waters of swamps and backwaters. Further north, along the river bottoms, the pin oak forms dense forests. The rich soils of the Mississippi River delta area have come down the large rivers draining the vast area between the Rocky Mountains and Appalachian ranges. Seasonal flood waters have added to these deposits for centuries.

The southern forest supplies more than a third of the nation's lumber and more than half its pulpwood. It also supplies nearly all of the nation's turpentine, rosin, and other by-products of the forest classified as *naval stores.*

Fig. 53-3. Engelman's spruce of the Rocky Mountain region is valuable wood resembling white pine.

Tropical forest. Farthest south is the smallest region, the tropical forest. It includes only the southern tip of Florida where mahogany, mangroves, and bay trees grow, and a small area in southeastern Texas in which no commercially important species grow.

Rocky Mountain forest. About half of the western forest belt occupies the slopes of the Rocky Mountain ranges. Forests grow here because of decreased temperature and increased rainfall due to elevation. Deserts, sagebrush lands, and plains occupy the valleys between mountains. The forests occupy definite zones, extending up the slopes to the tree line. Among the most prominent trees of the western forest are ponderosa pine, lodgepole pine, Engelmann spruce, Colorado spruce, Douglas fir, Idaho white pine, true firs, and aspen. Millions of tourists admire the

beauty of the Rocky Mountain forest each year as they travel to National Parks and other scenic areas.

Pacific Coastal forest. The most beautiful of all evergreen forests extends along the Pacific Coast from middle California to Alaska. This forest grows along the western slopes of the Cascades and on the coastal ranges. Here, clouds hang low and moisture laden breezes blow in from the Pacific Ocean. The annual rainfall is more than 100 inches. The most famous trees of this magnificent forest are the giant redwoods in a narrow belt along the northwest coast of California. Along the west slopes of the Sierras in western California and extending up into southern Oregon grows the majestic sugar pine, the largest of our native pines, in a mixture with ponderosa, digger, and jeffrey pines, Douglas firs, true firs, and tan oak.

In separated groves at elevations of from 5,000 to 8,000 feet grow the giant sequoias or " Big Trees," many of which are 4,000 to 5,000 years old and are the largest trees in the United States. Farther north, the Douglas fir, western red cedar, western hemlock, western larch, Idaho white pine, and true firs form the towering forests of Oregon and Washington. The Sitka spruce and western hemlock follow the coastal region to the far north, where they form dense forests in Canada and Alaska.

All these forests have contributed greatly to the building of America. The varied trees which form them have supplied wood for nearly every purpose. They constitute a major part of the natural heritage of America.

Lumber, our chief forest product. The greatest drain on the forests has been the demand for construction lumber. Once it was for log cabins and rail fences. Later, it was lumber for frame buildings. Even in this age of brick and stone buildings, four out of every five homes are still made of wood. Regardless of the exterior building material, the average home uses 10,000 board feet of lumber for flooring, trim, window casings, and other wooden construction parts.

The evergreen forests supply most of the construction lumber today. This is due to the fact that our commercial forests have always contained more softwoods than hardwoods and also to the ease with which the soft wood of conifers can be worked.

The most important timber trees now supplying lumber are given in the table on page 692.

Lumber for furniture. Much of the supply of hardwood timber now goes to the furniture industry. Among some of the hardwood trees supplying lumber for making furniture are: red gum, oak (white and red), maple (sugar, or rock), black walnut, wild black cherry, and birch. Mahogany is imported from the tropics. Rising production costs have increased the cost of furniture made of solid wood to the point that veneer finish furniture is now much more popular. Less expensive furniture can be constructed of other wood, then covered with a layer of veneer.

Veneer is made by peeling a thin layer of wood from a hardwood log. The expensive wood shows on the surface, but is not used in the basic construction. Radio and television cabinets, pianos, and other pieces of furniture have beautiful grain designs produced by matching pieces of veneer.

Transportation and communication. Early in the history of our country, vast quantities of trees were used to build wooden ships and provide naval stores. The decks and planking of "Old Ironsides," now anchored in Bos-

Fig. 53-4. This stand of magnificent Douglas fir of the Pacific Coastal forest completely shades the forest floor. Large ferns, common to the region, are competing with the small firs for light and growing space beneath the giant trees.

ton Harbor, are native oak. But even though the wooden ships are gone, transportation and communication industries still need an enormous amount of timber. Had you ever thought about how much wood our railroads use?

There are about 3,000 crossties in a mile of track. Crossties have to be replaced as often as once in five to nine years. At this rate, railroads use about 40 million crossties each year on the average.

Add to this the wood used to construct and repair the countless buildings along the right-of-way. Then consider the wood used in certain freight car construction.

Communication depends to a great extent on the countless telephone poles which run across the nation. An entire tree is required for a single pole. In the case of high voltage lines, trees of

IMPORTANT TIMBER TREES

NAME OF TREE	FOREST REGION
Southern pine { loblolly, slash, shortleaf, longleaf	Southern forest
Douglas fir	Pacific Coastal forest
Ponderosa pine	Rocky Mountain forest
Oak	Central hardwood forest
Hemlock (eastern and western)	Northern and Pacific Coastal forest
Eastern white pine	Northern forest
Red Gum	Central hardwood and Southern forest
White fir	Rocky Mountain and Pacific Coastal forest
Poplar	Central hardwood and Southern forest
Maple	Northern forest
Redwood	Pacific Coastal forest
Tupelo	Southern forest and Central hardwood forest
Spruce	Northern forest
Cottonwood and aspen	Northern forest and Rocky Mountain forest
Cedar	Pacific Coastal, Northern, and Southern forest
Sugar pine	Pacific Coastal forest
Beech	Northern and Central hardwood forest
Larch	Rocky Mountain and Pacific Coastal forest
Idaho white pine	Rocky Mountain and Pacific Coastal forest
Cypress	Southern forest
Birch	Northern forest
Lodgepole pine	Rocky Mountain forest
Balsam fir	Northern forest

great size are needed. The tall straight trunks of the spruce, fir, pine, and white cedar are ideal for use as telephone poles.

Newsprint for your daily paper. A single New York daily newspaper needs the paper produced from the pulp from 44 acres of timberland to print a single edition! When you consider the number of daily newspapers in the nation, the timber required for a day's supply of newsprint is almost staggering. In addition to newsprint, high quality book paper, stationery, packaging paper, toweling, and a great many other kinds of paper must be supplied daily.

Distillation products. Various hardwoods yield valuable products as a result of distillation. When certain kinds of wood are heated in closed iron cylinders, various products are given off as vapors. These vapors are condensed by cooling into a variety of substances called **distillation products.** The wood turns black during distillation and becomes carbon or charcoal. Some of the

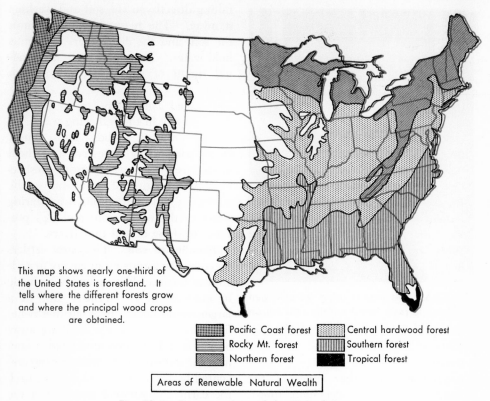

This map shows nearly one-third of the United States is forestland. It tells where the different forests grow and where the principal wood crops are obtained.

Pacific Coast forest	Central hardwood forest
Rocky Mt. forest	Southern forest
Northern forest	Tropical forest

Areas of Renewable Natural Wealth

Fig. 53-5. Forest regions of the United States.

products of hardwood distillation include: wood alcohol used as a solvent; acetic acid; lampblack used in making certain inks; oxalic acid, used for dyeing and bleaching; and charcoal used as a fuel, in water purification, and in other industrial processes.

Beech, maple, and birch are commonly used in hardwood distillation. For this reason, the distillation industry centers are in Wisconsin, Michigan, Ohio, Pennsylvania, and New York.

Pine products. The South, as a region, leads the nation in the production of pine products. The fast-growing pines of the southeastern evergreen forest supply nearly two-fifths of our nation's lumber. Nearly half the pulpwood used in making paper comes from this productive forest.

Turpentine, rosin, and pine tar are products of southern pines. When certain species of pine are tapped, they yield a large quantity of **resin,** a thick gummy sap. Resin is removed from the trees by cutting diagonal gashes through the bark into the wood. Resin is collected in jars or pots. When the resin is boiled, turpentine comes off as a vapor. It is condensed to liquid form by cooling. After extraction of turpentine, tar and rosin remain. Do not confuse pine tar with the asphalt tar we use on streets and roofs.

Rosin has many uses. You've probably seen a baseball pitcher reach for the rosin bag and a batter dust rosin onto the bat handle.

Maple sugar. Maple sugar is an important product of Vermont, New

Fig. 53-6. This man is using an acid gun to stimulate resin flow from the new cut on the face of a pine tree that is being prepared for turpentining.

York, Ohio, and other states of the northern region of the deciduous forest. Maple sugar comes from the sap of the sugar maple tree, which is collected in buckets attached to tapped trees in the early spring. The sap is boiled to remove much of the water, after which it becomes a thick syrup.

Tanning materials. The tanning industry depends on the forests of the world for bark containing tannic acid which is used in the tanning of hides. Chestnut wood, chestnut oak bark, eastern hemlock bark, and tanbark oak are the chief American sources. About 70 per cent of the nation's tanning supply comes from foreign woods, however. The tanning industry is centered mostly in the Lake States, Appalachian, and northeast forest regions.

Control of the water supply. The forest area acts like a sponge by absorbing the rainfall in its layers of humus. The leaves of trees keep the rain from falling directly on the soil and washing it away. The network of roots binds the soil, and the deep layers of humus hold water. Therefore, there is a gradual runoff of soil water, not a flash flood.

Forested land helps to control the water supply in the following ways: (1) Prevents floods and causes steady stream flow by reserve water held in humus; (2) prevents spring freshets by slower melting of snow due to the shade; (3) prevents drought by storing water in the wet season; and (4) prevents washing of soil into rivers.

Benefits to soil. The early settlers regarded the forests as an enemy to agriculture because clearing had to be made to make room for farms. But in a larger sense, forests are a distinct benefit to soil. *Erosion,* the washing away of soil by rain, is one of the worst enemies of agriculture. But this is prevented by forests whose roots hold back the earth and whose leaves protect the surface. Furthermore, the humus which collects on the forest floor supplies an essential element to all fertile soils.

In some areas, the forest performs another function in preventing the spread of wind-blown sand over fertile areas which are thus saved for use.

Effect of forests on climate. While this may not rank in importance with the two preceding, it is certain that by their retention of moisture, forests modify the climate over large areas and apparently influence rainfall. To a lesser extent, forests affect climate by giving protection from wind and sun.

Homes for birds and animals. Forests supply shelter, homes, and food for a great many birds and animals which are of direct importance to man. Many valuable birds seek the shelter of forest trees for nests, and feed on the wild

Fig. 53-7. This second growth of Ponderosa pine was burned by fire. All vegetative cover was destroyed and the intense heat burned down standing trees.

fruit and berries which grow there. Fur-bearing animals, like the raccoon, opossum, and squirrel, depend on the forest for food and cover. Forest streams supply cool clear water for many varieties of game fish, as well as smaller aquatic animals such as frogs and salamanders. Destruction of a forest destroys the entire woodland society of life. The loss of these forest birds and animals would be nearly as tragic as the loss of the trees themselves.

Forests — their use and misuse. More and more Americans are learning to regard forests as a crop. We are learning to harvest trees when mature and to leave seed sources to replace them as they are used. Our forest lands could have supplied all the timber required for building America without their serious depletion if they had been used wisely. Instead, they were destroyed by a rapidly growing nation with little regard for the future.

As early as 1905 officials in Washington, among them President Theodore Roosevelt, became alarmed about the critical condition of the forests. Accordingly, Congress created the United States Forest Service under the control of the Department of Agriculture. When Theodore Roosevelt signed the act creating this agency on February 1, 1905, the forest conservation movement in America was begun. Vast tracts of timber, especially in the West, were set aside as natural forests.

The United States Forest Service has established a splendid record through its years of activity. State and local agencies of conservation have looked to this agency for guidance and assistance in carrying out forest conservation programs. A well-trained staff of foresters work untiringly in research laboratories in an effort to discover better conservation methods, controls for forest diseases, more efficient lumbering practices, and new uses for timber products. Even more remarkable are the changes which have come on privately owned forest lands. Since it has become possible to manage forests properly and still make a financial profit, forestry has been spreading rapidly. More professional foresters are hired by forest industries today than by the Federal government. No small task in both the administration of the national forests and the management of millions of acres of private woodlands is the protection of these valuable timberlands from fire.

Fire — the forest's worst enemy. During 1953, 154,160 fires burned over 9,975,750 acres of forest in the United States. This is a staggering loss to our nation. Fire protection has been extended to more and more forest areas in recent years, but at the beginning of 1954, 52,902,000 acres still lacked organized fire protection.

Aside from the danger to human life, a forest fire destroys standing timber and consumes the seeds and young trees of the future forest. A large fire may even burn into the rich humus of the forest floor. The toll of animal life cannot be determined. Disaster continues as rains pour over the blackened earth and debris, washing the remaining humus into streams.

Causes of forest fires. According to reports of the United States Forest Service in recent years, the following are the most common causes of forest fires. The causes are listed in the order of frequency:

1. Incendiarists (those who set fires deliberately).

2. Debris burners (those who let brush fires get out of control).

3. Smokers (especially those who throw lighted cigarettes, cigars, and matches from automobiles).

4. Lightning.

5. Campers (especially those who leave live coals in a campfire).

6. Railroads.

7. Lumbering.

8. Miscellaneous.

It is shocking to learn that incendiarists are the leading cause of forest fires. Fires resulting from debris burners and smokers could be avoided if people were more careful and considerate of others. Lightning, the only natural cause, is responsible for less than ten per cent of the forest fires a year.

Fire prevention. In protected forests, fire towers are placed at strategic points. Usually all areas of the forest are visible from at least two towers. Trained rangers survey the forest from the towers and report any evidence of fire to headquarters. A ranger cannot determine the exact distance of a fire from his tower, but he can report its direction. The same fire, spotted from another tower, will be reported from another angle. The point where the two lines of direction cross indicates the exact location of the fire. Fire fighters equipped with trucks, water tanks, and chemical fire extinguishers can often bring a fire under control before it becomes extensive. **Fire lines,** which resemble roads, penetrate the forest at regular intervals. They serve as avenues for reaching a fire and provide gaps at which a fire can be stopped. In some places, however, fires can be reached only by dropping fire-fighting crews from airplanes by parachute.

Our forests are protected from fire at a risk of many lives and at a cost of millions of dollars. It would seem a simple matter for all of us to cooperate in observing these simple rules in forest areas.

1. Never throw away lighted tobacco or matches.

2. Build campfires only in protected

MAJOR CAUSES OF FOREST FIRES

Fig. 53-8. Principal causes of forest fires.

areas and *put the fire out completely*.

3. Watch for fire while driving through a forest. If you see a small one, stop and put it out. If the fire is too large to extinguish by yourself, report it at once.

4. Report any suspicious person attempting to start a fire.

5. Never burn a field or debris close to a forest or without adequate help to keep the fire from spreading.

6. Become acquainted with your state's forest fire laws.

7. Get to know your nearest fire warden or foresters.

Insect enemies. In our study of insects we mentioned the damage some of them cause to trees. The saw flies, bark beetles, spruce budworm, wood-boring beetles, western pine beetle, white pine weevil, gypsy moth, hemlock looper, browntail moth, pine shoot moth, tent caterpillar, and tussock moth are among the worst forest pests. Sprays containing DDT and other powerful insecticides are effective against these pests. However, it is difficult to spray an extensive forest. We must depend principally on control by natural enemies of these insects.

Fig. 53-9. Fire towers, set up in forest areas, enable forest rangers to locate fires before they have a chance to become too widespread.

Birds are valuable although assistance is rendered also by frogs, toads, snakes, ichneumon flies, and other insect destroyers.

Nearly all of the American chestnut trees still standing in our forests are dead. Not many years ago, it was a common and valuable timber tree of the Northeast, Appalachian, and Ohio Valley regions. The chestnut tree fell victim to a blight, introduced accidentally from Asia in 1892. However, the wood of the dead trees is still being harvested for tannin extraction. Disease-resistant crosses of American and Chinese chestnut trees have been developed which show promise of restoring chestnuts to the American forest. This is another way in which man works with nature to develop new weapons with which to fight forest diseases.

Dutch elm disease is also spreading through the Middle West. The only hope of saving this elm and several other species is control of a bark beetle which carries the disease. Such control cannot be done on a large scale. Individual infected trees must be cut down as soon as the disease has been diagnosed.

We mentioned the white pine blister rust when studying the fungi. This serious disease can be controlled by destroying the wild currant and gooseberry, since the rust alternates between these plants and the white pine.

A disease first diagnosed and classified in 1942 as oak wilt has now spread from Wisconsin to several surrounding states as far east as Pennsylvania and south to Arkansas. It threatened to destroy all our great oak forests, source of some of our most valuable wood. Research was undertaken to halt the wilt's spread and, if possible, to cure the infested trees. In early 1954 scientists said that a remedy seemed in sight.

We depend on foresters and other specialists in the laboratories of the United States Forest Service, state forestry departments, universities, and private laboratories to find answers to the insect and disease problems.

Grazing and gnawing animals. In many of the deciduous forest states, pasturing is the greatest forest enemy. Pasturing of cattle, horses, sheep, or hogs in wood lots will completely destroy the trees in time. First, the animals eat or trample the young trees and reduce the woods to an open grove. Later they destroy the leaves on the lower limbs and injure roots and trunks. Aside from shelter, the animals receive very little value from a woods pasture. Trees and other plants of the forest are high in cellulose but very low in protein — an essential substance for the production of flesh and milk.

Weather conditions. Wind, ice, and snow are beyond our power to control. However, damage done to forests by natural forces should receive attention.

Broken limbs open a tree to attack by fungus diseases and insect pests. Forest litter resulting from ice storms creates a fire hazard and should be cleared out regularly.

Reforestation. The return of a forest to an open area is a slow process. *Reforestation* is a lengthy and costly process, but it is a vital part of the conservation program. Large sections, useless for agriculture, have been cleared unwisely in past years. These regions, as well as eroded, heavily lumbered, and burned-out areas, should be returned to trees as rapidly as possible.

The various forest states, the United States Forest Service, and many private lumber and paper companies maintain large nurseries where seedlings of timber species are grown. Private land owners planted more than 574,000 acres in 1953, and plan to increase this number substantially in the future. Some associations of wood-using industries now grow their own seedlings and give them free of charge to forest landowners in their operating areas. Pine is being used in reforestation of many hardwood forest regions because it matures rapidly and yields valuable construction lumber.

Forest management. How valuable is a virgin forest? You may be surprised to learn that it is not as valuable as a planted and second-growth, managed forest. A brief description of a virgin forest will tell why.

A virgin forest is always dominated by large, overripe trees. They have occupied their places for centuries — long past their period of rapid growth and many of them are dying at the top. Some have been damaged by storms and are liable to attack by disease and insect pests. Much of the forest space is occupied by trees which have no commercial timber value. Other trees have

Fig. 53-10. Insects killed these trees. Skeletons of once mighty trees stand stark against the sky in this photograph made in the Douglas fir region of the Pacific Northwest.

grown crooked in their race for light. The floor is littered with fallen trees in various stages of decomposition.

Compare this forest with a managed forest, operated on a **sustained yield** basis. A forest so planned will yield trees for cutting regularly. All the trees are valuable timber species. Weed trees, damaged trees, crowded trees, crooked trees, and diseased trees are removed in **improvement cutting.** As timber trees mature, they are removed by **selective cutting.** The forest is a source of constant revenue to the owner and yet is never cut extensively. Every inch of space produces good timber, and every tree is a perfect specimen.

Today, all national forests are using good cutting practices. Furthermore, private owners of nearly 34 million acres of timber in 36 states have pledged co-

Fig. 53-11. Selective cutting in a managed forest means more revenue and perfect specimens of trees. By this practice, a good reserve stand of fast growing trees is constantly maintained.

operation in a tree-farm program. You can identify these managed timber tracts by posted tree-farm signs.

Block cutting is another kind of lumbering used in stands of timber in which all the trees are about the same age. Here it is desirable to cut out a complete block and reseed it or replant it. In block cutting, stands of timber are left around the block for natural reseeding and protection of the exposed land. When small trees are established, another block can be cut. This method of lumbering is used in extensive stands of Douglas fir and a modified method called "strip cutting" is used in the harvesting of spruce.

National parks and national forests. The six million acres of forest in the 28 national parks have been preserved for-ever. They are part of game preserves and recreational areas dedicated to those who seek natural beauty which is completely undisturbed.

In addition, there are 153 national forests covering more than 181 million acres. The national forests supply timber for about 10 per cent of the nation's needs for forest products. In addition, they supply homes for wildlife and aid greatly in restoring birds and animals which have been reduced in number in past years. During summer months, when drought strikes the Great Plains, they are opened to cattle and sheep as grazing areas under supervision. In addition, they are *recreational areas* which attract campers and sportsmen who fish in their lakes and streams.

In Conclusion

What of tomorrow's forests? Will future generations be forced to find substitutes for wood and wood products because the forests were destroyed before their time? Or is there hope that the America of future years will receive a rich heritage in forest resources because our generations corrected the costly mistakes of the past?

True, the virgin forests of pioneer days will never be restored. But in their places even better forests are already producing crop after crop of trees. They are protected from fire and disease and are being scientifically managed to yield the maximum timber production. As this scientific management increases and spreads to all of our forests, our future wood supply will be assured. Little space will be wasted with over-age giants, diseased and injured trees, or species with low economic value. Trees will be a crop to be harvested when they are mature. Cutting will be a continuous process. At no time will the forest be completely destroyed.

Forestry today is a highly specialized science. Forest management and conservation is its most important business.

Questions for Review

1. What are the forest areas of America?

2. (a) List at least ten valuable timber trees. (b) From what forest regions do we get each species?

3. How do the railroads make various uses of lumber?

4. Name several products of the distillation of hardwoods.

5. (a) List the principal products of pine resin. (b) What forest region supplies nearly all of these products?

6. What are some of the trees which supply bark for the tanning industry?

7. In what respects are forests essential to wildlife?

8. (a) What are the various causes of forest fires? (b) Indicate which ones are deliberate, the result of carelessness, or unavoidable. (c) How can forest fires be prevented?

9. How can two forest rangers, viewing a fire from towers, pinpoint the location of the fire?

10. List several of the worst insect enemies of forest trees.

11. What types of trees are removed from a managed forest during improvement cutting?

12. Under what conditions are whole sections of a forest cleared by block cutting?

Biologically Speaking

block cutting
boreal forest
central hardwood forest
deciduous forest
distillation products
fire line
improvement cutting
lake forest

maple sugar
northern forest
Pacific Coastal forest
pine tar
pulpwood
reforestation
resin
Rocky Mountain forest

rosin
selective cutting
southern forest
sustained yield
tannic acid
tropical forest
turpentine
veneer

Applying Facts and Principles

1. The climate of the lake forest and southern forest regions is ideal for broad-leaved trees. Yet, these areas support pine forests, for the most part. Account for this.

2. Explain why the soil of the southern forest region is different from the coastal plain areas to the east and to the west.

3. The largest conifers in the world grow in the Pacific Coastal forest. What conditions in this forest area are responsible for these enormous trees?

4. Much of the forest wealth of our nation was wasted in past years. Find out various ways in which forests have been destroyed needlessly and discuss these.

5. Discuss the scientifically managed forest operated on a sustained yield basis and show how this forest is more productive and more valuable than a virgin forest.

CHAPTER 54

Wildlife Conservation

When the pioneers pushed westward through the North American wilderness, they found abundant wildlife on every hand. Inland waters teemed with fish, birds, and aquatic mammals. Large and small game roamed the forest and grassland. The woods bison, now extinct, lived in the forests as far east as New York State. Its western cousin, the plains bison (buffalo), thundered across the grasslands in herds numbering tens of thousands. The white-tailed deer thrived in millions of acres of forest lands and supplied the early settlers with both meat and buckskin. The wildcat and cougar (mountain lion), timber wolf and fox, beaver and muskrat, weasel and mink were some of the mammals of the wilderness.

As the settlers began their conquest of the wilderness, wildlife began its slow retreat. What caused this gradual decline? Was it the rifles of the pioneers? Was it the trapper or the market hunter? All these have been factors, but none has played a principal role. It was silt and poisoned water, drained marshes and leveled forests as well. It was useless destruction of vast areas of natural habitat — areas man really did not need and should have left to the native wildlife.

We learned our lesson a few years ago. Deer now roam the forests of many states that had exterminated their native deer a century ago. Raccoons, opossums, squirrels, skunks, and many other small mammals are multiplying in every wilderness that is left to them within their natural ranges.

Can wildlife flourish in 20th century America with its sprawling cities and vast agricultural lands? It can and will if we give it a chance. Conservation is showing us how.

Divisions of wildlife. The term *wildlife* includes all native animals. However, the wildlife conservation program is concerned primarily with those native animals which have a direct food, fur, or sporting value. Divisions of wildlife include:

1. Fish, especially fresh-water game and food fish.

2. Birds, including our many song birds of forest, field, yard, and park.

3. Waterfowl, including ducks, geese, and wading birds.

4. Upland game birds.

5. Smaller game mammals with food, fur, and sporting value.

6. Big game mammals.

Since management problems in each of these divisions differ, we will consider each one separately.

Fish conservation. We often hear that a stream or a lake is "fished out." It would probably be more correct to say that a body of water is no longer suitable for a fish population. More rigid laws regulating fishing are not the

Fig. 54-1. A lake provided with vegetation such as this is important as a spawning ground and as a place for fish fry to grow.

solution. Nor will restocking help in many cases. Give the fish the proper environment and they will hold their own and even increase in heavily fished streams and lakes.

In the study of fish conservation, we must first find out the characteristics of productive waters. Then we will consider various practices which destroy fish and make waters unproductive. Finally, we will discuss conservation measures which can restore ideal habitats and return the fish to our waters.

Characteristics of a productive lake and stream. A lake which supports a thriving fish population must supply many different environments suitable for large species and smaller ones, frogs, insects, and other vital parts of a complicated society and food chain. Deep channels and holes are necessary to protect fish during both the cold of winter and the extreme heat of summer. The depth at which fish live varies greatly with water temperature. During the

spawning season, sunfish, bass, and many other species leave the deep water and enter clear, shallow pools and backwaters. Here the fry hatch and live protected by water plants in shallow areas.

Protozoa, tiny crustaceans, and larvae of various insects supply food necessary for small fish. As the smaller fish leave the shallow water and enter deep water, they become food for predatory game fish, such as the bass, pike, trout, and perch. *Forage fish,* including such species as shiners, chubs, and other minnows, while they have no sport or food value for man, are vital as a food for the larger species of game fish.

The productive stream has rapids and riffles, shallows and depths, channels and undercut banks. Larger rivers are fed from productive backwaters. Fallen logs and driftwood provide ideal habitats for many species. Abundant water plants are necessary to oxygenate the water, provide food for vegetarian fish

Fig. 54-2. Fish ladders enable fish to travel upstream during the spawning season.

and other aquatic animals, and supply the organic matter required by bacteria, protozoans, and organisms essential in the food chain.

Destruction of aquatic habitats. Many practices, some careless and others deliberate, have destroyed aquatic habitats. In regions where the water table has been lowered by removal of vegetation, soil erosion, and other misuse of the land and water resources, the level of lakes and ponds has fallen. Small ponds may dry out completely during the summer. The water in larger lakes may recede to the point that shallow areas and backwaters are left dry. This destroys both spawning areas and regions where much of the food supply develops. In many cases, backwaters and marshes have been drained deliberately because they were thought to be useless wasteland.

The channels of many rivers have been dredged and straightened to increase the flow of water. Such open channels may be good from the standpoint of flood control, but they are not good surroundings for fish. Fish thrive better in a river with natural bends, rapids, and deep pools.

Dams across rivers interfere with fish migrations unless fish ladders are provided. A **fish ladder** is a channel around a dam through which fish can travel upstream. The fast flow of water is broken by a series of staggered plates projecting into the water from the sides. In other fish ladders, a long slope is broken into a series of steps like terraces, which can be leaped by fish traveling upstream.

Serious floods are tragic, not only to man, but to fish and aquatic animals as well. When flood waters overflow the lowlands, many fish leave the channel and follow the rising water. Large numbers are left stranded in isolated pools when the waters recede.

Water unfit for fish. Many game fish cannot survive in water containing a large amount of mud and silt. Mud coats the surface of the gill filaments and prevents oxygen from reaching the blood stream. This causes suffocation, especially in species with a high oxygen requirement.

Sewage, garbage, cannery waste, and other organic refuse dumped into water kill fish for another reason. Organic matter decays in water as a result of bacterial action. Oxygen is used during this process and fish die for want of oxygen in water.

Industrial and chemical wastes poured into streams poison fish and other aquatic animals. Cyanide, acids, alkalies, and other industrial wastes may affect the stream's inhabitants for many miles downstream.

Hatchery programs. Both state and federal fish hatcheries produce large numbers of game fish in their rearing ponds. The hatcheries maintain a stock of adult breeders which are kept in special spawning pools. After spawning, the breeder fish are removed to prevent destruction of the small fish. Fry hatched in late spring reach stocking size by midsummer or early fall. Many hatcheries use special trucks equipped with aerated tanks for transporting small fish to distant streams and lakes.

Artificial propagation and stocking

Fig. 54-3. These are trout eggs from a fish hatchery. The white eggs are infertile. When the eggs hatch, the young fish are raised in tanks and pools. Later they are used to stock streams and lakes.

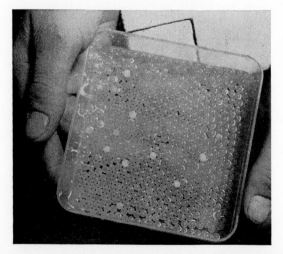

are essential parts of fish conservation programs. However, it is useless to stock polluted waters or those that lack conditions necessary to supply adequate food.

Private rearing ponds and lakes. Many farmers have constructed earthen ponds in low corners of fields by building up banks. These farm ponds are stocked with crappies, bluegills, catfish, and other species. The pond supplies recreation, conserves water, helps prevent soil erosion, and supplies many strings of fish for the dinner table.

Great numbers of artificial lakes have been made by building dams and backing up water in valleys. Lakes of this type are ideal for fishing and boating.

Laws protecting fish. While laws governing fishing vary in different states, they usually contain the following provisions:

1. Closed seasons for certain species, usually during the spawning season.

2. Length limit, or a size under which a fish may not be kept.

3. Bag limit, or a limit to the number of individuals of a given species a person can take in a single day.

4. Possession limit, or the number of a species a person may have in his possession from several days' catch.

5. Laws prohibiting the use of explosives or draining ponds to kill fish.

6. Restriction as to the size, mesh diameter, and use of nets or mechanical traps.

7. Laws prohibiting or restricting the spearing of fish.

8. Laws requiring the construction of fish ladders at dams.

9. Laws prohibiting the dumping of chemical wastes and other polluting materials into streams, rivers, and lakes.

10. Laws requiring the purchase of a fishing license for use on inland waterways.

Importance of fishing. Perhaps you think one of the best ways to conserve fish is to prohibit fishing. However, this is not true. A small lake or pond, especially, should be fished regularly to remove large fish and make food supply and space for new crops. This also prevents the fish population from growing beyond the available food supply.

Useless destruction of valuable allies, the birds. The advancing tide of civilization has made dangerous inroads into the population of song birds and game birds. Much of this destruction was useless and avoidable.

The cutting of forests, clearing of underbrush, and burning of fields have removed vast areas of bird homes. Unnecessary drainage of marshes and lowering of the water in ponds and lakes have deprived water birds and wading birds of both food and nesting sites.

In former years many thousands of birds were slaughtered for flesh or feathers. Fortunately, such *market hunting* is forbidden now, both by federal and state laws. But conservation measures came too late to save some species that were once common but are now extinct.

In the early 1800's Audubon described flocks of passenger pigeons so large they darkened the sky. When such flocks settled in trees to roost for the night, their enormous weight bent the branches and sent many crashing to the ground. We have reports of pigeon hunters who climbed the trees and knocked thousands of pigeons from their perches with clubs. Thousands of others were gathered in sacks to be sold for a few cents each or left on the ground as food for hogs. The last survivor of what is estimated to have been over 2,000,000,000 passenger pigeons died in the Cincinnati zoo in 1914. What caused the complete extermination of

Fig. 54-4. Fishing is a sport that appeals to all ages. However, the true fisherman is an active supporter of the conservation program.

this valuable bird in less than 100 years? Perhaps the introduction of an epidemic disease hastened the end of those that escaped the ruthless market hunting. Certainly no thought was given to conservation until too late.

Rare birds we may still save. Bird societies are watching several other species which are nearing extermination, but which may still be saved.

Only a few ivory-billed woodpeckers remain in the forests of southern river bottoms. Anyone seeing one of these rare birds should report it immediately to the National Audubon Society.

The whooping crane is disappearing from the region of the Great Plains. During the Christmas count in 1953–1954, only seven whooping cranes were found. These were in the Arkansas National Wildlife Refuge.

The prairie chicken was hunted widely for market in earlier times. More recently its numbers have been further reduced by plowing native grasslands in the prairie states.

Fig. 54-5. The California condor (left) and the Trumpeter swan (right) are nearing extinction. Conservation measures must be used to protect these species.

The California condor, largest bird of prey, is a rare species of the mountainous regions of the far west. Less than 100 of these great birds are left. The condor, with a body three feet long and a wing spread of ten feet or more, lives on decaying flesh. Lack of food and the fact that it lays only one or two eggs each season may doom it to extinction.

Problems relating to game birds. Migratory ducks and geese have been favorite game for hunters. However, the decline in their populations during the past 50 years has been due only partially to hunters. The draining of marshes which supply natural food such as wild rice, as well as nesting places and cover have presented a serious problem in conserving these birds. Large numbers of ducks die of alkali poisoning on ponds and lakes of the western prairies when the water is low and the salts become concentrated. In some regions, thousands of ducks and geese have died of botulism when they consumed the deadly toxin while probing for food in the mud of ponds and lakes

at low water. Lead poisoning takes its toll when game birds are wounded by lead pellets instead of being killed outright by hunters.

Upland game birds, including the quail, partridge, grouse, wild turkey and pheasant, are widely hunted by sportsmen. They can survive regulated hunting only if adequate food and cover are provided, especially during winter months. Many farmers allow trees, shrubs, and tall grass to grow along their fence rows and roadsides as cover. A few rows of grain left at the margin of fields provides winter food for these and other birds.

Laws to protect our birds. As early as 1885 the Ornithological Union drafted a law known as the *Audubon Law*. This law was adopted in most states.

In general, bird laws of the states and the federal government include the following provisions:

1. Non-game birds such as song birds may not be killed at any time.

2. Closed seasons are provided for game birds.

Fig. 54-6. Farmers who leave a few rows of grain along the borders of fields do much to conserve these ring-necked pheasants and other birds. (Male pheasant on the right; female pheasant on the left.)

3. English sparrows, starlings, sharp-shinned hawks, Cooper's hawks, great horned owls, ravens, and crows are not protected.

4. Laws protecting song birds apply to their eggs.

5. Birds and eggs may be taken for scientific purposes only with official permission.

The Federal Tariff Bill prohibits the importation of feathers, skins, plumes, wings, or quills of wild birds except for educational purposes.

The Migratory Bird Treaty Act is an international agreement between the United States and Canada. The Canadian Parliament approved it in 1917 after which our Congress approved it in 1918. The Act was amended by Con-

gress in 1936 to include an agreement with Mexico to protect both migratory birds and animals.

The work of bird societies. One of the most active and best known of many bird societies is the National Audubon Society and its various state and local organizations. The Audubon Society supplies literature regarding birds and bird habits and other educational material including pictures, slides, and motion pictures. In addition, the Society is a powerful influence in legislation to protect our wildlife. A yearly census is taken to determine the bird population. Many bird students and scientific workers support the activities of the Wilson Society, another national bird organization.

Private agencies work closely with the Fish and Wildlife Service, a department of the United States Department of the Interior. This important Bureau has charge of the conservation of birds and other animals, controls the national wildlife reservations, administers laws regarding commerce in game, and publishes many educational bulletins and other information.

Destruction of fur-bearing animals. The first drain on the mammal population of North America occurred early in our history. Long before the pioneers began their journey westward, trappers had explored the wilderness in search of fur-bearing animals. As long ago as 150 years, trappers were penetrating the forests of the Pacific Northwest. Their prize was the beaver, highly valued in the eastern and European markets. "Empire builder" is an appropriate name for this valuable fur-bearer which played a major role in the settlement of this vast wilderness country. Fortunes were made in the fur business during these times. The pelts of beaver, mink, otter, muskrat, fox, skunk, and other fur-bearers brought an annual revenue of more than $100,-000,000. Early trappers were ruthless hunters. They gave no thought to conservation of the animals they sought. The numbers of fur-bearing animals decreased rapidly. Later the settlers began clearing and cultivating the land. Mammals which had escaped the trappers retreated farther and farther into the remaining wilderness.

Destruction of larger mammals. The slaughter of the plains bison is a story of useless waste. In the middle of the last century, herds of bison numbering many thousands thundered across the Great Plains. For centuries, this noble animal had supplied both flesh and hides to plains Indians. But as calves replaced the mature animals taken from the herds by hunting, both the Indians and the bison flourished. Then came the buffalo hunters. Bison were slaughtered in tremendous numbers as food for workmen building railroads through the west or for pure sport. At one time, passengers on trains amused themselves by firing at bison from open platforms. It is shocking to learn that great numbers of bison were killed deliberately to starve the plains Indians into submission. Within 50 years, bison herds were reduced from tens of thousands to mere remnants. At one time it appeared likely that the bison might die out entirely.

The white-tailed deer and black bear vanished from the remaining forests of most of the central and eastern agricultural states. Elk, mule deer, and antelope were slaughtered on the western ranges.

What did the destruction of so much of the game resources profit America? It supported a rich fur trade for a time. And it provided food and clothing to pioneer families. But this could have been accomplished by sacrificing only a small portion of the wildlife population. Much of the destruction of wildlife was useless, careless waste.

Wildlife restoration. Most small mammal and big-game mammal species have survived in greatly reduced numbers in the remaining wilderness regions. Can they return with our help to at least a portion of their former ranges? Can we make room for them among our many farms and ranches with their enormous population of domestic animals? This will require careful planning and scientific management. But it can be done.

Restoration of small animals. The residents of New England have noticed an increase in the population of raccoons, fox, opossums, squirrels, beavers, and other mammals in recent years. The increase in number of these species has been natural and not the result of artificial stocking from game farms. Why are they coming back? The answer can be found in the forests which have returned to hillsides once cleared for agriculture but since abandoned because they proved unprofitable. In other words, these mammals can live in heavily populated regions if cover and food supply are available.

Many residents of large cities are surprised to see an opossum, raccoon, groundhog, or even an occasional fox on a street at night. These animals are thriving in small sections of woodland in the vicinity.

Fur farming. Fur farms have spared large numbers of native fur-bearing animals which might otherwise have been taken to meet the demand for pelts. Many marshy areas have been converted to profitable muskrat farms. It is interesting to learn that the muskrat is the most widely used fur-bearing animal, and that Louisiana leads all other states in fur production because of the number of these animals in the Mississippi delta.

Game management. You might think that the best way to conserve our native mammals is to establish large areas where hunting is prohibited. Unfortunately, the problem is not that simple. On several game preserves, deer and elk have multiplied to the point that they have exhausted the food supply. Large herds of starving animals defeat all the principles of conservation.

Those who manage game preserves know exactly how much food and cover are available for the various mammals in the area. A census at regular intervals tells them the size of the big game population. When the numbers become too large, the preserve is opened to restricted hunting. Thus a managed game preserve supplies both food and sport in addition to conserving native mammals.

In Conclusion

The wildlife of America belongs to you. What can you do to conserve it? The most basic contribution you can make is an active interest in wildlife conservation. If you live on a farm or a ranch, think of the birds and animals along your fence rows or in the brush and woodland you have not cultivated. If you are one of the many city dwellers, protect the squirrels in the park and the rabbits in the vacant lot. If you fish and hunt, respect the laws and limits. They protect your interests and add to your outdoor pleasures.

Have you thought of joining the Audubon Society or the Wilson Club? Have you heard of the Isaak Walton League? These organizations would welcome you if you are interested in wildlife and conservation. Ducks Unlimited, The National Wildlife Federation, and The American Wildlife Institute are other civilian agencies which are carrying on important work. They deserve your full support and cooperation.

Questions for Review

1. What six divisions of wildlife are important in wildlife conservation?

2. What are some features of a productive river or stream?

3. How has lowering of the water table caused serious loss of fish even in bodies of water which do not dry out?

4. Describe the operation of a fish ladder around a dam.

5. How are farm ponds made?

6. List six or more restrictions placed on fishing in most states.

7. Make a list of bird species which are now very rare or nearly extinct.

8. Discuss various problems relating to conservation of ducks and geese.

9. Name several species of upland game birds in your region.

10. List five provisions of the Audubon Law.

11. What fur-bearing mammal has been called the " empire builder " and why?

12. Name several valuable mammals which are raised profitably on fur farms.

Biologically Speaking

Audubon Society	fur-bearing mammal	market hunting
farm pond	game bird	pollution
Federal Tariff Bill	game fish	upland game bird
forage fish	game preserve	wildlife

Applying Facts and Principles

1. Discuss the role of sportsmen in the fish and wildlife conservation program.

2. Discuss the work of the Audubon Society and other societies in conservation.

3. List various problems in restoring big-game mammals in the agricultural states.

4. Why are predatory birds and animals essential to proper game management?

5. Discuss the problem of destruction of wildlife on the highways.

Research On Your Own

1. Using soil or plaster of Paris, build models of slopes illustrating contour farming, strip farming, and terracing. Crops may be indicated with small straws or sticks, or painted (if plaster is used).

2. Prepare a soil profile in a glass cylinder, using gravel in the bottom, then sand, clay, and topsoil. Pour water through it and study its movement to the bottom of the cylinder. Add water until it stands about halfway from the bottom of the soil profile. Over a period of several days, study the movement up through the soil as the surface loses water.

3. If a soil test kit is available, test various soils for the following: acidity, nitrates, phosphates, and potash. Individual kits are available for each of these tests; large kits include all of the tests.

4. Locate on an outline map of the United States the major dams and water power projects.

5. Conduct a wildlife census of a woods, a section of forest, a field, or a marsh in your area. Record the various birds, mammals, and other animals you see and the numbers of each.

 ———————————————— **More About Biology**

Allen, Durward L. *OUR WILDLIFE LEGACY.* Funk and Wagnalls Co., New York. 1954

Butcher, Devereux. *EXPLORING OUR NATIONAL PARKS AND MONUMENTS.* Houghton Mifflin Co., Boston. 1954

Dupuy, William Atherton. *OUR BIRD FRIENDS AND FOES.* John C. Winston Co., Philadelphia. 1940

Graham, E. H. and Van Dersal, W. R. *WILDLIFE FOR AMERICA.* Oxford University Press, New York. 1949

Grange, Wallace. *THOSE OF THE FOREST.* The Flambeau Publishing Co., Babcock, Wisc. 1954

Headstrom, Richard. *GARDEN FRIENDS AND FOES.* Ives Washburn, Inc., New York. 1954

Holberg, Ruth. *RESTLESS JOHNNY APPLESEED.* The Thomas Y. Crowell Co., New York. 1950

Kieran, Margaret and Kieran, John. *JOHN JAMES AUDUBON.* Random House, Inc., New York. 1954

Lathrop, Dorothy P. *LET THEM LIVE.* The Macmillan Co., New York. 1951

McElroy, Thomas. *HANDBOOK OF ATTRACTING BIRDS.* Alfred A. Knopf, Inc., New York. 1950

Milne, Loreus. *FAMOUS NATURALISTS.* Dodd, Mead and Co., New York. 1952

Morgan, Ann Haven. *FIELD BOOK OF ANIMALS IN WINTER.* G. P. Putnams Sons, New York. 1939

Panshin, Harrar. *FOREST PRODUCTS.* McGraw-Hill Book Co., Inc., New York. 1950

Shippen, Katherine Binney. *GREAT HERITAGE.* The Viking Press, New York. 1947

Smith, F. C. *THE FIRST BOOK OF CONSERVATION.* Franklin Watts, Inc., New York. 1954

Appendix

A SIMPLIFIED CLASSIFICATION OF ORGANISMS

PLANTS

PHYLUM I Thallophyta (thah-*loff*-ih-tah) [110,000 species]

One-celled or many-celled plants lacking usual tissues and without roots, stems, or leaves. Some possess chlorophyll; others do not. Reproduction by fission, spores, or gametes. Spore and gamete producing structures usually unicellular.

SUBPHYLUM 1. ALGAE: Thallophyte plants possessing chlorophyll, in addition to other pigments in certain groups.

    Class 1. Cyanophyceae (sy-an-oh-*fy*-sih-ee): Blue-green algae [*Nostoc; Oscillatoria* (ah-sih-lah-*toh*-ree-ah)]

    Class 2. Chlorophyceae (kloh-roh-*fy*-sih-ee): Green algae [*Protococcus; Spirogyra; Ulothrix* (*yoo*-loh-thriks)]

    Class 3. Chrysophyceae (kry-soh-*fy*-sih-ee): Golden-brown algae [diatoms]

    Class 4. Phaeophyceae (fay-oh-*fy*-sih-ee): Brown algae [*Fucus;* kelp; *Sargassum*]

    Class 5. Rhodophyceae (roh-doh-*fy*-sih-ee): Red algae [seaweeds]

SUBPHYLUM 2. FUNGI: Nongreen parasitic or saprophytic thallophyte plants.

    Class 1. Schizomycetes (skiz-oh-my-*see*-teez): Fission fungi [bacteria]

    Class 2. Myxomycetes (mik-soh-my-*see*-teez): Amorphous slimy growths resembling animals in form but reproducing by spore formation in plant manner [slime fungi or slime molds]

    Class 3. Ascomycetes (as-koh-my-*see*-teez): Sac fungi, producing, usually, eight ascospores in an ascus; many forms producing conidiospores [*Penicillium; Aspergillus* (as-per-*jil*-us); morel; yeast; cup fungi]

    Class 4. Phycomycetes (fy-koh-my-*see*-teez): Algalike fungi [bread mold; water mold; white " rust "]

    Class 5. Deuteromycetes (doo-ter-oh-my-*see*-teez): Imperfect fungi [athlete's foot]

    Class 6. Basidiomycetes (bah-sid-ih-oh-my-*see*-teez): Basidium fungi [smuts; rusts; mushrooms: puffballs; bracket fungi]

    Class 7. Lichenes (ly-*kee*-neez): Plant body consisting of an alga and a fungus in combination [lichens]

PHYLUM II Bryophyta (bry-*off*-ih-tah) [23,000 species]

Multicellular green plants living on land, in most cases; alternation of generations with the gametophyte the conspicuous generation; vascular tissues lacking; reproduction by spores and gametes.

    Class 1. Hepaticae (heh-*pat*-ih-see): Liverworts [Riccia (*rik*-sih-ah); Marchantia (mar-*kan*-shih-ah)]

    Class 2. Musci: True mosses [Polytrichum (poh-*lit*-rih-kum), or pigeon-wheat moss; Sphagnum moss]

PHYLUM III Pteridophyta (ter-ih-*doff*-ih-tah) [10,000 species]

Mostly terrestrial plants with alternation of generations; both generations green; conspicuous generation the sporophyte leafy frond; vascular tissues and roots, stem, and leaves present; reproduction by spores and gametes.

    Class 1. Filicineae (fil-ih-*sih*-nee-ee): Ferns [wood fern; Boston fern; bracken fern]

    Class 2. Equisetineae (ek-wih-seh-*tin*-eh-ee): Horsetails [*Equisetum* (ek-wih-*see*-tum)]

    Class 3. Lycopodiaceae (ly-koh-poh-dih-*ah*-seh-ee): Club mosses [*Selaginella* (sel-ah-jih-*nel*-ah) *Lycopodium* (ly-koh-*poh*-dih-um)]

PHYLUM IV SPERMATOPHYTA (sper-mah-*toff*-ih-tah) [250,700 species]

Seed plants in which the plant body is the sporophyte generation; highly specialized tissues; roots, stems, leaves, and reproductive organs.

Class 1. Gymnospermae (*jim*-noh-sper-mee): Seeds not enclosed in an ovary; mostly large, woody plants; mostly evergreen

Order 1. Cycadales (sy-kah-*day*-leez): Primitive fernlike gymnosperms [cycads or sago palms, including *Cycas; Dioon; Zamia*]

Order 2. Ginkgoales (gink-goh-*ay*-leez): Large trees with two kinds of branches, one bearing most of the wedge-shaped leaves in clusters [*Ginkgo*]

Order 3. Coniferales (koh-nif-er-*ay*-leez): Cone-bearing gymnosperms, mostly evergreen; leaves in the form of needles or scales [pine; spruce; fir; cedar; larch; cypress; redwood]

Order 4. Gnetales (nee-*tay*-leez): Possible forerunners of the flowering plants; two seed leaves on the embryo; vessels in the wood; only three remaining genera [*Ephedra; Welwitschia; Gnetum*]

Class 2. Angiospermae (*an*-jee-oh-sper-mee): Flowering plants; seeds enclosed in an ovary which ripens into the fruit

Subclass A. Monocotyledonae (mon-oh-kot-ih-*lee*-dun-ee): Embryo with one cotyledon; fibrovascular bundles scattered through stem tissues; flower parts in 3's and 6's; leaves parallel veined [grass; lily; iris; orchid; sedge; palm, including about 9 orders]

Subclass B. Dicotyledonae (dy-kot-ih-*lee*-dun-ee): Embryo with two cotyledons; vascular bundles forming a cylinder around the pith in the stem; leaves with netted veins [buttercup; rose; apple; elm, including about 35 orders]

ANIMALS

PHYLUM I PROTOZOA [20,000 species]

Unicellular animals or simple colonies of cells lacking specialization into tissues; reproduction by fission or spores.

Class 1. Sarcodina (sar-koh-*dy*-nah): Protozoa which form pseudopodia; pellicle at cell surface lacking; reproduction principally by fission; many forms marine [*Ameba; Arcella* (ar-*sell*-ah)]

Class 2. Mastigophora (mas-tih-*gof*-oh-rah): Protozoa which propel themselves with one or more flagella; pellicle usually present; fission longitudinal; many forms parasitic [*Euglena; Trypanosoma*]

Class 3. Sporozoa (spoh-roh-*zoh*-ah): Parasitic protozoans; processes for locomotion lacking; reproduction by spores at some stage in the life cycle [*Plasmodium malariae; Isospora hominis*]

Class 4. Ciliata (sil-ih-*ay*-tah): Locomotion by means of cilia; both free-living aquatic and marine forms and parasitic forms; macronucleus and micronucleus present in many forms [*Paramecium; Stylonichia* (sty-loh-*nik*-ih-ah); *Vorticella* (vor-tih-*sel*-ah); *Stentor*]

PHYLUM II PORIFERA (poh-*rih*-fer-ah) [2,500 species]

Including marine and fresh-water sponges; body in two layers, penetrated by numerous pores; " skeleton " formed by silicious or calcareous spicules or horny spongin.

Class 1. Calcispongiae (kal-kih-*spon*-jih-ee): Simple sponges of shallow waters; calcareous spicules forming " skeleton " [ascon sponges and sycon types including *Grantia*]

Class 2. Hylospongiae (hy-loh-*spon*-jih-ee): Deep water sponges; " skeleton " composed of silicious spicules in a relatively open framework [Venus's flower-basket]

Class 3. Demospongiae (dee-moh-*spon*-jih-ee): Large sponges, often brightly colored; " skeleton " of spongin or a combination of spongin and silicious material; fresh-water and marine [finger sponge; crumb of bread sponge; bath sponge]

PHYLUM III Coelenterata (seh-len-ter-*ay*-tah) [10,000 species]

Usually free-swimming metazoans with a baglike body of two layers of cells with a noncellular substance between them; gastrovascular cavity with one opening leading to the outside; solitary or colonial forms; many have tentacles and all have stinging capsules.

Class 1. Hydrozoa (hy-droh-*zoh*-ah): Solitary or colonial; fresh-water and marine; reproduction by asexual buds and gametes; alternation of generations in many forms [*Hydra; Obelia; Gonionemus* (go-nee-oh-*nee*-mus) *Physalia*]

Class 2. Scyphozoa (sy-foh-*zoh*-ah): Exclusively marine forms; most have mesenteries inside the body; polyp stage usually absent [Portuguese man-of-war and other large jellyfish]

Class 3. Anthozoa (an-thoh-*zoh*-ah): Marine forms; solitary or colonial; without alternation of generations; body cavity with mesenteries; many tentacles [sea anemone; coral; sea fan]

PHYLUM IV Platyhelminthes (plat-ee-hel-*min*-theze) [6,500 species]

Flatworms with a ribbonlike body; no true segments; no body cavity nor skeletal, circulatory, or respiratory systems; head provided with sense organs; nervous system composed of two longitudinal nerve cords.

Class 1. Turbellaria (tur-beh-*lay*-rih-ah): Mostly free-living aquatic or terrestrial forms; many with cilia on the epidermis [*Planaria*]

Class 2. Trematoda (tree-mah-*toh*-dah): Parasitic forms with mouth at anterior end; intestine present; no cilia on adults [sheep liver fluke; human liver fluke]

Class 3. Cestoda (ses-*toh*-dah): Parasitic forms; body a series of detachable proglottids; intestine lacking; hooked scolex adapted for attachment to intestine of host [tapeworm]

PHYLUM V Nemathelminthes (nem-ah-thel-*min*-theze) [3,500 species]

Roundworms with unsegmented bodies; body wall in three layers; body cavity present.

Class 1. Nematoda (nem-ah-*toh*-dah): With intestine but without a proboscis; some forms free-living, others parasitic [vinegar eel, *Ascaris,* hookworm, pinworm, *Trichina*]

PHYLUM VI Rotifera (roh-*tih*-fer-ah) [1,500 species]

" Wheel animals " with rows of cilia around the mouth which beat with a motion suggesting the rotation of a wheel; chitinlike jaws and a well-developed digestive system; body usually cylindrical, ending in a forked grasping foot; smallest of the metazoans [rotifers].

PHYLUM VII Annelida (an-*neh*-lih-dah) [5,000 species]

Segmented worms with the body cavity separated from the digestive tube; brain dorsal and the paired nerve cord ventral; body wall containing circular and longitudinal muscles.

Class 1. Polychaeta (pol-ih-*kee*-tah): Marine forms; fleshy outgrowths, or parapodia extending from segments (sandworm)

Class 2. Archiannelida (ar-kih-ah-*nel*-ih-dah): Similar to Polychaetae but without parapodia and with two rows of cilia [*Polygordius* (pol-ih-*gor*-dee-us)]

Class 3. Oligochaeta (ol-ih-goh-*kee*-tah): Fresh-water or terrestrial forms; bristles on side of body; head not well-developed [earthworm; *Tubifex; Chaetogaster* (kee-toh-*gas*-ter)]

Class 4. Hirudinea (hir-oo-*din*-eh-ah): Body flattened from top to bottom; mostly fresh-water forms, but may also occur as marine or terrestrial organisms; parasites and predators; no bristles on body; suckers at both ends [leeches]

PHYLUM VIII ARTHROPODA (ar-*throp*-oh-dah) [674,500 species]

Animals with segmented bodies, the segments bearing jointed appendages; chitinous exoskeleton; terrestrial, aerial, and aquatic forms.

Class 1. Crustacea: Mostly aquatic; breathe by means of gills; head and thorax usually joined in a cephalothorax; two pairs of antennae; many members have calcareous deposits in the exoskeleton [crayfish; lobster; crab; shrimp; water flea; sow bug; barnacle]

Class 2. Chilopoda (kih-*lop*-oh-da): Body flattened and consisting of from 15 to 170 or more segments; one pair of legs attached to each segment; maxillipeds developed into poison claws [centipedes]

Class 3. Diplopoda (dip-*lop*-oh-dah): Body more or less cylindrical and composed of 25 to 100 or more segments; most segments bearing two pairs of legs [millepedes]

Class 4. Insecta: Head, thorax, and abdomen separate; three pairs of legs; one pair of antennae; usually, two pairs of wings; breathe by means of tracheae.

Order 1. **Thysanura** (thy-sah-*noo*-rah): Wingless; chewing mouth parts; no metamorphosis; primitive insects (silver-fish)

Order 2. **Orthoptera** (or-*thop*-ter-ah): Two pairs of wings, the outer pair straight and leathery; chewing mouth parts; incomplete metamorphosis [grasshopper; cockroach; walking stick; mantis; cricket]

Order 3. **Isoptera** (eye-*sop*-ter-ah): Some forms wingless, others with two pairs of long, narrow wings lying flat on back; chewing mouth parts; incomplete metamorphosis; social insects [termites]

Order 4. **Neuroptera** (noo-*rop*-ter-ah): Four membranous wings of equal size, netted with many veins; chewing mouth parts; complete metamorphosis; larvae of some forms aquatic [dobson fly or hellgrammite; ant lion]

Order 5. **Ephemerida** (ef-eh-*mer*-ih-dah): Two pairs of membranous wings, the front pair larger than the hind pair; mouth parts nonfunctioning in adults; metamorphosis incomplete; adults short-lived [may fly]

Order 6. **Odonata** (oh-doh-*nah*-tah): Two pairs of strong, membranous wings, the hind pair as large or larger than the fore pair; chewing mouth parts; incomplete metamorphosis; compound eyes very large; larvae aquatic [dragonfly; damsel fly]

Order 7. **Mallophaga** (mah-*loff*-ah-gah): Wings absent; chewing mouth parts; incomplete metamorphosis; biting lice [chicken louse]

Order 8. **Anoplura** (an-oh-*ploo*-rah): Wingless; piercing and sucking mouth parts; no metamorphosis; external parasites on mammals [human body louse]

Order 9. **Hemiptera** (heh-*mip*-ter-ah): Wingless, or with forewings leathery at the base and folded over the hindwings; piercing and sucking mouth parts; incomplete metamorphosis [true bugs; water bug; water strider; water boatman; back swimmer; bedbug; squash bug; stink bug]

Order 10. **Homoptera** (hoh-*mop*-ter-ah): Wingless, or with two pairs of wings held in a sloping position like the sides of a roof; piercing and sucking mouth parts; incomplete metamorphosis [cicada; aphid; leaf hopper; tree hopper; scale insect]

Order 11. **Coleoptera** (koh-lee-*op*-ter-ah): Four wings, the front pair hard and shell-like, the second pair folded and membranous; chewing mouth parts; complete metamorphosis [beetles; lady " bug "; firefly; boll weevil]

Order 12. **Lepidoptera** (lep-ih-*dop*-ter-ah): Four wings covered with colored scales; mouth parts modified into a coiled sucking proboscis; complete metamorphosis [butterfly; moth; skipper]

Order 13. **Diptera** (*dip*-ter-ah): Forewings membranous, hindwings reduced to knobbed threads; mouth parts for piercing, rasping, and sucking; metamorphosis complete [housefly; bot fly; blowfly; midge; mosquito; crane fly; gall gnat]

Order 14. Siphonaptera (sy-foh-*nap*-ter-ah): Wingless; piercing and sucking mouth parts; complete metamorphosis; legs adapted for leaping; external parasites on mammals [flea]

Order 15. Hymenoptera (hy-meh-*nop*-ter-ah): Wingless or with two pairs of membranous wings, the forewings larger; forewings and hindwings hooked together; chewing and sucking mouth parts; complete metamorphosis; many members living in social colonies [bee; ant; wasp; hornet; ichneumon fly]

Class 5. Arachnida (ah-*rak*-nih-dah): Head and thorax usually fused into a cephalothorax; no antennae; four pairs of legs; breathe by means of lung books or trachea [spider; daddy longlegs; scorpion; mite; tick]

PHYLUM IX MOLLUSCA (mol-*luss*-kah) [90,000 species]

Soft-bodied invertebrates without segments or jointed appendages; most forms secrete a valve, or calcareous shell from a mantle; muscular foot usually present; terrestrial, fresh-water and marine organisms.

Class 1. Amphineura (am-fih-*noo*-rah): Elongated body and reduced head, without tentacles; many forms with a shell composed of eight plates [chiton]

Class 2. Pelecypoda (peh-leh-*sip*-oh-dah): Axe-footed with bivalve shell; gills in mantle cavity; head, eyes, and tentacles lacking [clam; mussel; oyster; scallop]

Class 3. Gastropoda (gas-*trop*-oh-dah): Flat-footed; with or without coiled shell; head and distinct eyes and tentacles [snail; slug; whelk]

Class 4. Scaphopoda (skah-*fop*-oh-dah): Marine forms; body elongated and enclosed in a tubular shell, open at both ends; gills lacking [tooth shell]

Class 5. Cephalopoda (sef-ah-*lop*-oh-dah): Head large; foot modified into grasping tentacles; marine forms [squid; octopus; chambered nautilus; cuttlefish]

PHYLUM X ECHINODERMATA (eh-kyne-oh-der-*mah*-tah) [5,000 species]

Marine forms, radially symmetrical when adult; spiny exoskeleton composed, in some types, of calcareous plates; most forms with tube feet for locomotion.

Class 1. Crinoidea (kry-*noy*-dee-ah): Five branched rays and pinnules; tube feet without suckers; most species with stalk for attachment [sea lily; many fossil forms]

Class 2. Asteroidea (as-ter-*oy*-dee-ah): Body usually with five rays and double rows of tube feet in each ray; eyespot [starfish]

Class 3. Ophiuroidea (off-yoo-*roy*-dee-ah): Usually with five slender arms or rays [brittle star]

Class 4. Echinoidea (ek-ih-*noy*-dee-ah): Body spherical, oval, or disc-shaped; no rays; tube feet with suckers [sea urchin; sand dollar]

Class 5. Holothurioidea (hol-oh-thoo-rih-*oy*-dee-ah): Elongated, thickened body with tentacles around the mouth; no rays or spines [sea cucumber]

PHYLUM XI CHORDATA (kor-*day*-tah) [40,000 species]

Notochord present at some time; disappearing early in many forms; paired gill slits temporary or permanent; dorsal nerve cord; never more than four legs or paired limbs.

SUBPHYLUM 1. HEMICHORDATA (hem-ih-kor-*day*-tah): Wormlike chordates; body in three regions with a proboscis, collar, and trunk [acorn or tongue worm]

SUBPHYLUM 2. UROCHORDATA (yoo-roh-kor-*day*-tah) **also called Tunicata** (tuh-nih-*kay*-tah): Marine animals with saclike body in adult; free-swimming or attached [sea squirts and other tunicates]

SUBPHYLUM 3. CEPHALOCHORDATA (sef-ah-loh-kor-*day*-tah): Fishlike animals with a permanent notochord [*Amphioxus* (am-fih-*oks*-us) or lancelet]

SUBPHYLUM 4. VERTEBRATA: Chordates in which most of the notochord is replaced by a spinal column composed of vertebrae and protecting the dorsal nerve cord.

Class 1. Agnatha (ag-*nah*-thah), **also called Cyclostomata** (sy-kloh-*stoh*-mah-tah): Fresh-water or marine eel-like forms without true jaws, scales, or fins and with a skeleton of cartilage [lamprey " eel "; hagfish]

Class 2. Elasmobranchii (eh-lass-moh-*brang*-kih-eye): Fishlike forms with true jaws and fins; gills present but not free and opening through gill slits; no swim bladder; cartilaginous skeleton [shark; ray; skate]

Class 3. Osteichthyes (os-tee-*ik*-thih-eez), **also called Pisces:** Fresh-water and marine fishes with gills free and attached to gill arches; one gill opening on each side of body; true jaws and fins; bony skeleton.

    Subclass 1. Ganoidei (gah-*noy*-deh-eye): Mostly extinct forms with armored body, heterocercal tail and swim bladder with duct [sturgeon; garpike; amia; fossil armored fish]

    Subclass 2. Teleostomi (tel-ee-*os*-toh-my): Common bony fish; tail rarely heterocercal; swim bladder (with or without duct) present or absent [perch; trout; salmon; eel; bass; catfish; sucker; shiner; flounder; cod; haddock]

    Subclass 3. Dipnoi (*dip*-noy): Swim bladder connected with throat and used as a rudimentary lung [lungfish]

Class 4. Amphibia: Fresh-water or terrestrial forms; gills present at some stage; skin slimy and lacking protective outgrowths; limbs without claws; numerous eggs, usually laid in water; metamorphosis.

    Order 1. Apoda (ah-*poh*-dah): Wormlike amphibians with tail short or lacking; without limbs or limb girdles; small scales embedded in the skin in some forms [caecilians]

    Order 2. Caudata (kow-*day*-tah): Body elongated and with a tail throughout life; scales lacking; most forms have two pairs of limbs [salamander; newt; siren]

    Order 3. Salientia (sal-ee-*en*-tih-ah): Body short and tailless in adult stage; two pairs of limbs, the hind limbs adapted for leaping; gills in larva stage but replaced by lungs in adult stage [frog; toad; tree frog]

Class 5. Reptilia: Terrestrial or semi-aquatic vertebrates; breathe by lungs at all stages; body scale-covered; feet, if present, provided with claws; eggs relatively few, large, and leathery; oviparous or ovoviparous.

    Order 1. Testudinata (tes-too-dih-*nay*-tah): Body enclosed between two bony shields or shells, usually covered with large scales or plates; toothless [turtles; terrapins; tortoises]

    Order 2. Rhynchocephalia (ring-koh-seh-*fay*-lih-ah): Skeletal characteristics of the oldest fossil reptiles; lizardlike in form; parietal eye in roof of cranium [*Sphenodon* (*sfee*-noh-don), sole surviving species]

    Order 3. Squamata (swah-*may*-tah): Body elongated; with or without limbs (vestigial in snakes); body covered with scales which are molted with outer skin at regular intervals [*Iguana; Gila* (*hee*-lah) monster; horned toad; swift, skink, and other lizards; snakes]

    Order 4. Crocodilia (kroh-koh-*dih*-lee-ah): Large, heavily-scaled body with strong, muscular tail; heart approaching four-chambered condition [alligator; crocodile; cayman; gavial]

Class 6. Aves (*ay*-veez): Body covered with feathers; front limbs modified into wings; four-chambered heart and double circulation; hollow bones; lung breathing throughout life.

    Order 1. Gaviiformes (gay-vih-ih-*for*-meez): Loons [common loon]

    Order 2. Colymbiformes (koh-lim-bih-*for*-meez): Grebes [pied-billed grebe]

    Order 3. Pelecaniformes (peh-leh-kan-ih-*for*-meez): Tropic birds [white pelican; brown pelican; cormorant]

    Order 4. Ciconiiformes (sih-koh-nih-ih-*for*-meez): Wading birds with long legs [heron; ibis; spoonbill; flamingo]

    Order 5. Anseriformes (an-ser-ih-*for*-meez): Short-legged gooselike birds [duck; goose; swan]

    Order 6. Falconiformes (fal-con-ih-*for*-meez): Large birds of prey [hawk; falcon; eagle; kite; vulture; buzzard; condor]

Order 7. Galliformes (gal-ih-*for*-meez): Fowl-like birds [pheasant; turkey; quail; partridge; grouse; ptarmigan]

Order 8. Gruiformes (groo-ih-*for*-meez): Cranelike birds [crane; rail; coot]

Order 9. Charadriiformes (kah-rad-rih-ih-*for*-meez): Shore birds [snipe; plover; sandpiper; gull; tern; auk; puffin]

Order 10. Columbiformes (koh-lum-bih-*for*-meez): Pigeons and doves [mourning dove]

Order 11. Psittaciformes (sit-ah-sih-*for*-meez): Parrots and parrotlike birds [Carolina paroquet; parrot; parakeet]

Order 12. Cuculiformes (koo-kyoo-lih-*for*-meez): Cuckoos [cuckoo; road runner]

Order 13. Strigiformes (strih-jih-*for*-meez): Nocturnal birds of prey [owl]

Order 14. Caprimulgiformes (kap-rih-mul-jih-*for*-meez): Goatsuckers [whip-poor-will; chuck-will's-widow; nighthawk]

Order 15. Apodiformes (ah-poh-dih-*for*-meez): Swifts [hummingbird, chimney swift]

Order 16. Coraciiformes (kor-ah-sih-ih-*for*-meez): Fishing birds [kingfisher]

Order 17. Piciformes (pis-ih-*for*-meez): Woodpeckers [woodpecker; sapsucker; flicker]

Order 18. Passeriformes (pas-ser-ih-*for*-meez): Perching birds [robin; bluebird; sparrow; warbler; thrush]

Class 7. Mammalia (mah-*may*-lee-ah): Body more or less covered with hair; warm-blooded with four-chambered heart; mammary glands; diaphragm; central nervous system highly developed; viviparous except in one order.

Order 1. Monotremata (mon-oh-*tree*-mah-tah): Egg-laying mammals. [duckbill; spiny anteater]

Order 2. Marsupialia (mar-soo-pih-*ay*-lih-ah): Mammals with young born immature and carried in a pouch [opossum; kangaroo; Koala bear]

Order 3. Edentata (ee-den-*tay*-tah): Toothless mammals or nearly so [armadillo; sloth]

Order 4. Cetacea (seh-*tay*-she-ah): Marine mammals with flippers instead of legs [whale; porpoise; dolphin]

Order 5. Sirenia (sy-*ree*-nee-ah): Aquatic mammals; forelimbs finlike; hindlimbs absent; tail with horizontal fin; body whalelike but with definite neck [sea cow]

Order 6. Insectivora (in-sek-*tih*-vor-ah): Insect-eating mammals mostly [mole; shrew]

Order 7. Chiroptera (ky-*rop*-ter-ah): Flying or bone-winged mammals [bat; vampire]

Order 8. Rodentia (roh-*den*-she-ah): Mammals equipped with incisor teeth adapted for gnawing [squirrel; woodchuck; prairie dog; chipmunk; mouse; rat; muskrat; porcupine]

Order 9. Lagomorpha (lah-goh-*mor*-fah): Rodentlike mammals with highly developed hindlimbs adapted for jumping [rabbit; hare; pica]

Order 10. Ungulata (un-gu-*lay*-tah): Hoofed mammals; vegetarians with large, grinding molars [odd-toed: horse; tapir; rhinoceros; even-toed: cow; bison; goat; sheep; deer; antelope; camel; llama; pig; hippopotamus]

Order 11. Proboscidea (proh-boh-*sid*-ee-ah): Upper lip and nose lengthened to form a long, prehensile trunk; incisor teeth forming long tusks; molars very broad [elephant; fossil mammoth and fossil mastodon]

Order 12. Carnivora (kar-*nih*-vor-ah): Mammals with sharp teeth with cusps for eating flesh; claws usually present [bear; raccoon; ringtailed cat; weasel; mink; skunk; otter; lion; tiger; cat; dog; fox; wolf]

Order 13. Primates (pry-*may*-teez): More or less erect mammals with forelimbs adapted for grasping and holding [monkey; gorilla; champanzee; orangutan; gibbon] [man is structurally classified by biologists as a primate]

Glossary

Abdomen, the body region posterior to the thorax.

Abdominal cavity, the cavity in the lower part of the trunk, below the diaphragm, in man and other mammals.

Abscission (ab-*sis*-shun) **layer,** two rows of cells near the base of a leaf petiole, causing the natural fall of leaves.

Absorption (ab-*sorp*-shun), the process by which water and dissolved substances pass into cells.

Accessory fruit, an enlarged stem receptacle bearing numerous hard scattered fruits, as in the strawberry.

Acetylcholine (as-et-il-*ko*-leen), a powerful chemical substance, released at the end of a motor nerve, causing a muscle to contract.

Achene (ah-*keen*), a dry, indehiscent fruit in which the ovary wall separates from the seed, as in the sunflower.

Acne (*ack*-nee), a condition in which pimples appear in groups on the face and neck.

Acquired immunity, a type of immunity established during the lifetime of an individual.

Acromegaly (ak-ro-*meg*-ah-lee), abnormal development, especially of the bones of the face and extremities, associated with a disease of the anterior lobe of the pituitary gland.

Adaptation, modification to perform a specialized activity.

Adenoid, a mass of lymph tissue which grows from the back wall of the nasopharynx, behind the internal nares.

Adipose (*ad*-ih-poze) **tissue,** fatty tissue.

Adrenal gland, a ductless gland located above each kidney, often referred to as the "gland of emergency."

Adventitious (ad-ven-*tish*-us) **root,** one which develops from the node of a stem or from a leaf.

Aerial root and stem, those which do not enter the ground.

Aerobic (ay-*roh*-bik), requiring free atmospheric oxygen for normal activity.

Agglutinin (ah-*gloo*-tuh-nin), an immune substance in the blood which causes specific bacteria to clump.

Aggregate fruit, many tiny drupes clustered on a single receptacle, as in the raspberry.

Albino (al-*by*-no), an organism lacking the genes for normal pigmentation.

Alga (*al*-gah), a thallophyte plant possessing chlorophyll.

Alimentary canal, those organs composing the food tube in man and animals.

Allergy (*al*-er-jee), an abnormal reaction in some people to certain foods, drugs, and pollens.

Alveoli (al-*vee*-oh-ly), air sacs of the lungs.

Amino (ah-*mee*-no) **acid,** a substance from which organisms build proteins.

Amylopsin (am-ee-*lop*-sin), an enzyme of the pancreatic fluid which changes starch to maltose sugar.

Anabolism (an-*ab*-o-lizm), constructive processes of metabolism.

Anaerobic (an-air-*oh*-bik), deriving oxygen for life activity from chemical changes and, in some cases, being unable to live actively in free oxygen.

Analogous (an-*al*-o-gus) **organs,** those organs which are similar in function.

Anaphase (*an*-ah-faze), a stage of mitosis, during which chromosomes migrate from the equator to opposite poles.

Anatomy, study of gross structure of living things.

Androgen (*an*-droh-jen), the male sex hormone.

Anemia (ah-*nee*-mee-ah), a deficiency of red corpuscles, hemoglobin, or both.

Angina pectoris (an-*jy*-nah *pek*-to-ris), a term referring to cardiac pain.

Annual, a plant which lives for only one season.

Annual ring, a circle in the stem of a plant marking a season's growth of wood.

Annulus (*an*-you-lus), the ring on the stipe of a mushroom marking the point where the rim of the cap and the stipe were joined.

Anoxia (an-*ok*-see-ah), the condition of oxygen starvation in the tissues.

Antenna, a large "feeler" in insects and certain other animals.

Antennule, a small "feeler" in the crayfish and certain other animals.

Anterior, head or front end.

Anther, that part of the stamen which bears the pollen grains.

Anthocyanin (an-tho-*sy*-an-in), a red pigment produced in certain plants.

Anthropoid, manlike.

Anthropology, the complete study of man and the societies in which he groups himself.

Antibiotic (an-tih-by-*ot*-ik), a germ-killing substance produced by a bacterium, mold, or other fungus plant.

Antibody, an immune substance in the blood and body fluids.

Antigen (*an*-tih-jen), a substance, usually a protein, which, when introduced into the body, stimulates the formation of antibodies.

Antihistamine (an-tee-*his*-tah-meen), a drug which counteracts the effect of histamine in a mucous membrane.

Antiseptic, a substance used locally in contact with body tissue to destroy bacteria.

Antitoxin (an-te-*tok*-sin), a substance in the blood which counteracts a specific toxin.

Antivenin, a serum used against snakebite.

Anus (*ay*-nus), opening at the posterior end of the intestine.

Anvil, a small bone of the middle ear.

Aorta (ay-*or*-tah), the great artery leading from the heart to the body (arising from the left ventricle of the bird and mammal).

Aortic arch, an arching curve in the aorta, near the heart.

Appendage, an outgrowth of the body of an animal, such as a leg, fin, or antenna.

Appendix, a worm-shaped outgrowth of the caecum at the lower end of the ascending colon.

Aquatic, a fresh-water environment.

Aqueous (*ay*-kwee-us) **fluid** (humor), the watery fluid filling the cavity between the cornea and lens and iris of the eye.

Areolar tissue, a connective tissue.

Arteriole (ar-*tee*-ree-ohl), a tiny artery which eventually breaks down into capillaries.

Arteriosclerosis (ar-*tee*-ree-oh-skler-*oh*-sis), hardening of the arteries.

Artery, a vessel carrying blood away from the heart.

Artificial pollination, controlled pollination to produce a hybrid plant from selected parents.

Ascorbic acid, vitamin C.

Aseptic, free of pus-producing bacteria and other organisms.

Asexual reproduction, reproduction without eggs and sperm.

Assimilation (as-sim-ih-*lay*-shun), the process by which protoplasm is organized from non-living foods.

Association, the property of the brain which links the memory of past experiences with present behavior.

Association neuron, a nerve of the brain or spinal cord which carries impulses from one nerve to another.

Atabrin (*at*-uh-brin), a synthetic drug used in treating malaria.

Atoll, a circular coral reef with an open pool in the center.

Atom, a basic unit of matter.

Auditory, pertaining to the ear or the sense of hearing.

Aureomycin (aw-ree-oh-*my*-sin), an antibiotic drug.

Auricle (*aw*-rih-kul), a thin-walled, upper chamber of the heart.

Autonomic nervous system, a division of the nervous system which influences or controls the vital internal organs in an involuntary manner.

Axil, the angle between a leaf stalk and a stem.

Axillary bud, a lateral bud produced in a leaf axil.

Axon (*ak*-son), a nerve process which carries an impulse away from the cell body of the nerve.

Bacitracin (bah-si-*tray*-sin), an antibiotic substance produced by certain types of bacteria.

Bacteria, a group of microscopic, one-celled fungus plants.

Bacteriology, the study of bacteria.

Bacteriolysin (bak-*tee*-ree-oh-*lie*-sin), a specific blood antibody which causes a definite kind of bacteria to dissolve.

Bacteriophage (bak-*tee*-ree-oh-faj), one of several kinds of viruses which can destroy bacteria.

Barb, a tiny ray in the vane of a feather.

Barbel, a slender projection close to the mouth of a fish, such as a catfish.

Barbule, one of the divisions of the barb of a feather.

Bark, the outer region of a woody stem, composed of several kinds of tissue.

Basal metabolism, the activities needed to supply the energy to support the basic life processes and to maintain the body.

Bast fiber, a tough, thick-walled plant fiber serving as a supporting structure in the phloem region.

BCG (Bacillus-Calmette-Guerin), a vaccine made from bovine (cow) tuberculosis organisms.

Belly (muscle), the body of a striated muscle.

Berry, a thin-skinned fleshy fruit with numerous scattered seeds.

Bicuspid, a kind of tooth situated between the cuspids and molars.

Biennial, a plant which lives two seasons.

Bile, a brownish-green fluid secreted by the liver.

Binomial nomenclature, the system of giving an organism a scientific name composed of at least two parts.

Biochemistry, the biological aspects of chemistry.

Biological factor, the influence of one organism on another.

Biology, the science of life.

Bivalve, a mollusk possessing two valves, or shells.

Bladder (urinary), a membranous sac in the pelvic region of vertebrates for the temporary retention of urine. Any thin-walled sac enclosing a fluid.

Blastula, an early stage in the development of an animal in which the body is in the form of a ball-shaped mass of cells.

Bleeding, the loss of water through a cut plant stem, or the loss of blood through a severed vessel.

Block cutting, the clearing of a stand of

timber, usually in a square or rectangular patch, surrounded by other trees.

Blood, the fluid tissue of the body.

Blood corpuscle, a blood cell, or solid element of the blood.

Blood letting, an early effort to treat infection by deliberately bleeding a patient.

Blood plasma, the fluid portion of blood.

Blood platelet, the smallest form of blood cell, essential in clotting.

Bone, a connective tissue which deposits mineral matter in its intercellular spaces and strengthens the body framework.

Bony layer, the hard region of a bone between the periosteum and the marrow.

Botany, the specialized study of plant life.

Breathing, a mechanical process involved in getting air into and out of the body.

Bronchial tube (bronchiole), a subdivision of a bronchus within a lung.

Bronchus (*bron*-kus), a division of the lower end of the trachea, leading to a lung.

Bud, an undeveloped shoot of a plant, often covered by scales.

Budding, the uniting of a bud with a stock.

Bulb, a large underground bud protected by scales.

Bursa, a fluid-filled sac in a joint which serves as a cushion between bones.

Caecum (*see*-kum), a blind pouch extending from a region of the alimentary canal; from the pyloric region of certain fish and at the lower end of the ascending colon in man and some other mammals.

Calorie (large), the amount of heat required to raise the temperature of 1,000 cc. of water one degree Centigrade.

Calorimeter, a device for measuring heat production.

Calyptra (ka-*lip*-trah), a thin hoodlike covering of the capsule of a moss.

Calyx (*kay*-liks), the sepals of a flower, collectively.

Cambium (*kam*-bee-um), the tissue in roots and stems which is responsible for growth in diameter.

Camouflage (*kam*-oo-flaje), the blending of an animal with its surroundings.

Cancer, a malignant growth of abnormal tissue.

Canine, an enlarged tooth for tearing.

Cap, the spore-bearing part of a mushroom.

Capillarity, a force causing the rise of a liquid along the surface of a tube or vessel.

Capillary, a tiny blood vessel which carries blood to individual cells.

Capsule (Bowman's), a group of specialized cells surrounding the glomerulus of a kidney.

Capsule (fruit), a dry dehiscent fruit with several chambers.

Capsule (moss), a spore-producing structure at the top of the stalk.

Carapace (*kar*-ah-pace), the shell covering the cephalothorax of a crustacean; the upper shell of a turtle.

Carbohydrate, the class of foods including sugars, starches, and cellulose.

Cardiac muscle, the heart muscle.

Cardiovascular-renal disease, involvement of the heart, blood vessels, and kidneys during high blood pressure.

Carotid artery, the great artery from the heart to the head region.

Carotene (*kar*-oh-teen), an orange pigment found in certain chloroplasts.

Cartilage, a connective tissue, often called gristle, composing part of the body framework.

Catabolism, the destructive phase of metabolism.

Catalyst (*kat*-ah-list), a substance that causes a chemical reaction without entering into the reaction.

Caudal, pertaining to the tail, as the caudal fin.

Cell, the unit of structure and function of all living things.

Cell membrane, the thin, living membrane surrounding the protoplast of a cell.

Cellulose (*sel*-you-lohs), carbohydrate substance present in the walls of plant cells.

Cell wall, the outer, nonliving wall secreted around plant cells.

Cement, the covering of the root of a tooth.

Central cylinder, the central core of a root, where conduction occurs.

Central nervous system, the brain and spinal cord.

Cephalothorax, a body region of crustaceans and certain other animals consisting of the head and thorax.

Cerebellum, the brain region between the cerebrum and medulla.

Cerebral cortex, the outer region of the cerebrum.

Cerebral hemorrhage, the rupture of a blood vessel in the cerebrum of the brain or on its surface.

Cerebrospinal (*ser*-ee-bro-*spy*-nal) **fluid,** a clear fluid in the brain ventricles and surrounding the spinal cord.

Cerebrum (*ser*-ee-brum), the largest region of the human brain, considered to be the seat of emotions, intelligence, and other nervous activities.

Chemical change, matter changing from one substance to another as a result of chemical reactions.

Chemotherapy, the use of specific chemicals in treating infectious diseases.

Chemotropism, the response of protoplasm to a chemical stimulus.

Chitin (*ky*-tin), a material present in the exoskeleton of insects and other arthropods.

Chloromycetin (klo-roh-my-*see*-tin), an antibiotic substance.

Chlorophyll (*klo*-roh-fill), a green pigment essential to food manufacture in plants.

Chloroplast (*klo*-roh-plast), a plastid containing chlorophyll.

Choroid (*ko*-roid) **layer,** the second, inside layer of the eyeball.

Chromatin (*kroh*-ma-tin), the substance forming genes and chromosomes.

Chromosome (*kroh*-moh-soam), a rod-shaped, gene-bearing body formed in the nucleus during division.

Chrysalis (*krih*-sah-lis), a hard case containing the pupa stage of a butterfly.

Cilia (*sill*-eh-ah), a tiny hairlike projections of cells.

Circulation, the movement or flow of nutritive fluids, such as sap or blood in living organisms.

Classification, the systematic grouping of organisms.

Climate, the long-range result of weather changes.

Climax plant, a plant which assumes final prominence in a region.

Cloaca (kloh-*ay*-kah), a chamber below the large intestine in certain vertebrates, into which the alimentary canal, ureters, bladder, and reproductive organs empty.

Cochlea (*kok*-lee-ah), the hearing apparatus of the inner ear.

Cocoon (kuh-*koon*), a silken case containing the pupa stage of a moth.

Cohesion, the clinging together of molecules, as in a column of liquid.

Colloid (*kol*-oid), a substance, such as protoplasm or egg albumen, in which one or more solids are dispersed through a liquid and thereby forming a gelatinous material.

Colon, the large intestine.

Complemental air, air which can be inhaled with force in addition to the amount inhaled during normal breathing.

Complete flower, one containing all parts — calyx, corolla, stamens, pistil.

Complete metamorphosis, four stages of development of certain insects — egg, larva, pupa, and adult.

Complex sugar, sugar requiring chemical simplification and conversion before it can be absorbed by the blood and body tissues.

Compound (chemical), two or more elements combined chemically.

Compound eye, an eye composed of numerous lenses and containing separate nerve endings as in insects and crustaceans.

Compound leaf, a leaf in which the blade is divided into leaflets.

Cone, a reproductive part of a conifer; also a color-sensitive nerve ending in the retina of the eye.

Conifer, a cone-bearing Gymnosperm.

Conjugation, a primitive form of sexual reproduction in *Spirogyra* and certain other algae and fungi in which the content of two cells unite; exchange of nuclear substance in *Paramecium* resulting in rejuvenation of the cells.

Connective tissue, a group of tissues, including bone, cartilage, blood, adipose, yellow elastic, white fibrous, areolar, and reticular tissue.

Conservation, the preservation and wise use of natural resources.

Contact infection, a disease spread through direct contact with an infected person.

Contact poison, an insecticide which kills on coming in contact with the body of an insect.

Contour farming, the plowing around a slope or hill rather than up and down.

Contractile vacuole, a large vacuole in protozoans associated with the discharge of water from the cell; it regulates osmotic pressure.

Contraction (muscle), the shortening of a striated muscle.

Control experiment, an experiment performed to check the validity of another experiment.

Convolution, an irregular, rounded ridge on the surface of the brain.

Coordination (muscular), the combined action of several muscles in a movement.

Coracoid (*kor*-ah-koid) **bone,** a bone found in birds which braces the shoulder from each side against the breastbone.

Cork, a tissue formed by the cork cambium which replaces the epidermis in woody stems and roots.

Cork cambium, a layer of cells in the outer bark which produces new cork.

Corm, a shortened underground stem in which the leaves are reduced to thin scales.

Cornea (*kor*-nee-ah), a transparent bulge of the sclerotic layer of the eye in front of the iris.

Corolla (kor-*ol*-uh), the petals of a flower.

Coronary, pertaining to the circulation to the heart muscle.

Coronary occlusion, a block in a coronary vessel due to a blood clot formed in the vessel (thrombosis) or a migrating clot which lodges there (embolism).

Cortex, a storage tissue in roots and stems; outer region of a kidney, or of the cerebrum.

Cortin, a hormone complex secreted by the cortex of the adrenal glands.

Cotyledon, a seed leaf, present in the embryo plant and, in some plants, serving as a food reservoir.

Countershading, a form of protective coloration in which darker colors on the upper side fade into lighter colors on the lower side.

Cover crop, a crop, such as wheat, oats, etc., in which the plants grow close together and bind the soil with their closely mingling roots.

Cranial cavity, the cavity in the skull containing the brain.

Cretinism, a condition resulting from lack of thyroid secretion.

Crop, an organ of the alimentary canal of the earthworm, bird, and certain other animals which serve for food storage.

Crop rotation, alternation in the planting of crops which use nitrates with those which replace nitrates.

Cross-breeding, the mating or crossing of two different pure lines.

Cross-pollination, transfer of pollen from the anther of one plant to the stigma of another.

Culture medium, a nutrient mixture used for growing bacteria, molds, and other fungi.

Cuspid, a canine tooth.

Cuticle (*kew*-tih-kul), a waxy, transparent layer covering the upper epidermis of certain leaves.

Cyst (*sist*), a resting stage.

Cytoplasm (*sy*-toh-plazm), the protoplasm of the cell, outside the nucleus.

Dandruff, normal scaling of the outer layer of scalp tissue.

Daughter cell, a newly formed cell resulting from the division of a previously existing cell.

Decay, the reduction of the substances of a plant or animal body to simple compounds by the action, usually, of bacteria.

Deciduous, woody plants which shed their leaves seasonally.

Deficiency disease, a condition resulting from lack of one or more vitamins.

Dehiscent, a class of fruits which open and discharge seeds.

Dehydration, loss of water from body tissues.

Deliquescent (del-ih-*ques*-sent), a type of branching in which the trunk divides into several main branches, resulting in a wide, spreading crown.

Dendrite (*den*-dryte), a branching nerve process which carries an impulse toward the nerve cell body.

Denitrifying bacteria, those which reduce soil nitrates to ammonia and lose soil fertility.

Dentine, a relatively softer substance than enamel that forms the bulk of a tooth.

Deoxygenation, the process during which oxygen is removed from the blood or tissues.

Depletion, mineral exhaustion of the soil through continued planting of agricultural crops without proper fertilizing.

Dermis, the skin layer beneath the epidermis.

Diaphragm (*dy*-uh-fram), a muscular partition separating the thoracic cavity from the abdominal cavity in a mammal.

Diastase (*dy*-ah-stase), an enzyme that changes starch to sugar.

Diastolic blood pressure, arterial blood pressure maintained between heart beats.

Diatomaceous earth, deposits formed from the accumulated remains of vast numbers of diatoms.

Dicotyledon, a seed plant with two seed leaves, or cotyledons.

Diffuse root system, one composed of spreading roots of similar size.

Diffusion, the spreading out of molecules of one substance through another.

Digestion, the process during which foods are made simple and soluble so they can be used by cells.

Digestive fluids, cell secretions containing enzymes.

Dihybrid, an offspring having genes for two contrasting characters.

Dioecious (dy-*ee*-shus), a condition in which a single plant bears only staminate or pistillate flowers.

Disease, any condition which interferes with the normal function of the body of an organism.

Disease carrier (human), a person who harbors pathogenic organisms of a disease to which he is immune.

Disease-resistant, an organism which has an inherited immunity to a specific disease.

Disinfectant, a substance used in the chemical destruction of microbes.

Distribution, the spreading out of a species in an environment.

Division of labor, specialization of cell functions resulting in interdependence.

Domestic, pertaining to animals and plants which are bred and improved by man.

Dominant, a trait which appears in a hybrid character.

Dormancy, a period of inactivity, such as the resting stage of a seed before germination.

Dorsal, pertaining to the upper surface of an animal.

Drone, the male bee.

Droplet infection, a disease spread through coughing or sneezing droplets bearing microbes from the respiratory tract or mouth.

Drug, a substance used as a medicine or in the making of a medicine.

Drupe, a stone fruit.

Ductless gland, a gland which secretes one or more hormones directly into the blood stream.

Duodenum, the region of the small intestine immediately following the stomach; in man it is about 12 inches long.

Ecology, the study of the relations of living things to their surroundings.

Ectoderm, outer layer of cells of a simple animal body; in vertebrates, the layer of cells from which the skin and nervous system develop.

Ectoplasm (*eck*-toh-plazm), an outer layer of thin, clear cytoplasm, as in *Ameba*.

Eczema, a skin condition of allergic or emotional origin in which red, swollen, scaly areas appear.

Egg, a female gamete, or germ cell.

Element, a basic form of matter composed of one kind of atoms.

Elongation region, the region behind the embryonic region of a root or stem, in which cells grow in length.

Embryo, an immature, developing organism.

Embryo sac, the tissue in a plant ovule which contains the egg and other cells.

Embryonic region, the area near the tip of a root or stem in which cells are formed by division.

Emotional stress, a stress resulting from emotional tension or upset.

Enamel, the hard covering of the crown of a tooth.

Endocrine gland, a ductless gland.

Endoderm, the inner layer of cells of a simple animal body; in vertebrates, the layer of cells from which the lining of the digestive system, the liver, lungs, etc. develop.

Endodermis, a single layer of cells located at the inner edge of the cortex of a root.

Endoplasm, the inner layer of cytoplasm, as in *Ameba*.

Endoskeleton, the internal skeleton of vertebrates.

Endosperm, the tissue in some seeds containing stored food.

Endosperm nucleus, a nucleus formed by the union of two polar nuclei in the embryo sac just before fertilization.

Endothelium, epithelial cells which line the blood vessels, heart, chest, and abdominal cavities.

Endotoxin, an insoluble toxin which remains in a bacterial cell until the cell disintegrates.

Energy, the ability to do work or cause a change.

Entomology, the specialized study of insects.

Environment, all those factors, both living and nonliving, which make up the surroundings of an organism.

Enzyme, a chemical present in a digestive fluid, which causes a chemical change in a food.

Epidermis, the outer layer of the skin; an outer tissue of a young root or stem, a leaf, and other plant parts.

Epiglottis (ep-ee-*glot*-tiss), a leaflike lid which partially covers the opening of the trachea during swallowing.

Epithelial tissue, that composing the coverings of various organs of the body.

Ergosterol, a compound present in the hu-

man skin from which vitamin D is produced on exposure to the sun's rays.

Erosion, the loss of topsoil by the action of water or wind.

Esophagus (ee-*sof*-ah-gus), the food tube or gullet, connecting the mouth and the stomach.

Essential parts, the stamens and pistil of a flower.

Estivation (es-ti-*vay*-shun), a period of summer inactivity in certain animals.

Estrogen (*es*-troh-jen), a female hormone.

Eugenics, the science of human heredity.

Eustachian tube, a tube connecting the pharynx with the middle ear.

Evaporation, the process during which a liquid changes to a vapor.

Evaporation pull, one of the forces involved in the rise of water through the vessels of a stem, brought about by the evaporation of transpired water on the surfaces of leaves.

Evergreen, a plant which does not shed its leaves seasonally.

Excretion, the process during which waste materials are removed from living cells or from the body by specialized organs of excretion.

Excurrent, a form of branching in which a single stem extends through a plant as a shaft.

Exoskeleton, the hard, outer covering or skeleton of certain animals, especially arthropods.

Exotoxin, a soluble toxin excreted by certain bacteria and absorbed by the tissues of the host.

Expiration, the discharge of gases from the lungs.

Extensor, a muscle which straightens a joint.

Extinct, no longer in existence.

Fang, a hollow tooth of a poisonous snake through which venom is ejected.

Feces (*fee*-seez), solid intestinal waste material.

Fertilization, the union of sperm and egg.

Fever, elevation of the normal body temperature.

Fibrin, a substance formed during blood clotting by the union of thrombin and fibrinogen.

Fibrinogen (fy-*brin*-oh-jen), a blood protein present in the plasma.

Fibrous root, a small, slender secondary root that is generally very much branched.

Fibrovascular (fy-broh-*vass*-kyoo-lar) **bundle,** a strand containing xylem and phloem tissues in higher plants.

Filament, the stalk of a stamen, bearing the anther at its tip.

Filth-borne infection, one spread by the contamination of food and water with human excretions.

Filtrable virus, an extremely small organism which invades living tissue.

Fin, a membranous appendage of a fish and certain other aquatic animals.

Fire line, a lane cut through a forest to prevent a possible fire from spreading.

Fission (*fish*-un), division of a cell into two parts.

Flaccid, a limp condition of a cell due to lack of water.

Flagellate (*fla*-jell-ate), a protozoan bearing one or more whiplike appendages, or flagella.

Flagellum (fla-*jell*-um), a whiplike projection of protoplasm used in locomotion by certain plant and animal cells.

Fleshy root, an enlarged root which serves as a reservoir of food for the plant.

Flexor, a muscle which bends a joint.

Flower, an organ of a flowering plant specialized for reproduction.

Food, any substance absorbed into the body which yields material valuable for energy, growth, and repair of tissue and regulation of the life processes without harming the organism

Food infection, the introduction of infectious organisms into the body by means of food.

Food poisoning, a condition resulting from the action of preformed toxins present in food.

Foot, a muscular organ used for locomotion in many mollusks.

Fossils, preserved remains or mineral replacements of living things of previous ages.

Fovea, a small, sensitive spot on the retina of the eye where cones are especially abundant.

Frond, a leaf of the sporophyte generation of a fern.

Frontal lobe, anterior lobe of the cerebrum of a mammal, especially of man.

Fruit, a ripened ovary, with or without associated parts.

Fumigant, a gaseous insecticide or chemical used in destroying animal pests.

Functional disorder, a condition resulting from impaired activity of a body organ.

Fungus, a thallophyte plant lacking chlorophyll and, therefore, deriving nourishment from another organism.

Gall bladder, a sac in which bile from the liver is stored and concentrated.

Gamete (*gam*-eet), a male or female reproductive cell or germ cell.

Ganglion, a mass of nerve cells lying outside of the central nervous system.

Gangrene (*gan*-green), death of tissue occurring in a localized area.

Gastric, referring to the stomach.

Gastrovascular cavity, the central cavity of Porifera and Coelenterata.

Gastrula, a stage in development in which the primary germ layers are formed.

Gemmule (*jem*-mule) **formation,** a method of asexual reproduction in fresh-water sponges.

Gene, a determiner of heredity, located in a chromosome.

Generation, a group of individuals, existing at the same time, all of whom are equally removed from a common ancestor.

Generative nucleus, the one in a pollen grain which divides to form two sperms.

Genetics, the science of heredity.

Genus, a group of closely related species.

Geotropism (jee-oh-*troh*-pizm), the response of plants to gravity.

Germination, growth of the seed when favorable conditions occur.

Gestation period, the period between fertilization and birth of a mammal.

Gill, an organ modified for absorbing dissolved oxygen from water.

Gizzard, an organ in the digestive system of birds modified for grinding food; a division of the alimentary canal of an earthworm.

Gland, a group of secretory cells.

Glandular disease, a condition resulting from over- or underactivity of a gland.

Glomerulus (glow-*mer*-you-luss), a knob of capillaries in a kidney capsule.

Glottis, the upper opening of the trachea in land vertebrates.

Glycogen (*gly*-ko-jen), animal starch, formed in the liver and muscles.

Goiter (simple), an enlarged condition of the thyroid gland resulting from iodine deficiency.

Gonadotropic hormone, a hormone of the anterior lobe of the pituitary gland which influences activity of the reproductive organs.

Grafting, the union of the cambium layers of two woody stems, one the stock and the other the scion.

Grain, the fruit of a monocot in which the ovary wall is fastened securely to a single cord.

Gray matter, nerve cells in the cerebral cortex and spinal cord. These lack a myelin sheath.

Green gland, an excretory organ of crustaceans.

Ground water, that which enters the soil following precipitation.

Guard cell, one of the two epidermal cells surrounding a stoma.

Gullet, the esophagus, or food tube leading to the stomach.

Gully erosion, an advanced stage of water erosion following rill erosion.

Guttation, the loss of excess water through veins at the margin of a leaf.

Hammer bone, one of the three small bones forming a chain across the middle ear.

Hapten, a substance obtained from washed red cells in blood banks which helps prevent the destruction of red blood cells by the *Rh* factor.

Haversian (ha-*vur*-shan) **canals,** numerous channels penetrating the bony layer of a bone.

Heartwood, inner, inactive wood usually darker in color than sapwood.

Hemoglobin (*hee*-moh-glow-bin), an iron-containing protein compound giving red corpuscles their color; combines easily with oxygen.

Hepatic, pertaining to the liver.

Herbaceous stem, a non-woody stem.

Heredity, the transmission of traits from parents to offspring.

Hibernate, to spend the winter months in an inactive condition.

Hilum, the scar on a seed where it was attached to the ovary wall.

Homologous organs, those similar in origin and structure but not, necessarily, in function.

Hormone, the chemical secretion of a ductless gland producing a definite physiological effect.

Horns (spinal cord), the tips of the wings of the gray matter of the spinal cord.

Host, the living body from which a parasite gets its nourishment.

Humerus, the bone of the upper arm.

Humus, black organic matter in the soil formed by the decomposition of plant and animal remains.

Hybrid, an offspring from a cross between parents differing in one or more traits.

Hybridization, the crossing of two different varieties to produce a new one.

Hybrid vigor, a vigor present in a hybrid organism which was lacking in both parents.

Hydrotropism (hy-droh-*troh*-pizm), the response of roots to water.

Hyperthyroidism, overactivity of the thyroid gland.

Hypha (*hy*-fah), a threadlike filament of the vegetative body of a fungus.

Hypocotyl (*hy*-poh-kot-til), that part of a plant embryo from whose lower end the root develops.

Hypothesis, a scientific idea or guess.

Hypothyroidism, underactivity of the thyroid gland.

Imbibition (im-bih-*bih*-shun), the absorption of liquids by a solid with the result that the solid swells.

Immune therapy, the assistance and stimulation of the natural body defenses in treating disease.

Immunity, the power to resist a disease through natural or artificial means.

Imperfect flower, one in which either the stamens or the pistils are missing.

Improvement cutting, the removal of diseased, injured, or undesirable trees from a managed forest.

Incendiarist, one who sets fires deliberately.

Incisor, a tooth in the front of the jaw; highly developed for gnawing in rodents.

Inclusion, a nonliving substance in a cell.

Incomplete dominance, the equal appearance or blending of two unlike characters in the offspring resulting from a cross of these characteristics.

Incomplete flower, one in which one or more of the parts is missing.

Incomplete metamorphosis, the life stages of certain insects consisting of the egg, several nymph stages, and the adult.

Incubate, to provide ideal conditions for growth and development, as in the incubation of eggs or the growth of bacteria.

Indehiscent (in-dee-*hiss*-ent), a class of fruits which do not open to discharge the seeds.

Individual characteristic, an hereditary trait of an individual not necessarily present in other members of the species.

Infection, the entrance and establishment of pathogenic organisms in the tissues of a host plant or animal.

Inheritance, that which is transmitted by descent from parent to offspring.

Inoculation, voluntary addition of germs or viruses to a culture medium or to a living organism.

Inorganic, the materials of the physical earth, lacking the element carbon.

Insecticide, a chemical used to destroy insects.

Inspiration, the intake of air into the lungs.

Instinct, a natural urge, or drive.

Insulin, a hormone secretion of the islet cells of the pancreas which regulates the oxidation of sugar in the tissues.

Integumentary system, the body covering and such outgrowths as scales, nails, feathers, and hair.

Intelligence, the capacity to reason and act accordingly.

Interdependence, the dependence of cells on other cells for complete functioning, or of organisms on the activities of other organisms.

Internode, the space between two nodes.

Interstitial cells, cells of the testes which secrete male sex hormones.

Intestine, the portion or portions of the alimentary canal extending beyond the stomach.

Invertebrate, an animal below the subphylum *Vertebrata* in classification; lacking a backbone.

Involuntary muscle, a muscle which cannot be controlled at will.

Iris, the muscular, colored portion of the eye, behind the cornea and surrounding the pupil.

Irrigation (soil), diversion of water into an area during dry periods.

Irritability, the ability to respond to a stimulus.

Joint, the point at which two separate bones are joined by ligaments.

Kidney, a glandular organ which excretes urine.

Kinetic energy, energy at work.

Koch Postulates, the steps in Robert Koch's procedure in the investigation of anthrax.

Labium, the lower portion or "lip" of an insect's mouth.

Labrum, the two-lobed upper portion or "lip" of an insect's mouth.

Lacteal (*lak*-tee-al), a lymph vessel which absorbs digested fat from the intestine wall.

Larva, the stage which follows the egg in the development of certain animals.

Larynx, the voice box.

Lateral bud, a bud which develops at a point other than the end of a stem.

Lateral line, a row of pitted scales along each side of the fish, functioning as a sensory organ.

Law of Dominance, Mendel's first law of heredity, stating that in a hybrid cross involving two characters, one character may dominate over the other.

Law of Segregation, Mendel's second law of heredity, stating that recessive characters will reappear in the F_2 generation when two hybrids are crossed.

Law of Unit Characters, Mendel's third law of heredity, stating that individual genes, and not all the genes as a whole, illustrate dominance, segregation, and ratios of appearance.

Layering, the development of adventitious roots from the tip or a node of a stem where it contacts the ground.

Leaching, loss of soluble soil minerals as a result of the movement of ground water.

Leaf scar, a mark on a twig left at the point of attachment of a leaf stalk of a previous growing season.

Leaflet, a division of a compound leaf.

Legume, a dry, dehiscent pod fruit with many seeds attached in a row along the side of the fruit.

Lens, the transparent disk, by means of which light rays are directed to the retina of the eye.

Lenticel (*len*-tih-sel), a small pore opening through the epidermis or bark of a young stem.

Lesion, a localized tissue damage resulting from an injury or disease.

Lethal gene, one which bears a characteristic which is usually fatal to an organism.

Leukoplast (*lew*-koh-plast), a colorless plastid serving as a food reservoir in certain plant cells.

Lichen (*like*-en), a thallophyte composed of an alga and a fungus living together to their mutual advantage.

Life function, a vital function or activity of a plant or animal.

Life span, period of existence of an organism.

Ligament, a tough strand of connective tissue which holds bones together at a joint.

Line breeding, the selection of closely related individuals as parents in order to keep a strain pure; the opposite of hybridization.

Lipoid, a fatty substance in nerve tissue.

Liquid tissue, blood and lymph, in which cells are dispersed through a liquid medium.

Litmus, an organic dye which turns red in the presence of an acid and blue in the presence of an alkali.

Liver, the largest organ within the human body, and associated with several vital activities including excretion and storage.

Locomotion, the spontaneous movement of an organism from one place to another.

Lung, an organ of aerial breathing.

Lymph, the clear, liquid part of blood which enters the tissue spaces and lymph vessels.

Macronucleus, the large nucleus of *Paramecium* and certain other protozoans.

Maggot, the larva stage of a fly.

Maltase, an enzyme which acts on maltose sugar

Mammal, a hairy vertebrate whose young are born alive and nourished on milk.

Mandible, a strong, cutting mouth-part of arthropods; a jaw, as in the beak of a bird or the bony structure of a mammal.

Mantle, the tissue covering the soft parts of a mollusk.

Marine, plants and animals living in salt water.

Marrow, the soft tissue in the central cavity of a larger bone.

Mass selection, selection of ideal plants or animals from a large number to serve as parents for further breeding.

Matter, anything which occupies space and has weight.

Maturation region, region of a root or stem where embryonic cells mature into tissues.

Maxilla, a mouth part of an arthropod; the upper jaw of vertebrates.

Maxilliped (max-*ill*-ih-ped), a jaw "foot" of certain arthropods.

Medulla (me-*dul*-ah) **oblongata,** the enlargement at the upper end of the spinal cord, at the base of the brain.

Meiosis (my-*oh*-sis), a type of cell division in which there is a reduction of chromosomes to the haploid number during oögenesis and spermatogenesis.

Membrane, a thin material through which substances may pass.

Meninges (men-*in*-jeez), the three membranes covering the brain and spinal cord.

Mesentery (*mes*-en-ter-ee), a folded membrane which connects to the intestines and the dorsal body wall of vertebrates.

Mesoderm (*mes*-oh-derm), the middle layer of cells in an embryo.

Mesothorax, the middle portion of the thorax of an insect, bearing the second pair of legs and, usually, a pair of wings.

Metabolism, the physiological and chemical processes of the body.

Metamorphosis (met-ah-*mor*-foh-sis), the various life stages of an insect and certain other animals.

Metaphase, the stage of mitosis in which the chromosomes line up at the equator.

Metathorax, the posterior division of the thorax, in the grasshopper bearing the third pair of legs and the second pair of wings.

Metazoan, a many-celled animal.

Microbe, a bacterium, virus, or other minute organism associated with infectious disease.

Micronucleus, a small nucleus found in *Paramecium* and certain other protozoans.

Microorganism, a microscopic organism, such as a bacterium or protozoan.

Micropyle (*my*-kroh-pile), the opening in the ovule wall through which the pollen tube enters.

Microscopic, invisible, except with microscopic enlargement.

Midrib, the large, central vein of a pinnately veined leaf.

Migration, seasonal movement of animals.

Mildew, one of several forms of fungus plants.

Milt, the spermatic fluid of a male fish.

Mimicry, a form of protective coloration in which an animal resembles another kind of animal or an object in its environment.

Mineral matter, inorganic substance such as salt.

Mitosis (my-*toh*-sis), the division of chromosomes preceding the division of cytoplasm of a cell.

Mixture, two or more substances which intermingle without chemical combination.

Modified berry, a fruit like a berry but with a tough outer covering, as in the orange and lemon.

Molar, a large tooth for grinding, highly developed in herbivores.

Mold, one of several types of filamentous fungus plants.

Molecule (*mol*-lih-kyool), a unit mass of a compound, formed by the chemical combination of two or more atoms.

Mollusk, a member of the phylum *Mollusca*.

Molting, shedding of the outer layer of exoskeleton of arthropods, or of a scale layer of reptiles or plumage of birds.

Monocot, a flowering plant which develops a single seed leaf or cotyledon.

Monoecious (mon-*ih*-shus), a condition in which staminate and pistillate flowers are borne on different parts of the same plant.

Mother cell, a cell which gives rise to other cells by division or budding.

Motor end plate, the terminus of the processes of a motor nerve in a muscle.

Motor neuron, a nerve which carries impulses from the brain or spinal cord to a muscle or gland.

Mucous membrane, a form of epithelial tissue which lines the body openings and digestive tract and secretes mucus.

Mucus, a slimy secretion of mucous glands.

Multiple fruit, a compound fruit formed from several flower clusters, as in the mulberry and pineapple.

Muscle, a tissue found in all animals, except the lowest, which produces movement by contraction.

Muscular coordination, the combined action of muscles to produce a movement.

Mushroom, a form of basidium fungus.

Mutation, a change in genetic make-up resulting in a new characteristic which may be passed on to offspring.

Mycelium, the vegetative body of molds and other fungi, composed of hyphae.

Narcotic, a substance which, in small doses deadens nerve activity, but in larger doses acts as a poison.

Natural immunity, one which is natural in the individual and not artificially acquired.

Natural selection, the result of survival in the struggle for existence among organisms possessing those characteristics which give them an advantage.

Nectar, a sweet secretion formed at the base of the petals.

Nerve, a cell specialized for the reception and transmission of impulses.

Nerve body, the body of a neuron containing cytoplasm and a nucleus.

Nerve process, a delicate filament along which an impulse travels.

Neuron, a nerve cell.

Niacin, nicotinic acid.

Nictitating membrane, a thin, transparent covering, or lid, associated with the eyes of certain vertebrates; a third eyelid.

Nitrate, a soluble mineral containing nitrogen and oxygen and frequently associated with another element, such as sodium or potassium.

Nitrification, the action of a group of soil bacteria on ammonia which produces nitrates or nitrites.

Nitrite, a chemical compound formed by soil bacteria in the process of forming nitrates.

Nitrogen-fixing bacteria, those which live in root nodules of legumes and form nitrates from atmospheric nitrogen.

Node, a growing region of a stem, from which leaves, branches, or flowers develop.

Non-protein nitrogen, nitrogen-containing

waste products of cell activity which are taken up by the blood.

Notochord (*no*-tuh-kord), a rod of cartilage running longitudinally along the dorsal side of lower chordates and always present in the early embryological stages of vertebrates.

Nuclear membrane, a living membrane surrounding the nucleus.

Nucleolus (new-*klee*-oh-lus), a small, spherical body within the nucleus and composed of chromatin.

Nucleoplasm (*new*-klee-oh-plazm), the dense, gelatinous material of the nucleus.

Nucleus, a division of the protoplast of a cell; the central mass of an atom, containing protons and neutrons.

Nut, a dry, indehiscent fruit with a hard ovary wall surrounding one or more seeds.

Nutrition, the processes concerned with food and its uses in cell oxidation and the growth and repair of tissue.

Nymph, one of several stages between egg and adult in the incomplete metamorphosis of an insect.

Occipital (ok-*sip*-ih-tal) **lobe,** the posterior region of the cerebrum.

Occupational therapy. The treatment of disease by developing manual skills.

Oculist, a Doctor of Medicine who specializes in treatment of defects and diseases of the eyes; an ophthamologist.

Olfactory lobe, a brain region specialized in the sense of smell in many vertebrates.

Omnivorous organism, one which eats both plant and animal substance.

Oöcyte (*oh*-oh-syte), an early stage in egg formation.

Ootid, a cell which matures into an egg.

Oogonial (oh-oh-*goh*-nee-al) cells, egg producing structures.

Operculum (oh-*per*-kew-lum), the gill cover in fish.

Opsonin, a blood antibody which prepares bacteria for ingestion by white corpuscles.

Optic, pertaining to the sense of sight or to the eye.

Optic nerve, the nerve cable connecting the eye and the brain.

Optometrist, a specialist who tests vision and fits glasses.

Oral groove, a deep cavity along one side of the *Paramecium* or similar protozoan.

Organ, different tissues grouped together.

Organic, carbon-containing substances produced by living things.

Organic diseases, those originating in an organ and not due to pathogenic organisms; non-contagious.

Organic nutrients, the three classes of foods: carbohydrates, fats, proteins.

Organism, the entire body of any living thing.

Ornithology, the study of birds.

Osculum, an opening allowing water to leave the central cavity of sponges.

Osmosis, the movement of water and dissolved materials through a semi-permeable membrane from a region of greater concentration to a region of lesser concentration.

Osmotic pressure, a technical term referring to the degree of concentration of a solution within a semi-permeable membrane impermeable to the solute, which must be attained to prevent further increase in volume by the inward osmosis of water.

Ossification (oss-ih-fih-*kay*-shun), the process by which cartilage cells in childhood are replaced by bone cells, resulting in a hardening of the body framework as the organism grows older.

Ovary, the basal part of the pistil containing the ovules which become seeds; a female reproductive organ.

Overcultivation, the cultivation of too much land rather than increasing yields from land already cultivated.

Overproduction, the growing of crops year after year on the same soil.

Oviduct, a tube in a female through which eggs travel from an ovary.

Oviparous (oh-*vip*-ar-us) **animals,** those which lay eggs.

Ovipositor (*oh*-vih-*poz*-ih-ter), an egg-laying organ in insects.

Ovoviviparous (oh-voh-vy-*vip*-ar-us) **animals,** those which bring forth their young alive, but do not nourish them during development.

Ovule, a structure in the ovary of a flower which, when fertilized, can become a seed.

Oxidation, the union of any substance with oxygen thereby releasing the energy stored in that substance.

Oxygenation, the process whereby the blood is supplied with oxygen from the lungs.

Oxyhemoglobin, hemoglobin with which oxygen has combined.

Palate, the roof of the mouth.

Paleontology, the study of fossils and their relationship to life of past ages.

Palisade, a dense tissue in green leaves and twigs consisting of closely packed elongated cells.

Palmate, a type of veining in leaves in which the main veins radiate somewhat like fingers; a type of compound leaf.

Palpus, an appendage of a mouth part of an arthropod.

Pancreas, a gland located between the stomach and intestine.

Pancreatic duct, a tube which carries pancreatic fluid to the small intestine.

Pantothenic acid, a vitamin of the B-complex.

Papillae (pah-*pill*-ee), projections of the tongue containing taste buds.

Parallel venation, a vein pattern characteristic of the leaves of monocots.

Parasite, an organism which gets its food entirely from another living organism.

Parasympathetic system, one part of the autonomic nervous system.

Parathyroid, one of the small ductless glands embedded in the thyroid.

Parietal lobes, the parts of the cerebrum lying behind the frontal lobes.

Parotid (pah-*rot*-id), one of the pair of salivary glands near the ear.

Pasteurization, the process of killing and/or retarding the growth of bacteria in milk by heating.

Pathogenic organism, one capable of causing disease.

Pathology, the study of diseases of living things.

Peat, a substance formed by the decomposition of plants in the presence of water.

Pectoral, pertaining to chest or shoulders; pertaining to the anterior set of paired fins in a fish.

Peduncle (peh-*dunk*-al), the stalk of a flower.

Pellicle (*pell*-ih-kal), a thickened membrane surrounding the cell of *Paramecium*.

Pelvic fin, one of a pair of fins in fish corresponding to legs.

Pelvis, the pelvic or hip girdle, in man consisting of ilium, ischium, and pubis bones.

Penicillin, an antibiotic derived from the fungus *Penicillin* and used to kill certain bacteria.

Pepsin, a digestive ferment of the gastric juice.

Peptid, a stage in protein digestion.

Peptone, a stage in protein digestion prior to the formation of amino acid.

Perennials, plants which grow more than two growing seasons.

Perfect flower, one which has both stamens and pistils.

Perianth, the sepals and petals of a flower.

Pericardium, the tissue surrounding the heart.

Pericycle, the tissue in roots from which secondary roots arise.

Periostium (per-ee-*oss*-tee-um), the tough membrane covering the outside of a bone.

Peripheral nervous system, the communication between the central nervous system and parts of the body.

Permeable membrane, one which allows substances to pass through it.

Personality, those qualities which make you a person.

Petal, a colored part of the flower. (In some flowers the sepals may also be colored.)

Petiole, the stalk of a leaf.

Pharynx (*fair*-inks), the back of the mouth, extending up over the soft palate to the nasal cavity.

Phloem (*flow*-em), the tissue in roots and stems which conducts dissolved food substances.

Phosphate, a chemical compound containing phosphorus and oxygen.

Photosynthesis (foh-toh-*sin*-the-sis), the process of carbohydrate formation in leaves, i.e. uniting carbon dioxide and water in the presence of light.

Phototropism (foh-toh-*troh*-pizm), the response of plants to light.

Phylum, one of the large divisions in the classification system of plants and animals.

Physical change, one in which no change occurs in the composition of a substance.

Physical factors, the external influences of environment.

Physiology, the study of the functions, or life activities, of living things.

Pineal gland, a ductless gland located between the cerebral hemispheres and near the pituitary gland.

Pinnate venation, leaves with a single large vein extending through the center of the blade from the petiole to the leaf tip.

Pistil, the part of the flower bearing the ovary at its base.

Pistillate flower, one containing only pistils.

Pith, a tissue of roots and stems consisting of thin-walled cells and used for food storage.

Pith rays, cellular strands reaching from the pith to the bark in stems of dicotyledons; medullary rays.

Pituitary gland, a ductless gland composed of two lobes, located beneath the cerebrum.

Plasma, the liquid portion of blood tissue.

Plasma membrane, a thin living membrane, where cytoplasm lies against the cell wall.

Plasmolysis (plaz-*moll*-ih-sis), the collapse of cell protoplasm due to loss of water.

Plastids, living bodies in the cytoplasm of plant cells.

Platelet, the smallest of the blood cells.

Pleural membrane, one of two membranes surrounding each lung.

Plexus, a body of nerve cells.

Plumule (*ploo*-mule), that part of a plant embryo from which the shoot develops.

Pod, a dry, dehiscent fruit produced by a legume plant.

Pollen grain, the male reproductive tissue of flowering plants.

Pollen sacs, sacs in the anther containing pollen grains.

Pollen tube, the tube formed by a pollen grain when it grows down the style.

Pollination, the transfer of pollen from anther to stigma.

Pollution, any substance which makes food,

water, or surroundings unhealthy for any living thing.

Pome, an applelike fruit, consisting of a ripened receptacle surrounding the ovary.

Portal vein, the large vein which carries blood from the intestine to the liver.

Posterior, tail or rear end of an animal.

Potential energy, stored energy.

Precipitation, the movement of water to the earth from the atmosphere.

Precipitin (pre-*sih*-pih-tin), a blood antibody which causes bacteria to settle out.

Predator (*preh*-dah-tor), any animal which preys on other animals.

Prehension, the ability to grasp.

Premolars, large teeth for grinding.

Primary root, the first root of the plant coming from the seed.

Primates, the highest order of Mammalia, including monkeys, apes, and man.

Proboscis (proh-*boss*-is), a tubular mouth part in certain insects; the trunk of an elephant.

Propagation, multiplication of plants by stems.

Prophase, a stage of mitosis, in which the chromatin forms a network in the nucleus.

Protective coloration, when the organism blends into the color of its surroundings.

Protective resemblance, resemblance to shape of the environment.

Proteins, extremely complex class of foods containing not only C, H, O, but also N, S, and usually P as well, plus other elements.

Prothallus, the tiny, delicate, heart-shaped structure which develops from the spore of the fern.

Prothorax, the first segment of an insect's thorax to which the head and first pair of legs are attached.

Prothrombin, an enzyme produced in the liver and an inactive part of blood plasma except during clotting.

Protonema (proh-tow-*nee*-ma), a filamentous structure produced by a spore in mosses.

Protoplasm, the living substance composing cells.

Protoplast, all the living content of a cell.

Protozoa, one-celled animals.

Pruning, the cutting off of surplus branches of trees and shrubs.

Pseudopodium (soo-doh-*poh*-dee-um), a "false foot" of *Ameba* or ameba-like cells.

Pulmocutaneous (pull-moh-kew-*tain*-ee-us) **arteries,** arteries in the frog, branching to the lungs, skin, and mouth membrane.

Pulmonary, pertaining to the lungs.

Pupa, the stage in a complete metamorphosis of an insect following the larva.

Pupil, the opening in the front of the eyeball, the size of which is controlled by the iris.

Pyrenoid, a small protein body on a chloroplast of *Spirogyra* and certain other algae.

Pyridoxine, vitamin B$_6$.

Quadrate bone, a bone in the snake's skull to which the lower jaw is attached.

Quill feathers, the large stiff feathers in the wing or tail of a bird.

Rachis (*ray*-kis), the axis of quill feathers of a bird.

Radiant energy, energy transmitted through space, as light from the sun.

Receptacle, the end of the flower stalk bearing the reproductive organs.

Recessive, the trait in a cross of two contrasting characters which does not appear in the first generation of offspring but is inherited by them.

Rectum, the posterior portion of the large intestine; above the anus.

Red corpuscles, the cells in blood which contain hemoglobin.

Red marrow, the tissue in a bone giving rise to red and white blood corpuscles.

Reflex action, an act in which a stimulus causes the passage of a sensory nerve impulse to the brain or spinal cord, from which, involuntarily, a motor impulse is transmitted to a muscle or gland.

Reforestation, the planting of forest trees in an open area from which previous trees have been removed.

Regeneration, the ability of cells to form new parts.

Relaxation (of muscles), the lengthening of a striated muscle.

Renal, relating to the kidneys.

Rennin, the milk-curdling enzyme of the gastric juice.

Reproduction, the process during which plants and animals produce new organisms of their kind.

Reptile, a scaly vertebrate, breathing by means of lungs throughout life.

Respiration, the exchange of gases between cells and their surroundings.

Reticular tissue, a connective tissue.

Retina, the inner layer of the eyeball, the expanded end of the optic nerve.

***Rh* factor,** any one of six or more protein substances present in the blood of certain people.

Rhizoid, a root-like growth which carries on absorption.

Rhizome, an underground stem.

Rib, one of the several pairs of bones protecting the chest and attached to the spine.

Riboflavin, vitamin B$_2$.

Rickets, a disease of childhood characterized by lack of calcium in bones due to absence of vitamin D from the diet.

Rickettsiae, a group of organisms, midway between the viruses and bacteria, which cause disease.

Rill erosion, the formation of tiny rills by rain across the surface of the land.

Rind, outer covering of monocot stem, composed of thick-walled hard cells.

Rod, a cell of the retina of the eye that receives impulses from light rays and which is sensitive to shades but not to colors.

Root cap, a tissue at the tip of a root protecting the tissues behind it.

Root hair, a projection of an epidermal cell of a young root.

Root pressure, a factor which forces water into the stem.

Root system, all the roots of a plant.

Rostrum (*ros*-trum), a protective area which is an extension of the carapace in crustaceans.

Row crop, a crop grown in rows with soil exposed between them.

Ruminant, a cud-chewing ungulate.

Runoff water, rain water which runs off the surface of the ground and enters the drainage system.

Saliva, a digestive fluid secreted into the mouth by the salivary glands.

Samara, a winged fruit, as in the maple.

Saprophyte (*sap*-roh-fite), a plant which lives on nonliving organic matter.

Sapwood, active tissue in the outer area of wood in a stem.

Science, the branch of knowledge which deals with many facts from which we draw conclusions.

Scientific method, the procedure by which knowledge is gained or verified by observation or experiment, resulting in sound conclusions and applications.

Scion (*sy*-on), the portion of a twig grafted onto a rooted stock.

Sclerotic (skle-*rot*-ick) **layer,** the outer layer of the wall of the eyeball.

Scurvy, a disease caused by lack of vitamin C in the diet.

Secondary root, a branch root, developing from the pericycle of another root.

Secretion, production of essential substances by glands.

Sedimentary rock, one formed of sediment, usually deposited in water.

Seed, a complete embryo plant protected by one or more seed coats.

Seed dispersal, the scattering or distribution of seeds from the fruit.

Seedling, a young plant which develops from the germinating seed.

Segregation, the reappearance of recessive characters in the F_2 generation, resulting from a cross of two hybrid individuals.

Selective absorption, the phenomenon in a root by which certain dissolved minerals enter a root hair independently of water intake and others are excluded.

Selective cutting, cutting timber trees from a managed forest only when they are mature.

Selective membrane, a membrane allowing some substances to enter while rejecting others.

Self-pollination, the transfer of pollen from anther to stigma in the same flower or another flower of the same plant.

Semi-aquatic, plants and animals living both in water and on land.

Semi-circular canals, the three curved passages in the inner ear and associated with balance.

Seminal vesicles, organs that store the sperm cells of certain animals.

Semi-permeable membrane, one which is permeable to different substances to different degrees.

Sensitivity, the response of protoplasm to its surroundings.

Sensory neurons, a nerve carrying an impulse from a receptor to the spinal cord or brain.

Sepal, the outermost part of a flower, usually green and not involved in the reproductive process.

Serum (*seer*-um), a substance used in treating a disease after it has struck and to produce immediate passive immunity.

Serum albumin, a protein in the plasma of the blood.

Serum globulin, a protein in blood plasma giving rise to antibodies.

Sessile, attached by the base without a stalk or stem.

Setae (*see*-tae), bristles on earthworm.

Sex-linked characters, those which are carried on an X or sex chromosome.

Sexual reproduction, that involving the union of a female gamete or egg and a male gamete or sperm.

Sheet erosion, loss of a thin layer of soil due to standing water.

Shelterbelts, rows of trees planted at intervals to break the force of the wind.

Sieve tube, a conducting tube of the phloem.

Simple leaf, one in which the blade is in one piece.

Simple sugar, one which can be absorbed by the body without further simplification.

Sinus node, a small mass of tissue on the top of the heart where the automatic beat originates.

Skeletal muscle, a striated muscle attached to a bone.

Skull, the bone structure of the head of a vertebrate animal.

Soil, a mass of rock particles and humus which form the basic materials from which plants obtain essential materials for growth.

Soil binder, a plant whose roots bind exposed land.

Soil exhaustion, depletion of soil minerals as a result of overproduction.

Solar plexus, the large nerve ganglion of the

sympathetic nervous system located in the abdomen.

Soluble substance, one which can be dissolved.

Sori (*soh*-ry), small clusters of sporangia which appear on fern leaves when they are mature.

Spawn, the eggs of aquatic creatures, especially when laid in masses.

Specialization, development of special organs for different functions.

Species, an individual kind of plant or animal which has the same characteristics as its parents.

Species character, a characteristic of all members of a species.

Sperm, a male reproductive cell.

Spicule (*spih*-kule), the material forming the skeleton of certain sponges.

Spinal cord, the main dorsal nerve of the central nervous system in vertebrates, extending down the back from the medulla.

Spinal nerve, a nerve leading directly from the spinal cord.

Spindle, the numerous fine threads formed between the poles of the nucleus during mitosis.

Spinnerets, organs in spiders through which silk passes from the silk glands.

Spiracles (*spih*-rah-kals), external openings of the insect's respiratory system on thorax and abdomen.

Spirochete (*spy*-roh-keet), a group of spiral-shaped, one-celled organisms resembling both bacteria and protozoa which produce diseases in animals and man.

Spleen, an abdominal organ of most vertebrates which filters disintegrated cells from the blood.

Spongin, fibers comprising the skeleton of certain sponges.

Spongy, a term applied to loosely constructed tissue with many spaces, as in a leaf or a sponge.

Sporangium (spor-*an*-jee-um), a structure which produces spores.

Spore, an asexual reproductive cell, as in mushrooms, mosses, and ferns.

Spring wood, wood containing many large vessels mingled with tracheids and fibers.

Stamen, a part of the flower bearing anthers at their tips.

Staminate flower, one containing only stamens.

Steapsin, an enzyme of the pancreatic juice which digests fats and oils.

Sternum, the breastbone.

Stigma, the part of the pistil which receives the pollen grains.

Stipe, the stalk of a mushroom.

Stipule, one member of a pair of small, leaflike structures usually found at the base of the petiole.

Stirrup bone, one of the three bones forming a chain across the middle ear.

Stock, a line of descent; to supply with seed, plants, eggs, or animals; the plant on which a scion has been grafted.

Stolon, a transverse hypha of a mold.

Stomach poison, an insecticide which acts in the alimentary canal.

Stomates (*stoh*-mates), pores regulating the passage of air and water vapor to and from the inside of the leaf.

Stone cell, a thick-walled, supporting cell.

Streptomycin, an antibiotic.

Striated muscle, skeletal, voluntary muscle.

Strip cropping, the alternation of strips of row crops and cover crops.

Style, the stalk of the pistil.

Sublingual, one of the pair of salivary glands lying under the tongue.

Submaxillary, one of the pair of salivary glands lying in the angle of the lower jaw.

Subsoil, soil which lies below topsoil and which is usually poor in plant nutrients.

Sulfa drugs, a group of drugs used in chemotherapy.

Sucrose, white sugar made from sugar cane or sugar beets.

Summer wood, wood containing few vessels and a large number of fibers.

Supplemental air, that which can be forced from the lungs after normal exhalation.

Sustained yield, a forest so managed as to give regular crops for cutting.

Swim bladder (fish), a thin-walled elliptical sac which allows the fish to maintain a level in the water.

Swimmerets, appendages of the abdomen of a crustacean.

Symbiosis (sim-bee-*oh*-sis), the relationship in which two organisms live together for the mutual advantage of each.

Sympathetic nervous system, the part of the autonomic nervous system consisting of a series of ganglia and nerves.

Synapse (*sin*-apse), the space between nerve endings.

Synovial (sin-*ov*-ee-al) **fluid,** a secretion of cartilage, lubricating a joint.

Systemic circulation, the general circulation as distinct from the pulmonary circulation.

Systems, group of organs performing similar functions.

Systolic blood pressure, arterial pressure when the heart beats.

Tadpole, a young amphibian.

Talon, the foot of a hawk or owl, adapted for seizing prey.

Taproot, the main root of a plant, often serving as a food reservoir.

Taxonomy, the branch of biology which groups and names living things.

Telophase, the last stage of mitosis.

Telson, the posterior segment of the abdomen of certain crustacea such as the crayfish.

Temporal lobes, those lying below the frontal and parietal lobes of the cerebrum in man.

Tendon, a strong band of connective tissue in which the fleshy portion of a muscle terminates.

Tendril, a part of a plant modified for climbing.

Tentacle, a long appendage or feeler of certain invertebrate animals.

Terminal bud, the terminal growing point of the stem.

Terracing, the checking of water on sloping land by building level areas to prevent soil erosion.

Terramycin, an antibiotic.

Terrestrial (ter-*res*-tree-al), land plants and animals.

Testa, outer seed coat.

Testes, male reproductive organs of higher animals.

Theory, a belief based on a hypothesis but supported by further evidence.

Therapy, the treatment of disease.

Thiamin, vitamin B_1.

Thoracic (thor-*ass*-ik), pertaining to the chest cavity.

Thorax, the middle region of the body of an insect between the head and abdomen; the chest region of mammals.

Thrombin, a substance formed in blood clotting as a result of the reaction of prothrombin, thromboplastin, and calcium.

Thromboplastin, a substance essential to blood clotting formed by the disintegration of blood platelets.

Thymus, one of the ductless glands, situated near the breastbone, which begins to atrophy at puberty.

Thyroid, a ductless gland, located in the neck on either side of the larynx.

Thyroid hormone, the secretion of the thyroid gland.

Tidal air, air involved in normal, relaxed breathing.

Tissue, one of the basic parts of which an organ is formed, composed of cells similar in structure and function.

Tissue destruction, the destruction of cells by pathogenic organisms.

Tone (muscle), the condition when flexor and extensor muscles oppose each other and this results in a state of slight contraction.

Topography, the physical features of the earth.

Topsoil, that top part of the soil consisting of mineral matter combined with organic matter.

Toxin, a poison produced by certain microorganisms.

Toxin-antitoxin, a mixture of diphtheria antitoxin and toxin, formerly used to develop immunity.

Toxoid, toxin weakened by mixing with formaldehyde or salt solution, used extensively to develop immunity to diphtheria, scarlet fever, tetanus, and polio.

Trachea (*tray*-kee-a), the windpipe in air-breathing vertebrates; an air tube in insects and spiders.

Tracheids (*trake*-ee-ids), thick-walled conducting tubes, used for strengthening of wood.

Translocation, the movement of dissolved foods in plants.

Transmit, to transfer; to conduct; to pass on by heredity.

Transpiration, the loss of water from plants.

Trichocysts (*trik*-oh-sists), sensitive protoplasmic threads in *Paramecium*, concerned with protection.

Tropism (*troh*-pizm), the involuntary response of an organism to a stimulus.

Trunk, the main body or stock of a tree; the body of an animal as distinguished from its appendages.

Trypsin, an enzyme of the pancreatic juice which converts protein to proteases and peptones.

Tuber, an enlarged tip of a rhizome swollen with stored food.

Tuberculin, a substance containing dead tuberculosis organisms, used in testing for tuberculosis.

Turbinates, the three layers of cavities in the nasal passages.

Turgor, the stiffness of plant cells due to the presence of water.

Tympanic (tim-*pan*-ick) **membrane,** the eardrum.

Tyrothrycin, an antibiotic substance.

Ungulate, a member of the order Ungulata or hoofed animals.

Univalve, a single-shelled mollusk, such as the snail.

Unstriated muscle, smooth, involuntary muscle.

Urea, a nitrogenous waste substance found chiefly in the urine of mammals but formed in the liver from broken down proteins.

Ureter, a tube leading from a kidney to the bladder or cloaca.

Urethra, the tube leading from the urinary bladder to an external opening in the body.

Urine, the liquid waste filtered from the blood in the kidney and excreted by the bladder.

Uvula, extension of the soft palate.

Vaccine (*vack*-seen), a substance used to produce active immunity.

Vacuolar (*vack*-you-oh-lar) **membrane,** a membrane surrounding a vacuole which regulates the movement of materials stored in the cavity in and out of the general cytoplasm.

Vacuole (*vack*-you-ole), any space scattered through the cytoplasm of a cell which contains a fluid.

Vagus nerve, the principal nerve of the parasympathetic system.

Valve, a structure regulating the flow of blood in the heart and in veins.

Vane, part of a quill feather of a bird.

Variations, changes in the characteristics of organisms.

Vegetative reproduction, reproduction by any organ of a plant except the flower.

Veins, structures carrying blood to the heart; strengthening and conducting structures in leaves.

Venation, the arrangement of veins through the leaf blade.

Venom, the poison secreted by glands of poisonous snakes or other animals.

Ventral, front or lower (abdominal) surface of animals.

Ventricle, a thick-walled chamber of the heart.

Vertebra, a bone of the spinal column of a vertebrate.

Vertebrate, animal with a spinal column and endoskeleton.

Vessel, a conducting tube.

Viability (vy-ah-*bill*-ih-tee), the ability of seeds to germinate after dormancy.

Virus, the simplest form of living matter.

Vitamins, substances, present in foods, and essential for normal growth and body activity.

Vitreous humor, a transparent substance that fills the interior of the eyeball in back of the lens and iris.

Viviparous (vy-*vip*-ar-us) **animals,** those whose young are nourished before birth by the mother through a placenta. The young are born alive.

Voluntary, pertaining to actions under the control of the will.

Voluntary muscle, that controlled by the will of the organism.

Vomerine teeth, those in the roof of the mouth of the frog which aid in holding prey.

Water-borne infections, those produced by certain pathogenic organisms present in water.

Water cycle, a continuous movement of water from the atmosphere to the earth and from the earth to the atmosphere.

Watershed, a hilly region, usually over a large area which conducts surface water to streams.

Water table, the level at which water is standing in the ground.

White corpuscles, colorless cells of the blood.

White fibrous tissue, strong, pliable white fibers arranged in bundles.

White matter, the fibers of nerve cells in the brain and spinal cord which are surrounded by a fatty sheath.

Wigglers, the larvae of the mosquito.

Wildlife, all native animals.

Wind erosion, removal of soil by wind.

Wood, the solid part of a woody stem, made up of xylem, and found between the pith and cambium.

Woody stem, any woody, perennial stem.

X-chromosome, a sex determining chromosome present in both males and females.

Xanthophyll (*zan*-thoh-fill), a yellow pigment found in chloroplasts.

Xylem (*zy*-lem), the woody tissue of a root or stem which conducts water and dissolved minerals upwards.

Y-chromosome, a sex chromosome found only in males.

Yellow elastic tissue, tough, yellowish fibers which add flexibility to tissue.

Zoology, the specialized study of animal life and the relation of animals to other living things.

Zygospore, a zygote surrounded by a thick wall.

Zygote (*zy*-goat), the fertilized egg cell in plants and animals.

Acknowledgments

The authors gratefully acknowledge the courtesy and cooperation of the following individuals and organizations who have been kind enough to supply the photographs used in this book.

American Forest Products: Figs. 53–4, 53–6, 53–9, 53–11

American Hereford Assoc.: Fig. 50–7

American Institute of Baking: Figs. 4–2, 35–4

American Museum of Natural History: Figs. 2–10, 2–11, 6–9, 7–4, 8–1, 10–2, 15–5, 15–6, 20–5, 21–4, 22–7, 22–9, 23–9, 23–17, 24–6, 24–8, 27–5, 28–1, 28–4, 29–4, 29–5, 29–13, 30–2, 30–13, 31–3, 31–5, 31–6, 31–7, 32–1, 32–16 (top), 33–1, 33–2, 33–15, 51–2, 51–3, 51–7, Unit 5 Preview

American Red Cross: Fig. 36–7

Argonne National Laboratory: Fig. 14–6

Bausch and Lomb: Figs. 3–3, 47–3, Unit 1 Preview

Bettmann Archives: Figs. 1–2, 3–1, 43–1, 43–2, 45–3

Black Star: Figs. 16–5, 22–2, 25–6, 32–13, 36–8

Bodger Seed Co.: Fig. 13–16

Brooklyn Botanic Garden: Figs. 9–8, 14–10, 20–10, 51–9

Burpee, Atlee W. Co.: Figs. 10–4, 10–7, 10–9, 15–7, Unit 3 (top)

Carboloy News Bureau: Fig. 46–8

Cornell University: Fig. 32–15 (right)

Cushing, Charles Phelps: Figs. 16–6, 38–5, 38–7

Devaney, A.: Figs. 19–7, 31–13, 49–1

Dow Chemical Co.: Fig. 27–7

Eli Lilly Co.: Fig. 45–13

Encyclopædia Britannica Films: Figs. 2–8, 6–8, 8–13, 15–17, 28–5

Field and Stream Magazine: Figs. 2–13, 8–6, 8–7, 29–3

Galloway, Ewing: Figs. 6–6, 6–10, 7–6, 7–12, 8–3, 8–9, 11–12, 12–8, 15–19, 16–12, 24–5, 35–1, 40–8, 51–1

Gendreau, Philip: Figs. 3–8, 8–4, 18–3, 18–5, 25–7, 26–2, 26–6, 26–12, 32–14, 33–8, 53–7

General Biological Supply House: Fig. 3–9, Unit 4 Preview

General Electric Co.: Figs. 1–7, 5–15

Indiana University Medical Center: Figs. 37–4, 46–6

International News Photo: Fig. 14–14

Lederle Laboratories: Fig. 44–6

Lewis, Frederick: Figs. 24–9, 49–4

Lilo Hess: Fig. 31–2

Los Angeles City Health Dept.: Fig. 45–10

Marine Studios: Figs. 22–4, 23–14, 23–18

Massachusetts General Hospital: Figs. 46–1, 46–2

Monkmeyer Press Photo Service: Figs. 2–4, 2–7, 9–2, 13–5, 15–11, 18–6, 20–6, 25–9, 26–6, 30–3, 36–9, 54–1, Unit 2 Preview

Muench, Josef: Fig. 7–8

National Audubon Society: Figs. 1–8, 2–5, 8–12, 32–11, 33–16, 48–9, 54–6

National Board of Fire Underwriters: Fig. 5–2

National Foundation for Infantile Paralysis: Fig. 18–8

National Park Service: Fig. 4–6

National Safety Council: Fig. 42–2

National Tuberculosis Assoc.: Figs. 45–7, 45–8, 45–9

New York Botanic Garden: Figs. 10–2, 10–4, 10–8, 10–11, 13–7, 13–15, 17–10, 19–13

New York Zoological Society: Figs. 2–3, 7–11, 30–5, 31–11, 32–16, 33–3, 33–10, 33–12, 33–17

Northwestern University: Fig. 42–1

Notre Dame University: Fig. 18–4

Ohio Forestry Assoc.: Fig. 16–9

Oliver Corporation: Fig. 4–1

Popular Gardening Magazine: Fig. 10–10

Presbyterian Hospital: Figs. 39–3, 40–5

Radio Corporation of America: Fig. 3–4

Roberts, Armstrong H.: Fig. 42–1

Santa Fe Railway: Figs. 8–30, 54–4

Schulz, Peggie, Unit 9 Preview

Shell Oil Co.: Fig. 5–9

Society of American Bacteriologists: Figs. 43–6, 43–7

Southern Pacific Railway: Fig. 7–7

Spencer, Hugh: Figs. 1–6, 4–11, 19–1, 19–4, 20–2, 20–3, 20–8,

23–6, 23–10, 23–12, 23–13, 23–16, 25–3, 30–4, 31–1, 31–8, 31–12, Unit 3 Preview

Squibb, E. R.: Figs. 35–3, 44–5

Standard Oil Co. (N.J.): Figs. 2–6, 27–6

Teaching Films Custodian: Figs. 45–1, 45–2

Texas and Pacific Railway Co.: Fig. 14–9

Tokugawa Institute, Tokyo, Japan: Fig. 17–1

Triarch Botanical Products: Fig. 47–5

United Press Assoc.: Figs. 42–4, 49–2

United States Air Force: Fig. 36–10

United States Dept. of Agriculture: Figs. 1–5, 1–9, 6–5, 8–8, 15–16, 25–8, 26–4, 26–10, 27–2, 27–9, 50–1, 50–2, 50–5, 50–8, 52–1, 52–2, 52–3, 52–7, 52–8, Unit 3 Preview (bottom right)

Bureau of Entomology and Plant Quarantine: Figs. 9–7, 26–7, 26–8, 26–9, 27–1, 27–8, 43–8

Bureau of Home Nutrition: Figs. 5–11, 5–12

Bureau of Plant Industry: Fig. 7–10

Forest Service: Figs. 2–9, 3–10, 7–1, 7–2, 7–13, 7–14, 7–15, 9–4, 10–5, 11–11, 13–3, 13–4, 13–6, 13–8, 15–12, 52–10, 53–1, 53–2, 53–3, 53–6, 53–10, 53–12

Soil Conservation Service: Figs. 7–9, 14–15, 52–4, 52–5, 52–6, 52–11, 53–8, Unit 10 Preview

U.S. Dept. of Health, Education, and Welfare: Fig. 45–12

U.S. Fish and Wildlife Service: Figs. 2–12, 6–7, 7–3, 7–5, 8–10, 8–11, 9–1, 9–6, 29–1, 29–2, 30–5, 33–4, 33–6, 33–11, 33–13, 33–14, 54–2, 54–3, 54–5

U.S. Public Health Service: Figs. 1–4, 37–3, 45–5, 46–3, 46–4

U.S. Steel Corporation: Fig. 5–1

Williams and Wychoff, Drs.: Fig. 18–10

Wisconsin Conservation Dept.: Fig. 15–18

Yale University: Fig. 34–2

The authors also gratefully acknowledge the contributions of the following artists who prepared the illustrations for this book: Joseph Guerry for the scientific line drawings in the text; Edward Malsberg for the chapter introductions; Dr. Louise Bush for the cover, title page, and "Trans-Vision" of the frog.

Index

Page references for illustrations are printed in **boldface type.**

1. Pond snail (*Planorbis sp.*)
2. Giant water bug (*Lethocerus americanus*)
3. Protozoan (*Epistylis sp.*) colonies growing on snails
4. Snail (*Physa sp.*) eggs
5. Water lily (*Castalia odorata*)
6. Leopard frog (*Rana pipiens*)
7. Mallard duck (*Anas platyrhynchos*) female
8. Dragonfly (*Anax junius*)

9. Water striders (*Gerris sp.*)
10. Pond snail (*Physa sp.*)
11. Duckweed (*Lemna minor*)
12. Leopard frog (*Rana pipiens*) tadpole
13. Predaceous diving beetle (*Dytiscus marginalis*) larva
14. Common or pumpkinseed sunfish (*Lepomis gibbosus*)
15. Green alga (*Cladophora sp.*)
16. Crayfish (*Cambarus sp.*)